Teacher's Edition

SCIENCE

B

Third Edition

BJU PRESS
Greenville, South Carolina

SPACE AND EARTH SCIENCE Teacher's Edition
Third Edition

R. Terrance Egolf, CDR, USN (retired)
Franklin S. Hall, MA
Rachel Santopietro
Linda Shumate

Consultants
Eugene Chaffin, PhD
Joseph Henson, PhD
Ron Samec, PhD
Emil Silvestru, PhD

Bible Integration
Bryan Smith, PhD
William L. Gray, MA

Project Editor
Michael Santopietro

Compositor
Kelley Moore

Cover Designers
John Bjerk
Aaron Dickey

Designers
John Bjerk
Kristin Boyles
Aaron Dickey
Timothy French
David Siglin

Photo Acquisition
Brenda Hansen
Joyce Landis
Susan Perry
Visuals Unlimited

Illustrators
Peter Crane
Aaron Dickey
Terrance Egolf
Preston Gravely
James Hargis
Brian D. Johnson
Jonathan Johnson
Nathan Kirsop
Sarah Lyons
David Schuppert

Project Manager
Victor Ludlum

This book is based on original materials by Dr. David Anderson and Richard Seeley, with George Mulfinger Jr. and Donald E. Snyder. Originally published as *EARTH SCIENCE* Teacher's Edition.

Photograph credits appear on pages 331–34 (Book A) and 603–6 (Book B). BJU Press extends special thanks to Dr. Joseph Henson, Dr. Ron Samec, Mr. Michael Oard, Dr. Andrew Snelling, and Dr. Emil Silvestru for providing introductions to each of the five units of the student text and biographical information for the Teacher's Edition.
The student text is based on original materials by George Mulfinger Jr. and Donald E. Snyder. Revised by Dr. David Anderson and Rosemary Lasell. Originally published as *EARTH SCIENCE*.

Produced in cooperation with the Bob Jones University Division of Natural Science of the College of Arts and Science.

© 2005 BJU Press
Greenville, South Carolina 29614
First Edition © 1979 BJU Press
Second Edition © 1992, 1999 BJU Press

ISBN 978-1-59166-309-6

15 14 13 12 11 10 9 8 7 6 5 4 3 2

**We asked customers what they were looking
for in their teaching materials.**

You told us.

> I am Looking For
> Teacher's Editions that
>
> ☑ are easy to use
> ☑ aim at teaching comprehension
> ☑ improve test scores
> ☑ have lots of teaching ideas
> ☑ help me reach different
>   learning styles
> ☑ have four-color throughout
> ☑ are reasonably priced

> I want student books that have
>
> ☑ grade-appropriate activities
> ☑ challenging information
> ☑ engaging presentations
> ☑ photographs
> ☑ lots of color everywhere

We listened.

**And we did as you asked. We think you will like
what you see in this book. Enjoy your teaching.
We're still listening – contact us any time.**

CONTENTS

APPENDICES

Student Activities

THE LITHOSPHERE

unit 4

Andrew Snelling, who was raised in a Christian family, came to Christ at nine years of age. Through study of the Creation/evolution debate, he was called to a lifelong ministry in creationist geology. Dr. Snelling received his BS in Applied Geology in 1975 from the University of New South Wales in Sydney, Australia, and a PhD in geology in 1982 from the University of Sydney. He has been a field geologist, and in 1983 he became affiliated with the Creation Science Foundation. Since 1992, Dr. Snelling has been an Associate Professor of Geology with the Institute for Creation Research. He writes for creationist publications and lectures on Creation science in churches and schools.

Andrew Snelling: Geologist

A visit to some copper mines when I was 9 years old stimulated my interest in rocks and minerals. By the time I was in junior high, geology had become my passion. God used this passion to lead me to train in geology at two Australian universities, eventually receiving my Ph.D. After working $4^1/_2$ years in northern Australia in mineral exploration and geological research, I have researched full-time for more than 20 years in Creation and Flood geology, studying extensively in the Grand Canyon.

I have been excited to see the fruits of this research. Creationist scientists have found overwhelming evidences of a recent, global, cataclysmic, biblical Flood. Global patterns of geologic features, such as fossils, rock deposition, large-scale geologic structures, and indicators of strong water currents all point to the Flood. The scientific case for a young earth is increasingly irrefutable as radioactive methods for dating rocks are being shown to be totally unreliable.

We need more people to research, and to spread and teach what we find. I warmly encourage you to consider whether God might be calling you to an exciting life of Creation science.

Andrew Snelling

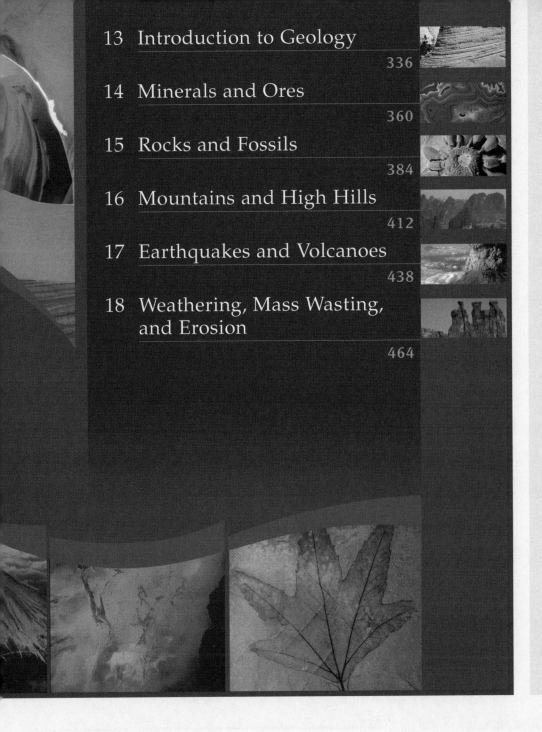

Overview

Since Unit 4 addresses the lithosphere, or the solid matter of the earth, it is appropriate that Chapter 13 start the unit with an introduction to geology. The surface and structure of the earth is, for the majority of students, the most visible and tangible part of God's creation. As we delve into the study of the earth itself, we believe it is appropriate to first remind students of the presuppositions that permit us to interpret the physical evidence from a biblical viewpoint. Once this foundation is established, the examination of the earth's structure, design, processes, and history becomes a fascinating and God-honoring activity that can grow into a lifelong calling and vocation.

Section 13A illustrates unique features of our Earth that make it especially suitable for life. Characteristics such as the earth's mass, rotation, atmosphere, and liquid water point to the design of the Creator God and His sustaining hand.

The earth's interior structure and layers are the subject of Section 13B. Analysis of seismic waves traveling through the earth's interior has revealed the presence of the crust, mantle, and core of the earth as well as other structures within these layers.

Section 13C investigates the earth's history as viewed by Creationists and evolutionists. Creationists that hold to a young-earth model view the world in terms of its divine Creation, the Fall and Curse, and the devastating effects of the Genesis Flood. This section also discusses valid and not-so-valid methods for assigning an age to the earth and its materials.

Schedule Summary

Section 13A: 1–2 periods

Section 13B: 1–2 periods

Section 13C: 3–4 periods

Investigation Summary

13H "The Radiocarbon Method"

 Bulletin Board Ideas

1. A Creation bulletin board is easy to make. Title it "In the Beginning . . . " and illustrate the six (or seven) days of Creation week, incorporating the ideas and conjectures mentioned in the textbook.

CHAPTER

13

INTRODUCTION TO GEOLOGY

SUGGESTED TEACHING SCHEDULE

DAY 0

Assignment

Reading: Section 13A, "The Earth's Design"

DAY 1

Discuss what is involved in the study of geology. Highlight unique features of the earth that affirm a divine design rather than random happenstance.

Assignment

Complete: 13A Section Review Questions

Applications 13A, "What is Geology?"

Reading: Section 13B, "The Earth's Structure"

DAY 2

Quiz—Section 13A, "The Earth's Design"

Describe the layers of the earth's interior and explain how geologists can deduce this information.

Assignment

Complete: 13B Section Review Questions

Applications 13B, "The Earth's Interior"

Applications 13C, "The Structure of the Earth"

Reading: Section 13C-1 (§13.11–13.17), historical geology and Earth's history according to Creationists

DAY 3

Quiz—Section 13B, "The Earth's Structure"

Examine the nature of historical geology. Discuss the key functional and physical attributes of the newly created Earth. Describe the events through history that have reshaped the earth according to the Bible.

13A THE EARTH'S DESIGN

13.1 Geology Defined

What is geology? The word literally means the study of (*-logy*) the earth (*geo-*). A study of the earth can include the study of its atmosphere, its oceans, and its solid structures. However, the name **geology** has historically been assigned to the science of the earth's rocks and minerals, their structures, and the processes that affect those structures. A *geologist* is a scientist who specializes in the study of the solid part of the earth. Geology is both interesting and practical. Geologists who study rocks and minerals can locate natural resources. They find unusual substances such as oil, uranium, and gold as well as more common materials such as clay, limestone, and gravel. Other geologists study natural phenomena, such as glaciers, earthquakes, and volcanoes. Geology also involves the study of earth processes, such as erosion (caused by wind, water, and waves), the formation of sediments, and the movement of energy within the earth. Some geologists study the geology of the moon and planets.

Creationary scientists believe that the many characteristics of the earth make it unique among all the planets in the universe. Earth has the unique purpose of providing a perfectly designed world for all life *as created by God*. Before we press forward in our study of geology, it is worthwhile to review the aspects of the design of the earth and how each works with the others to provide the necessities for life.

13.2 Evidence for Design: Earth's Mass

The earth contains 3 billion trillion metric tons of the right materials to support life. The mass and size of the earth are directly responsible for the strength of gravity at the earth's surface. Too little gravity would not seem to have an adverse effect on organisms directly, but too much gravity would rapidly fatigue muscles and cause bones to break more easily. Organisms would have to use much more energy to oppose gravity in growth and movement. Different gravity would require different biological designs to achieve the same function, and some, like bird flight, might not be possible in much stronger gravity.

Gravity is also responsible for the earth's atmosphere. With too little mass, the atmosphere would have too low a density to support animal life. With too much mass, the atmospheric density of certain gases, especially of oxygen, could approach poisonous levels for animal and plant tissues.

13.3 Evidence for Design: Earth's Rotation

The speed of the earth's rotation is perfectly matched to other aspects of the earth. If the earth turned too slowly or not at all, very few organisms would be able to survive under the sun through the long or constant day. Temperatures would soar, and living things would be scorched. Plants that get their energy through photosynthesis would not be able to live in long periods of darkness and cold.

13-1 Earth was designed for life. In contrast to Earth's optimal living conditions (top), the other planets, such as Mars (bottom), have unbreathable atmospheres, intense radiation, extreme temperatures, and virtually no water or oxygen.

2. A diagram of the earth's interior makes a vivid and effective bulletin board.

 Field Trip Ideas

Check with a laboratory or hospital in your area to see if they have a mass spectrometer that your students may observe. Ask the technician to explain how a mass spectrometer makes readings, how samples are prepared, and perhaps how carbon-14 content is measured in a sample.

Objectives—Section 13A

Upon completing this section, students should be able to

- identify examples of God's design in the earth's unique features.
- discuss the features and limitations of the canopy theory.

The phrase "as created by God" in the second paragraph is significant. The world and the creatures in it are one completely integrated and coordinated design. The earth is designed for the living things, and the living things are designed to inhabit the earth.

In spite of the evolutionary assumption that life could have appeared and evolved repeatedly throughout the universe, recent evolutionary writers have declared that Earth may be a very special case where fortuitous, or even unique, conditions permitted the appearance of life.

None of the evidences presented here provide credible evidence in themselves for a special Creation. For example, the beneficial consequences of the earth's mass discussed in §13.2 could be explained by stating that life would have evolved structures as needed for mobility in whatever gravity was present. It is when all the evidences are considered together that it becomes apparent that the earth was uniquely designed to support life.

Assignment

Complete: 13C-1 Section Review Questions

Applications 13D, "The Earth's History According to Creationists"

Reading: Section 13C-2 (§13.18–13.20), the earth's history according to evolutionists

DAY 4

Describe the basic tenets of uniformitarianism and discuss why the physical and scriptural evidence does not support a uniform past or future.

Assignment

Complete: 13C-2 Section Review Questions

Applications 13E, "Uniformitarianism"

Reading: Section 13C-3 (§13.21–13.27), methods for dating the earth

DAY 5

Describe the various methods used for dating the earth and its materials from the prehistoric past. Analyze the technique, assumptions, and validity of each method.

Assignment

Complete: 11C-3 Section Review Questions

Applications 13F, "Dating the Earth"

Applications 13G, "Three Methods of Dating the Earth"

Reading: Investigation 13H, "The Radiocarbon Method"

DAY 6

Quiz—Section 13C, "The Earth's History"

Do Investigation 13H, "The Radiocarbon Method."

Assignment

Complete: Selected Chapter Review Questions

(schedule continued on p. 338)

Too fast a rotation would also be harmful to life as God created it. The rapid day and night cycles would provide insufficient periods for hunting or food gathering, and sleep periods would be too short. Many familiar plants could not survive the rapid cycle of day and night. The entire nature of the earth's wind and ocean circulation patterns would be significantly different, and weather would probably be more violent.

13.4 Evidence for Design: Atmospheric Mixture

Our atmosphere also contains an optimal amount of oxygen. Nitrogen dilutes the oxygen to the proper concentration for use by living organisms. Interestingly, no appreciable quantities of oxygen have been found in any of the other planetary atmospheres in the solar system. Furthermore, those atmospheres contain gases that are poisonous to terrestrial life. Although green plants continually replenish our atmospheric oxygen, they in no way account for its origin, since green plants need oxygen to grow, just like all living things.

13.5 Evidence for Design: Atmospheric Protection

The earth's atmosphere also protects the surface from most meteors. Of the tens of thousands of small meteors that enter our atmosphere each day, very few—perhaps a hundred per day—actually impact the earth's surface as meteorites. At the same time, the ozone layer in the stratosphere protects organisms from harmful ultraviolet rays. The earth also contains a magnetic field (well outside the atmosphere) that traps high-energy solar and cosmic particles before they reach the earth's surface.

13.6 Evidence for Design: Liquid Water

Probably the most striking evidence of God's design of the earth for life is the presence of liquid water. Although astronomers have not found liquid water on the surface of any other planet, this vital substance covers 71% of the earth's surface. The physical properties of water are unique and remarkable. They include its transparency, its expansion before freezing, its dissolving properties, and its relatively strong surface tension. Life and physical processes important to life rely heavily upon these properties of water.

13-2 Water, the remarkable compound that is so vital to life, is plentiful on the earth.

When water freezes, the resulting ice floats. The solid states of most other liquids would sink to the bottom. If ice sank, lakes and the ocean would freeze solid from the bottom up. Bottom-dwelling organisms would die in freezing climate zones.

Stones of Witness

People who cannot or will not name the Designer of the universe and the Author of life must produce an intelligent cause that is great enough to have accomplished these tasks. These people must wonder why an unidentified intelligence would have gone through the effort of creating such a complex entity without revealing himself/herself/itself. They are avoiding the question of their own mortality and missing the fact that the Designer is also their Savior.

Many of these people are part of the modern Intelligent Design Movement (IDM). Those in the IDM object to Darwinism and the fact that, despite numerous evidences of design, Darwinism is promoted by government, schools, and the scientific establishment as a strictly naturalistic and only valid description of origins. Many of the evidences IDM advocates cite are similar to those we have discussed (though most proponents of IDM are concerned mainly with biological design). IDM supporters may also be comfortable with directed evolution, billions of years of time, and even *panspermia* (establishment of life on other planets by aliens). Most supporters take the IDM position to avoid appearing biased or influenced by religious beliefs. On the other hand, most evolutionists view the IDM as a backdoor or Trojan Horse approach to forcing religion, in particular Christianity, into schools. As with other attempts to account for the existence of the universe and life apart from the biblical account (see the Facet on pp. 10–11), the Intelligent Design Movement fails to be acceptable to the people it is attempting to convince because of fundamentally different presuppositions.

Stones of Witness
In this section, you have reviewed a few of the earth's design features. Some people believe that something or someone designed the natural universe, but they cannot—or do not want to—identify the Designer. What philosophical problem does this position cause?

DAY 7

Review for a chapter test.

Assignment

Study for a chapter test.

DAY 8

Test—Chapter 13

Assignment

Reading: Section 14A, "Components of Minerals"

The Canopy Theory

Imagine Noah and his family as they listened to the rain pounding on the roof of the ark for forty days and nights. Where did that huge amount of water come from? Many Christians have suggested that the water that flooded the earth came from a shell or canopy of dense water vapor suspended above the atmosphere. This theory helped explain conditions before the Flood, like the large sizes of animals, humans' long lives, and a widespread tropical climate. Was a water vapor canopy part of the originally "very good" design of the earth?

The concept of a water vapor canopy was first proposed in 1874 by the Quaker Isaac Vail. He suggested that millions of years ago, seven vaporous layers (or canopies) of various materials surrounded the molten, evolving earth. As the earth cooled, these layers collapsed, one at a time, millions of years apart. Each formed a distinct geologic layer, which Vail believed was most clearly visible in the rock layers of the Grand Canyon. The final, lightest canopy was water, which collapsed in the days of Noah. This idea, designed to unite the evolutionary origin of the earth and the Genesis account, was the start of the single-canopy theory that was eventually adopted by many Creationists.

But what does the Bible say? Genesis 1:7 is the proof text of those who believe in the vapor canopy theory. *"And God made the firmament, and divided the waters which were under the firmament from the waters which were above the firmament: and it was so."* The interpretations of this passage differ. The key to understanding this passage is the Hebrew word for "firmament," the word *raqiya*. This Hebrew word can be translated "expanse" or "the visible arch of the sky." Accordingly, John Calvin in his commentary on Genesis concluded that the "waters above the firmament" were simply clouds. But the word *raqiya* is also used in Genesis 1:14 and 1:20 as being the place where God put the sun, moon, and stars, as well as the place where the birds fly. This would lead us to think that the firmament contained both the atmosphere as well as interstellar space. Russell Humphreys, in his book *Starlight and Time*, suggests that a shell of water expanded with interstellar space as the universe was created and is actually the boundary of physical space. In any case, the Bible does not clearly say that a canopy of water existed between the atmosphere and space.

In 1990 and 1998, Larry Vardiman and other creationary scientists used supercomputer models of the atmosphere to investigate the surface temperatures on an earth surrounded by a water vapor canopy. The results of these computer simulations indicate that a runaway greenhouse effect, with an average surface temperature of several hundred degrees, would have occurred under a canopy that could have produced the kind of flood described in Genesis. A vapor canopy that could rain 2 m of water was the thickest that would allow some forms of life to survive on the earth. A canopy that could have rained just 10 cm (4 in.) would have maintained an average of 63 °C (143 °F) on the earth's surface!

Based on the results of these computer models, most creationary scientists today do not believe the canopy theory is scientifically feasible. There are several other possible sources of water for a 40-day deluge. These include the miraculous creation of rain by God Himself, condensation from worldwide volcanic activity that occurred with the rupturing of the "fountains of the great deep" (Gen. 7:11), subterranean water discharged into the atmosphere from these fountains, or even atmospheric bombardment by swarms of comet nuclei. No one knows for sure where the rainwater of the Flood came from, but the source was probably not a water vapor canopy.

According to the most straightforward interpretation of the Bible, the sun, planets, and stars are placed in the firmament of space between the waters below and the waters above.

Additional Resources

The research of Dr. Vardiman et al. that concludes a runaway greenhouse effect would have made the pre-Flood earth too hot can be found in the following papers:

D. E. Rush and L. Vardiman, "Pre-flood Vapor Canopy Radiative Temperature Profiles" (Paper presented at the Second International Conference on Creationism, Pittsburgh, PA, 1990).

L. Vardiman and K. Bousselot, "Sensitivity Studies on Vapor Canopy Temperature Profiles" (Paper presented at the Fourth International Conference on Creationism, Pittsburgh, PA, 1998).

These papers may be obtained by contacting the Creation Science Fellowship, Inc., Pittsburgh, PA, USA.

The constellations Canis Major, Orion, and Taurus are visible in the photograph.

Box Summary: The Canopy Theory

This box discusses a theory of the proximal cause of the Flood that many Bible-believers hold to with almost the same tenacity as they do the authority of Scripture. The best preparation for presenting this material is to know your students so that you can anticipate their response. Discuss the topic respectfully and with humility, reminding students that because of the limitations of human science, we will never know for sure what actually caused the Flood until we reach heaven. There are no vocabulary terms in this box.

Objectives—Section 13B

Upon completing this section, students should be able to

- explain how scientists have deduced the inferior structures of the earth.
- correctly label a diagram of the earth's interior structures.
- compare and contrast the characteristics of the different layers of the earth.
- discuss the significance of the asthenosphere and the outer core.

Concepts Students Find Difficult

Your students may not understand why earthquake waves travel differently in different substances if they do not know that sound travels at different speeds in solids, water, and air. The denser the material (the closer together the particles of the substance are), the more efficiently the wave energy is transferred and the faster the wave travels. Also mention that some kinds of waves do not travel through liquid-like materials. We will discuss this aspect of earthquake waves in more detail in Chapter 17.

13A Section Review

1. How is geology distinct from the other sciences in this book that you have studied so far?
2. What aspects of the existence of life on Earth depend on the earth's mass? (Consider things that we have discussed in earlier chapters as well.)
3. What is the most striking evidence that the earth was designed to support life?
4. List four special properties of water that living organisms depend on for survival.
5. (True or False) The protective features of the earth's atmosphere are completely separate from the gases necessary to support the life it contains.

13B THE EARTH'S STRUCTURE

13.7 The Layers of the Earth

How is the earth's mass distributed? Is the earth a uniform ball of rock, or a hollow shell, or something else? Is there any way we can find out? Geologists learn about the earth's interior by studying the way earthquake waves travel through it. Earthquake waves are sound waves that cannot be heard as they move through the earth and along the surface of the earth. We will study earthquakes in Chapter 17. Using earthquake waves, geologists have created computer models of the earth's interior. It has three basic layers: the crust, the mantle, and the core. These layers contain different materials through which earthquake waves travel at different speeds and in different forms.

Earthquake waves are not the only way geologists can learn about the structure of the layers of the earth. Geologists can create their own shock waves, using explosives, and record the reflections. Other techniques that are growing in popularity are photography and ground-penetrating radar operating from a satellite in orbit around the earth. These methods are especially helpful in locating mineral deposits and oil. Another approach is overflying a region with specially equipped aircraft that record minute variations in the earth's magnetic or gravitational fields.

13-3 Scientists gain much of their knowledge of the earth's structure from studying earthquakes. A scientist reading a seismogram (top); a seismogram can also be read on computer monitor (middle); a computer-generated epicenter map (bottom left); a siesmologist checking a device that takes field measurements (bottom right).

Answers to 13A Section Review Questions

1. Geology is the science of the earth's rocks and other solid materials, its structures, and the processes that affect those structures. In contrast, meteorology is the study of the earth's atmosphere, and astronomy is the study of everything beyond the earth's atmosphere. (§13.1)

2. Answers will vary. The earth's mass chiefly affects its gravitational force. The earth's gravity is responsible for the density of the atmosphere and the layers of gases in the atmosphere, and the atmosphere in turn provides protection from cosmic radiation and meteoric bombardment. The characteristics of the moon's orbit depend on the earth's mass. Differences in the earth's mass would affect tide cycles and range, and lunar calendars would be different. The earth's gravity also influences ease of movement, especially in regard to flight. (§13.2, 13.5; Chap. 9)

3. The most striking design feature of the earth is the presence of large quantities of liquid water on the earth's surface. (§13.6)

4. Water's special properties include its transparency, ability to dissolve many substances, freezing properties, and strong surface tension. (§13.6)

5. False. One of the wonderful aspects of God's creation is the complex way in which everything works together. Oftentimes, many benefits come from a single design feature such as the earth's atmosphere. (§13.4, 13.5)

13.8 The Crust

The earth's outer layer, the **crust**, is solid, relatively low-density rock. This rock's thickness ranges from about 7 km (4.5 mi) under the oceans to 30–50 km (19–31 mi) or more under the mountain chains on continents. The crust averages about six times as thick under the continents as under the ocean basins. In 1909, Andrija Mohorovičić discovered that earthquake waves change speed suddenly at a specific distance below the upper surface of the crust. Such a change in speed is called a **discontinuity** and marks the boundary between two layers of the earth. The boundary between the crust and the mantle is called the **Mohorovičić discontinuity** (**Moho** for short).

13.9 The Mantle

The **mantle** extends from the Moho to a depth of about 2900 km (1800 mi). It occupies about 84% of the earth's volume. The mantle can be subdivided into several regions according to the way earthquake waves pass through it. Directly below the Moho is the upper mantle, a layer of solid matter chemically different from the crust but attached to it. This layer includes a segment about 70 km (40 mi) thick beneath the ocean basin crust and 125–250 km (80–160 mi) thick under the continents. Geologists call the combination of this segment of the upper mantle and the crust the **lithosphere**, since it seems to form the rocky plates that make up the surface of the earth. We will discuss these plates in more detail in later chapters.

Earthquake waves normally go faster with increasing depth. However, below the lithosphere, the upper mantle contains a curious layer in which earthquake waves unexpectedly slow down. Geologists call this layer the **asthenosphere**. It extends from the bottom of the lithosphere to a thickness of perhaps 200 km (125 mi), or even deeper under continents. Scientists believe that the rock material in this zone is nearer to melting compared to the rock above or below it due to the combination of heat and pressure at this depth. These conditions could be why earthquake waves move slower in this zone.

The upper mantle continues downward to a depth of about 670 km (420 mi), which is the deepest point where earthquakes seem to occur. Below this boundary is the lower mantle, which extends to a depth of 2900 km, or about 3480 km from the center of the earth. Analyzing earthquake waves with a technique similar to the way doctors analyze ultrasounds or brain scans, geologists have been able to map huge regions of rising, hot mantle material and sinking, slightly cooler material. The mantle in this region may consist of a semi-liquid rock that flows extremely slowly. This motion is similar to the convection currents we saw in the sun's interior and in thunderstorms. Note that the mantle's dense, hot, plastic-like solid material is *not* the same thing as lava or magma, which is molten (liquid) rock that forms within the lithosphere.

Andrija Mohorovičić (MOH huh ROH vuh chik) (1857–1936) was a Croatian **seismologist** (earthquake scientist) who was far ahead of his time in studying earthquakes and the damage they caused to buildings.

13-4 Section of the earth's interior showing the relative size of each part

Visual 13-1: The Earth's Interior

This visual is a reproduction of Figure 13-4. Use this visual as you discuss the interior structures of the earth. Point out that the crust is thicker under mountain ranges and much thinner under the oceans. The lithosphere rests on top of the asthenosphere, which geologists believe is a layer of rock very near its melting point and easily deformable (plastic) in nature.

The stated thicknesses and depths of the earth's layers vary depending on the source of the information. The values given in this text are typical of those stated in scientific sources.

Additional Resource

Additional insight into the complex model of the production of the earth's magnetic field and its decay may be found in the following technical article:

D. Russell Humphreys, "The Earth's Magnetic Field Is Still Losing Energy," *Creation Research Society Quarterly* 39:1 (2002): 3–13.

Some geologists estimate that the outer core has a temperature of 4000–5000 °C (7200–9000 °F) and a density of about 12 g/cm³, and the inner core has a temperature of 5000–6000 °C (9000–11,000 °F) and a density of 15 g/cm³.

13.10 The Core

The earth's **core** contains 15–16% of the earth's volume. It occupies all the earth's remaining volume below the mantle. Many geologists are unwilling even to guess what the core material is like because it is so different from anything humans have experienced. The core must be extremely hot and dense, possibly more than twice as dense as ordinary iron. The core has two parts. The outer core is about 2260 km (1400 mi) thick, and geologists believe it to be liquid or to have liquid properties. The inner core's radius is about 1220 km (800 mi). It is likely that the flow of the liquid portion of the core is at least partly responsible for earth's strong magnetic field. Geologists believe that the core is probably 85% iron and 4–5% nickel, with the remainder being lighter elements such as oxygen. The pressure and temperature in the core are tremendous. Any material under these conditions would be almost unrecognizable.

FACETS OF GEOLOGY

JOURNEY TO THE CENTER OF THE EARTH

Man knows less about the earth beneath his feet than he does about the stars in the heavens. No "telescope" can penetrate the thick crust down to the mantle only a few kilometers away. Our ignorance has encouraged fantastic accounts of the earth's interior, such as Jules Verne's *Journey to the Center of the Earth*. Only recently have modern drills been able to discover some of the earth's deep secrets.

The first effort to break through the crust began in 1961. An area with a thin crust on the bottom of the Pacific Ocean off the coast of La Jolla, California, was selected. The project was named *Mohole* in honor of the earthquake scientist Andrija Mohorovičić.

Engineers and oceanographers converted a navy barge into a floating drill rig, called *CUSS I*. It lowered pipes 3650 m (12,000 ft) to the Pacific Ocean floor. The drill then pushed through 165 m (550 ft) of sediment and bit 15 m (50 ft) more into basalt rock (the crust). Mohole proved that deep-sea drilling was possible, but it barely pierced the crust, stopping many kilometers short of reaching the Moho, the boundary between the crust and the mantle. A bigger rig, more money, and many more kilometers of drill pipe would be needed to complete the job. Not willing to bear the cost, Congress voted to end the project in 1966.

A follow-on program involved six American oceanographic institutions. It was called the Deep Sea Drilling Project (DSDP) (1968–83) and used the drill ship *GLOMAR Challenger*. The deepest hole this ship drilled was 1080 m (3543 ft) into the crust. In addition to gathering core samples at 624 sites, this program solved many technical problems, such as how to get the drill back into the same hole after changing drill bits. Additional agencies joined the program as it progressed until 21 nations were participating.

The next program, called the Ocean Drilling Program (ODP) (1985–2003), employed a special for-the-purpose drill ship called *JOIDES* Resolution*. The ODP enlisted scientists from 10 different countries. Of the 1797 holes drilled, the deepest was 2111 m (6926 ft) into the crust beneath the Pacific.

JOIDES stands for Joint Oceanographic Institutions for Deep Earth Sampling. Their ship, the *Resolution*, was named after the ship used by Captain James Cook in his famous explorations.

The Japanese drilling ship *Chikyu*, to be used by the IODP

Facet Summary: Journey to the Center of the Earth

This Facet discusses man's many attempts to directly access to the interior of the earth by drilling. Initially, scientists intended to drill to the Moho, the boundary between the crust and the mantle. At present, technology cannot meet the rigorous demands of such a project. There are no vocabulary terms in this Facet.

Drill bit being lowered through the drilling deck of the *JOIDES Resolution*

In 2003 a new program called the Integrated Ocean Drilling Project (IODP) was begun. It will use three drill platforms: an upgraded *Resolution*, a large, modern ship built by Japan called *Chikyu* (*World*) that will begin research operations in 2007, and a Swedish vessel, the *Vidar Viking*, which is specially equipped for drilling in arctic waters. The *Vidar Viking* will be assisted by the Swedish ice breaker *Oden* and the nuclear-powered Russian icebreaker *Sovetskiy Soyuz*. This program not only brings together the oceanic research capabilities of many contributing nations, but it also includes a student trainee program and a system for scientists and science students from all fields to make suggestions for fruitful tasks and areas of research.

The most interesting discoveries have occurred in land drill holes, though efforts in the United States have been modest. Most deep holes are dug by commercial companies searching for oil and gas. The deepest purely scientific dig in the United States was in California and went only 3.5 km (2.2 mi), stopping far short of the 5 km (3.1 mi) goal because of high temperatures, high costs, and budget cuts. Some shallow digs have practical aims, such as the Energy Department's drilling near the volcanic regions of Yosemite National Park, to test whether magma can be tapped as an alternative source of energy.

The efforts of the former Soviet Union have exceeded anything else done in the world. The deepest hole on Earth was begun in 1970. For over two decades the Soviets bored into the crust of the Kola Peninsula above the Arctic Circle. They picked this spot because the upper crust is thinner in this location than elsewhere in the world. The project's finds were revolutionary, overturning widely accepted theories put forward by evolutionists.

The Kola project took samples over 12 km (7.6 mi) deep. One of their first discoveries was veins of minerals, including copper and nickel, deep in the upper crust. Farther down they expected the pressure of the earth to have closed any cracks in the rock, but they were dumbfounded to find channels of superheated water streaming through huge cracks in the granite. As they dug, the temperatures rose 2.5 times faster than they had estimated. When they reached the lower crust, where scientists expected granite would be replaced by dense volcanic basalt, they broke into a layer of hard granite. Apparently rock is much more impervious to high pressure than once thought.

The Germans also completed a deep, 9.1 km drill hole in 1994, obtaining results similar to the Soviets'. If these moderate digs have already turned up so many surprises about the crust, can we be sure about our theories of the deeper mantle? Perhaps a more important question is this: If scientists cannot predict basic information about the earth on which they live, how can they be sure about an earth in the past that they have never seen?

High pressures and high temperatures make drilling to the mantle too difficult for the near future. Instead, drilling projects have been started or are being planned by many countries to drill into the crust for reasons other than finding the Moho. Drilling projects include monitoring earthquake and volcanic activity, exploiting oil, mineral, or natural gas reserves, finding geothermal energy sources, discovering the structure of the crust, confirming and investigating meteorite impact craters, and seeking clues to global climate change. Planned holes will penetrate the crust to more than 6 km (3.7 mi).

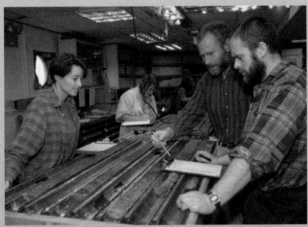

Scientists examining ocean floor core samples to study the earth's crust

Stones of Witness

You will need to guide students on what we know from Scripture about the place called hell. We know that it is eternally hot (Luke 16:24, Mark 9:44), that one goes down to it (Job 11:8, Matt. 11:23), and that it is dark (Job 10:21). All of these characteristics could correspond to a physical region within the earth.

However, prior to the final resurrection, hell is the abode of lost, disembodied souls. For this latter reason, hell is probably not a physical place in the earth but instead is a spiritual place. You can point out that in the end times, Satan will be bound by a chain in the bottomless pit for a thousand years. We do not know the nature of this chain, but the bottomless pit is not likely to be in the earth, which has finite physical dimensions. It is thus probable that the chain and the pit are spiritual restraints, not physical.

According to what we know about the interior of the earth, there are no signs of an immense hollow region deep under the crust. However, due to our limited ability to study the earth's interior, science alone cannot rule out the existence of a physical hell there.

Objectives—Section 13C

Upon completing this section, students should be able to

- describe how scientists engage in the study of historical geology.
- summarize the Creationist view of the history of the earth.
- outline the basic tenets of uniformitarian geology.
- list several ways commonly used to arrive at an age for the earth.
- summarize the validity of several modern radiometric dating methods and note the weaknesses of each.
- describe the radiocarbon dating method, its usefulness, and limitations.

Stones of Witness

For several years, there was a popular but fictional story circulating about how Soviet scientists at one of the deep drilling sites in Siberia noted that their drill seemed to break through into an open space. They lowered a microphone into the hole and thought they heard the screams of souls sent to hell, which terrified the workers. As a result, the drill hole was permanently shut down. The story was circulated among religious organizations and widely published as truth. How would you refute the validity of this story?

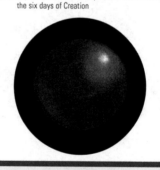

13-5 Representation of the sequence of events during the six days of Creation

13B Section Review

1. List in order, from the surface to the interior, the three major layers of the earth.

2. What determines the boundary between the crust and the interior of the earth? How does the location of this boundary vary from place to place?

3. What unusual layer exists in the mantle, and what do geologists believe gives this layer its properties?

4. What molten metals do some geologists think the earth's core is made of? What important feature of the earth's design may be produced by these materials?

5. Which country has drilled the deepest hole in the earth? Did they reach the mantle?

6. (True or False) The asthenosphere is a zone of lower temperature in the mantle, just below the lithosphere.

13C THE EARTH'S HISTORY

13.11 The Science of Historical Geology

Some geologists try to study the earth's history—where the earth came from, how long ago it was formed, and what produced the visible features on its surface. Theories and models developed from such studies are grouped under **historical geology**. In any discussion of historical geology, geologists recognize certain truths: (1) No human was present to view the origin of the earth. (2) No human records exist for events prior to about 4500 years ago. (3) The historical records that contain information of interest to geologists are incomplete. These facts place very strict limits on what can be discovered about the history of the earth.

When a scientist cannot study something directly, he proposes a model that he believes describes what he wants to study. A scientific model can be used to predict unknown information, so the scientist then sets up experiments to observe the predicted effects of his model. If the effects are observed, then the scientist is more confident that his model accurately describes what he believes exists even though he cannot observe it directly. The modern model of the atom, for instance, was developed in this way.

One interesting aspect of historical geology is that geologists can observe thousands of effects in nature that should be predictable by

Answers to 13B Section Review Questions

1. The major layers of the earth are the *crust, mantle,* and *core*. (§13.8)

2. The speed of earthquake waves changes at the Mohorovicic discontinuity (Moho) between the crust and the mantle. The depth of the Moho is shallower under ocean basin crust and much deeper under mountain ranges and continental crust. (§13.8)

3. A layer of decreased sound velocity called the *asthenosphere* exists below the lithosphere. It is believed that the rock in this zone is closer to melting than the rock above or below it, causing sound waves to slow down. (§13.9)

4. Some geologists believe that the earth's core is iron or some other metal having good electrical and magnetic properties. They believe that the earth's magnetic field may be generated by the flow of these metals in the liquid outer core of the earth. (§13.10)

5. The former Soviet Union has drilled the deepest hole in the earth. Although they drilled 12 km, they still did not reach the mantle. (Facet, p. 342)

6. False. The asthenosphere is a region in the upper mantle where earthquake waves are slower than they are above or below the zone. (§13.9)

some model of the earth's origin. The difficulty lies in proposing a model that can account for every observation without creating contradictions between different observations or violating scientific laws in other disciplines.

Developing a scientific model requires that a scientist make certain assumptions. These assumptions can have a great influence on what kind of model is chosen. In the case of historical geology, one can assume that (1) the earth has always existed, (2) the earth came into existence through a natural process, or (3) the earth was created supernaturally. After its beginning, the earth's history could have followed one of three paths: (1) the processes that existed at the beginning continued to operate relatively undisturbed to the present day; (2) the original processes that we see today operated continuously except when briefly interrupted by significant geologic events, such as an asteroid impact; (3) the earth's history consists of phases separated by one or more major geologic events that permanently changed the earth and its processes. Without any other information, the geologist could combine these assumptions and develop many different models. However, if he has some way of limiting the choices to only one possible origin of the earth and only one possible historical framework, the model-making process becomes much simpler.

ACCORDING TO CREATIONISTS

13.12 A Biblical Framework

As a Christian studies the earth's history, he must remember three major events described in Scripture that affected the physical earth: the Creation, the Fall and Curse, and the Flood. These three events form the framework on which the Christian builds his understanding of the earth's natural history—not only for past events, but for the future as well. The authority of Scripture concerning these events is sure because the Author of the Book is the Creator Himself—He was present at Creation and throughout the unrecorded periods of Earth's history. His Word is His inerrant record of His own works.

13.13 The Creation

"In the beginning God created the heaven and the earth" (Gen. 1:1). When God finished Creation at the end of the sixth day, He surveyed His handiwork and declared that it was "very good" (Gen. 1:31). We can only imagine the magnificent beauty of the earth in its original state of perfection. Until a person is willing to face the fact of a supernatural Creation—complete, miraculous, and rapidly

The concepts mentioned in this paragraph are important. Be sure that students understand the problems and limitations facing scientists who make it their work to study aspects of the earth's history.

 Visual 13-2: Creationary Historical Timeline

Use this visual to identify the key geologic events in the earth's history. The horizontal time scale is subdivided into 1000-year intervals. Refer to this visual frequently in subsequent chapters where historical geology is addressed. Emphasize those observations that have biblical support. Question marks indicate statements that are conjectural, based on reasonable interpretation of the biblical narrative and after examination of physical evidence today according to a biblical worldview.

It is the view of all young-earth Creationists that the days mentioned in Genesis 1 represent periods of time marked by one complete rotation of the earth on its axis. Whether a day was 24-hours long or slightly longer is open to question, but any significant departure from literal days will simply not stand up to the scriptural evidence.

Point out to students that we are conditioned to think of mature living things as having age. There is no reason to believe that God *had* to create things with the appearance of age—they were likely functionally mature but did not show the ravages of time and growth as in the fallen biological world of today. Thus, rough tree bark, which results from the gradual growth and swelling of the wood tissues underneath, didn't necessarily have to be present at Creation, since trees were probably created fully formed. Encourage your students to avoid uniformitarian assumptions when trying to imagine what the earth must have been like following Creation week.

Topics such as the existence of growth rings in original trees and whether Adam had a navel could generate some lively discussion. However, it would all be pointless since there is no way of verifying the facts. Use such an opportunity to deprogram your students from the uniformitarian way of looking at the earth. None of what we have grown up believing looks old is old in the sense of millions or billions of years.

Remind students that the ideas in this subsection are completely conjectural. No human was present at Creation, and Scripture is silent on matters such as soil structure. However, by using a biblical model and purposely avoiding unjustifiable uniformitarian assumptions, one can hypothesize about the conditions present at Creation. The important thing to remind students is that no matter how appealing a creationary hypothesis may be, without affirmation by Scripture it will always remain just a hypothesis.

13-6 At the time of the original creation, trees the size of the one pictured might not have shown the effects of time, such as knots and weathered bark. They might not even have had growth rings in their wood!

Organic materials are those that contain the element carbon or are obtained from living or once-living organisms.

13-7 Soil at the instant of Creation probably did not look like any soil found today. Its age could not have been estimated based on today's natural processes.

accomplished—he will not have a realistic appreciation for the world in which he lives. Although God has not told us all the details about how He created, He has told us how long Creation took and how complete it was. "*For in six days the Lord made heaven and earth, the sea, and all that in them is, and rested the seventh day: wherefore the Lord blessed the sabbath day, and hallowed it*" (Exod. 20:11). The Sabbath was a commemoration of the completed Creation.

13.14 A Fully Functional Earth

The Bible says that God created a world that was fully functional—it contained everything needed and was abounding with life. He created Adam and Eve, not as infants, but with enough physical and mental maturity that they could take care of themselves and communicate with Him. Plants were also fully developed: they had fruit and seeds at Creation (Gen. 1:11–12). While some of these trees may have been very large, it is unlikely that they bore the marks of age seen in modern trees, such as knots and weathered bark.

The soil in which the first plants grew probably looked like no natural soil found today. Fertile soil in today's world contains an irregular mixture of clay, sand, pebbles, minerals, and **organic** materials. Most of these materials came from the erosion of rock and sediment and the decay of previously living plants and animals. Plants grow well in such material. For many plants, soil must be at least several inches deep to provide proper support. An inch of soil usually takes about a century to form today. However, if a modern geologist could have examined the soil after Creation week, he might have been perplexed. Expecting to find soil that looked hundreds of years old, he probably would have found a perfect, uniform mixture of materials that provided nutrients, water, air, and strong support to the roots of plants. It probably would not have looked like any soil he had seen before. The soil would have been completely functional, but its age by modern standards probably could not have been estimated because it was formed supernaturally.

13.15 The Natural Dominion

The original earth was ready for man's use by the time God placed him on it and gave him dominion over it. It was undoubtedly beautiful and complete, with lush vegetation covering low, rolling hills; with mammals, dinosaurs, and other vertebrates inhabiting the grasslands and forests; and with birds and pterodactyls soaring through the air. Insects and other arthropods would have been everywhere. Likewise, the ocean teemed with living creatures, many of which are known only as fossils today. Beneath the surface of the ground, elements and minerals awaited man's use. In His omniscience (complete foreknowledge), God knew exactly what man would need, and in His omnipotence (complete power) He supplied this need in the miraculous way His Word describes.

Not only the earth but also the celestial bodies were ready to fulfill their purposes. God placed the sun, moon, and stars in their proper locations "*to divide the day from the night*," and to be "*for signs, and for seasons, and for days and years*" (Gen. 1:14). The light from these astronomical bodies was already visible from the earth by the end of the Creation week. God created not only the universe but also everything in it in substantially its present form. "*Thus the heavens and the earth were finished, and all the host of them*" (Gen. 2:1). The creation was complete; it lacked nothing.

The concept of a young, fully functional creation is important for the Christian student of science. Using this approach, we can see that the apparent vast ages of rocks determined by various dating methods must be erroneous. By examining the assumptions made in such methods, we can show that the old-earth dates are scientifically invalid. Nearly all people have grown up with the idea that the world is billions of years old—or that it at least looks that old. Both of these views originate with the belief that it takes a long time for certain processes to occur. When these processes are carefully examined with the intent to honor God's Word, we discover that either they take very little time to occur after all, or else we did not fully understand the original process. It is exciting to see what God reveals about His creation when we set aside the preconceived notions that we have absorbed from a naturalistic view of the world.

13.16 The Fall and Curse

The earth did not remain in its perfect state. Because man sinned, God cursed the earth. "*Cursed is the ground for thy sake; in sorrow shalt thou eat of it all the days of thy life; Thorns also and thistles shall it bring forth to thee. . . . In the sweat of thy face shalt thou eat bread, till thou return unto the ground*" (Gen. 3:17–19). We do not know all that happened at the Curse, but we do know that the earth and living things experienced profound changes. It may be that God withdrew some of His sustaining power so that natural systems began to degrade and the perfect balance of various aspects of creation was disturbed. Weather may have become more severe, erosion from rains and waves may have increased, earthquakes may have been felt for the first time, and so on. The effects on living things were even more severe—the death of vertebrate animals first occurred. Death of animals was not mentioned in Scripture prior to this point and probably had not occurred. Some Creationists believe that animals first became carnivorous at the Fall. In other words, the Curse included some minor physical modifications and significant behavioral changes in animals that led to mindless carnivorous violence (see Gen. 6:11–12). Others believe these changes took place after the Flood, when fear of humans was instilled into animals (see Gen. 9:2).

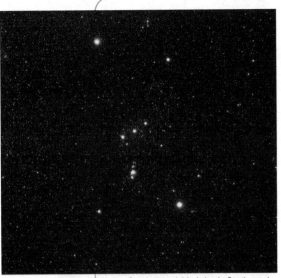

13-8 Stars became visible during the Creation week.

 Stones of Witness

We assume or have been taught that the following features in nature take many thousands or millions of years to occur.

Deep canyons
Glacial valleys
Mountain ranges
Sedimentary strata hundreds of meters thick
Rocks
Starlight from distant galaxies
Thick continental glaciers

Which of these could have been formed fairly rapidly by processes that are no longer occurring? Which may depend on physical laws that have changed over time?

body of both creationary and naturalistic research indicates that the speed of light is not constant and is, in fact, decreasing.

2. Time (that is, the rate of time) is or was not constant at every place in the universe. According to Einstein's general theory of relativity, clocks run slower in high gravitational fields and faster in low gravity. Many creationary scientists agree with a theory that during the first days of the Creation week, the earth was at the center of a huge, extremely dense, expanding "white hole" (called the "deep" in Genesis), from which God created the rest of the universe. While only a few days passed on Earth, which was subject to intense gravity within the white hole, billions of years passed during the creation of the rest of the universe distant from the earth. Since starlight was shining throughout the entire period of the expansion of the universe, it was visible on Earth when the heavens became visible.

Regardless of how we may try to explain the apparent disagreement between stellar distances and time, we can be assured that it is the interpretation of the scientific data and the inadequacies of our theories that are at fault, not the revelation of God's Word.

 Stones of Witness

All of these features (except perhaps distant starlight) could have come into existence through processes that are no longer occurring. Most creationary scientists believe that the Flood and its aftermath are sufficient causes for these features. Starlight from distant galaxies may depend on physical laws that have changed or perhaps on physics that we do not fully understand.

 Web Resource: Antediluvian Carnivory

Some creationary scientists hold that if some of the animals on the ark were carnivorous, then Noah would have had to butcher and dry enough meat to feed them for perhaps two or three years so that they would not eat all the herbivores as soon as they left the ark. The Bible does not say Noah did this in addition to building the ark, therefore these scientists do not believe he did it, and they conclude that carnivorous behavior must have developed sometime after the Flood. Others say tooth marks on fossilized bones buried by Flood sediment show that carnivory existed before the Flood. About 75 percent of the animal kinds released from the ark are now extinct, many of which may have disappeared through carnivory. See more on this topic on the Answers in Genesis (AiG) website, which is linked from the BJU Press Online Resources/Sciences webpage. Under General Science, click on the link *How Did Bad Things Come About?*

This description of the devastation of the earth is generally referred to as the catastrophic plate tectonics (CPT) theory. Nearly all geologists today accept a plate tectonics theory in one form or another as the best description of the process that determined the locations and contours of the continents, but only the CPT theory is consistent with the biblical timeframe of the Flood. Chapter 16 presents and compares two plate tectonics models.

Additional Resources

Consult *The World that Perished* by John C. Whitcomb and *The Genesis Flood* by John C. Whitcomb and Henry Morris for more on the effects of the Flood. Both are available from ICR and AiG as well as other booksellers.

Noah's Ark

It can be argued that Noah's ark was the most important feat of human engineering, carried out under God's direction, in the history of the earth. According to the Bible, the ark was constructed of gopher wood, a strong but unidentifiable wood, and sealed with a thick, waterproof tree sap (Gen. 6:14).

The ark was not a sea-going ship but a floating barn. There was no need for streamlining, since it was not propelled. It simply had to float upright during the Flood. The dimensions given in Scripture indicate it was a large rectangular box, 300 cubits long (450 ft or 137 m) by 50 cubits wide (75 ft or 23 m) and 30 cubits high (45 ft or 14 m) (Gen. 6:15). The ark had three enclosed decks, or floors, and a window "above" (Gen. 6:16). Many creationary engineers believe this window was a shuttered opening one cubit high that ran the length of the ark in a rooftop cupola to provide ventilation. A single door was built into one side, probably providing access to the third deck so as to be above the water line when the ark was loaded.

The ark is often depicted as being constructed of crude, partially dressed bark-covered logs and held together with wooden pegs (tree nails). But consider that humans living prior to the Flood (1656 years after Creation) were probably extremely intelligent, having long lives that permitted continuous learning and acquisition of vast experience. Also, metallurgy was a well-established art if not a science (Gen. 4:22). It would not be surprising if Noah had iron saws, drills, fasteners (nails and bolts), and other fittings at his disposal. Noah and his sons could have had as many as 120 years (Gen. 6:3) to do the extra work of squaring and dressing the timbers, possibly with the aid of some sort of sawmill. It is probable that the ark was used as a source of building timbers for urgently needed human and animal shelter after the Flood. It is even conceivable that additional milled lumber was loaded into the ark for this very purpose. Therefore, it would have been prudent to dress the timbers used in the ark when time was available before the Flood rather than trying to do it afterward when all efforts were devoted to basic survival.

Additional Resource

For an interesting study of technical issues surrounding the ark, read *Noah's Ark: A Feasibility Study* by John Woodmorappe (Institute for Creation Research, 1996). This book covers topics such as the space into which animals had to fit on the ark, the feeding of the animals, waste management, the recovery of the biosphere after the Flood, and the repopulation of the earth after the floodwaters subsided.

Web Resource

For a technical evaluation of the ark's design and sea-keeping ability, visit the BJU Press Online Resources/*SPACE AND EARTH SCIENCE* webpage. Under Chapter 13, click on the link *Ark Sea-Keeping Analysis*.

13-9 Artist's rendition of the antediluvian world (top); the first 40 days of the Flood (top middle); the recessionary stage of the Flood (bottom middle); Noah and his family giving thanks after leaving the ark at the end of the Flood year (bottom)

13.17 The Flood and Its Aftermath

Later, God again judged the world because of man's overwhelming sin. "*And the waters prevailed exceedingly upon the earth; . . . and the mountains were covered*" (Gen. 7:19–20). The worldwide Flood of Noah's time completely changed the face of the earth. It eroded and redeposited vast amounts of **sediment** (loose material that sinks to the bottom of a body of water). Nearly all sedimentary rock layers of the earth's crust, called **strata**, and the fossils they contain, are likely the results of this Flood. The geologic disruptions of the Flood raised great chains of volcanic mountains and likely rearranged the earth's surface as huge plates of the crust slid against each other, creating mountain ranges and deep chasms.

Many creationary scientists believe that the original climate after Creation varied from mild to tropical, nearly from pole to pole. The fact that the overall world climate today is cooler and is different from place to place and from day to day fits the biblical framework. Creationary scientists believe that there was much less water on the earth's surface in its early days. According to their theories, the existence of a few landmasses, or possibly only one large continent covered by lush, dense vegetation, produced a much more uniform global environment. The Flood may have introduced two to three times more liquid water onto the surface of the earth than originally was present. It is thought that the dense haze from worldwide volcanic activity and increased water vapor in the atmosphere drastically cooled the earth, causing a single ice age of no more than several hundred years duration. Eventually, the skies cleared, the earth warmed, and the present-day climate was established.

Most geologists deny that these three important events (Creation, Fall, and Flood) ever happened. They believe that the Bible is full of errors and exaggerations. The Bible says that such people are willingly ignorant because they have refused to believe God (2 Pet. 3:5–6).

13-10 Sedimentary rock strata in Pugh Canyon, Kanah, Utah

The Flood

Next to Creation, the Genesis Flood is the most significant event in geologic history. The chronology of the Flood is carefully recorded in Genesis 7:11–8:14. Although the geologic details are only briefly mentioned in tantalizing generalities, we can draw some educated inferences based on biblical presuppositions. We know that the Antediluvian calendar consisted of 30-day months. The five months between the dates given in Gen. 7:11 and 8:4 contain 150 days (Gen. 8:3). With this knowledge, the following Flood chronology can be constructed:

Day 7 before the Flood: Noah and his family boarded the ark. It can be surmised that it took some or all of the next seven days to load and berth the estimated 16,000 animals and birds (Gen. 7:6–11).

Day 1: On this day "*were all the fountains of the great deep broken up, and the windows of heaven were opened*" (Gen. 6:11). Creationary geologists suggest that great rents in the earth's crust opened, possibly where the mid-ocean ridges are today, releasing unimaginable torrents of hot subterranean water and steam along with floods of magma. One potential source of the rains could have been the condensing of these waters ejected into the atmosphere.

Days 1–40: The floodwaters covered all land features by at least 15 cubits (7 m or 22 ft) (Gen. 7:19–20). It has been estimated that the fully loaded ark had a draft of about 15 cubits, so this depth would be necessary for the ark to float free of all submerged terrain. This period of the Flood is called the *inundatory phase* by many creationary geologists.

13C-1 Section Review

1. What problems face one who would create a geologic history of the world?

2. In the absence of an eyewitness account, what three possibilities exist for the origin of the earth?

3. Name the three events that must be considered when studying the earth's history from a biblical worldview.

4. What is the main reason that one cannot directly determine the age of the earth by studying it?

5. Name some things in nature that are different from the original creation as a result of the Flood.

6. (True or False) It is not possible to determine the actual age of an object or organism just by examining it.

ACCORDING TO EVOLUTIONISTS

13.18 Uniformitarianism

Evolutionists deny the truth of God's Word and insist on discovering earth's history from the earth itself. They interpret the earth's history by using the **doctrine of uniformity**, or uniformitarianism. As we mentioned in Chapter 1, this principle depends on the idea that the processes occurring today are the same processes that have shaped the earth throughout its history; that is, *the present is the key to the past*. To an extent, this is true. God has set up certain laws of science that do not change. If this were not so, science would be useless because the laws (and the processes they control) could change as quickly as scientists formulated them. But evolutionists believe that these processes existed before the earth was formed and that the earth came into existence by these laws and processes. If these scientists believe in God, they do not recognize that He is not bound by natural laws. Thus, they say that the earth formed according to current scientific laws, and they deny the possibility of supernatural events or miracles.

13.19 Earth's History Is Not Uniform

According to the doctrine of uniformity, processes that are occurring today should have worked in the past to form features similar to those that we see today. For example, sedimentation of sand and silts occurs mainly at the mouths of rivers in the shallow coastal areas of the ocean. Therefore, when a uniformitarian geologist examines a stratified rock containing sandstone or siltstone, he sees evidence for sedimentation in a shallow sea. Interestingly, all the major continents contain extensive deposits of stratified sediments, implying that most of the world was continuously covered by shallow coastal seas near river mouths. This theory does not fit with the other uniformitarian models of the ancient earth, nor does it agree with what is seen today.

Uniformitarianism also fails to explain why we see evidence for processes that worked in the past that are not operating today. Some kinds of rocks—red sandstone, for example—have never been observed to form. Coal is not being formed today in the vast quantities it once was. No one has observed **fossil graveyards** forming, yet

Day 40: The rains fell for 40 days and nights. Evidently the geologic events that released the subterranean waters ceased on this day (Gen. 7:12, 17).

Days 40–150: As the waters began subsiding in the *recessionary phase*, the ark floated until the 150th day after the Flood began, when it grounded on the mountains of Ararat (Gen. 8:4).

Day 224: Nearly 2½ months after the ark grounded, the waters had subsided enough so that tops of the local mountains became visible on this day—It took nearly 2½ months after the ark grounded for the waters to subside enough to begin to see the tops of the local mountains (Gen. 8:5). Geologically, the newly formed ocean basins were subsiding and the continents were rising, making room for the additional waters on the earth's surface. The waters covering the continents were compacting the sediments and scouring loose materials as they flowed toward the ocean basins between the continents.

Day 264: Noah opened the ark's window covering to glimpse out for the first time. He released a raven and a dove. There evidently was much water still remaining that prevented the birds from landing.

Day 271: Noah sent out the dove again, which returned with a twig from an olive sapling, proving that somewhere plants were reestablishing themselves, probably in the higher elevations (Gen. 8:10–11).

Day 278: The dove was released again and did not return, indicating that she had found some sort of habitation (Gen. 8:12).

Day 314: Five weeks later, Noah opened the great door in the side of the ark that God had sealed on the first day and gazed out on a barren and alien Earth (Gen. 8:13). The ground appeared dry, which meant that the sediments had compacted enough to squeeze out most of the residual waters, at least in the mountain elevations.

Day 370: After almost two more months, God commanded Noah and his family to disembark and begin the job of filling the earth with life again (Gen. 8:14–17).

Answers to 13C-1 Section Review Questions

1. (1) No human was present to view the origin of the earth. (2) No human records exist for events prior to about 4500–5000 years ago. (3) The existing historical records that contain information of interest to geologists are incomplete. (§13.11)

2. Three origins of the earth are possible: (1) the earth has always existed, (2) the earth came into existence through some natural process, or (3) the earth was created supernaturally. (§13.11)

3. The three key events in the earth's history are the Creation, the Fall and Curse, and the Flood. (§13.12)

4. The earth and everything in it was created supernaturally, so there is no direct way of determining how old it is or even how old it appears to be. (§13.14)

5. Answers will vary but may include the amount of water on the earth's surface; the shape and distribution of landmasses; the weather; the number of volcanoes and mountains; the number of kinds of animals; the existence of huge numbers of fossils; the existence of oil, coal, and natural gas deposits; and global sedimentary and igneous rock formations. (§13.17)

6. True. To assign an age simply from examination usually requires making assumptions that may not be verifiable. (§13.15)

■ known or suspected coal beds

13-11 The doctrine of uniformity is insufficient to explain nonvolcanic mountain formation (top), fossil graveyards (middle), or coal formation (bottom). These processes have not been observed taking place.

Another great Bible verse for refuting uniformitarianism is Hebrews 11:3: *"Through faith we understand that the worlds were framed by the word of God, so that things which are seen were not made of things which do appear."*

these tangled heaps of mixed fossils abound in the earth's rocks. Chalk beds exist in many locations over the world. These deposits, hundreds of meters thick, consist of the innumerable shells of tiny one-celled animals that live and die in the ocean as plankton. Their shells settle to the floor of the ocean to form a sedimentary ooze. Although there are thick deposits of this ooze in the ocean basins today, no observable process is turning it into chalk.

Much of the sedimentary rock layers also lack evidence of processes that we see operating today. For example, in many locations strata rest undisturbed one on top of another, supposedly representing millions of years in evolutionary time. The boundaries between parallel layers do not show evidence of stream erosion, of worm holes, or of other biological activity. No soil formation is evident. These conditions would be highly unlikely if there were really millions of years between layers. If erosion appears to have occurred, it was in a manner that indicates the removing of huge amounts of material in a short period of time. The freshly eroded surface was then quickly covered by other sediment, often having layers settled at a different angle.

Evolutionists claim that after the earth condensed from the dusty disk surrounding the sun, it became a mass of "molten rock" containing steam and other gases dissolved in it. The surface eventually solidified into a rocky crust pierced with numerous volcanoes. Many evolutionists say that all the water in the oceans condensed from steam separating from the molten rock emitted by volcanoes. Modern volcanoes do emit steam, but in such great quantities that they could have filled the present ocean basins in less than 350 million years. Geologists know that up to 70% of the volcanoes today are extinct, which means that volcanic activity must have been much greater in the past. If the doctrine of uniformity were correct, and if the earth were truly 4.5 billion years old, the world would be completely covered by water. Where did all of the excess water go?

13.20 Earth's Future Will Not Be Uniform

The Bible warns against the error of uniformitarianism in 2 Peter 3:3–4. *"Knowing this first, that there shall come in the last days scoffers, walking after their own lusts, And saying, Where is the promise of his coming? for since the fathers fell asleep, all things continue*

13-12 The earth and all living things will experience great disruption during the end times as described in the book of Revelation.

Figure 13-12 is a montage of future events mentioned in the book of Revelation that point to a failure of the uniformitarian model. Shown are the impact of an immense meteor (8:9–11, 9:1), devastation by earthquakes (six references) and accompanying tsunamis, the waters of the earth turning to blood (11:6, 16:3–4), and widespread famine (18:8).

as they were from the beginning of the creation." All things have not continued simply as they were since the Creation, regardless of how loudly the scoffers of today protest. God has intervened supernaturally many times, and He may do so again at any moment. Our hope of the Lord's soon return is a rejection of uniformitarian doctrine.

13C-2 Section Review

1. Name the doctrine that states "the present is the key to the past." What does this phrase mean to naturalistic scientists?

2. What are some evidences accepted by scientists that conditions have not always been what they are today?

3. Why are these evidences problems for people holding to a uniformitarian view?

4. What future event demands a rejection of uniformitarianism? Why does the event not fit into that doctrine?

5. (True or False) The doctrine of uniformity is used more to reject the possibility of miracles than it is used to show the uniformity of natural processes throughout earth's history.

DATING METHODS

13.21 How Old Is the Earth?

One dispute between evolutionists and many Creationists is the earth's age. Evolutionists, and those who would compromise with what the Bible says, believe that the earth is nearly 4.5 billion years old. People who accept the literal account of Creation given in Scripture believe that the earth is only a few thousand years old. How can we decide who is right? Is there a reliable way to know the age of the earth?

13.22 The Candle Analogy

Present-day observations are no basis for determining the earth's age. Trying to find the earth's age from present processes is like trying to figure out how long a dripless candle has been burning. Even if you know how fast the candle is burning, you cannot tell how long the candle has been burning unless you know how tall it was when it was lit and whether it has been burning at a constant rate. Similarly, we cannot tell how long the earth has existed by looking at how rapidly sediments are deposited today.

One reason for disagreement on the earth's age is disagreement about the origin of the earth. Young-earth Creationists believe God's Word when it says that the earth was complete after Creation. It had land, seas, rocks, plants, animals, and two humans. The Bible also gives reliable evidence that this event happened relatively recently. Evolutionists believe that the earth condensed from space dust into a molten mass of rock, which later cooled and developed seas and dry land, formed mountains, and started life. These processes supposedly required billions of years to occur. Finally, there are those who claim to believe the Bible but try to compromise with modern science on matters of origins by saying that God somehow continued creating over billions of years or used evolutionary processes to create. In any case, these people agree with evolutionists that the earth is billions of years old.

13-13 Just as the height of a candle cannot indicate how long it has been burning, sediments on the earth cannot reveal how old the earth is.

 Demonstration: The Candle Analogy

Have several different candles burning on your desk as students enter the room for class. At the beginning of class, ask the students to identify which candle has been burning the longest. You can pick candles of the same type and cut them off to form candles of different lengths. You can also place a candle near a fan to increase the rate of burning. Point out to your students that some factors can cause a process to occur faster than "normal."

 Visual 13-3: Biblical Chronology of the Earth's History

Use this visual to show your students the biblical and historical evidence for the age of the earth. The horizontal time scale is subdivided into 1000-year intervals. Note that not all Bible scholars agree on the date given for the birth of Abraham, but the variance is less than 100 years.

Answers to 13C-2 Section Review Questions

1. *The doctrine of uniformity*, or *uniformitarianism*, states that the present is the key to the past. Naturalistic scientists believe that only the processes and laws that can be observed today, or localized catastrophic natural events such as meteor strikes, were responsible for processes and physical features formed in the past. Therefore, since miracles are not observed to be occurring today, they had no part in past times either. (§13.18)

2. Answers will vary. Examples given in the text of features not forming today include certain kinds of rock, coal, fossil graveyards, and thick chalk deposits. Other evidences include the absence of thick salt deposits, the indications that climate varied greatly in the past, continental glaciation, and asteroid impacts. (§13.19)

3. These evidences show that earth's history was not uniform and that processes not observed today occurred in the past. (§13.19)

4. The return of Christ for His people demands a rejection of uniformitarianism because Christ's return is a miraculous, supernatural, one-time event. (§13.20)

5. True. (§13.18)

FACETS OF GEOLOGY

DATING A YOUNG EARTH

Here is an easy math problem that anyone should be able to solve. If a city currently dumps 1 m of trash into a landfill each year and the trash is now 3 m deep, then how old is the landfill? Three years, right?

Think again! You did not take into account the other circumstances. The landfill was built on an older landfill. The city dumped trash at different rates in the past. Sometimes construction crews took away soil for projects. But there is no way you could have known about these other factors.

Modern scientists face a similar difficulty in determining the age of the earth. They measure current amounts and accumulation rates of dust, gas, and so on; then they estimate how many years were

necessary for the accumulations to occur. However, they do not know all the factors that affect the accumulation:

1. What quantities existed in the beginning?
2. How quickly did these quantities accumulate in the past?
3. What unusual factors altered the rate of accumulation and removal?

If evolution is correct, then the earth's accumulations should reflect an old age of 4 or 5 billion years. But the accumulations do not even come close. Each accumulation is different. Even

Material	Age based on observed change	Explanation based on uniform rates alone
human population	4000	Starting with one human couple, it is possible to reach the current population of the world in only a few thousand years, even when accounting for wars and disease.
river deltas	5000	Modern deltas at the ends of rivers required a relatively short time to develop.
helium in zircon crystals	4–8000	Radioactive decay of uranium atoms trapped in "Precambrian" zircons at the time of their formation produces helium atoms. The rate of leakage of helium from zircon crystals indicates a recent formation and very high radioactive decay rates.
magnetic field*	<4500	Even though the earth's magnetic field is decaying rapidly, it is still very large today. Evidence indicates many fluctuations around the time of the Flood.
linguistic families	<4500	Every 1000 years, 19.5% of the core of any language changes. Presently we can identify 20 different linguistic families. The number of families should be higher if human language has existed for more than 5000 years.
ocean salinity	<10,000	The salt content of ocean waters would be much greater if Earth were more than about 10,000 years old.
petrified wood	<4500	Evolutionists claim that petrified wood (such as that found in the Petrified Forest of Arizona) requires many millions of years to form. Creationists have found instances where petrified wood formed in less than 100 years.
growth rate of stalactites and stalagmites	<4500	Evolutionists claim cave formations take millions of years to form. Creationists have shown (experimentally) that one or two hundred years is more than adequate.
ocean sediment	<12,000,000	Ocean sediment accumulates 25 times more rapidly than it is removed. The existing amount of mud could have accumulated in only 12,000,000 years, which is much less than 4–5 billion years.

* Age based on decay, not accumulation. Information is from multiple sources.

Facet Summary: Dating a Young Earth

This Facet turns the naturalistic assumptions of uniformitarians against them. By taking a simplified view of accumulation rates, or rates of change observed today, and then looking back to the logical start of the process, we find that all of the rates point to a beginning that is much more recent than the billions of years suggested by physical evolutionists. This Facet is worth discussing in class. There are no vocabulary terms in this Facet.

more embarrassing for evolutionists, most dating techniques based on accumulations indicate that the earth is young, not billions of years old.

The evolutionists reject dating methods that indicate a young earth, not because the methods are wrong, but because they do not fit their theory. Evolutionists choose the few dating techniques that happen to support an old earth and an old ocean, which the evolutionary theory demands. Is their method scientific?

Creationists can estimate the age of the earth, not because they rely on dating techniques, but because the Bible contains an eyewitness account of the Creation and events before the Flood. We can only guess at conditions in the early days because the Flood destroyed nearly all the evidence. Modern accumulations of various materials in the earth help us study changes since the Flood, but their value is limited in studying conditions before that time. Any attempt to give an age for the earth based on accumulations of different materials is misleading and unscientific. There are almost as many different ages of the earth as there are accumulating materials.

Accumulations, such as these rock strata in the Grand Canyon, are of limited use in determining the age of the earth.

Because these different views of the earth's beginning start with "candles" of different "heights," different ages of the earth are assumed. Which idea is more reliable? Creationists base their conception of the early earth on the Bible, but evolutionists have only their own speculations on which to base their ideas.

13.23 Genealogical and Prophetical Evidence

Dates in the past can be established in several ways. One way is to examine historical records. Evolutionists generally dismiss historical records for this purpose because they believe man's appearance on Earth is too recent for him to have documented much of Earth's history. Creationists use the historical records in the Bible to attempt to date the age of the earth. Specifically, they study the genealogical records (lists of ancestors and descendants) in the Old Testament along with the prophecies of Daniel and other prophets.

James Ussher calculated from these records that Creation occurred in 4004 BC. Johannes Kepler undertook the same task and concluded that Creation took place in 4977 BC—almost a millennium earlier. Ussher's date has been generally regarded as the more accurate of the two. Early scholars had difficulty determining whether the manuscripts of Scripture that were available in their time contained complete and accurate genealogies. However, many copies of ancient manuscripts not available to these men have been discovered in recent centuries. Careful reanalysis of genealogical information from all the known Bible manuscripts gives assurance that the age of the earth is approximately 6500 years, not the millions or billions of years required by the theory of evolution.

13-14 Archbishop James Ussher

James Ussher (1581–1656) was the Protestant Archbishop of Armagh, Church of Ireland. He is best known for calculating the date of Creation and other key biblical dates, but he also traveled widely and was a prominent theologian.

Careful analysis of Scripture tells us that the earth is approximately 6500 years old.

The first practical electronic radiation detector was invented by the German physicist Hans Geiger in 1911. It consisted of a sealed glass detector tube containing a central electrode with a high voltage relative to a metallic sheath inside the tube. When a radiation particle or ray entered the detector and ionized a gas molecule in the tube, the resulting ions were rapidly accelerated toward one of the charged electrodes. In the process, they collided with other gas molecules, forming a cascade of many gas ions. The resulting voltage dip in the circuit connected to the tube was registered as an audible click and indicated by a meter. Most people associate the Geiger counter with radiation detection, and the principles on which it operates are still in use. However, many new methods have been developed to detect and measure radiation and radioactivity. (See PHYSICS, 2nd Edition, Chapter 29.)

 Visual 13-4: Carbon-14 Decay

This visual simply illustrates radiocarbon decay over one half-life. Interestingly, this span of time is about the age of the earth according to the young-earth model.

You may find it difficult to discuss radioactive dating methods without referring to the *isotopes* of various elements. If this is the case, explain that the nucleus (center) of most atoms consists of tiny particles—positively charged protons and neutral neutrons. The number of protons in the nucleus determines the element. For example, an atom with 6 protons is always carbon and an atom with 7 protons is always nitrogen. Atoms of a given element can have different numbers of neutrons. These forms of an element are called isotopes. Each isotope is identified by a mass number, which is the sum of the protons and neutrons in the nucleus. For example, the isotope of the most common form of carbon that has 6 protons and 6 neutrons is called carbon-12 (C-12). The isotope of a carbon atom that has 8 neutrons is called carbon-14 (C-14). Isotopes of elements are chemically identical, but they have different masses. The nuclei of carbon-12 atoms are stable. Carbon-14 nuclei are radioactive, decaying into nitrogen-14 with time.

Radiocarbon dating is based on an assumption that the atmospheric ratio of C-14 to C-12 has been more or less 1:1 trillion as it is now. But we also know that this ratio has varied with time, sometimes significantly. Immediately after Creation the amount of C-14 probably would be undetectable, assuming God did not create any in the atmosphere. We know objects whose dates are positively established by historical methods do not always yield equivalent radiocarbon ages, which indicates that the initial C-14/C-12 ratio must have been different from what it is presently. We also know that nuclear explosions and the burning of fossil fuels create changes in the atmosphere that affect the C-14 to C-12 ratio. This is why calibration curves are required. Ultimately, radiocarbon dating of objects no older than 5000 years may be fairly accurate, but beyond that limit the dates become increasingly questionable.

There is increasing evidence that the rates at which radioactive elements decay into other elements may not be constant and, in fact, may have been much more rapid in the past.

13.24 Radioactive Dating

Another way to determine the age of an object is to examine a process that occurs at a constant rate. If we can tell how long the process has been going on in the object, then we just subtract that time from the current date to find the age of the object. For example, many materials are **radioactive**; their atoms are unstable and they break down or **decay** into different forms of the same element or atoms of other elements. Radioactive materials seem to decay at a constant rate, which scientists believe makes them useful as "clocks" for measuring the earth's age. The rate of radioactive decay can be measured by an instrument called a Geiger counter, as well as other instruments.

There are some problems with radioactive dating methods in general. These methods require assumptions that rely directly on the doctrine of uniformity. Scientists make assumptions about the rates of formation and decay of radioactive materials. They also make assumptions about the history of the sample they are analyzing—that it has not changed during its existence, or that they know how it changed in ways that might affect its apparent age (the age indicated by the dating method). So, what are the problems? There is no reliable way to know that decay rates were the same in the past as they are now. And there is certainly no way of knowing for sure whether or how the sample was changed during its existence.

13.25 Radiocarbon Dating

The tissues of plants and animals contain extremely small amounts of a form of the element carbon called **carbon-14**. Carbon-14 forms in the upper atmosphere when cosmic rays bombard atmospheric gas atoms and produce neutrons, which then strike nitrogen atoms and replace one of the nitrogen's protons. Carbon-14 is chemically identical to the normal form of carbon, carbon-12, so it readily combines with oxygen to form carbon dioxide. Carbon-14 in carbon dioxide eventually moves into the lower atmosphere where it is used by plants to form plant tissues. Animals and humans eat plants, so their tissues contain carbon-14 as well.

Because carbon-14 is radioactive, it slowly changes back into nitrogen through nuclear decay. While an organism is living, the amount of carbon-14 entering its tissues balances the amount that decays, so the ratio of carbon-14 to carbon-12 within the organism is constant. When it dies, however, it no longer eats or breathes; thus, it can no longer take in carbon-14. The amount of carbon-14 that is present begins to decrease through radioactive decay. Half of any remaining carbon-14 will decay away every 5730 years.

13-15 The 800 Dead Sea Scrolls have been given dates between 335 BC and 78 AD by the radiocarbon method. Photo © The Israel Museum, Jerusalem

To determine the date of an organism's death, a scientist uses special tests. Among the more modern tests is **liquid scintillation counting (LSC)** and the use of an instrument called an **accelerated mass spectrometer (AMS)**. These tests measure the amount of carbon-14, or the ratio of carbon-14 to carbon-12, in the sample material. The smaller the ratio, the longer the time since the organism died. To account for variations in the amount of carbon-14 present in the atmosphere when an organism died, the researcher uses a **calibration curve**, a graph of carbon-14 in objects of known ages. That is, scientists date an object by historical clues, or a tree by counting its rings, and then determine the amount of carbon-14 that is in it for a given age. They plot the carbon-14 age on the vertical axis and the actual age on the horizontal axis. Then they draw a best-fit curve through the points. To date another object, they measure the carbon-14 it contains and then find the actual age on the curve that corresponds to the carbon-14 age of the sample.

Radiocarbon dating has limitations. The most significant of these is that the calibration curve can be historically verified only for ages less than about 5000 years. Although some scientists have claimed that analyses of tree rings have extended the calibration curve several thousand years farther back in time, these results are controversial even among uniformitarian scientists. No object has been reliably dated through historical records as more than 4500–5000 years old. Thus, a scientist cannot be confident about an apparent radiocarbon date of more than 5000 years.

Another problem is that some radiocarbon ages do not agree with ages that can be verified by other means. These are called **anomalous samples**. Scientists do not always understand why the dates are wrong or how to correct them.

Many factors affect the amount of carbon-14 that an organism takes in. The tissues of some organisms "prefer" one form of carbon over another form. This may produce apparent ages that are older or younger than the actual age. The rate of carbon-14 production and its occurrence in the atmosphere are known to have varied throughout history as well. Radiocarbon dating is also limited to materials that contain organic carbon, such as wood, charcoal, shells, and bones. It is useless for dating most rocks or metal artifacts.

13-16 A mass spectrometer used to determine carbon-14 content

anomalous (uh NAHM uh lus): an- (Gk. *an*—not) + -omalous (Gk. *homalos*—even, same)

A young-earth Creationist would not expect carbon-14 dates to be older than about 4500 BC since that is about the date of Creation obtained from biblical evidence. Much older carbon-14 dates are anomalous.

Calibration Curve Based on Tree-ring Data

Relative Amount of C-14 Remaining / Years Before Present (BP)

— C-14 Calibration
— C-14 Decay Curve

13-17 One kind of radiocarbon calibration curve is based on counting tree rings. The black line shows the amount of carbon-14 remaining in a sample if atmospheric carbon-14 has been constant throughout history. The colored line shows the amount of carbon-14 remaining after a given time due to variations in atmospheric concentrations over time.

13-18 Some scientists use overlapping records of tree growth rings to extend the radiocarbon dating technique to more than 11,000 years into the past. This method is based on some unreliable assumptions.

The LSC counting technique chemically converts a sample of organic material into a very pure organic liquid whose molecules are formed from rings of carbon atoms. This organic liquid may be in the form of either benzene or toluene. The organic liquid is mixed with another chemical that glows when a carbon-14 atom decays. The tiny flashes of light (scintillations) produced by the decays are counted by a special optical instrument. The rate of decays gives the radioactivity of the sample.

An AMS measures the mass and relative quantities of the different atoms in a sample. Since different isotopes of a radioactive element have different masses, their presence in a sample can be detected. This instrument is much more sensitive but also much more complex and expensive to use than LSC counting.

Visuals 13-5A, B: Various Carbon-14 Calibration Curves I & II

These visuals illustrate radiocarbon-dating calibration curves. The first visual is a curve based on the IntCal98 dendrochronology calibration curve but displays the data in a different way. The curve is truncated at 6500 years before present (BP), even though the data set extends more than 11,000 years BP. The second visual shows a calibration curve that uses historical artifacts and is similar to the one originally used by Willard Libby's research team. Libby's team perfected the carbon-14 analytical technique shortly after WW II. The vertical lines at each datum indicate the potential error of each age determination. These lines are called *error bars* by scientists.

Other dating methods have been used by scientists in an attempt to achieve independent correlation of the dates obtained by the methods discussed in the text. One of these methods that has become very controversial is ice core layering. Glaciologists drill out long cylindrical cores of ice from thick glacial sheets in places such as Greenland and Antarctica. According to their model, the layers of compacted ice represent annual snowfall cycles that can indicate the age of the ice at each level. They also measure various isotopes of oxygen to identify the annual boundaries of these layers. However, they have run into the same problem as the dendrochronologists (see the Stones of Witness Teacher's Edition note on p. 356). Recent ice accumulations have shown the assumption that each layer of ice represents an annual deposit of snow and ice to be flawed. Also, the deposition of different oxygen isotopes seems to depend on other factors besides seasonal air temperature.

Scientists who study the fine layering of mud in lakes and shallow seas, called *varves*, have discovered the same kinds of problems. Scientifically, there is no reliable way of determining dates and ages for the unobservable past.

Stones of Witness

These scientists are assuming that one tree ring equals one year of growth. According to evidence provided by the Bible, the earth is no older than 6500 years. In addition, any dead tree trunk that now exists on a mountaintop must have grown since the Flood, placing an upper limit on its age of about 4500–5000 years. Therefore, the trees must have grown multiple rings in one year. This hypothesis has been confirmed by people who have studied modern trees and discovered that they have grown multiple rings in a single year. This finding brings the underlying assumption of dendrochronology into question.

"Deep time" is a concept we will return to again and again in this unit as we discuss the features of the evolutionary model of the earth's history.

Two kinds of uranium, U-235 and U-238, decay into two different types of lead, Pb-207 and Pb-206, respectively. A third kind of lead, Pb-204, usually occurs in the same rocks. Pb-204 does not come from radioactive sources. In pure lead, the ratio of Pb-204 to Pb-207 is usually constant. Scientists assume that the rock being tested originally contained lead in this constant ratio. They assume that all Pb-206 and Pb-207 above this ratio is a result of uranium's decay. This assumption may seem plausible, but it has no scientific data to support it since the original assumption cannot be verified.

Stones of Witness

Another dating technique that is gaining popularity is the counting of tree rings to determine the age of long-lived trees. This dating method is called **dendrochronology** from the Greek words for tree and dating. Certain species of trees, such as the bristle-cone pine, grow high on mountains in cold, dry climates that preserve their wood after they die. By comparing overlapping tree ring records from very old dead trees, some scientists claim they can accurately determine the age of the oldest trees back 11,000 years.

What is the basic assumption about tree rings and time that these scientists are making? Using the Bible as the standard for dating the earth, how would you explain these dendrochronology dates? What evidence in living trees of these species would you look for to confirm your explanation?

In spite of these limitations, radiocarbon dating is a worthwhile tool. With proper precautions, it is reasonably accurate. Interestingly, radiocarbon dating has provided significant evidence against evolution and long ages of time. Because it decays away relatively quickly, the amount of carbon-14 in a sample should be undetectable after only 40,000–60,000 years. Therefore, samples of coal and oil (originally land plants and sea creatures, respectively) that evolutionists estimate are millions of years old should have *no* detectable carbon-14. Yet these materials have been radiocarbon dated at only a few thousand years old.

13.26 Uranium-Lead Method

Other radioactive materials are theoretically able to remain detectable for millions or billions of years because they decay so slowly. These materials are used by geologists for determining ages of rocks far back in time ("**deep-time**" ages). The **uranium-lead method** is based on the radioactive decay of uranium into lead by a chain of other radioactive elements. Many rocks contain both uranium and lead. The dating method assumes that the ratio of lead to uranium in a rock shows its age. The more lead and less uranium in a rock, the older it is. The problem with this method is that it is not known how much lead (or uranium) was in the original rock. Scientists using this method also do not know whether uranium or lead atoms were added or removed by groundwater solutions during the rock sample's existence.

Because two kinds of uranium decay into two kinds of lead, each process gives a different age for a rock. Scientists can therefore check these ages to see if they are nearly the same. In theory, if they are, the age is considered more likely; if they are not, the age is doubtful. Scientists have found that the ages from the uranium decays are rarely the same. In one rock the two uranium decays as well as two other dating methods gave four different ages, ranging from 100 million years to 10.5 billion years. Rather than being an exceptional case, these kinds of disagreements are the rule, showing how unreliable the uranium-lead method is. Numbers like 10.5 billion years highlight another problem with the uranium-lead method: it sometimes gives results that are clearly wrong even to evolutionary scientists. Rocks in Texas gave ages as high as 11 billion years—more than twice as old

13-19 The age of rock from near Pikes Peak was determined from two different uranium isotopes. They differed by 80 million years.

as evolutionists believe the earth is. The rocks cannot be older than the earth.

13.27 Potassium-Argon Method

The **potassium-argon method** is similar to the uranium-lead method but uses different elements. Potassium-40, a metal, decays into argon-40, a gas. The method uses the ratio of argon to potassium to find the age of a rock. Again, to use this method to date a rock, scientists must decide how much argon the rock had originally. They usually assume that it had none, especially if the rock is an igneous type that was molten when it was formed. Geologists formerly believed that gases completely boiled out of molten rock. This assumption has been disproved by sampling fresh lava flows.

The potassium-argon dating method has been tested and found wanting. Some volcanic rocks in Hawaii were observed as they formed in 1800 and 1801. About 170 years later, scientists dated these rocks using the potassium-argon method. They found ages ranging from 160 million to 3 billion years. Other volcanic rocks known to be less than 200 years old gave potassium-argon ages ranging from 12 million to 22 million years. Such results prove conclusively that the potassium-argon method is unreliable.

What conclusions can we reach about attempts to date the earth? For one thing, some highly regarded, so-called scientific dating methods are thoroughly unreliable. True science involves observation. Therefore, scientific research cannot provide a true age for the earth because no human was present until the very last stage of Creation. On the other hand, God has provided us a reliable record in His Word from which we can know the earth is only a few thousand years old.

13-20 Lava rocks such as these were seen forming during a volcanic eruption. About 170 years later they were given potassium-argon dates of millions to billions of years. The potassium-argon dating method is unreliable.

13C-3 Section Review

1. How did James Ussher determine the date of Creation? What was the date?

2. Name one of the assumptions made by scientists when they use the radiocarbon method to determine the age of an object.

3. How does the ratio of carbon-14 to carbon-12 in a live organism change with time? after it has died?

4. When using the uranium-lead or the potassium-argon dating methods, scientists assume that a rock sample was a "closed system" throughout its existence. In other words, none of the elements were added or removed from the time it was formed. Is this a good assumption? Explain.

5. Name the instruments used to measure the amount of radioactive elements in a sample.

6. What scientific evidence is there that the radioactive methods used to date rocks at millions or billions of years are not reliable?

7. (True or False) Using the latest digital AMS to measure radiocarbon content, a scientist determines that a sample of coal is 55,000 years old. This is probably a fairly accurate date.

Answers to 13C-3 Section Review Questions

1. Ussher calculated the date of Creation from genealogical and prophetical information in the Bible. He arrived at a date of 4004 BC. (§13.23)

2. Answers will vary. Responses may include that the decay rate of carbon-14 is constant, that the original ratio of carbon-14 to carbon-12 in the organism is known, and that the amount of carbon-14 in the sample is not anomalous. (§13.24–13.25)

3. The ratio of carbon-14 to carbon-12 in an organism remains constant as long as the organism is living. It begins to decrease after the organism dies. (§13.25)

4. No. Groundwater can dissolve and add or remove elements from rock. Gases such as argon can pass easily into and out of a sample. (§13.26–13.27)

5. The instruments include the *Geiger counter*, the *liquid scintillation counter*, and the *mass spectrometer*. (§13.24–13.25)

6. Volcanic rocks that formed from lavas within recent historical times have been dated at millions or billions of years old using these methods. Also, significantly contradictory ages have been supplied for the same rock by different dating methods. (§13.27)

7. False. From a biblical viewpoint, the age is significantly greater than the accepted age of the earth. From a strictly scientific viewpoint, the accuracy of carbon-14 dating becomes very unreliable beyond about 4500–5000 years due to the lack of a verifiable calibration curve. (Technically, the amount of C-14 required to yield such a date is hardly detectable and would be subject to significant measurement errors. The average C-14 concentration in living tissues is about 1.5×10^{-12} g C-14 per gram of carbon. The amount of C-14 remaining after 55,000 years would be less than 0.0004% of the original quantity present in the living plant, or about 6×10^{-15} g C-14 per gram of carbon.) (§13.25)

Answers to Chapter Review Questions

What Did You Learn?

1. A geologist is a scientist who studies mainly the solid structures of the earth and the processes that affect those structures. A meteorologist is more interested in the processes and structure of the earth's atmosphere. (§13.1)

2. The text mentions the earth's optimal mass, which holds just the right amount of atmosphere while permitting ease of mobility; its optimal rotational period, which allows for even heating and cooling and a daily cycle of light and dark well matched to the needs of living things; the atmosphere's optimum mixture of oxygen, nitrogen, and other gases necessary to support life while not creating unnecessarily hazardous conditions; the atmosphere's protection of living things from a number of hazards from space; and the provision of the vast quantities of liquid water necessary to sustain life. (Water has a unique combination of properties and is an important factor in many of the processes on Earth.) (§13.2–13.6)

3. Geologists use earthquake waves to study the structure of the interior of the earth. They also drill deep holes into the crust in order to sample the composition and types of rock deep underground, to determine the amount of water and gases present, and to measure the change in temperature with depth. This information is used to construct computer models of the earth's interior. (§13.7)

4. The Bible mentions that the ground was cursed, and as a result humans would have to grow their food from then on. It would be hard work, including weeding and dealing with thorns and thistles. Death entered the world, affecting all animals and humans. The text conjectures that weather may have become more severe, erosion and other forms of degradation may have become significant, earthquakes may have first occurred, some animals may have become carnivorous, and a general fear of predators may have settled over animals and humans. (§13.14)

5. Answers will vary. Responses may include verses 11–12 (plants yielding seed and fruit), verses 14–16 (sun, moon, and stars signaling signs, seasons, days, and years as well as giving light), verses 20–21 (birds could fly), verse 21 (whales were "great," implying they were large if not full grown), verse 22 (sea creatures and fowl were capable of reproduction), verse 28 (commandment to mankind to reproduce), verse 28 (mankind capable of understanding commandments and having dominion), and verses 29–30 (plants were given as food to all creatures and mankind).

6. Answers will vary. Responses from scientific knowledge include the following: Earth features that formed in the past are not forming now (vast sedimentary rock deposits, red sandstone, coal, oil, chalk, fossil graveyards) although the earth is assumed to have been continually changing (evolving) since its beginning; water production from volcanoes today is excessive compared to the amount of water on the earth's surface, if the earth is as old as evolutionists say it is; the earth's climate was significantly different in the past compared to today. (§13.12)

7. The most important assumption concerns the origin of the earth. Creationists base their assumption on the narrative of supernatural Creation in the Bible. Evolutionists reject a supernatural beginning for the earth and base their naturalistic assumptions on their own reasoning. (§13.22)

8. The earth is approximately 6000–6500 years old according to a careful analysis of available Bible manuscripts. (§13.23)

9. A radiocarbon calibration curve is necessary because the amount of C-14 in the atmosphere has varied with time. Just measuring the current ratio of C-14 to C-12 does not indicate the correct age of the sample. Different curves may be needed because some organisms show a preference for different forms of carbon. (§13.25)

10. The deep-time methods often produce greatly different ages for the same sample of rock, ages that are far older than the accepted age of the earth, or ages that are millions or billions of years old for a rock that is known to be only

In Terms of Geology

Chapter Summary

- Geology is the study of the earth, its composition, processes, and history.
- The earth was designed to be inhabited. Its mass, rotation, protective atmospheric mixture, and liquid water provide all the necessities for life.
- The earth's internal structure has been deduced by analyzing earthquake waves.
- The earth's structure consists of the crust, the Mohorovičić discontinuity, the upper mantle (which includes part of the lithosphere and the asthenosphere), the lower mantle, the outer core, and the inner core.
- The core is likely responsible at least partly for the earth's strong magnetic field.
- Historical geology can be viewed from two perspectives based on one's assumption of a young earth or an old earth.
- Young-earth Creationists believe the earth is no older than about 6500 years.
- Creationary scientists are motivated by the Creation Mandate to practice science. They view geology as a product of a fully functional, supernatural creation that was permanently altered by the Curse and the Flood.
- Evolutionists believe the earth evolved by observable, uniform, naturalistic processes from around 4.5 billion years ago.
- Creationists rely on biblical genealogies and prophesies to establish an age for the earth.
- Evolutionists rely on various radioactive dating techniques, such as uranium-lead and potassium-argon, to establish an age for the earth.
- Although radiocarbon dating is a useful tool, radioactive dating techniques for determining the age of rocks are generally scientifically unreliable.

What Did You Learn?

1. What is a geologist? How might his activities differ from a meteorologist's?

2. List several examples of the earth's design that show God's care for living organisms, and describe how each design feature is beneficial.

3. Discuss some methods by which geologists study the interior of the earth.

4. Name two things that were changed about the earth as a result of the Curse.

5. What verses in Genesis 1 support the conclusion that the earth was created fully functional?

6. Give an example in which the doctrine of uniformity fails to account for observations.

7. What is the most important assumption made when attempting to determine the age of the earth? What is the basis for this assumption?

8. What is the age of the earth according to a scholarly analysis of all available manuscripts of the Bible?

9. Why is a calibration curve required for using radiocarbon dates? Why is it possible that different calibration curves will be needed for different kinds of organic matter (say, wood versus bone)?

10. In what ways are deep-time dating methods unscientific?

True or False

11. A geologist could study satellite photos of the earth in the search for oil deposits.

12. The existence of fossils all over the world is evidence for the supernatural design of the original earth.

13. The Moho is the dividing line between the lithosphere and the mantle.

14. The liquid core is believed to be a possible source of the earth's magnetic field.

15. A proper framework for studying the earth must account for the supernatural Creation, the Fall of man, God's Curse on the world, and the global Flood.

16. Fortunately, God's Curse was limited to only the earth and not the remainder of the universe.

17. There is no reason to think that a modern oak tree would look in all respects like an oak tree formed on the third day of Creation week.

18. The Flood not only completely and permanently changed the surface of the earth, but also permanently changed the earth's weather and climates.

19. Even though a uniformitarian sees evidence that processes in the past were not like those he sees today, he just assumes that this is due to random changes in the environment that occur according to scientific laws.

20. Because James Ussher's date of 4004 BC for Creation was obtained from a careful study of Scriptures, we should accept that date in the same way we accept the truth of salvation given in the Gospels.

What Do You Think?

1. Seasons were mentioned during the fourth day of Creation, but the first mention of cold and winter in the Bible occurs immediately after the Flood (Gen. 8:22). What do these facts, along with other information you have learned in this chapter, indicate about the earth's climate before and after the Flood?

2. In a court of law, an eyewitness account by a credible person is regarded as much more trustworthy than circumstantial evidence (facts that happen to exist that can point to one or more conclusions). Which evidence for the age of the earth presented in this chapter falls into each of these categories?

3. If you were a geologist, which areas of that profession do you think would benefit mankind the most in fulfilling God's command to have dominion over the earth and subdue it? Recall what you learned in Chapter 1.

My Review Checklist

☐ I have carefully read the entire chapter.
☐ I have reviewed all of the photographs, illustrations, and graphs.
☐ I have reviewed all of my notes in the margins.
☐ I have reviewed and corrected the quizzes on this chapter.
☐ I have studied all of the vocabulary terms.
☐ I have had all of my questions answered.

---

a few years old. These methods all make unverifiable, unreasonable, and therefore unscientific assumptions. (§13.26–13.27)

True or False

11. True. (§13.1)

12. False. The existence of fossils is not by itself evidence for supernatural design but rather evidence of supernatural judgment. (§13.1–13.6, 13.15)

13. False. The Moho is the dividing line between the crust and the upper mantle. (§13.8)

14. True. (§13.10)

15. True. (§13.12)

16. False. Romans 8:22 shows that the Curse affected the whole creation. (Chap. 1)

17. True. This is an important concept that students need to understand. God did not necessarily create the earth and everything in it with the "appearance of age." A botanist looking at the newly created tree might intuitively think that the tree must have been growing for decades, but it is probable that the tree would not bear the leaf scars, knots of broken branches, rough bark, or even tree rings that are all part of growth in a cursed world. All mammals were probably created without navels (why would those scars be necessary?), and tiny zircon crystals existing today contain evidence from radioactive decay products that they were formed recently in an instant—not over long periods of

time. Humans are fixed on the idea that fully formed objects and organisms imply age. This is only natural. However, nearly everything in the original creation, especially those things created on Earth, might superficially have had the appearance of age, but upon closer examination, their age would have been indeterminate. It is more accurate to state that the earth was formed "fully functional." (§13.14)

18. True. (§13.17)

19. True. (§13.18)

20. False. Unlike the gospel message, which is clearly repeated in many ways throughout Scripture, Ussher's date for Creation is never explicitly stated in the Bible. It is information obtained indirectly through educated guesses based on other information in the Scripture as well as sources outside of the Bible. Since it is a result of human reasoning, it is potentially in error. Therefore, Ussher's date for Creation cannot have the same authority as the gospel message. (§13.23)

What Do You Think?

1. Answers will vary, but consider the following thoughts: (a) It is believed that the world's climate before the Flood was fairly uniform, varying from mild to tropical from pole to pole. After the Flood there were more dramatic seasonal changes, including cold and winter. (b) Seasons can involve more than just temperature—the amount of sunlight, winds, and precipitation vary seasonally as well.

2. The eyewitness account of the earth's early history is contained in the book of Genesis in the Bible. It is an account given by the Holy Spirit to Moses (2 Pet. 1:20–21). The circumstantial evidence for Earth's history consists of all of the theories from science, which are obtained from human reasoning and may or may not be based on God's Word.

3. Answers will vary. Some areas of geology that most directly affect human welfare are in seismology and volcanology, resource exploration and management (oil, coal, water, and minerals), landfill design, and landslide warning and prevention. Many other answers are possible.

Overview

Chapter 14 is the first of two chapters that introduce the materials that form the crust of the earth. In this chapter, students will study pure substances found in the crust—minerals. The emphasis is placed on an overview of the subject, such as general mineral-identification properties, classification of minerals, and their sources and usefulness. The providence of God is emphasized in how He created beautiful things and placed them in the earth for man's use.

Section 14A defines the term *mineral* and introduces the basic kinds of matter so that minerals can be placed in their proper chemical context. The origin of minerals in connection with the Genesis Flood is also discussed.

Minerals can be classified according to certain common properties. In Section 14B, students will learn about these properties and tests that are used for each. This section also covers special properties that are held by only certain classes of minerals.

Section 14C describes the prominent native minerals, their sources, and uses. The major compound mineral classes are listed along with brief descriptions of their characteristics and importance.

Schedule Summary

Section 14A: 1 period

Section 14B: 2–3 periods

Section 14C: 2–3 periods

Investigation Summary

14D "Accretion of Crystals"

14E "Accretion of Crystals—Going a Step Further"

14F "Properties of Minerals"

 Bulletin Board Ideas

1. Make a collage of photographs of various gems and minerals. These photographs help students relate to the material in the chapter.

2. Make a montage of artwork or photographs showing people performing the tests used to identify minerals. Photographs of students from your class will attract a lot of attention.

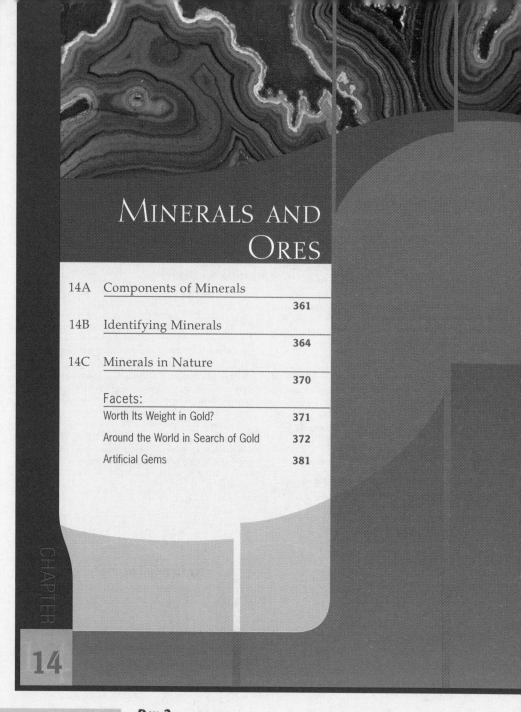

MINERALS AND ORES

CHAPTER

14

SUGGESTED TEACHING SCHEDULE

DAY 0

Assignment

Reading: Section 14A, "Components of Minerals"

DAY 1

Begin by emphasizing that minerals are a gift of God for beauty and for usefulness. Define the word *mineral*. Discuss ores. Differentiate between the terms *element*, *compound*, and *mixture*.

Assignment

Complete: 14A Section Review Questions

Applications 14A, "Types of Matter"

Reading: Section 14B-1 (§14.7–14.14), properties of all minerals

Investigation 14D, "Accretion of Crystals"

DAY 2

Quiz—Section 14A, "Components of Minerals"

Set up Investigation 14D, "Accretion of Crystals." You may also initiate Investigation 14E, "Accretion of Crystals—Going a Step Further," at the same time.

Discuss the general properties of minerals that allow us to identify them. Plan to use examples from your classroom specimen collection and be sure to have the necessary apparatus for demonstrating the various properties.

Assignment

Complete: 14B-1 Section Review Questions

Reading: Section 14B-2 (§14.15–14.20), properties of some minerals

DAY 3

Have students observe crystal growth today and throughout the rest of the chapter (Investigations 14D/E).

14A COMPONENTS OF MINERALS

14.1 Introduction

Minerals in the earth are a gracious gift of God. Job 28:1–11 presents minerals as elements waiting to be used. Here the Bible does not speak of the earth's depths as a sanctuary that men and women must not violate. It rather presents this mineral-rich region as a storehouse designed to meet human needs and desires: "*As for the earth, out of it cometh bread*" (Job 28:5). By uncovering the earth's silver, gold, brass, stones, and sapphires, mankind discovers and explores the glory of being human. This passage refers to the mines that humans dig as "*a path which no fowl knoweth, and which the vulture's eye hath not seen*" (v. 7). A few lines later, it states that the search for minerals demonstrates our race's marvelous strength: "*He [mankind] putteth forth his hand upon the rock; he overturneth the mountains by the roots*" (v. 9). Job 28:1–11 presents minerals as resources waiting to be harnessed.

It should not surprise us, therefore, to learn that minerals have always played an important role in our history. The same day that God called man to exercise dominion over the earth, He placed him in a garden not far from some of the most precious minerals mankind has ever discovered (Gen. 2:11–12). Throughout the Old Testament, the people of God are shown making use of minerals in order to fulfill their divine calling. The Israelites used precious stones in jewelry (Exod. 35:22) and in making Aaron's holy garments (Exod. 39:6–13); they used hewn stone in houses (2 Chron. 34:11) and uncut stones in altars (Exod. 20:25). In addition, from the New Testament we learn that twelve minerals will have a prominent place in New Jerusalem (Rev. 21:19–20).

Minerals are significant in God's Word, and they should therefore be important to us. They are raw materials from which people made in His image are to fashion useful and beautiful things. In studying how best to harness these materials, we can declare the glory of our God because we are learning how to fulfill our divine calling. We are learning to keep the Creation Mandate—maximizing the usefulness of the world He has placed under our authority.

14.2 Minerals

What exactly are minerals? A **mineral** is a naturally occurring, inorganic, crystalline solid with a definite chemical composition. This definition excludes items such as steel and artificial gems because they are manmade. It excludes coal and pearls because they are organic; that is, they came from the tissues or processes of once-living organisms. It excludes air and water because they are not solid. It excludes various forms of glass because they do not have the definite arrangement of atoms that crystals have. Minerals include substances such as gold, natural gems, asbestos, and quartz, along with oxides, sulfides, and carbonates (minerals that are principal sources of metals).

Stones of Witness

Since the Bible recognizes man's great capacity for digging up the earth in search of minerals, how should man approach huge mining and smelting activities that have the potential to open great scars on the earth's surface (as in open pit mining) or to produce large piles of toxic slag (as from gold refining)?

14-1 God directed the Israelites to use specific minerals in the high priest's breastplate to represent the twelve tribes.

Field Trip Ideas

1. Take a trip to a lapidary museum if one is located near you. Many university geology departments also have collections that are available for viewing, either in display cases or by appointment.

2. Organize a mineral hunt, either at a public site that is a good prospect for some finds or at a pay-to-dig operation. This may involve going to a nearby stream, road cut, or quarry to look for minerals. Be sure to obtain permission before entering private property, and follow proper safety precautions.

3. Organize a trip to a government minting facility if you live near Denver, San Francisco, or Philadelphia.

Objectives—Section 14A

After completing this section, students should be able to

- show that minerals have been provided by God as materials for both function and beauty.

- list the characteristics that define a mineral and, given its composition, be able to classify any substance as a mineral or non-mineral.

- categorize all matter according to its composition.

- distinguish between native minerals and compound minerals.

Stones of Witness

Man must obey all aspects of the commandment to subdue the earth and have dominion. To indiscriminately dig up the good earth and spread toxic wastes over its surface is not good stewardship of what has been given to mankind. These activities can upset the processes that keep environments and ecosystems running as God intended. Uncontrolled wastes can eventually pollute water sources and kill wildlife, which are also gifts of God. Responsible mining along with reasonable efforts to minimize the impact of these activities on the surroundings is proper stewardship.

The definition of "organic" given in §14.2 differs from the traditional definition given in chemistry textbooks. An organic compound in chemistry is a hydrocarbon or is a compound of life (DNA, amino acids, proteins, etc.) based on carbon. Technically, diamond could fall under this definition. In mineralogy, however, an organic substance is any compound or mixture that originates from the activities or tissues of plants or animals. Thus, diamond is correctly categorized as a mineral because its origin is inorganic, even though it is composed entirely of carbon. The definition also excludes samples of chalk, which because of the organic origin may be homogenous solids of calcium carbonate.

Explain the tests that are used to identify the unique properties of some minerals. Demonstrate the tests with the apparatus and materials that you have available.

Assignment

Complete: 14B-2 Section Review Questions
          Applications 14B, "Mineral Tests"

Reading: Investigation 14F, "Properties of Minerals"

DAY 4

Quiz—Section 14B, "Identifying Minerals"

Do Investigation 14F, "Properties of Minerals."

Assignment

Reading: Section 14C-1 (§14.22–14.27), native minerals

(schedule continued on p. 362)

Review: Atomic Structure

Students may have to dig deeply in order to re-call the structure of the atom from earlier grades. Briefly review the nomenclature if needed. You may want to discuss the Periodic Table (App. B4) at this point, which is also available as Visual App-2. Show students where the metals and nonmetals are located and point to a few prominent examples of each (sodium, calcium, iron, copper, gold, and silver for metals; oxygen, sulfur, and chlorine for nonmetals). Emphasize that the elements are arranged by atomic number (number of protons in the nucleus) and that the vertical columns contain elements with similar chemical properties. It would not be profitable to go into electron structure or other such details due to lack of time.

Visual 4-1: Classification of Matter

Use this visual as you discuss the various cate-gories of matter. Review the definitions at the bottom of the visual.

Mixtures that are completely homogeneous are called *solutions*. A homogeneous mixture of salt and water is a *saltwater* (saline) *solution*.

An *ore* is rock containing one or more minerals that are the source of elements or compounds important to industry or agriculture.

14-2 This mass of pure gold was found uncombined with any other element and thus is a native mineral.

14-3 The mineral *quartz* is a compound since it has a fixed ratio of silicon and oxygen.

14-4 This rock contains several minerals in no particular ratio and is therefore a mixture.

14.3 Origin of Minerals

Where did minerals come from? It would be simple enough to say that God created them, and that would be a true statement. How-ever, it is likely that not all minerals that exist today existed in their current form at Creation. Only the minerals gold, bdellium, onyx, brass (copper), and iron are mentioned in the first six chapters of Genesis. That is not to say that other minerals did not exist at Cre-ation, but it is worth noting that at least an additional 36 rocks and minerals are mentioned in the Bible following the Flood. The Flood resulted in a complete overturning of much of the earth's surface, re-arranging the originally created mineral deposits and likely causing the formation of new minerals and **ores** from processes that did not take place before the Flood. Just as the Flood is a testimony of God's judgment, the provision of minerals, even in the devastated earth, is a testimony of God's grace.

14.4 Matter and Elements

Minerals, like all other matter, have mass and take up space (that is, they have volume). Also, they are made up of atoms, the tiny par-ticles that are the building blocks of matter. Atoms are identified by the number of protons in their nuclei. The number of protons deter-mines the **element** that the atom belongs to. Almost four thousand different minerals are known to exist, as well as many other kinds of matter that are not minerals. Does each kind of mineral contain a dif-ferent element? No. Scientists have found only about 116 different elements, and 24 of these are man-made. A **native mineral**, how-ever, contains only one kind of atom and is therefore a pure element. Gold, silver, and diamond are examples of native minerals.

14.5 Compounds

Atoms of several elements can combine to form a **compound**. Most minerals are compounds. A pure compound contains elements in a fixed ratio. For example, the mineral quartz is a compound of silicon and oxygen. Pure quartz always contains twice as many oxy-gen atoms as silicon atoms. If the ratio were different, the compound would be something else, not quartz.

14.6 Mixtures

Some forms of matter contain several elements or compounds in proportions that vary. These substances are not chemically com-bined, which means that nonchemical processes such as sifting, melting, or evaporation can separate them. Salt water, for example, may contain various amounts of salt mixed in water and still be salt water. This form of matter is called a **mixture**. Minerals are never mixtures but consist of relatively pure elements or compounds, al-though they may contain small amounts of impurities. Most rocks are a single mineral or a mixture of two or more minerals.

Day 5

Discuss the characteristics of the most significant native minerals. Explain their uses and give information about locations of deposits and mining meth-ods. Answer the Summing Up questions to Investigation 14D and/or 14E.

Assignment

Complete: 14C-1 Section Review Questions

Reading: Section 14C-2 (§14.28–14.31), compound minerals

Day 6

Explain that the most important minerals fall into certain chemical cate-gories. Discuss the general chemical formulas for silicates, oxides, and sul-fides. Note that silicates are the most abundant class of mineral in the earth's crust and that oxides and sulfides can be significant economically because they are the chief ores for important metals. Begin Applications 14C, "Elements and Compounds."

Assignment

Complete: Remaining questions in Applications 14C, "Elements and Compounds"

Selected Chapter Review Questions

Day 7

Quiz—Section 14C, "Minerals in Nature"

Review for a chapter test.

Day 8

Test—Chapter 14

Assignment

Reading: Section 15A, "Introduction to Rocks"

EXPLORING MINERALS

Staurolite often appears as six-sided crystals that intersect with others at either 60° or 90° angles.

The blue color of chrysocolla comes from the presence of copper.

Impurities can make quartz any color. This specimen is called smoky quartz.

Bornite, also called peacock ore, is an important copper ore.

Pyrite, also known as fool's gold, is composed of iron and sulfur.

Tourmaline is usually black; however, multicolored crystals are used as gems. If heated, tourmaline will develop electrical charges.

Galena, or lead sulfide, is the ore of lead.

Cinnabar, or mercury sulfide, is the ore of mercury.

Orpiment, or arsenic trisulfide, is very poisonous. It was once used to make a yellow dye.

Objectives—Section 14B

After completing this section, students should be able to

- list physical properties that are common to all minerals.
- list properties that are unique to some minerals.
- explain or demonstrate the different tests of physical properties used to identify minerals.
- use a mineral identification key to identify a mineral.

Web Resources: Identifying Minerals

Workers in many areas of science classify or categorize the things they study. Classification guides that contain branching decision trees to facilitate the proper identification of an unknown sample are called classification keys. Easy-to-use mineral identification aids are available online. Visit the BJU Press Online Resources/*SPACE AND EARTH SCIENCE* webpage. Under Chapter 14, click on the link *Physical Characteristics of Minerals*, which will take you to a site that provides in-depth information and photos of minerals. Click on the link *Mineral Identification Guide* for a site that features an interactive mineral identification guide.

Visual App-4A, B: Mineral Identification Key (Appendix B5)

This visual is a reproduction of Appendix B5. If you elect to identify mineral specimens in class, this key will be useful in eliminating unlikely candidates. The key itself is of a general nature that will introduce students to the way such classification aids work.

Nestled in the Andes at the place where Chile, Bolivia, and Peru meet lies a high-elevation, desertlike plain called the Altiplano—an area characterized by volcanoes, mineral deposits, and unusual lakes. These lakes are vividly colored by the minerals in the surrounding soil. Laguna Verde is a greenish colored lake because of the sulfur and calcium carbonates dissolved in the water. Laguna Colorada is colored rusty brown by borax and other minerals. Flamingos feed on the algae and plankton in these lakes.

14A Section Review

1. What evidence do we have that God intends humans to mine for minerals in the earth? Give at least one of these evidences.
2. What are materials that come from living things called? Give at least three examples of these materials.
3. What happened to the mineral deposits that were originally created in the earth?
4. What is a mineral composed of a single element called?
5. What are pure materials that are composed of two or more different kinds of atoms in a fixed ratio called?
6. What are materials that are made up of pure elements or compounds in varying proportions called?
7. Pure gold is called 24-carat gold because it is $^{24}/_{24}$ gold. When combined with other metals, one resulting mixture is called 18 carat gold because it is $^{18}/_{24}$ gold. What proportion of gold is there in 12-carat gold?
8. (True or False) All salt water contains 3.5% sodium chloride.

14B IDENTIFYING MINERALS

14.7 Introduction

Geologists have the task of identifying minerals. Geologists who specialize in identifying minerals are called *mineralogists*. Although some minerals have distinctive characteristics that make identification easy, many minerals resemble other minerals or contain impurities that make identification difficult.

To accomplish their task, mineralogists observe and test specimens carefully. They observe the specimen's appearance and physical characteristics. Sometimes they also use chemical tests to determine the elements present in the specimen and the percentage of each element. Such tests might be used to determine whether a mine would be profitable or not. To be sure of their results, geologists use many different tests, not just one test. A simple identification key of some common rock-forming minerals has been provided as Appendix B5 in the back of this volume.

PROPERTIES OF ALL MINERALS

14.8 Color

Geologists begin to identify a specimen by observing its color. Only rarely does the task stop here because many minerals have the same color. Moreover, minerals sometimes change color when they are exposed to air because their surfaces oxidize or tarnish. Often the same mineral has several or even many different colors because of tiny amounts of impurities. Quartz, for example, may be green, pink, blue, violet, milky, or smoky. A small amount of manganese as an impurity changes clear quartz to the violet gem amethyst. The mineral corundum, another example, is usually colorless. Yet with traces of chromium, corundum becomes ruby, and with traces of iron and titanium, it becomes sapphire.

14-5 Small amounts of impurities give this quartz its rose color.

14-6 Amethyst is quartz with a small amount of manganese.

Answers to 14A Section Review Questions

1. Several passages in Scripture mention obtaining minerals through mining-like activities. The text mentions Job 28:1, 2, 6, 9, and 10. Other answers are possible. (§14.1)

2. Materials that come from living things are called *organic* materials. Examples will vary but may include coal, oil, pearls, wood, animal skins, and food. (§14.2)

3. Most of the original mineral deposits were probably disrupted and redistributed throughout the sediments following the Flood. New minerals may have been produced after the Flood that were different from the minerals originally created. (§14.3)

4. A mineral composed of a single element is called a *native mineral*. (§14.4)

5. Materials that are composed of two or more different kinds of atoms in a fixed ratio are called *compounds*. (§14.5)

6. Materials that are made up of pure elements or compounds in varying proportions are called *mixtures*. (§14.6)

7. Twelve-karat gold is $^{12}/_{24}$, or 50% gold and 50% other metals.

8. False. A saltwater mixture (solution) may have any amount of salt in it as long as it is still liquid. (§14.6)

14.9 Streak

More reliable than the apparent color is the mineral's **streak**, the color of its powder. Rubbing a specimen across a **streak plate**, a piece of unglazed porcelain, makes its streak evident. As the specimen rubs across the plate, it leaves a trail of fine powder that has a characteristic color. Even though a specimen may vary in color because of impurities, its streak remains the same. Iron pyrite, one type of "fool's gold," is a good example of a mineral whose streak is different from its outward color. This brassy yellow mineral has a greenish black streak, while gold's streak is the same as its color.

14.10 Luster

Another characteristic of a mineral is its luster. **Luster** is the quality and intensity of the light reflected from a mineral's surface. Mineral copper, for example, has a *metallic* luster. Quartz reflects light like glass, and therefore mineralogists say that it has a *glassy* (also called *vitreous*) luster. The luster of gypsum is *pearly*. The brilliant luster of a diamond is called *adamantine*. Asbestos, with a fibrous texture, has a *silky* luster. Other recognized lusters include *greasy*, *waxy*, *earthy* (dull), and *resinous*.

14.11 Crystal Shape and Growth

Crystals come in assorted shapes and have always been a curiosity of creation. The earliest description of crystals was by the Roman philosopher Pliny shortly after the time our Lord was on the earth. Their sizes range from the small microscopic crystals of kaolin (clay) to the giant crystals of beryl or feldspar that sometimes weigh several tons. If allowed to form without space restrictions, crystals take their shape from the arrangement of the atoms in the mineral. Each mineral has a characteristic crystal shape with fixed angles between corresponding faces. For example, simple quartz crystals are hexagonal (six-sided) rods, having 120° between each side face. Halite (common salt) crystals are cubic (square, boxlike) with 90° between faces. Mineralogists have classified mineral crystals into seven systems and at least 32 classes.

Crystals enlarge by adding particles to their structure on their exposed surfaces, a process called **accretion**. During accretion, particles arrange themselves in a definite pattern. This often occurs in water solutions containing high concentrations of elements or compounds or from vapors containing minerals. Crystals also may form when molten rock cools. For a long time, uniformitarian geologists believed that the cooling rate of molten rock was the only factor that determined mineral crystal size. According to their model, when

14-7 Even though impurities change the color of a mineral, its streak remains the same.

adamantine (AD ah MAN teen): (Gk. *adamas*—a hard stone from Greek mythology considered unbreakable)

14-8 Asbestos has a silky luster (left), and gypsum has a pearly luster (above).

Gaius Plinius Secundus (Pliny the Elder) (23–79 AD) was a prominent Roman philosopher who wrote an encyclopedia on his observations of nature called *Natural History*. He died in the famous eruption of Mt. Vesuvius that destroyed Herculaneum and Pompeii.

kaolin (KAY uh lin)

accretion (uh KREE shun)

For minerals harder than an unglazed porcelain plate (6–7 on Mohs scale), an equivalent technique to the streak is powdering the mineral by using a fine hardened steel machinist's file (7+ Mohs) or a diamond file (9–10 Mohs) on an edge of the mineral. View the resulting powder on a white background.

 Visuals 14-2A, B: Basic Crystal Systems I & II

If you believe it would be profitable to introduce your students to the basic crystal systems, use these visuals. Not all recognized systems are included. For each system, there is an idealized crystal shape, a stick diagram illustrating the essential symmetry of the system, and a photo of a typical mineral crystal in the system. The stick diagrams represent the orientation of the axes of symmetry within the crystals. Perpendicularity is denoted by the right-angle symbols. Axes with different letters are of different lengths. Note that the last two photos on the second visual show examples of crystal *twinning*, which can significantly alter the shape of a crystal from what is normal for its system. Twinning occurs when a second symmetrical crystal-lattice growth pattern develops during the accretion of the crystal.

14-9 Shapes of crystals vary from the long needle-like crystals of aragonite (left) to the cubic crystals of halite (right).

molten rock cooled slowly, the atoms had time to arrange themselves and form large crystals, but when the molten rock cooled rapidly, the atoms had little time to arrange themselves; thus, the crystals were small, if they existed at all. Today geologists recognize that many other factors besides the cooling rate control crystal size. Glasses, solids that do not contain crystals, often form when molten rock cools under low-pressure conditions when it contains little or no dissolved gases or liquids.

14.12 Cleavage and Fracture

Cleavage is the characteristic of some minerals to separate into flat sheets or along certain planes. Minerals split in this way when the bonds between the atoms in the crystals are not equally strong in all directions. Though the bond in one direction of a crystal may be strong so that cleaving is difficult, the bond in another direction may be weak enough to allow cleaving. Mineralogists have established five ratings for mineral cleavage: *perfect, good, fair, poor,* and *none*. At one end of the scale are minerals such as mica, which separate easily into thin sheets; these have perfect cleavage. At the other end of the scale are minerals such as quartz, which do not cleave along flat surfaces at all. Cleavage also involves the number of directions or planes in which a mineral will cleave. Mica cleaves in only one direction, halite cleaves in three directions, and sphalerite cleaves in six directions.

14-10 Mica is easily identified by its ease of cleavage into thin sheets.

Minerals that do not show cleavage planes but seem to have some pattern in their breaking have the property of **fracture**. The different types of fracture include *conchoidal, fibrous, uneven,* and *hackly*. Minerals with conchoidal fracture, such as flint, break along curved, smooth surfaces. The chips or pieces have the shape of a shell. Fibrous fracture is breakage that produces surfaces having splinters or fibers, as with asbestos. Uneven fracture produces surfaces that are irregular and rough, as in chalcocite (another kind of fool's gold). Hackly fracture is breakage that produces a surface of fine, sharp points, as in iron or copper.

14.13 Hardness

A simple procedure in identifying a mineral is the **hardness test**, which determines the ability of a mineral to withstand scratching and abrasion. Some minerals are so soft that they can be scratched with a fingernail; others are so hard that virtually nothing can scratch them. In 1822 a German mineralogist named Friedrich Mohs devised a hardness scale for classifying and identifying minerals by their hardness. On the **Mohs scale**, minerals range from 1 (very soft) to 10 (very hard). Mohs assigned a hardness of 1 to talc and 10 to diamond. The test for a mineral's hardness is whether it can scratch or be scratched by certain minerals that Mohs assigned to each number

14-11 Obsidian's characteristic of breaking along smooth, curved surfaces is called conchoidal fracture.

conchoidal (kahn KOID al)

Friedrich Mohs (1773–1839) was a German mineralogist and college professor.

Demonstration: Cleavage and Fracture

Provide several minerals to demonstrate cleavage and fracture. Include mica and slate and perhaps quartz for contrast. Allow the students to split apart the cleavage samples.

Visual 14-3: Mohs Hardness Scale

Use this visual as you discuss the Mohs scale. It is more comprehensive than Table 14-1 on page 367.

in his hardness scale. For example, if a mineral scratches gypsum (number 2) but is scratched by calcite (number 3), its hardness is between 2 and 3. Table 14-1 lists the Mohs scale and gives the hardness of some common materials used by geologists to determine the hardness of minerals in the field.

14-12 Mineral set used to test the hardness of other mineral specimens

14-1 MOHS HARDNESS SCALE

Diamond	10
Corundum	9
Topaz	8
Quartz	7
File	**$6^{1}/_{2}$**
Feldspar	6
Apatite	5
Knife blade	**$5^{1}/_{2}$**
Glass	**$5^{1}/_{2}$**
Fluorite	4
Copper coin	**$3^{1}/_{2}$**
Calcite	3
Fingernail	**$2^{1}/_{2}$**
Gypsum	2
Talc	1

14.14 Specific Gravity

Another characteristic used for identifying a mineral is its **specific gravity**. Specific gravity is the ratio of the mass of a substance to the mass of an equal volume of water at 4 °C (39 °F). If a mineral sample with a volume of 1 cm³ has a mass of 5 g, and the mass of 1 cm³ of water is 1 g, then the mineral's specific gravity is

$$\frac{\text{mass of 1 cm}^3 \text{ of mineral}}{\text{mass of 1 cm}^3 \text{ of water}} = \frac{5 \text{ g}}{1 \text{ g}} = 5.$$

Sometimes a geologist can estimate the specific gravity of a mineral by lifting or handling a sample of each of two different minerals. If the samples are about the same volume, the geologist can compare their weight to estimate the specific gravity. Some minerals, such as gypsum, have low specific gravities; others, such as gold, are dense and have high specific gravities. With practice in lifting minerals, a person can become proficient in estimating whether a specific gravity is low, average, or high.

14B-1 Section Review

1. What color test used in identification of minerals is more reliable than simply observing the color of the mineral sample? Why is it more reliable?

2. What familiar mineral has adamantine luster? What luster would you expect a sample of native silver to have?

3. What name is given to the process of enlarging crystals by adding particles? What are two methods of crystal formation?

4. Name the identification feature that is determined by the breakage of a crystal along distinct planes. Give an example of a mineral that does not have this characteristic.

5. (True or False) A geologist cannot look at the size and shape of the mineral crystals in a rock and tell relatively how long the rock took to form.

To determine a sample's specific gravity, you would use the sample's actual experimental values for mass and volume of water displaced (which is equal numerically to the mass of water displaced).

$$\text{specific gravity} = \frac{\text{sample mass}}{\substack{\text{volume of water} \\ \text{displaced}}} = \frac{\text{sample mass}}{\substack{\text{mass of water} \\ \text{displaced}}}$$

14-13 The mass of a rock is measured on a balance (top), and its volume can be measured by the amount of water it displaces (bottom).

Answers to 14B-1 Section Review Questions

1. Performing a *streak test* is more reliable than observing apparent color when one is identifying minerals. Minerals often can be found in different colors that make them look like other minerals, but their streak is always the same color. (§14.9)

2. *Diamond* has an adamantine luster. Native silver should have a *metallic luster*. (§14.10)

3. The process of enlarging crystals by adding particles is called *accretion*. Students may list any two of the following methods: crystals can grow from water solutions containing dissolved substances, from deposition in vapors, or from molten rock. (§14.11)

4. *Cleavage* is the identification characteristic that is determined by breakage along distinct planes. Quartz does not show cleavage. Other answers are possible. (§14.12)

5. True. (§14.11)

14-14 Some minerals can be identified by the color of flame they produce.

A platinum wire is used in the flame tests of sodium, potassium, calcium, and other minerals because it does not degrade in the presence of most chemicals and imparts no color to the flame. See Figure 14-14.

14-15 The reaction of some minerals with acid is another method of identification.

lodestone: lode- (OE. *load*—course) + -stone

Most rocks and minerals are naturally radioactive because they contain trace amounts of radioactive isotopes of common elements as well as impurities. The emission of the radiation from the rocks and minerals in the ground contributes to what is known as the background radiation, to which we all are exposed every day of our lives. Some creationary scientists believe that these radioactive materials were originally deep in the earth at Creation but were brought to the surface by the action of the Flood. They suggest that exposure to the vastly increased background radiation flux after the Flood was the main contributing factor to the loss of genetic vitality and the shortening of lifespans documented in the Bible and as seen in reduced diversity of kinds compared to the fossil record.

14-17 Torbernite is a green mineral that is radioactive. It contains both uranium and copper.

PROPERTIES OF SOME MINERALS

14.15 Flame Test

Most minerals are identified by their color, streak, luster, crystal shape, cleavage, hardness, and specific gravity. A few minerals, however, have other properties that make them easy to identify.

Some minerals produce characteristic colors of flame or residue when they burn. The **flame test** identifies these minerals. For example, when a platinum wire is dipped into a small sample of table salt and then is held in a flame, the flame becomes yellow. The yellow color is due to the presence of sodium in table salt (sodium chloride). Potassium produces a violet flame, and lithium gives a red flame. Other minerals produce distinctive colors of flame.

14.16 Acid Test

Carbonates, sulfides, and sulfites can be identified by the **acid test**. If an acid, usually hydrochloric acid, is applied to these minerals, it fizzes, giving off bubbles of carbon dioxide, hydrogen sulfide, or sulfur dioxide, respectively. Calcite, dolomite, and galena are minerals that react with acids. For dolomite to react, the acid must be slightly heated or the sample powdered.

14.17 Magnetism

14-16 Magnetite is a natural magnet. It will pick up iron filings just as other magnets do.

Some minerals display **magnetism**. Not only can a magnet pick up these minerals, but also some of them are strong enough to pick up small pieces of iron. The best example of a magnetic mineral is magnetite. According to one legend, a shepherd discovered this mineral when he noticed that pieces of a black rock stuck to the iron point of his staff. During the twelfth century AD, mariners in China and Europe, apparently independently, developed the magnetic compass. This compass always pointed north and south to guide a ship. Because magnetite could be used in a compass, it was called **lodestone**.

14.18 Radioactivity

Geologists locate uranium-containing minerals, such as pitchblende, using radiation detectors because these minerals are radioactive (their atomic nuclei change by giving off particles and rays). Although uranium is more abundant in the earth's crust than silver, mercury, or iodine, its concentration in any area is so slight that mining operations are expensive. Geologists, therefore, prospect for highly concentrated deposits of pitchblende and other radioactive minerals.

14.19 Luminescence

Some minerals glow when they are placed under ultraviolet light. Minerals produce this glow, or **luminescence**, by absorbing the invisible ultraviolet light and giving off visible light. Minerals that emit light while absorbing radiation from another source are **fluorescent**. One common mineral that often fluoresces is calcite. Some minerals emit light not only when they are illuminated but also after the light source is removed. Such minerals are **phosphorescent**. Luminescence is a somewhat unreliable test since samples of even the same mineral may glow in different ways.

fluorescent (floo RES unt)

phosphorescent (FAHS fuh RES unt)

14.20 Refraction

All transparent minerals bend light as it passes through them, and the amount of bending can be used to identify the minerals. This bending is called **refraction**. The index of refraction of a mineral is an indication of how much it bends light. Diamond has a high index of refraction; this is the reason for its brilliance when cut and polished as a gem stone. Mineralogists have published tables giving the refractive indexes for all known transparent minerals.

14-18 This may look like an ordinary rock (left), but it contains two fluorescent minerals (right)—willemite (green) and calcite (red).

A few transparent minerals show **double refraction**; that is, they produce a double image as light passes through them. A form of calcite called Iceland spar is a good example of a doubly refracting mineral.

Many mineral crystals can bend light in another way. If a light wave is filtered so that it vibrates in only one direction (a process known as **polarization**), these minerals can rotate the polarized light entering them to a different angle. For example, if a light wave is polarized so that its waves are vertical when it enters the mineral crystal, it may exit the crystal rotated by 30°. Special microscopes that use this property can identify tiny mineral crystals in thin cross sections of rock samples.

14-19 Calcite (above) has double refraction. A polarizing mineral crystal (below) rotates light rays.

unpolarized light

polarized light beam

polarizing filter

mineral crystal

rotated light beam

14B-2 Section Review

1. If a flame test of a powdered mineral produced a green flame, which elements could you say were *not* present in the sample?

2. A sample of a mineral fluoresces and bubbles vigorously when tested with hydrochloric acid. What mineral could it be according to your reading in this section?

3. What mineral was the development of the compass dependent on? Why would copper or silver not have worked for this purpose?

4. What two kinds of luminescence can minerals produce?

5. What special properties should be checked when trying to identify a transparent mineral?

6. (True or False) All transparent minerals show double refraction.

A peculiar interaction of light with the mineral ruby is the stimulated emission of light. Under the right conditions, light of a particular wavelength injected into the crystal produces identical light waves emitted in phase with each other from energy stored within the crystal lattice. This is the physical basis for lasers.

Other interesting light-emitting properties of some minerals are *thermoluminescence* (glowing when heated) and *triboluminescence* (glowing when crushed, scratched, or rubbed).

Assigning a mineral collection project to your class is a practical way to introduce your students to mineralogy. You will need to do some research to determine what minerals are readily available locally. Develop a mineral classification guide or obtain one from a science supplier, a library, or the Internet. Provide students with detailed instructions for successfully completing the project. Consider a combined rock and mineral collection after completing Chapter 15.

Demonstration: Polarization

Take two pairs of polarizing sunglasses and overlap a lens in one pair at right angles to a lens in the other pair. Show that this orientation blocks nearly all light transmitted through the two lenses. The polarization axis in sunglasses is oriented vertically to block the horizontally polarized reflected sunlight.

Answers to 14B-2 Section Review Questions

1. According to the textbook, you could be sure that sodium and potassium were not present in significant quantities in the sample. Other answers are possible. (§14.15)

2. The sample is likely calcite. (§14.16, 14.19)

3. The development of the compass depended upon *magnetite*, or *lodestone*. Neither copper nor silver is significantly magnetic; therefore, neither could point to the earth's magnetic north pole. (§14.17)

4. Minerals can produce either *fluorescence* or *phosphorescence*. (§14.19)

5. A transparent mineral's index of refraction should be checked, along with whether the material exhibits double refraction. (§14.20)

6. False. Only a few minerals, such as Iceland spar, show double refraction. (§14.20)

Objectives—Section 14C

After completing this section students should be able to

- list examples of native minerals.
- describe methods for obtaining native minerals from their ores.
- indicate some useful properties and uses of native minerals.
- name four classes of compound minerals.
- name a representative of each type of compound mineral.

Demonstration: Stream Beds as Mineral Sources

To demonstrate how moving water helps to expose mineral specimens, put a mixture of soil, pebbles, sand, small stones, and large stones on a sloping driveway or on a plank elevated on a brick or wooden block. Using a watering can or a sprinkler attachment on a hose, pour water slowly down the incline. The water will carry the smaller sediments away but leave the larger rocks behind.

The world's leading gold-producing countries are South Africa, the United States, Australia, China, Canada, and the Russian Federation.

14C MINERALS IN NATURE

14.21 Introduction

As we study some of the most important minerals that humans use, we learn something about our God. He made this earth not just of stone and sand, but also of diamond and ruby and of gold and silver. God is not simply a God of function and usefulness. He is also a God of beauty. This observation has important meaning for us, being made in His image. If we are to exercise dominion in a way that declares God's glory, we must learn how to appreciate the beauty of minerals as well as their usefulness. We ought to show by our use of them that we understand dominion is not only a science but also an art.

NATIVE MINERALS

14.22 Gold

Gold is one of the densest minerals, having a specific gravity of about 19. Gold deposits nearly always contain about 10 to 15 percent silver. In most gold veins, the mineral is so finely distributed in quartz that it is invisible. As gold-bearing rock erodes away, the metal washes into nearby streams and sifts through the sand until it is deposited in crevices, in river sandbars, or along beaches. The stream deposits where eroded gold or other minerals are found are called **placer deposits**.

Gold in placer deposits can be separated from the sand and gravel in a number of ways. **Panning** washes away the lighter material and exposes the nuggets, the larger pieces of gold. **Sluicing** involves washing sediment so that the flecks of gold collect behind crossbars in a trough called a sluice. The crossbars are often coated with mercury because it holds the gold well. **Dredging** can separate the metal from thousands of cubic yards of sand and gravel. For several years the state of California used a fleet of dredging machines to dredge the bed of the American River. They recovered thousands of dollars worth of gold each day to help finance the state government.

Minerals that are formed from heavy pure elements such as gold, silver, and platinum are a particular problem for evolutionary geologists. The most popular evolutionary model for the origin of these elements proposes that they were formed in supernova explosions throughout the universe. The resulting dust of precious metal atoms moved through space until it became trapped in the proto-sun's nebula. Eventually, planets formed and the gold atoms were trapped in the crust of the earth. Of course, evolutionary geologists cannot explain why gold, which is $2\frac{1}{2}$ times as dense as iron, remained in the crust while the majority of the iron sank to the middle of the earth. This problem exists for all of the dense elements found in the earth's crust. The geologists try to explain that the gold has been brought to the earth's surface from its interior by volcanoes and by molten rock flowing into cracks and spaces within the crust. This is an inadequate explanation for why gold and other metal deposits can be found in many places throughout the earth.

sluicing (SLOOS ing)

14-20 Gold nuggets like the one above are often found by panning. A gold note from 1928 (below) shows that United States currency used to be backed by gold.

WORTH ITS WEIGHT IN GOLD?

You may never hold a gold or silver coin in your hand. Most of the coins in your pocket, including the dime, are primarily made of copper. The penny is almost pure zinc (97.5%) with 2.5% copper. The five-cent piece is a mixture of copper (75%) and nickel (25%), and dimes, quarters, half-dollars, and dollars are mostly copper covered by a thin layer of the same 75/25 mixture of copper and nickel. The metal in each coin is nearly worthless. The paper in our bills is worth less than a penny.

Coins and currency were once worth their face value. The $10 gold eagle, issued in 1795, was worth its weight in gold until the U.S. government stopped minting gold coins in 1933. Silver dollars were worth $1 until their minting ended in 1935. The government also issued certificates that you could exchange for gold or silver. But gold certificates ceased in 1933; silver certificates ceased in 1963.

Modern coins have almost no value in themselves. They are *tokens*, designed for durability and difficulty to counterfeit. Paper currency does not even have the advantage of durability. Most bills last no longer than a few years in circulation. Banks routinely send worn-out bills to the Federal Reserve Bank, where they are shredded and replaced with crisp, new bills.

Currency was not always worthless. Early coins had *intrinsic* value. They could be converted into something of value—knives, spoons, jewelry, bells, and so on.

Ancient people found three soft metals that they could extract from ores and shape into coins or jewelry: copper, silver, and gold. The first coins, as we know them, appeared in Asia Minor about the seventh century BC. They were made of a natural mixture of gold and silver known as electrum. The mixture varied

Modern coins have almost no value in themselves.

from one coin to the next, and thus the relative value of each coin was never certain.

Only with time did countries develop pure gold, silver, and copper coins. These metals seemed almost the ideal medium of trade around the world. They had a number of benefits: they were easy to carry, easy to measure and divide, and difficult to counterfeit. Also, they were common in most places of the earth.

God has placed different amounts of each of these three metals in the earth. Gold, which is rare, is more valuable than an equal amount of silver, and silver is likewise more valuable than copper. These metals have maintained their value relative to each other throughout history. The relative value of gold, silver, and copper is evident in the Bible. King David gathered 100,000 talents of gold, 1,000,000 talents of silver, and brass (copper mixed with some zinc) "without weight" for his son, King Solomon, to use in building the temple (1 Chron. 22:14). These talents were not coins but were lumps of metal stamped with different values. For years the relative value of the metals was reflected in America's coins: the ten-dollar gold piece, the silver dollar, and the copper penny (10 : 1 : 0.01).

When a country's economy runs on a metal standard, the value of money fluctuates constantly with the changing value of the metal. To prevent this problem, the government of the United States "froze" the value of gold at $32 per ounce for many years. During the Great Depression of the 1930s, most countries, including the United States, stopped minting gold coins because they wanted to be able to print and spend money without concern for backing it up with gold. Another reason for abandoning gold was that gold mines were not keeping up with the rapid in-

silver coin

$20 gold coin

Uses of gold—each of these items has gold in or on it.

crease in world population. The scarcity of silver coins later led the U.S. treasury to abandon silver certificates. And finally in 1964 most minting of silver ceased.

However, a few silver and gold coins are still being minted. The government mints a limited number of "silver dollars" each year for collectors. (They contain about 60% copper and sell for a much higher price than $1.) You can even buy $10 gold coins, but not for $10. Sometimes the government also mints commemorative coins to honor an individual or event, such as **George Washington Carver**. These coins are all legal tender, but you will find them only in the hands of collectors.

George Washington Carver (1865–1943), a former slave, was a chemurgist, educator, author, and businessman among other accomplishments. (A chemurgist is a chemist who specializes in developing industrial products from organic materials.)

Facet Summary: Worth Its Weight in Gold?

This Facet traces the intrinsic value of coins from ancient times to the present. It mentions some interesting historical information pertaining to monetary standards. There are no vocabulary terms in this Facet.

Gold is extremely soft. One ounce of gold can be rolled out to cover an area of 320 square feet, and gold leaf is used in many decorative applications. This softness makes pure gold inappropriate for jewelry, so it is usually alloyed with a harder metal. The *karat* system expresses the purity of gold as a fraction of 24—24-karat gold is pure gold, 18-karat is $^{18}/_{24}$ pure gold (by weight), and so on. *Karat* (used to measure purity) and *carat* (a measure of gem weight or mass) are different measurements.

14-21 A tick coated with an extremely thin layer of gold for viewing by a scanning electron microscope

Gold has many uses. Because it is beautiful and easy to work, it is used in jewelry and dentistry. Because it is valuable, it has been used as a standard for currency or as an investment. In the United States paper money could be redeemed for gold prior to 1933, but in 1971 the practice of determining the value of U.S. money by comparison to gold was abandoned. Gold's electrical properties and resistance to corrosion make gold an important material in the manufacture of reliable electrical contacts and components. Millions of extremely thin gold wires are attached to tiny microchips in computers all over the world. A thin film of gold on glass or clear plastic transmits light but not heat. Thus, it is used to make visors for astronauts and windows for aircraft and spacecraft. Gold is used in numerous medical applications, where its corrosion resistance prevents chemical reactions with body fluids. Many important buildings around the world have domes covered with gold.

14-22 An astronaut's visor is coated with a film of gold for protection from the sun's rays.

FACETS OF MINERALOGY

AROUND THE WORLD IN SEARCH OF GOLD

The dream of finding a treasure of gold has inspired some of the greatest migrations of men in history. The early conquistadors from Spain crossed the Atlantic to the New World in search of fabled cities of gold. Coronado found nothing but scorching heat and sagebrush in the American Southwest. Pizarro, on the other hand, found his city of gold at Cuzco, the capital of the Inca empire. The Incas filled an entire room with over six tons of gold artifacts to ransom their emperor, whom Pizarro had captured. But the Spaniards killed the emperor anyway and forced the Indians to work as slaves in the nearby mines, which were eventually emptied of all their wealth.

The first modern "gold rush" occurred in California in 1849. The discovery of two yellow nuggets in a stream near Sut-

ter's mill attracted over a quarter of a million men to California from 1849 to 1852. The rush turned a sparsely populated territory of fourteen thousand people into a full-fledged state of one hundred thousand inhabitants in less than two years. Tent camps mushroomed near gold sites as "forty-niners" crossed thousands of miles of ocean, plains, and deserts on foot, mules, wagon trains, and ships. They came from Europe, China, Australia, and South America, clamoring for a claim in this land.

The early miners looked for gold dust and nuggets that had washed into stream beds and gulleys. They used pans,

A California "forty-niner"

Facet Summary: Around the World in Search of Gold

This Facet briefly tells the stories of the gold rushes that occurred in North America and other places and how such events were indicative of man's covetous desire for the precious metal. There are no vocabulary terms in this Facet.

rocker boxes, and sluices of running water to wash out the lighter sand, gravel, and dirt, leaving the heavy gold. But placer deposits were soon exhausted. Some prospectors began digging shallow mines to find the origin of the gold. Most did not make enough to live on, and they eventually left the state or turned to other means of livelihood. Others worked for big mining companies that had the money and equipment to dig deep mines and follow the veins from which the gold originally came. In these "mother lodes," as they were called, sophisticated equipment dug out tons of rock, crushed it, and extracted the gold.

"Gold fever" was rekindled with the news of gold in Australia, discovered in 1851 by a forty-niner who had returned home. It drew eager miners from all parts of the world. Half a million men sailed from England alone. Many miners in California, disillusioned by overcrowded, disease-ridden, expensive mining towns, boarded ship and sailed "down under," halfway around the world. But the disappointment was repeated. A small find in the nearby islands of New Zealand drew more hopefuls. A string of small strikes and false claims continued in the American West throughout the second half of the century. But the next great finds came in South Africa's Transvaal (1886) and the Klondike region of Canada's Yukon Territory (1896). This find near the border of Alaska attracted the last of this hardy collection of men dreaming of getting rich quick in this frozen frontier. Many died from cold, starvation, and disease or turned back before they even reached their destination.

By the end of the 1800s, the last of the North American gold rushes was over. All that was left in many areas were ghost towns, such as Deadwood Gulch in South Dakota (gold rush of 1876). More gold had been mined in this half-century than in the previous 3½ centuries (since Columbus discovered America). Henceforth most major gold excavation has been controlled by big businesses using large machines, bulldozers, dump trucks, and processing mills. More than three-fifths of the world's gold now comes from

South Africa, where major gold deposits are still going strong. Other big producers are Brazil, Canada, and Australia. But today gold prospectors are either teams of trained geologists working for mining companies or amateurs pursuing a hobby that takes them away from the big cities on weekends and holidays. Recent finds, such as those in Kazakhstan and Uzbekistan in the 1990s, have attracted new mining towns, but they are all carefully surveyed and developed by companies and supervised by governments. Teams of geologists continue the search for new deposits although much is still not understood about the origin of gold deposits. The most important deposits in Canada and the U.S. appear as veins of quartz mixed with gold that spread upward from deep in the earth through cracks. Other deposits appear as placers washed out from these veins (Alaska), and still others are a mixture of veins and placers that appear as reefs (South Africa).

Here and there prospectors, still smitten by gold fever, can be seen poking around the mountains and making claims. Once in a great while they find something significant. In 1980 an Australian found a 267 oz nugget which he sold for $250,000. In 1983 a Brazilian found a 137 lb nugget worth $1,000,000. In 1989 an Alaskan found a 35 oz nugget, and a man in Montana found a

27 oz nugget worth about $8000. But for the most part their efforts are just an enduring testimony of the appeal of this amazing metal. If men can brave the Arctic cold, desert heat, privation, and shipwreck to find an elusive metal, cannot Christians brave much more in the service of God and in an effort to study, teach, and preach His Word, or do other worthwhile work?

Gold—like the earth itself—is God's gift to man. As a gift, gold and all that it can buy are to be used for God's glory. As fallen beings, however, we tend to love these gifts more than the Giver. We demonstrate this when we are willing to sacrifice our devotion to God for the sake of getting more of His gifts. Such a decision is in principle no different than the many foolish choices described in this discussion of the gold rush. Those who love God's gifts more than God will find that the Giver of all good things becomes their enemy. But those who love God best of all will enjoy God and His gifts forever. And gold in abundance is certainly among those gifts: "*And I John saw the holy city, new Jerusalem, coming down from God out of heaven, prepared as a bride adorned for her husband. And I heard a great voice out of heaven saying, Behold, the tabernacle of God is with men. . . . and the city was pure gold, like unto clear glass*" (Rev. 21:2–3, 18).

Panning for gold in 1889 in South Dakota (Dakota Territory at that time)

14.23 Silver

Silver has a specific gravity of 10.5 and a color and streak of silver-white. Native deposits of this mineral have various shapes: coarse or fine strands, thin sheets, and irregular masses. In the United States, most native silver came from the Keweenaw Peninsula in northern Michigan. During the 1800s there were many "silver rushes" in western states similar to the gold rushes already described.

Because silver is more common than gold, it is less valuable. One drawback of silver is its tendency to tarnish. Silver is commonly used for jewelry and tableware. Because silver conducts electricity better than any other metal, it is an important component in some electrical circuits. Silver is also used in photographic film and for the reflective surfaces of mirrors. It is found in dental inlays and used for brazing and soldering alloys in plumbing. In certain compounds, it is used as an antibacterial agent.

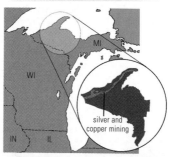

Keweenaw (KEE wuh NAW)

silver and copper mining

14-23 The Keweenaw Peninsula (top) was a major source of native silver and copper. Uses of silver include photographic film (middle) and tableware (bottom). Silver is stored as bullion (right).

14.24 Copper

Native **copper**, like silver, occurs in irregular masses, sheets, and twisted strands. The largest deposit of native copper in the U.S. was in the Keweenaw Peninsula of Michigan. Michigan copper was "discovered" in 1840 by settlers, but Native Americans used it much earlier. For the next seventy-five years, men exploited the region for copper. Although most of the copper was in small, irregular pieces, some large masses were found. One mass discovered in 1857 weighed over 420 tons. The United States has exhausted the native copper that was economical to mine and now gets most of its copper from the copper sulfide ores (chalcocite) in Nevada, New Mexico, Arizona, and other western states.

Copper, like silver, conducts electricity well. A major use of copper is in electrical wiring. It also transmits heat well, so it is used in refrigeration pipes, car radiators, cookware, and other places where heat conduction is important. When copper corrodes, a tough surface layer forms that seals out oxygen and resists further corrosion. Because of this resistance to corrosion, copper is considered a good material for plumbing pipes. It is also used in some jewelry and in sculptures. The Statue of Liberty is made of a copper skin on a frame of iron. Many buildings have high-quality roofs sheathed with sheets of copper.

14.25 Platinum

Platinum exists in a range of sizes, from small particles to nuggets. It has a steel gray color and a bright luster. Platinum has a specific gravity of 21.5, which makes it denser than gold. It is also more valuable than gold. The metal was first found in Colombia, South America, in 1735. It was named *platina* from the Spanish word for silver, *plata*. Today most of the world's supply of platinum comes from deposits in Russia and South Africa.

Platinum is often alloyed (mixed) with gold in jewelry. The metal is extremely resistant to corrosion. For this reason the international standard meter bar and kilogram mass were made of platinum alloyed with iridium. Platinum also acts as a catalyst for some reactions. A catalyst is a substance that increases the rate of a chemical reaction without being consumed itself. Platinum is the catalyst in automobile catalytic converters, and it will be important in the developing fuel-cell technology.

14.26 Diamond

By definition, minerals do not contain organic carbon. The mineral **diamond** is no exception. Diamond is a native mineral composed of pure inorganic carbon. Diamond, the hardest known mineral, has perfect cleavage, and it has a greasy luster before it is cut. The cut and polished gems, however, have a brilliant adamantine luster called the "fire of the diamond." This appearance is due to the multiple internal reflections of light from the gemstone's facets. Diamonds are usually pale yellow or colorless, but red, orange, green, blue, and brown diamonds exist. The famous Hope Diamond found in India in 1642 is the largest blue diamond. It has had at least twelve different owners, and because so many of them experienced tragedies while it was in their possession, a legend developed that it brought its owners bad luck. It is now owned by the Smithsonian Institution and is on display in the Harry Winston Room in the Hall of Geology.

Diamonds are sometimes found in placer deposits. Usually, however, they are found in **diamond pipes**, round vertical columns of formerly molten rock. The deepest diamond pipe ever mined, named Kimberley, is in South Africa. This pipe grew smaller in

14-24 Copper pipe fittings and tubing supply water to many homes because of copper's resistance to corrosion (top left). Because of its beauty, copper is also used for many decorative objects (above). Copper is an excellent conductor of heat, which makes it useful for cooking utensils (above, left).

14-25 The standard kilogram (top) and meter bar (bottom) are made of a platinum alloy. Platinum was chosen for this purpose because of its resistance to corrosion.

14-26 Diamonds in the rough (above) are of various sizes and colors. The accompanying rock is kimberlite.

carat (KAR ut)

Crater of Diamonds State Park, near Murfreesboro, Arkansas, is the only diamond digging site in the United States open to the public. For an entrance fee, you can keep whatever you dig up—not just diamonds but other precious and semiprecious stones as well.

Nearly three-fourths of all diamonds are industrial quality (called *bort*) rather than gem quality. These are either too small or too poor in quality to be sold on the gem market.

credit: DeBeers

diameter with greater depth. Though the pipe continued, mining stopped at a depth of about 1100 m (3500 ft). Until the 1990s, the world's most productive diamond mine was the Premier, located near Pretoria, South Africa. Since 1903 the Premier mine produced over 30 million carats (6 tons) of diamonds. A **carat**, a unit of weight for gems, is actually a unit of mass equal to 0.2 g. In 1905 the world's largest, the Cullinan Diamond, which weighed 3106 carats in the rough, was found in this mine. From this diamond over 100 gems were cut, which are now part of the British regalia. Today the most productive diamond mine in the world is the Argyle diamond pipe, located in western Australia. It has annual production rates of more than 60 million carats per year. The only diamond mine in the U.S. operating today is at Kelsey Lake, Colorado.

Separating diamonds once involved crushing the rocks into coarse chunks and spreading them out on platforms where the sun and rain disintegrated the rock after a short time. Men then shook the disintegrated chunks through screens that separated the diamonds from the rest of the rock. Today the rock is crushed finely so that the diamonds can be quickly separated. In the final stages of separation, the crushed rock with the diamonds is spread out on tables coated with grease. The diamonds stick to the grease, and the other rock is washed away.

Diamonds are best known for their beauty as gems. The value of gem diamonds depends on their color, purity, size, and the skill with which they are cut. Weight (or mass) is especially important. A one-carat stone is worth only one-fourth or one-third as much as a two-carat stone of equal color, purity, and cut. Many engagement rings contain diamonds as do other pieces of jewelry.

Diamonds are very hard (10 on the Mohs scale), and this makes them very useful. Diamonds that cannot be used as gems because of size or flaws are often ground into powder and used as abrasives. Drill bits and saw blades used to cut exceptionally hard materials often have diamond tips.

14-27 The "Big Hole" at Kimberley (above), now filled with water, was a diamond-bearing volcanic pipe. The world's most productive diamond mine is the Argyle (bottom) in Australia. The Hope Diamond (right) is the largest blue diamond known. It was cut from a 112-carat gemstone.

14.27 Sulfur

Native **sulfur** is identified by its yellow color and conchoidal fracture. Sulfur burns with a characteristic blue flame and produces a poisonous gas, sulfur dioxide, with an odor of rotten eggs. It is often found near the rims of volcanoes, in metal ores, coal, crude oil, "sour" natural gas, and in sedimentary beds deep underground. The United States has an abundant supply of this mineral in Louisiana and Texas. Today, most of the sulfur production in the U.S. is associated with fossil fuel (oil, natural gas, and coal) refining and processing. Electrical power generating plants that burn fossil fuels are required by environmental laws to use fuels from which most of the sulfur has been removed, and to recover any sulfur from their exhaust gases. This "involuntary" sulfur production produces more sulfur than the U.S. market demands. Chemical companies are conducting extensive research to create new uses for the surplus sulfur.

In the United States, native sulfur is no longer obtained directly from the deposits deep underground using the **Frasch process**. In this process, superheated water is pumped down to the sulfur deposit, and compressed air forces the melted sulfur up through another pipe to the surface. A few countries, such as Poland, may still be using the Frasch process as the United States once did, but the time will come when all of the world's sulfur supply will come from involuntary production.

U.S. sulfur production is "involuntary" in that the oil industries are required by law to remove the excess sulfur from crude petroleum in order to reduce the emission of sulfur compounds when the oil is burned. Since this process was not an essential part of producing oil and was not voluntarily adopted by the oil industry, it is considered an "involuntary" source of sulfur.

14-28 Sulfur crystals at a fumarole vent in Hawaii (left) (Fumaroles are discussed in Chapter 17.); sulfur extraction at the Geysers geothermal power plant in Sonoma County, California (top); crystalline form of the mineral sulfur (bottom)

Frasch (FRAHSH)

14C-1 Section Review

1. Where are placer deposits of gold and other metals found?

2. When and where did the first modern gold rush occur? What do you believe was the basic motivation for the gold rushes?

3. Name the native mineral that is the best conductor of electricity. What is one disadvantage of this precious metal?

4. What geologic feature seems to be a common location for finding diamonds?

5. What element(s) form diamonds? Why are diamonds considered minerals as defined in this chapter?

6. What unit of mass is used to measure gems?

7. (True or False) A Christian attempting to fulfill the Creation Mandate should not use the raw materials of the earth for decoration or beauty's sake. God intended us to use these materials in practical ways for man's benefit.

Answers to 14C-1 Section Review Questions

1. Placer deposits may be found in sediments deposited by streams and rivers in cracks and crevasses, on sand bars, or along beaches. (§14.22)

2. The first modern gold rush began in 1849 in California. The gold rushes were motivated by the greed of men who wanted to get rich quickly with little effort. (Facet, p. 372)

3. *Silver* is the native mineral that is the best conductor of electricity. Unlike the other so-called precious metals, silver tarnishes easily. (§14.23)

4. Diamonds are often found in the necks of extinct volcanoes, called *diamond pipes*. (§14.26)

5. Diamonds are formed of the element *carbon*. The carbon in diamonds is inorganic—it does not come from formerly living plants or animals. (§14.26)

6. The unit of mass for gems is the *carat*, which is 0.2 g. (§14.26)

7. False. God gave man, created in His image, the capacity to appreciate beauty in all of its forms. In addition to their usefulness as tools and raw materials, minerals are inherently beautiful and can be fashioned into objects of beauty, such as jewelry. (§14.21)

It is not necessary for students to memorize the information in this table or in Table 14-3. The formulas are provided in order to illustrate that some silicate minerals have a range of allowable compositions within each type. Some mineral groups form a multidimensional continuum that is almost impossible to illustrate in a single diagram. As the concentrations of three or four elements within the mineral vary between specified limits, three-dimensional graphs or phase diagrams must be created to plot the possible variations within a mineral type.

COMPOUND MINERALS

14.28 Silicates

The most abundant class of minerals is the **silicates**. Silicates make up about 25% of all known minerals and about 40% of the common ores. More than 90% of the earth's crust consists of silicates. This class of mineral is called silicates because the minerals in it contain mainly silicon and oxygen along with minor amounts of other elements. Quartz, the second most common mineral in the earth's crust, contains only silicon and oxygen. Feldspar, a type of silicate, is the most common mineral in the crust. Other silicates include chalcedony (a type of quartz), opal, mica, hornblende, olivine, garnet, talc, and kaolin (clay) (see Table 14-2).

14-2 SELECTED SILICATE MINERALS		
Mineral class	**Name**	**Formula (general)**
olivine	magnesium and iron silicate	$(Mg,Fe)_2SiO_4$
pyroxenes	augite	$Ca(Mg,Fe,Al)(Al,Si)_2O_6$
	beryl	$Be_3Al_2Si_6O_{18}$
amphibole	hornblende	$Ca_2(Fe,Mg)_4AlSi_7AlO_{22}(OH)_2$
micas	biotite	$K(Mg,Fe)_3(AlSi_3O_{10})(OH)_2$
	muscovite	$KAl_2(AlSi_3O_{10})(OH)_2$
feldspars	orthoclase	$KAlSi_3O_8$
	plagioclase	$(Ca,Na)(Al,Si)AlSi_2O_8$
quartz	quartz	SiO_2

14.29 Oxides

Mineral **oxides** are nonsilicates composed of oxygen and some other element, usually a metal. Many mineral oxides are important economically because they are the chief sources of important metals. Significant metal oxides include hematite and magnetite (iron ores), cassiterite (tin ore), and bauxite (aluminum ore) (see Table 14-3).

14-29 Some compound minerals are important metal ores. Chalcocite, copper sulfite, is found in the Bingham Canyon Mine in Utah, the largest man-made excavation in the world.

14-3 SELECTED NON-SILICATE MINERAL CLASSES

Mineral group	Name	Formula	Use
Oxides	corundum	Al_2O_3	gemstone, abrasive
	hematite	Fe_2O_3	red pigment, iron ore
	magnetite	Fe_3O_4	iron ore
Sulfides	chalcopyrite	$CuFeS_2$	copper ore
	cinnabar	HgS	mercury ore
	galena	PbS	lead ore
	pyrite	FeS_2	sulfuric acid production
	sphalerite	ZnS	zinc ore
Sulfates	anhydrite	$CaSO_4$	plaster
	gypsum	$CaSO_4 \cdot 2H_2O$	plaster, drywall board
Carbonates	azurite	$Cu_3(CO_3)_2(OH)_2$	copper ore, gemstones
	calcite	$CaCO_3$	Portland cement, lime
	dolomite	$CaMg(CO_3)_2$	Portland cement, lime
	malachite	$Cu_2CO_3(OH)_2$	copper ore, ornamental stoneware
	rhodochrosite	$MnCO_3$	manganese ore
Native Elements	copper	Cu	electrical wires
	diamond	C	gemstone, abrasive
	gold	Au	jewelry, money
	graphite	C	dry lubricant
	platinum	Pt	catalyst, jewelry
	silver	Ag	jewelry, photography
	sulfur	S	sulfuric acid, chemicals
Halides	fluorite	CaF_2	smelting steel and aluminum
	halite	$NaCl$	table salt
	sylvite	KCl	fertilizer

14.30 Sulfides

Mineral **sulfides** are composed of one or more metals and sulfur. Like oxides, these minerals contain the metals economically important to us today. Many sulfides are opaque. Yet they have characteristic colors and often have colored streaks. Galena (lead ore), chalcocite (copper ore), cinnabar (mercury ore), realgar (arsenic ore), stibnite (antimony ore), and pyrite (iron ore and a source of sulfuric acid) are all sulfides (see Table 14-3).

14-30 Galena, lead sulfide, is a lustrous, blue-gray mineral that usually crystallizes in cubes and is the principal source of lead.

14.31 Carbonates

Carbonates are minerals containing a metal ion and the carbonate ion (an ion containing a carbon and three oxygen atoms that combines with metals easily). When hydrochloric acid is applied to a carbonate mineral, a salt plus carbon dioxide is always produced. The carbon dioxide bubbles off as a gas. This acid test is commonly used to identify carbonates. Calcite (found in limestone), dolomite (calcium and magnesium carbonate), rhodochrosite (manganese ore), and malachite and azurite (copper ores) are some of the minerals in this class.

ARTIFICIAL GEMS

Many jewels you see in a department store are not genuine. They might be imitations, substitutes, or synthetics. The two most common *imitations* come to us from the ancient Egyptians and Romans. They are made of glass and glazed ceramic. Another popular type of imitation is a combination of materials, such as opal and glass.

Many cheap *substitutes* have been produced. One common crystal, made from strontium titanate, disperses light four times better than diamonds. Another common crystal, called cubic zirconia, almost matches the beauty of the true diamond, at a cost of only a few dollars. But the imitations lack the durabil-

ity and fire of true gems because they have a different atomic structure and chemical make-up.

For many years, scientists have dreamed of inventing *synthetic*, or man-made, gems. The difficulty was not finding the ingredients but imitating how God put them together. We have known for a long time that diamonds are made from the main element of coal and sugar. But not until 1954 were carbon atoms artificially forced into tiny diamonds. It required temperatures exceeding 2650 °C (4800 °F) and pressures of over 1,000,000 N/cm² (1.5 million lb/in.²). Today, economical manufacturing techniques have been developed for large artificial diamonds that rival natural gemstones for appearance and hardness.

Technically, pressure is reported in units of N/m² or pascals. However, in materials science N/cm² or lb/in.² is often substituted.

The components of other gems are also common, but it takes time to form the crystals. Usually the ingredients are melted and allowed to cool into a crystal. Rubies were the first synthetic gems produced this way. They are made from aluminum oxide, with a trace of chromium for color. Synthetic emeralds are made by placing beryl crystals in a solution with a solvent and then heating; about 2% of the aluminum atoms are replaced by chromium atoms, converting the beryl crystals to transparent emeralds. These crystals take months to form.

Although synthetics look like natural gems to the naked eye, they are much less valuable. The differences are fairly easy to spot under a microscope. Synthetics are "too perfect" and lack the irregularities and impurities that give natural gems their charm. Most sell for only a few dollars. Even synthetic emeralds, which are almost exact copies of their natural cousins, sell for only a few hundred dollars per carat, as opposed to the thousands of dollars paid for natural emeralds. It is important to recognize that God's creations will always be more marvelous than mankind's and that man's efforts to synthesize gems are only a weak imitation of God's handiwork. But in the mere fact that God has given man the skills and the raw materials to imitate His works, we can marvel at what man is able to do in God's image.

To an untrained eye synthetic diamonds (above) look genuine. The artificial green gem (right) was made from silica-containing volcanic ash.

14C-2 Section Review

1. Name the most abundant group of minerals in the earth's crust. What are the two most common minerals in this group?
2. Oxides, sulfides, and carbonates are good sources of what kind of materials?
3. What test is frequently used to identify carbonate-containing minerals?
4. What artificial gem is a substitute for diamond?
5. (True or False) Hydrochloric acid can be used to identify feldspars.

Facet Summary: Artificial Gems

This Facet explains the difference between imitation, substitute, and synthetic gems, none of which can rival God's creation in beauty. There are no vocabulary terms in this Facet.

Answers to 14C-2 Section Review Questions

1. The single most abundant group of minerals in the earth's crust is the *silicates*. *Feldspar* and *quartz* are the most common silicates. (§14.28)

2. These minerals are all good sources of various metals used in industry. (§14.29–14.31)

3. Carbonates are usually identified by reaction with dilute hydrochloric acid. The acid forms bubbles of carbon dioxide on the surface of the sample. (§14.31)

4. The artificial gem *cubic zirconia* is often used as a substitute for diamond in jewelry. (Facet, p. 381)

5. False. Hydrochloric acid is used primarily to identify carbonates although some sulfides, sulfates, and even a few rare silicates bubble when exposed to HCl. (§14.31)

In Terms of Geology

Chapter Summary

● A mineral is a naturally occurring, inorganic, crystalline solid with a definite chemical composition.

● An ore is a substance from which a valuable mineral or a metal can be extracted.

● Minerals can be elements or compounds, but they can never be mixtures.

● Most minerals can be identified by their color, streak, luster, crystal shape, cleavage, hardness, and specific gravity.

● Some minerals may be identified by using special tests such as flame tests or acid tests, or by identifying special properties such as magnetism, radioactivity, luminescence, and refractivity.

● Native minerals are pure elements: silver, gold, copper, platinum, diamond, and sulfur.

● Minerals are usually found as compounds such as silicates, oxides, sulfides, or carbonates.

What Did You Learn?

1. List the three distinguishing characteristics of minerals.

2. How did the Flood affect the kind and location of minerals in the earth?

3. What kinds of pure materials can form minerals? Give an example of each.

4. Why is color alone rarely used as positive identification of a mineral?

5. Discuss the different ways a mineral crystal may form. Contrary to what uniformitarian geologists believed, what factor is *not* the only one that controls crystal size?

6. Explain the difference between cleavage and fracture.

7. What tests can always be used to help identify a mineral?

Answers to Chapter Review Questions
What Did You Learn?

1. Minerals are (1) naturally occurring, (2) inorganic, and (3) crystalline solids. Students may also mention that they are of definite chemical composition. (§14.2)

2. Mineral deposits that were created in the earth before the Flood were probably completely disrupted and redistributed during and after the Flood. Processes that did not exist or were not important before the Flood may have produced new minerals. (§14.3)

3. Pure substances that can form minerals are called *elements* or *compounds*. Examples will vary. For elements, responses may include gold, silver, diamond, and so forth.

For compounds, examples may include any of the compound minerals or their classes as discussed in the text. (§14.4–14.5 and Section 14C)

4. Color alone is rarely used to identify minerals because many minerals have the same color as others or can exist in more than one color. (§14.8)

5. Mineral crystals may form by accretion in water or vapor solutions or when molten rock solidifies. Contrary to what used to be taught, the time it takes molten rock to cool and crystallize is not the only factor in determining crystal size. (Other factors include pressure, dissolved gases and liquids in the rock, concentration of dissolved minerals, number of sites where crystal formation may begin, and rate of crystallization.) (§14.11)

6. *Cleavage* is the characteristic of certain minerals to break easily along flat surfaces or along certain planes. Minerals that do not have cleavage may still have a characteristic breaking pattern known as *fracture*. (§14.12)

7. *Streak*, *cleavage* or *fracture*, *hardness*, and *specific gravity* can always be used to help identify a mineral. (§14.9, 14.12–14.14)

8. To find the specific gravity of a mineral, we must know the *mass* and the *volume* of the sample. (§14.14)

9. Some minerals are more dense than the surrounding sand and gravel in streams and rivers, so they settle to the lowest level in sedimentary deposits. (§14.22)

8. What two things must be known in order to find the specific gravity of a mineral sample?

9. How do some minerals become concentrated in placer deposits?

10. Where was one of the largest deposits of native silver and copper in the United States?

11. What characteristic of diamond is alluded to in Jeremiah 17:1?

12. What important mineral deposits are found in your state?

True or False

13. Mining to produce raw materials for manufacturing honors God for His provision for His creatures.

14. Coal is a very important mineral.

15. Minerals are mixtures of two or more elements or compounds.

16. Copper was among the first minerals in the new creation.

17. Nearly 4000 different minerals have been discovered.

18. Most minerals require more than one test for a positive identification.

19. Gold and fool's gold both produce a bright yellow streak.

20. Quartz will scratch a machinist's file.

21. Carnotite, a mineral of uranium, is easier to find if you use a radiation detector.

22. Phosphorescence is a characteristic of radioactive minerals.

23. Fuel cells powering the newest generation of automobiles will use silver as a catalyst for making the chemical reactions efficient.

24. The Premier mine is still the world's largest producer of diamonds.

25. Artificial gems are usually more perfect than natural gems.

26. When picking up a piece of gravel from your driveway, you would be correct in thinking that it likely contains silicate minerals.

27. Carbonates are most easily identified by their streak.

What Do You Think?

1. What factors make a mineral valuable? If someone were to develop a method for manufacturing unlimited numbers of near-perfect large diamonds very inexpensively, what would happen to the value of diamond jewelry?

2. Is ice a mineral?

3. Do you think it is possible to determine the hardness of fibrous minerals, such as those that form asbestos, using the Mohs scratch test?

4. Are geologists correct in calling a carbonate a mineral when it contains carbon?

5. Think about the great variety of colors, textures, and other properties of minerals and gemstones we have studied in this chapter. Does this suggest anything to you about what God's purpose might have been in creating precious stones?

My Review Checklist

☐ I have carefully read the entire chapter.

☐ I have reviewed all of the photographs, illustrations, and graphs.

☐ I have reviewed all of my notes in the margins.

☐ I have reviewed and corrected the quizzes on this chapter.

☐ I have studied all of the vocabulary terms.

☐ I have had all of my questions answered.

---

luminescent mineral in the same sample. However, phosphorescence is not a property of radioactive minerals per se. (§14.18–14.19)

23. False. Platinum will likely be used for this purpose. (§14.25)

24. False. The Argyle diamond pipe in Australia is now the world's most productive diamond pipe. (§14.26)

25. True. (Facet, p. 381)

26. True. (§14.28) However, in some locales limestone or marble gravel is common.

27. False. Carbonates are most easily identified by their effervescing when tested with dilute hydrochloric acid. (§14.31)

What Do You Think

1. Some of the factors that make a mineral valuable are its scarcity, beauty, durability, usefulness, and supply and demand. It may not be possible to predict gem values in a market flooded with perfect artificial stones, but it is likely that the value of large gem diamonds would eventually decline significantly. One thing to consider is that the slight imperfections found in natural diamonds tend to keep the value of diamonds high because they prove the gems are natural, and therefore rare.

2. Ice meets the definition of a mineral but usually is not considered one because water is not a solid under normal environmental conditions (for humans).

3. The individual crystals of the minerals in asbestos (actinolite-tremolite) are so fine that it is impossible to determine hardness using the standard hardness tests. However, these minerals do exist in larger individual crystals that yield a hardness of between 5 and 6 on the Mohs scale.

4. Minerals cannot contain carbon (or any other material) that has been produced by or within organisms. Carbonates that likely formed by chemical precipitation (Chap. 15) are inorganic in origin, so they meet the definition of a mineral. A mineralized fossil seashell consisting entirely of calcium carbonate does not meet the definition, since an organism formed it. For the same reason, the calcium carbonate chalk deposits found in many places around the world, formed entirely from the shells of innumerable microscopic organisms, cannot be considered a mineral.

5. Answers may vary. Perhaps precious stones were created especially for men and women to enjoy and use to demonstrate their creative talents. Numerous references in Scripture show that man has always placed great value on them. It is certain that God Himself affirms their inherent beauty, since He directed their use in the breastplate of the Jewish high priest and intends to use them for the foundations of New Jerusalem (Rev. 21:19–20).

---

10. One of the largest native silver and copper deposits was in the Keweenaw Peninsula in northern Michigan. (§14.23–14.24)

11. Jeremiah alluded to the diamond's extreme hardness by its use as an engraving tool. (§14.26, Jer. 17:1)

12. Answers will vary. Other sources must be consulted. Encourage students to use the Internet or the library.

True or False

13. True. (§14.1)

14. False. Coal does not meet the definition of a mineral—it is an organic substance. (§14.2)

15. False. Minerals by definition consist of a single element or pure compound although impurities may occur within their crystals. (§14.2) (*Note*: In compound minerals, some variation in composition within specified limits is permissible.)

16. True. (§14.3)

17. True. (§14.4)

18. True. (§14.7)

19. False. Gold produces a characteristic gold-colored streak; pyrites produce a characteristically greenish or brownish black streak. (§14.9, App. B5)

20. True. (Table 14.1, p. 367)

21. True. (§14.18)

22. False. Some rocks may glow due to the presence of both a radioactive mineral and a

Overview

The previous chapter described the minerals that comprise rocks. Chapter 15 shows that minerals are assembled to produce rocks. We examine the three kinds of rocks that make up the crust of the earth. This chapter examines the processes that formed or are forming the majority of rocks and interprets their origins according to both creationary and evolutionary models. The chapter also considers one aspect of geology most fascinating to students—fossils. Fossils give us a snapshot of the past—the kinds of plants and animals that lived at the time they were fossilized. This evidence can be interpreted in many different ways according to one's worldview. We hope that after this study, each time a student picks up a pebble, he or she will, at least momentarily, wonder what the history of that bit of rock might have been.

Section 15A presents to students the concept that the variety of rocks in existence is another aspect of God's provision for our needs. The three kinds of rocks that we will consider differ according to the processes that formed them. For completeness, the uniformitarian concept of the rock cycle is discussed, but the text shows that it cannot fit within a biblical, young-earth model.

Section 15B discusses sedimentary rocks and their two subcategories. Several common sedimentary rocks are presented to illustrate certain characteristics. Since fossils are found principally in sedimentary rocks, the section provides an overview of fossils, what can and cannot be learned from them, and their significance for interpreting the history of the earth through Scripture.

Section 15C discusses the characteristics and types of igneous rocks. This section describes the formation and characteristics of both extrusive and intrusive igneous rocks and provides many illustrations of the common igneous rock types.

Metamorphic rocks are the topic of Section 15D. These rocks began as either sedimentary or igneous rocks but were altered after their formation. We examine metamorphic processes and examples of the kinds of rocks produced through metamorphism.

Schedule Summary

Section 15A: 1–2 periods

Section 15B: 3–4 periods

Section 15C: 1–2 periods

Section 15D: 1 period

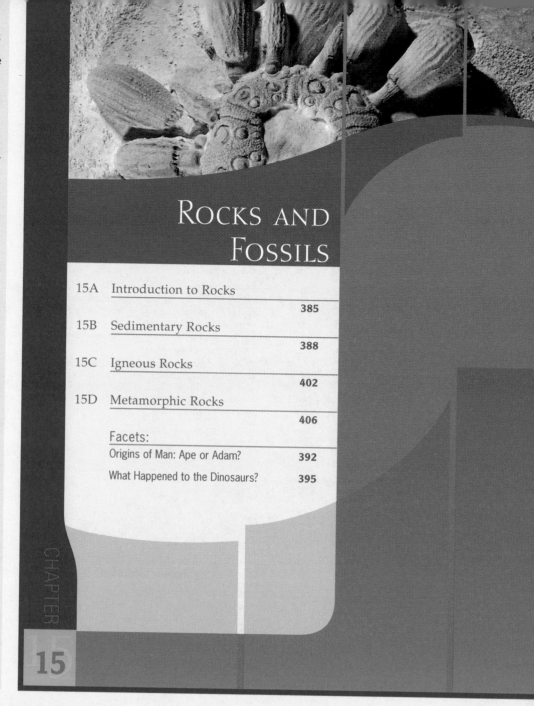

CHAPTER 15

ROCKS AND FOSSILS

SUGGESTED TEACHING SCHEDULE

DAY 0

Assignment

Reading: Section 15A, "Introduction to Rocks"

DAY 1

Differentiate between rocks and minerals and summarize the characteristics of the three types of rocks. Describe the uniformitarian rock cycle and evaluate it within a biblical, young-earth framework.

Assignment

Complete: 15A Section Review Questions

Applications 15A, "Classification of Rocks"

Reading: Section 15B-1 (§15.4–15.6), clastic and nonclastic sedimentary rocks

DAY 2

Quiz—Section 15A, "Introduction to Rocks"

Describe the two different types of sedimentary rocks. It is helpful to show students samples of each type.

Assignment

Complete: 15B-1 Section Review Questions

Reading: Section 15B-2 (§15.7–15.12), fossils, their origins, and the geologic column

DAY 3

Discuss the nature of the fossils that are found in sedimentary rock and how one's view of history affects the interpretation of these fossils. Examine how evolutionists use the geologic time scale.

15A INTRODUCTION TO ROCKS

15.1 The Importance of Rocks

The rocks of the earth are important for many reasons. The primary reason people study rocks is that they tell a story. However, different people read different stories in these rocks based on their worldviews. The evolutionist, who has a uniformitarian view of the earth's history, believes the rocks tell a story some four-and-a-half billion years long—one with no supernatural intervention by God. The Creationist, however, sees sobering reminders of God's hatred for sin everywhere. Sedimentary rock and the fossils found in it testify to a horrific year in history when God unleashed His anger on the entire world.

But this judgment is not the only message of the rocks. Their message to us is like Jonah's message to the Ninevites (Jonah 3:4). It is primarily about divine judgment, but it also suggests that God desires to forgive and restore His wayward creatures. If God has been careful to preserve physical evidence of His judgment and has allowed scientists all over the world to find this evidence, then surely He desires for us to call out to Him for mercy and seek forgiveness.

One of the main purposes of education is to teach students to read and analyze information. Education that is Christian must teach the Christian to read and understand the message that God has written in the rocks of the earth: God hates sin and has judged it in the past, but God constantly reminds us of that judgment so that we may *"be diligent that [we] may be found of him in peace, without spot, and blameless"* (2 Pet. 3:14).

We study rock not just for the story it tells us of the earth's history, but also because it is useful to us in many ways every day. It is a valuable building material that is both durable and ornamental. Gravel for roadbeds and blacktop comes from rock, as do concrete materials for sidewalks, marble for monuments, lime for improving the soil, and glass for windows. Coal, a rock that burns, is an important fuel for heating and for generating electricity as well as being a major source of dyes, medicines, and many other chemical products. Some rocks are storage places for petroleum, natural gas, coal, precious metals, precious stones, and ground water. Rocks also add to the scenic splendor of the world we live in. All around us we see testimony of the Creator's wisdom in the usefulness and the beauty of rock that remains in spite of the devastation of the Flood.

Rock, the solid material in the earth's crust, consists of one or more minerals or organic materials. Most rocks contain two or more minerals, though a few rocks, such as dolomite and halite, contain only one mineral. In some rocks the different kinds of mineral crystals are easy to see. Others have fine crystals that cannot be seen without a microscope. The study of rocks is called **petrology**. Geologists who specialize in identifying rocks are called petrologists.

15-1 Rocks, such as these folded strata formed from water-deposited layers of sediment, preserve the evidence of catastrophic events of the past.

dolomite (DOLE uh MITE)

petrology (pe TRAHL oh gy): petro- (Gk. *petra*—rock) + logy (study of)

Investigation Summary

15D "Properties of Rocks"

15E "Fallacies of the Geologic Time Scale"

15F "'Trilobite-ology'"

Bulletin Board Ideas

1. Reproduce the rock cycle diagram in Figure 15-5, but label the illustration "Processes That Can Change Rocks." This will get students thinking about the impermanence of rocks but will not associate the idea with the uniformitarian rock cycle.

2. Put a world map on your bulletin board and use straight pins or construction paper shapes to indicate places where fossils are found. Get your students to research locations of fossil finds.

3. Make a bulletin board of the geologic column similar to Table 15-1 in the text or Visual 15-4. Do some research in creationary geology literature and on websites, and assign the boundaries of the pre-Flood, Flood, and post-Flood rock strata to the column.

Field Trip Ideas

1. Visit a museum that displays fossils. Afterward, have students write a paper identifying how the exhibits favor the evolutionary worldview. You can also take photographs of articulated vertebrate skeletons with a digital camera and print out the photos back at the school. Distribute copies of the photos to students and have them create "artist's impressions" of what the animals looked like in the flesh by tracing over the skeletal photos. Display their illustrations in class.

2. Have your students do some field work, perhaps in a mountainous area, gathering samples from nearby rock outcrops, making sketches, drawing a map, and writing observations in a logbook. This type of exercise is the substance of geology.

Objectives—Section 15A

Upon completing this section, students should be able to

- see the providence of God in the types of rocks that exist in nature.

- distinguish between minerals and rocks.

- summarize the three types of rocks according to their modes of origin.

- describe the uniformitarian concept of the rock cycle and explain why it is inadequate to account for the origins of rocks seen today.

Concepts Students Find Difficult

Make sure that your students understand the difference between rocks and minerals. Rocks are made up of minerals and other substances. If a rock consists of only one type of mineral, then that rock is also a mineral. An example of such a rock would be a sample of limestone, which is chemically calcium carbonate, the same mineral that forms calcite. Generally, the existence of massive (noncrystalline) or microcrystalline forms of a mineral are called rocks.

Assignment

Complete: 15B-2 Section Review Questions
Applications 15B, "Fossils"

Reading: Investigation 15E, "Fallacies of the Geologic Time Scale"

Investigation 15F, "'Trilobite-ology'"

DAY 4

Do Investigation 15F, "'Triolobite-ology'." Review the instructions for Investigation 15E, "Fallacies of the Geologic Time Scale," which students will complete as homework.

Assignment

Complete: Investigation 15E, "Fallacies of the Geologic Time Scale"

Reading: Section 15B-3 (§15.13–15.16), fossil fuels

(schedule continued on p. 386)

15.2 Kinds of Rocks

As with everything else mankind studies in God's creation, the first thing a petrologist tries to do when examining a rock is to *classify* it, which means to determine which category it belongs to. He asks himself, "What basic process formed this rock?" and "Does the rock appear to have been altered in any way during its history?" After he has answered these questions, or perhaps as he answers them, he looks at the minerals that compose the rock and the way the minerals are arranged. He notes any other information that might give clues to the rock's composition or its history, such as the presence of fossils. Depending on his purpose, the petrologist may measure the angles between the cracks in the rock, sample the minerals for a detailed chemical analysis, determine the rock's specific gravity, and perform many other tests.

Let's look first at the basic processes that can form rocks. Rocks may be produced when moving water or wind lays down massive amounts of eroded sediment. Chemical reactions also appear to produce thick layers of solids in water. The sediments are then compacted under great pressure, possibly accompanied by high temperatures, resulting in **sedimentary rock**. This process can occur very rapidly—in a matter of days—as shown by the sedimentary rocks formed in the aftermath of the 1980 eruption of Mount St. Helens in Washington State.

Rocks formed by the cooling of molten rock are called **igneous rocks**. The molten rock may be either underground (magma) or on the earth's surface (lava). These rocks seem to be the only ones that are continuously forming in any significant quantities today. The world's many active volcanoes give much evidence for the movement of magma deep underground. In the past, the rapid wearing away of igneous rocks formed much of the raw material for sedimentary rocks.

Geologists have observed that many rocks were changed in some way after they were formed. Many creationary scientists believe that the movements and collisions of huge portions of the earth's crust created unimaginable pressures that crushed layers of sediment into folds during and following the Flood. Volcanoes rose in many places, venting great quantities of heat from the earth's interior that heated the rocks nearby. Masses of magma deep in the earth bubbled up through cracks in the crust, melting and heating the overlying rocks and changing their minerals and structures. All of these changes in the original igneous and sedimentary rock types produced **metamorphic rocks**. These rocks are still being formed today by the same processes, although probably at a much slower rate and on a much smaller scale.

Other rock types can be formed in other ways, but these are minor sources of rocks or else they are closely associated with the kinds of rocks noted above. Examples include rocks formed by the evaporation of groundwater from vents heated by magma and rocks formed from the dripping or flowing of water in caves. Many minerals that are sources of economically important compounds and elements are found in rocks formed from concentrated solutions of high-temperature water. This water is under great pressure and flows through the cracks in the crust deep underground. These kinds of rocks will be discussed in later chapters. In this chapter we will look at the three major rock types, discuss how to recognize them, and explore their usefulness.

15-2 These sedimentary rocks formed from a debris flow during the eruption of Mount St. Helens in 1980.

15-3 These rocks were formed from lava originating from Mauna Kea, Hawaii.

15-4 These metamorphic rocks appear to have been formed from sedimentary rocks folded under great pressure.

DAY 5

Focus on the different types of fossil fuels, their origin, and their characteristics.

Assignment

Complete: 15B-3 Section Review Questions

Reading: Section 15C, "Igneous Rocks"

DAY 6

Quiz—Section 15B, sedimentary rocks and fossils

Compare and contrast intrusive and extrusive igneous rocks, examining how each is different in crystal structure and texture. If possible, provide samples of each for students to examine. Describe intrusive and extrusive igneous rock formations.

Assignment

Complete: 15C Section Review Questions

Reading: Section 15D, "Metamorphic Rocks"

DAY 7

Quiz—Section 15C, "Igneous Rocks"

Discuss the different metamorphic processes and how metamorphism properly fits into a creationary model of a young earth. Compare and contrast foliated and nonfoliated metamorphic rocks, examining how each is different in appearance but similar in composition. If possible, provide representative samples of metamorphic rocks.

Assignment

Complete: 15D Section Review Questions
    Applications 15C, "Characteristics of Rocks"

Reading: Investigation 15D, "Properties of Rocks"

DAY 8

Do Investigation 15D, "Properties of Rocks."

Assignment

Complete: Selected Chapter Review Questions

15.3   The Rock Cycle

Most natural processes on Earth were designed to be cyclic. In other words, they follow a predictable set of steps that result in the materials in the process being reused. God created the earth to operate in cyclic processes so that essential materials would not run out. You should be familiar with the water cycle, which we discussed briefly in Unit Three. The winds and ocean currents also follow cyclic patterns. Nutrients in biological systems are continuously recycled as well.

It is not surprising, then, that uniformitarian geologists expect that rock is recycled just like nearly every other natural resource. According to their deep-time viewpoint, they believe igneous rock formed on or just under the surface from magma rising into the crust from the upper mantle. These rocks wore away over hundreds of thousands or even millions of years and were washed into the seas, forming sediments deep in the ocean basins. These sediments eventually turned into sedimentary rock after additional hundreds of thousands or millions of years. In some locations, plates of the ocean crust slid slowly down under stationary plates of the continental crust, which move only a few centimeters per year, returning sedimentary and igneous rocks back to the upper mantle to be melted again.

In other locations, the ocean crust seems to have broken apart as magma welled up from the mantle, forming mountains of igneous and sedimentary rocks in the ocean basins. Most geologists believe that, after millions of years, these mid-ocean mountains and other igneous rock masses became exposed as they were lifted above sea level and their covering layers wore away. Waves, rain, and wind then eroded these igneous rocks, producing sediments again and restarting the cycle.

This description of geologic events is known as the **rock cycle**. It is a uniformitarian model that relies on extending the slow geologic processes observed today into the supposed deep time of the past.

Creationary geologists agree that certain parts of the rock cycle are occurring today. Volcanic eruptions and erosion of rocks can be observed and measured. Plates of the earth's crust do seem to be sliding under other plates, which would result in rocks in the crust being melted in the mantle. However, because the creationary view of earth's history is so much shorter than in the evolutionary model, there has been insufficient time to complete even a small part of one uniformitarian rock cycle for a majority of the earth's surface. This means that erosion is wearing away the continents faster than they can be built back up. If a rock cycle actually exists, it is restricted to only a few locations on the earth and is likely a direct consequence of geologic events associated with the Flood.

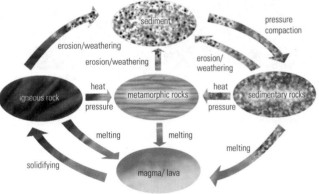

15-5 The evolutionary rock cycle supposedly explains the recycling of the earth's rocks between the crust and the mantle.

 Visual 15-1: The Uniformitarian Rock Cycle

This visual is a reproduction of Figure 15-5. Use this visual when discussing the rock cycle. Point out that examples of the transitions between the different "bubbles" can all be observed today. The error occurs when scientists presume that the transitions are all connected in a great cycle and are occurring more or less at the same rate in order to account for the postulated recycling of rocks in the earth's crust and mantle.

DAY 9

Quiz—Section 15D, "Metamorphic Rocks"

Review for a chapter test.

Assignment

Study for a chapter test.

DAY 10

Test—Chapter 15

Assignment

Reading: Section 16A, "Describing Mountains"

Objectives—Section 15B

Upon completing this section, students should be able to

- categorize samples of sedimentary rock as clastic or nonclastic.
- describe the characteristics of a fossil.
- explain how fossils and extinct species, especially dinosaurs, fit into the biblical view of the earth's history.
- discount fossil "evidences" of biological evolution.
- relate the geologic column to the geologic time scale.
- list and describe the types of fossil fuels and state evidences for their origins.

strata (STRA tuh), plural of *stratum*

15-6 Sedimentary strata in Pugh Canyon, Kanab, Utah (left); tilted strata in Denver, Colorado (right)

clastic: (Gk. *klastikos*—broken) A *clast* is a single piece of broken material or fossil in a clastic rock.

conglomerate (kun GLAHM ur it)

15A Section Review

1. What is the difference between a rock and a mineral?
2. How do we know that it does not require millions of years to form the three different rock types? How is each being formed today?
3. If the uniformitarian rock cycle were true, what would this imply about the age of the earth? How does your conclusion agree with the Bible?
4. According to 2 Peter 3:4–7, what should a Christian's response be to the claims of uniformitarian geologists?
5. (True or False) According to the uniformitarian rock cycle model, any rock can eventually become part of any other kind of rock, given enough time.

15B SEDIMENTARY ROCKS

15.4 Introduction

Sedimentary rock appears to be made of particles bonded together by natural cements or of solids that settled from water solutions. These rocks are abundant on the earth's crust, covering about three-fourths of its surface. Creationary geologists believe that the turbulent waters of the Genesis Flood were responsible for most sedimentary rocks, especially the layers that contain fossils. Such formations give evidence for a rapid, global process that no longer operates today. Sedimentary rocks characteristically form layers called **strata**. Water-deposited strata usually begin as horizontal layers (although layers at an angle are possible), but movements of the earth's crust can tilt them to almost any angle.

Sedimentary rocks are classified as **clastic**, or *fragmental*, if they appear to contain fragments eroded from other rocks. They are classified as **nonclastic**, or *chemical*, if they appear to come from minerals that were dissolved in water.

15.5 Clastic Rocks

The fragments in clastic sedimentary rock were formed from the breakup of previously existing rocks and in addition may contain numerous fossils or fossil fragments. Various mineral-like cements, and possibly pressure, bonded the fragments to make different kinds of sedimentary rock. Pebbles and gravel form *conglomerate*, sand forms *sandstone*, and silts and clays form *siltstone* or *shale*. Numerous rocks show some combination of two or three of these kinds of clastic sedimentary rocks.

Conglomerate, the coarsest grade of clastic sedimentary rock, contains gravels, pebbles, cobbles, and even large boulders held together by a mass of cemented sand grains. Most are rounded particles greater than 2 mm in diameter. Though almost any kind of rock

Answers to 15A Section Review Questions

1. Minerals have a specific, consistent chemical composition, but rocks are mixtures of one or more minerals or other substances. Minerals are inherently inorganic, but rocks can contain organic materials. (§15.1, Chap. 14)

2. Sedimentary and igneous rocks formed in a very short period following the eruption of Mount St. Helens in 1980. Metamorphic rocks depend only on heat and pressure, which are readily available in any active volcano. (§15.2)

3. In order for at least one complete rock cycle to occur on a large scale there must be sufficient time, on the order of millions of years. This necessitates a belief in an old earth, which is not supported by the Bible. (§15.3)

4. Christians should proclaim that uniformitarian geologists are willingly ignorant of the supernatural Creation of the earth, its judgment by a global Flood, and its coming judgment by fire. (2 Pet. 3:4–7)

5. True. (§15.3)

may appear in the mixture, most often the fragments in conglomerate are quartz or some other silicate. Conglomerate is often called "nature's concrete." The fragments in conglomerate were rounded by the effects of erosion prior to being combined into sedimentary rock. **Breccia** is similar to conglomerate except the fragments are sharp and angular. These sharp fragments often appear in a fine-grained matrix such as clay. A **matrix** is a material in which something else is enclosed or embedded. The sediments forming conglomerates and breccias are believed to have been deposited by rapidly flowing waters or winds, since large particles can be moved and supported only by strong fluid flows.

Clasts in conglomerates and breccias are larger than 2 mm in diameter.

15-7 Conglomerate and breccia are both composed of cemented rock fragments. Conglomerate (left) has incorporated rounded fragments, and breccia (right) includes angular fragments.

breccia (BRECH ee uh)

The clast sizes in sandstone are between 0.0625 mm and 2 mm in diameter.

In sandstone the fragments are smaller—between 0.0625 and 2 mm in diameter. Beds of quartz sand grains are compacted and cemented into deposits of sandstone; silica, calcite, or iron oxide cements the grains of sand, which are usually water-worn and rounded. These sediments were likely deposited by moderate water currents, wind, or wave action. The color of the rock results from its cementing material. If silica and calcite bind the rock, it is white, yellow, or buff. If iron oxide is the natural cement, the color is red to reddish brown.

Sandstones typically have air spaces between the sand crystals because the cements usually do not completely fill these spaces. This is especially true if the particles are all about the same size. If the sand particles vary widely in size, or if the sandstone contains clay, then these spaces between grains may be filled in. If relatively large spaces between grains exist in sandstone, then it has high **porosity**. Usually these spaces are interconnected, allowing the sandstone to be highly **permeable.** Liquids can pass easily through a bed of sandstone. The spaces between the particles of a porous rock often become reservoirs for water or, in some places, for oil.

Porosity is the ratio of the volume of empty space between the particles in a rock to its total volume. A rock that has high porosity has either large pores, or many pores, or both.

Permeability is the ability of a rock to permit liquids to pass through its pores. This happens when the pores are interconnected.

Siltstone and shale have the smallest particles of any clastic sedimentary rocks. Particles in these rocks average less than 0.0625 mm in diameter. They cannot be viewed without a microscope. Thick deposits of silt can occur only in relatively still water, such as at the bottoms of deep lakes or oceans. Shale and siltstone particles tend to be angular and thus have relatively large spaces between them. The porosity of siltstone and shale is usually only slightly lower than that of sandstone. However, because liquids flow with more difficulty through smaller spaces, siltstones and shales have much lower permeability. If there are no interconnected pores in the rock, it is **impermeable**. Shale is soft and splits easily into thin sheets. It is usually gray but

Shale and siltstone contain clasts less than 0.0625 mm in diameter.

15-8 A red sandstone cliff in Hanksville, Utah (left); shale from Montana, which easily splits into thin sheets (right)

Stones of Witness

An abundance of sedimentary rock over the earth's surface supports the biblical account of a worldwide Flood. If God had chosen to destroy the world with fire instead of water, we could expect to find the earth's surface covered with igneous rocks instead of sedimentary rocks.

Additional Resources

Take time to have a historical lesson with your students on salt and how it has affected the development of civilizations. Salt's use as a preservative, flavor enhancer, necessary nutrient, and medicine makes this mineral very important. Cities and the economies of civilizations have been built around salt trade and production. The Salt Institute has a six-page history online. Visit the BJU Press online Resources/SPACE AND EARTH SCIENCE webpage. Under Chapter 15, click on the link *History of Salt*. Several salt companies have information available on their websites. The International Commission for the History of Salt has an extensive bibliographic list.

Stones of Witness

Sedimentary rocks cover about 75 percent of the earth's surface and are found all over the planet. Given what you know about the formation of sedimentary rocks, what does an abundance of this kind of rock suggest?

15-9 Limestone takes many different appearances and can be nonfossiliferous (left) or fossiliferous (right).

permeable rock

salt dome

15-10 Diagram of a salt dome (top); a mass of halite (bottom)

may also be white, brown, red, green, or black. Siltstone is similar to shale but does not split into thin sheets.

15.6 Nonclastic Sedimentary Rocks

Nonclastic or chemical sedimentary rocks form from minerals dissolved in water. When the solution of minerals in water becomes supersaturated, the mineral may crystallize out of solution, settling as a solid to the bottom to form a **precipitate**. Alternatively, evaporation of the water can leave the minerals behind as an **evaporite**. Shells of microscopic water organisms can also contribute to these rocks.

Limestone, which contains mainly calcite, precipitates directly out of seawater. The presence of extensive limestone deposits on the continents indicates that they were all once under water. Creationary geologists suggest that global volcanic activity at the time of the Flood could have caused a higher level of atmospheric carbon dioxide, which in turn would have aided in the production of carbonate precipitates as the Floodwaters receded. This is one of many Flood-related theories that creationary geologists are investigating. Limestone is important economically because it is useful for neutralizing acidic soils, building roads, and making cement.

God may have created most halite (common or rock salt) as it is now. However, it is also possible that the halite deposits now found in the earth's rocks formed through evaporation or precipitation during or following the Flood. Strata of other materials often cover halite deposits. Geologists have found extensive beds of halite ranging from 1 m (3 ft) thick to over 60 m (200 ft) thick. Halite deposits occasionally occur deep underground as vertical cylindrical masses called **salt domes**. These structures seem to have been forced upward from below by great pressure. Deformed strata of impermeable rock penetrated by salt domes often collect oil and gas. Many such formations exist in the Gulf of Mexico, where numerous offshore oil wells are operating.

15B-1 Section Review

1. How do creationary geologists believe the sediments for most of the sedimentary rocks were deposited?

2. What are layers of sedimentary rocks called? What other natural formation that you have studied has a similar name?

3. What kind of rock consists of sharp, angular pieces of rock cemented in a matrix of finer sediment? To what class of sedimentary rocks does this kind of rock belong?

4. What is the property that indicates the amount of open space between particles in clastic rocks? How does this property relate to the permeability of rock?

5. What kinds of sedimentary rocks form from minerals dissolved in water?

6. (True or False) The larger the average particle size in a clastic sedimentary rock, the higher the rate of flow of the water or wind that deposited the original sediment.

Answers to 15B-1 Section Review Questions

1. Creationary geologists believe most of the sediments that formed sedimentary rock were laid down during the Flood. (§15.4)

2. Layers of sedimentary rocks are called *strata*. Horizontal layers of clouds are called *stratus*. (§15.4, Chap. 10)

3. A *breccia* is formed of sharp, angular pieces of rock cemented together. Sedimentary breccias are *clastic* sedimentary rocks. (§15.5)

4. The amount of open space between particles in clastic rock is known as *porosity*. A porous rock is permeable if the interconnected spaces are large enough so that liquid flow is not impeded. A porous rock of very fine particles will have a much lower permeability. (§15.5)

5. Sedimentary rocks that form from minerals dissolved in water are called *nonclastic* or *chemical* sedimentary rocks. (§15.6)

6. True. (§15.5)

15.7 Fossils in Sedimentary Rocks

A fascinating feature of sedimentary rocks is the fossils they sometimes contain. A **fossil** is any trace or remains of a living organism that has been preserved by natural means. According to this definition, a fossil may be remains of the organism itself, such as a shell; it may be a rock formed by mineral replacement of the tissues of the organism; it may be an impression of any part of the organism; it may be tracks, tubes, or burrows of an animal; or it may even be the waste products of the animal (*coprolites*). Ninety-five percent of all fossils are of marine organisms. There are fossils of both plants and animals, ranging in size from bacteria "microfossils" to huge dinosaurs.

Fossils are most frequently found in limestone, sandstone, and shale. The study of fossilized animals and plants is called **paleontology**. A scientist who studies fossils is a *paleontologist*. Paleontologists are often biologists who have specialized in this area of science.

15.8 Fossils and Evolution—Where Are the Missing Links?

Why are fossils so fascinating? Fossils tell us about the past by giving us a sample of what living things on the earth used to be like. We find many different kinds of creatures as fossils. It is important to remember that fossils, like rocks, minerals, and strata, are data that must be studied and interpreted by scientists who have biases. Evolutionary and creationary scientists all have the same data to work with. Their conclusions depend on what they believe about the original nature of things.

Some people who reject the biblical account of Creation think that living things went through gradual changes (biological evolution) from one kind to another. In order to support their beliefs, they find fossils that, when lined up, seem to show a continuous change from a simpler organism to a much larger and more complex one. But fossils for the most part do not show gradual changes from one kind to another. They are clearly one kind or another, not something between kinds. For example, fossils of mice exist and fossils of bats exist, but no fossils of half-winged, mouse-like creatures have been found.

Evolutionists believe, for example, that the fins of fish gradually changed into legs so that the resulting creatures could walk around on the land. In this process, the early fins were attached to thick lobes, the lobes lengthened and developed toes, and eventually the fin membranes disappeared. If such a change took place, we should be able to find many fossils of the transitional types having limbs with features of both fins and legs. It is true that many fossil fish (and living ones today) show thickened lobes supporting fins. But there are no fossils showing a clearly transitional form. Fossil appendages are either fins or legs. The same is true of the imagined change from the legs of reptiles to the wings of birds.

The fossils sought by evolutionists that might show intermediate forms are sometimes called "*missing links.*" Evolutionists have searched for these missing links for more than a century and a half without finding more than a small handful of fossils of doubtful classification. For many years, evolutionary biologists assumed it was just a

15-11 Fish fossil of the genus *Diplomystus* found in shale near Kemmerer, Wyoming

paleontology (PALE ee on TAHL uh gee): pale- (Gk. *paleios*—ancient) + -ontology (L. *ontologia*—the science or study of being)

15-12 A fossilized plant

"primitive" fish

"missing link"

"missing link"

"primitive" amphibian

15-13 Coelacanths (above) were thought to be an evolutionary link between fish and land animals (top), but they are still alive today. The Coelacanth's lobed fin (bottom right) is not transitional between a fin and a leg.

Fossils may be found in volcanoclastic sediments, which fall into a category that bridges sedimentary rocks and igneous rocks. In general, fossils do not occur in igneous rock because the organisms would be destroyed by the heat. Most metamorphic rocks do not preserve fossils. However, sections of marble rock frequently reveal fossils that have been stretched and smeared but not completely destroyed during the metamorphic process.

People are most familiar with vertebrate fossils and assume that the majority of fossil animals that have been found are vertebrates. The opposite is the case. While accurate percentages of the different kinds of fossils known to make up the fossil record are hard to obtain, Dr. John D. Morris of the Institute for Creation Research (ICR) has provided the following breakdown:

Category	Percentage of total fossil record
shallow marine invertebrates, mostly shellfish	95%
algae and plant fossils	4.75%
insects and all other invertebrates	0.2375%
vertebrates (fish, amphibians, reptiles, birds, and mammals)*	0.0125%

*Only 0.000125% of the total record consists of more than a single vertebrate bone!

Ref: John D. Morris, "Does The Geologic Column Prove Evolution?" *Back to Genesis* No. 67b (July 1994). http://www.icr.org/pubs/btg-b/btg-067b.htm (2004).

Though evolutionists may insist from time to time that they have discovered a "missing link," biblical Creationists need not worry. Evolutionists will never be able to disprove the record of biblical Creation through scientific discoveries. Their problem is not that they have not found *enough* "missing links," but that they have not found *any*. Many discoveries of so-called missing links have been exposed as hoaxes and others as misidentifications. Since biblical Creationists understand "missing links" to be an unbiblical concept, they realize that anything held up by evolutionists to be such a thing is at best an inaccurate interpretation of the evidence.

Stones of Witness

Answers will vary. Some differences between a boney fish and a typical amphibian are provided in the following table:

Fish	Amphibian
scaled skin	smooth skin (often with mucous glands)
fins; no jointed limbs	no fins; jointed limbs with toes, often webbed
gill respiration	lung respiration supplemented by skin respiration
two-chambered heart	three-chambered heart
swim bladder	no corresponding organ
streamlined body; aquatic	semi-aquatic; quadruped

One of the ways evolutionists account for the absence of intermediate species and gaps in their geologic record is a theory known as *punctuated equilibrium*, popularized by Stephen Jay Gould and other evolutionists. This theory's underlying principle is that a stable species (stases) may mutate rapidly in one geographical location, which could then have an effect on the species as a whole (allotropic speciation).

Another (albeit abandoned) explanation of the gaps in the fossil record is *saltationistic evolution*. A saltation is best described by a wind-blown sand grain that bounds along and lands among other sand grains, kicking them into the air. These grains then fall and dislodge additional grains until the air is full of bouncing sand grains. Similarly, a few organisms within a species undergo macromutations that allow them to change drastically in a short amount of time. These major mutations propagate throughout the species and replace it because the newer form survives more successfully. The theory was discredited because it was too *ad hoc*, and the sudden appearance of a viable, drastically different form would have required a miraculous coincidence of mutations.

Even though many organisms have become extinct since their creation, biblical Creationists do not believe that any of these were transitional organisms. Evolutionists assume that the missing links are yet to be found and that they will inevitably be organisms that have become extinct. From the biblical account, biblical Creationists know that since God created all things, even extinct organisms were part of His creation rather than products of evolutionary chance.

Stones of Witness

What kinds of changes would have to occur in a population of creatures for a fishlike creature to evolve into an air-breathing, four-legged animal, such as an amphibian? You may have to do some research in a biology book to answer this question.

matter of time before the fossils needed to prove their theory would be discovered. However, as time passes, evolutionists are wondering where these fossils might be. Very few of the tens of thousands of species represented in fossils could be considered transitional. The missing links are a powerful argument against biological evolution. Because creationary scientists believe that missing links never existed and that the apparent transitional forms are likely just variants of existing species, they do not believe these fossils will ever be found. They prefer to call missing links the "absence of intermediate species."

Many organisms preserved as fossils are the same as those living on the earth today. Many fossilized leaves, for example, match present-day leaves. Fossil seashells, starfish, insects, and many vertebrates (animals with backbones) also match those alive today. These counterparts show that no evolutionary change has occurred in that kind of organism between the time the fossil formed and the present. This is not surprising, since they lived only about 5000 years ago. Some fossils do not have living counterparts today. Their absence among the living is due to extinction (dying out).

FACETS OF GEOLOGY

ORIGINS OF MAN: APE OR ADAM?

The evolution myth has been almost universally accepted in the modern secular world. Evolutionists view evolution as the only reasonable and truly scientific framework from which to interpret evidence. As a result, they view fossil finds through "evolutionary glasses." Evolution demands "missing links" between different species, especially between modern humans and whatever evolved into humans—commonly believed to be an ape-like ancestor. The fossil finds claimed as "missing links" to *Homo sapiens* (HOH moh SAY pee unz) have turned out to be insubstantial evidence, such as a pig's tooth (Nebraska Man), human skeletons that had been classified as missing links (Neandertal Man, Cro-Magnon Man), meaningless chips of bone (Java Man), or outright hoaxes (Piltdown Man).

The fossil dubbed "Lucy" by its discoverer was originally thought to be a human ancestor with apelike characteristics that walked upright. It was classified in the species *Australopithecus* (aw STRAY loh PITH ih kus), or "Southern Ape." This evaluation was based on a skeleton that was only 40% complete and was missing some key parts, such as most of the skull and hand and foot bones. Later skeletons

of these creatures showed features of both tree-dwelling apes and knuckle-walking apes. Some evolutionists even speculate that the evidence is too skimpy to be sure that Lucy walked on its hind legs at all. They now believe Lucy may be nothing more than a unique, extinct, ape-like species. The evidence, even at its best, far from proves a missing link between a prehistoric ape and man.

Also consider the evidence for the species of the *Neandertals*, named for the Neander Valley in Germany, where the first fossils of this creature were discovered in 1857. Neandertals were said to be a prehuman species characterized by a sloping forehead, a large brain cavity, very heavy and thickened bones, and a hunched-over (apelike) appearance. Paleontologists later recognized that these fossils are very humanlike. Recent discoveries indicate Neandertals had an advanced culture that included clothing, ritual burials, and musical instruments. Creationists believe that these fossils are the remains of post-Flood peoples. The heavy Neandertal skeletal bones are characterized by arthritis and thickening, which could be due to a vigorous battle for survival in a harsh environ-

ment. Humans probably faced very difficult living conditions for centuries after the Flood. Modern peoples living in extreme climates show similar physical features.

Some evolutionists are honest enough to admit the problem of the lack of conclusive evidence to support human evolution. A child who believes the Word of God can see what the most brilliant minds of this day miss: all human beings were uniquely created by God in His image.

Facet Summary: Origins of Man: Ape or Adam?

This Facet focuses on the fossil hoaxes used to propagate the belief in human evolution. Be cautious when attacking evolutionists as deceivers that you do not commit the *ad hominem* fallacy in your presentation. Unsaved evolutionists are deceived fallen humans, just as we were before Christ redeemed us. There are no vocabulary terms in this Facet.

The occurrence of extinction alone does not refute Creation or evolution. Extinction fits both the biblical and evolutionary frameworks of the earth's history (Chapter 13). Creationists believe extinction should be expected in a degenerating world following the fall of man and the Curse. Also, the Flood and the drastic climatic changes following it would certainly cause the extinction of some organisms. Biologists believe that natural selection—the dying off of organisms that cannot successfully compete with other organisms—results in extinctions as well.

15-14 Fossils can be found for both living and extinct organisms. The shrimp and starfish are both very similar to living forms. The ammonites on the right were squid-like shelled creatures that are extinct.

Where to Look for Fossils

Shark teeth collected by spoil-sifting

Some people may have the idea that finding fossils is a difficult task—even for the experts. This is true if you are looking in the wrong places. The only hard part about finding fossils is discovering the right places to dig.

One of the very best sources of fossil locations is the USGS (United States Geological Survey). Most states have a USGS office located in the capital city. Simply write that office requesting information about fossil locations in your area. Most likely, what they will send you will be a list of publications. Decide what you would like to order or subscribe to, and then wait until it arrives.

Other sources of information are rock and gem shops or a university that has a paleontology or geology department.

However, if you cannot find any information about where to find fossils in your area, places that might yield some fossils include the following: along road or railroad cuts, in quarries or mines, on the beach, and in creek or river beds.

Probably your next concern should be obtaining permission to dig. If the site is on private property, the county

courthouse may be able to supply you with the owner's name. Usually, you will need to sign an injury disclaimer before searching commercial quarries and mines. In some locations, such as national parks, fossils are considered government property and you are prohibited from removing them without a permit.

The supplies that you need to take will depend on whether you will be "spoil-sifting" or "slab-splitting." Spoil-sifting is often done at mines or quarries where good fossil-bearing sediment has been moved to huge spoil piles in order to access limestone or gravel layers. Many fossils will be on the surface. However, by sifting through the pile using a claw-shaped hand rake, you can expose many more fossils. The shark's teeth in the photograph (above left) were collected in less than two hours by this method from a quarry in South Carolina.

Slab-splitting is most likely to occur at locations with shale rock. Attempt to remove as large a slab as possible. Set the slab on its side and split the rock apart parallel to the bedding planes, using a hammer and a wide, flat stone chisel. In order to get a perfect split, work all the way around the rock before trying to split the rock. The fish fossils shown in the figure were found by this method.

Be sure to take the time to write down as much information as possible about each find. This information will prevent your collection from becoming mere curiosities in the future.

Fish fossils from the green River formation in Wyoming (top); *homeosaurus pulonellus* in Kelheim, Germany (bottom)

Supply List

insect spray
sunscreen
hat and heavy gloves
sunglasses
paper and pencils
fossil field book
magnifying glass
brush for dusting
empty sample boxes
maps
masonry hammers
newspapers (for wrapping)

For Spoil-Sifting
claw-like hand rake
small shovel
small bag or carpenter's apron
coarse sifting screen box

For Slab-Splitting
wide, flat stone chisel
assorted other chisels
small sledge hammer

Box Summary: Where to Look for Fossils

This box discusses basic techniques of fossil hunting. Encourage your students to be involved in science outside the classroom. It is these types of activities that will develop your students into scientists and possibly influence them to prepare for a career in science. There are no vocabulary terms in this box.

Stones of Witness

According to Scripture, the Flood lasted about 370 days from start to finish. Since creationary geologists believe that nearly all fossils found in rock strata were formed during this single event, then the fossils were formed during a time span of a little more than a year in the history of the earth. Thus, though fossils are found all over the world and in different strata, they were essentially living all at the same time. Once again, the fossil record attests to the disastrous violence and global nature of this judgment.

Several theories of dinosaur extinction pervade the scientific community.

1. Mammals ate dinosaur eggs, resulting in the eventual extinction of the dinosaurs.

2. There was a general loss of the vegetation that supported the plant-eating dinosaurs. This affected the meat-eating dinosaurs as well.

3. The sun became either too hot or too cold for dinosaurs.

4. The world's climate became either too dry or too wet, possibly as a result of continental drift.

5. A nearby supernova sprayed the earth with radiation.

6. Earth's magnetic field reversed, and incoming radiation killed most life.

7. A passing comet poisoned the earth with chemicals.

8. A giant meteorite crashed into the sea, and a tsunami then swept the land and drowned life.

9. A giant meteorite impacted the earth, kicking up debris and possibly causing a near-global firestorm. The devastating effects on climate and habitat killed off the dinosaurs as well as most other animals.

10. Massive volcanic activity altered the earth's climate, making it impossible for dinosaurs to survive.

dinosaur: dino- (Gk. *deinos*—monstrous, terrible) + -saur (Gk. *sauros*—lizard)

Stones of Witness

The manner of fossilization of organisms is clearly a problem for paleontologists. Trees that die and fall over, fish that die in the ocean, and forest animals that die in the woods all rapidly decay away or their carcasses are eaten long before they can be covered with sediment. Only in cases where organisms are rapidly buried by flowing water laden with sediments do they have the opportunity to be fossilized. Given what you know about the global extent and duration of the Genesis Flood, how long a period in the earth's history do the fossils found in rock strata represent?

15-15 Tyrannosaurus Rex (above); crab (right); a crinoid (bottom right). Similar species of crabs and crinoids are alive today.

15.9 Dinosaurs

The fossils that are most interesting to many people are those of the giant reptilelike animals, the dinosaurs. Many kinds of dinosaurs became extinct long ago, probably during or shortly after the Flood. Dinosaur fossils have been found on every continent, even Antarctica. In most places that dinosaur fossils are found, dozens of them are relatively close together. Fossils of young and old dinosaurs piled in stacks like a logjam give evidence of having been caught in a violent disaster that deposited sediment and carcasses together in great layers. Afterward, the sediment hardened into rock and the bones fossilized.

To trap and preserve such large creatures, the catastrophe must have been tremendous. The biblical framework of the earth's history contains such a catastrophe, the Flood. Evolutionists do not think that all of the fossil graveyards found at many different places were formed by a single event. Instead, evolutionists propose that the dinosaurs died out as a group within a short period of time as the result of a large asteroid impact. Some even believe that they have found the culprit—a circular geologic formation near the town of Chicxulub in the Yucatan Peninsula, Mexico, believed by some to be the crater of a huge meteorite. The significance of the Chicxulub formation is controversial, however, even among evolutionary geologists.

WHAT HAPPENED TO THE DINOSAURS?

Imagine how William Foulke felt when he uncovered one of the first skeletons of a dinosaur in the gray slime of New Jersey in 1858. What did this creature look like when it was alive? How did it die? Scientists and nonscientists alike are fascinated by these huge beasts and wonder why such powerful creatures disappeared from the face of the earth.

The most popular theory of dinosaur extinction is the meteoric impact theory. This theory suggests that about 65 million years ago, the dinosaurs were wiped out by a meteorite, asteroid, or cometary impact with the earth. Such an event would have created a catastrophic blast for many hundreds of miles around the impact. But more importantly, the theory states that the dust and debris from the collision would have blocked out the sun for many years afterward, killing off green plants that need sunlight and the animals that feed on them.

Luis and Walter Alvarez formulated the impact theory in 1980. They used it to explain their discovery of a layer of clay containing large amounts of the element *iridium*. Iridium is commonly found in comets and meteorites but almost never in the earth's crust. This layer of iridium-containing clay was first found between the Cretaceous and Tertiary layers of the geologic column in Gubbio, Italy, and later was located at a similar geologic level at many other locations around the world. Evolutionists claim that dinosaurs became extinct between these two periods in the geologic time scale. All that remained was to find a large enough impact crater that matched this timeframe.

In 1987, a circular geologic formation about 180 km in diameter was found buried deep under the sediments of the Yucatan peninsula near the town of Chicxulub. Geologists drilled deep boreholes into the formation and conducted gravitational and magnetic studies. Evidence continued to accumulate that the geologic formation was an impact crater of the "right age." Scientists began to declare that Chicxulub was the crater left by a 10 km wide meteorite that resulted in the extinction of the dinosaurs as well as nearly 70% of all the species of animals represented in the Jurassic period. This view has been widely accepted without much critical analysis in the scientific community and has been repeated by the media and textbook publishers.

Creationary scientists, who hold to the Flood as the cause for the dinosaurian demise, recently were given an assist by evolutionary scientists. In their book *The Great Dinosaur Extinction Controversy*, Charles Officer, a geologist, and Jake Page, a science writer, discuss the problems with the impact theory. They argue that the iridium deposits in the clay layer discovered by the Alvarezes can be explained by regional volcanism and, in any case, are not usually present in impact craters. The date assigned to the supposed crater does not correlate with the fossil record of the dinosaurs' demise. Furthermore, the fossil record indicates that there was a gradual rather than a rapid decline in dinosaur fossils. And, strangely, organisms requiring light that should have been killed off in the aftermath of an asteroid impact seem to have survived and even flourished. The scientists mentioned above and others have proposed a revised theory of dinosaur extinction, involving multiple, smaller meteorite impacts rather than a single cataclysmic event. However, a large meteorite impact around 65 million years ago according to evolutionary "deep time" thinking is still recognized by most evolutionists as the cause of the dinosaur extinction.

What does the Bible say about dinosaur extinction? Dinosaurs were created on Day 6 of the Creation week along with all of the other land animals, about 6000 years ago. The Genesis Flood occurred about 1600 years later. Noah was instructed to take two of *every* unclean animal, including dinosaurs, and seven of every clean animal on the ark. Dinosaurs seem to have inhabited the earth after the Flood, as evidenced by eyewitness accounts (see Job 40:15). Most species of dinosaurs probably became extinct in the dramatic climate changes that followed the Flood, which may have included a global ice age. The Bible remains a conclusive and reliable historical source that will outlast all contradictory theories.

A radar image of the Chicxulub formation and surroundings

William Foulke, an Englishman and a member of the Academy of Natural Sciences, discovered the first complete skeleton of a dinosaur. Its species name *Hadrosaurus foulkii*, is based on Foulke's name. The skeleton is kept at a museum.

Evolutionary scientists describe dinosaur extinction as part of the great "K-T die-off." By this, evolutionists mean that the extinction of dinosaurs is at the boundary between the Cretaceous period (K) and the Tertiary period (T) in the geologic time scale, around 65 million years ago. (*Note*: K stands for *kreide*, or chalk, in German, deposits of which are dated to the Cretaceous period.) Dinosaur fossils are often found within layers of rock that correspond to these periods in the geologic column. The K-T boundary contains iridium, which many believe is an indication of a meteoric impact. However, iridium is more often associated with volcanism, which fits perfectly with a creationary view of dinosaur extinction during and shortly after the Flood, when volcanic activity is believed to have been extensive.

Facet Summary: What Happened to the Dinosaurs?

This Facet presents the latest information about the meteor impact theory of the demise of the dinosaurs. Since these large extinct animals are fascinating to nearly everyone, it is important that your students understand the facts pertaining to this theory. It will give them good witnessing opportunities if they authoritatively question this theory that is so glibly accepted and repeated in the media. There are no vocabulary terms in this Facet.

Stones of Witness

If there were no God who created everything, there would be no source of morality. In fact, the Genesis account records that God gave standards of morality to mankind after He created all things. If evolutionists reject the Creator God, then they are also rejecting the One who established moral standards. Without absolute moral standards or accountability, humans are left to define what is moral through their own reasoning. Societies that have adopted human standards of morality have often engaged in human atrocities and have eventually faded into obscurity.

It is likely that in the post-Flood era, much of mankind found survival very difficult, with summers growing colder, winters becoming longer, glaciers pushing ever southward, and people being forced into a hunter-gatherer mode of living. Scientists studying modern human populations have concluded that it is possible for people under extreme climatic conditions to develop unusual skeletal features. These features include arthritic buildup in joints and long bones as well as physiological adjustments to cold and frequent injuries (such as thickening of boney ridges in the skull and pelvis and increased bone density and thickness). Evolutionists claim that some of these traits found in fossil human skeletons are evidence that the human race has evolved. Biblical Creationists, however, should counter that these features may be the result of the difficult and hazardous living conditions following the Flood.

Visual 15-3: The Superposition Principle

This visual is a reproduction of Figure 15-19. Refer to the visual as you explain how the arrangement of rock strata and other evidence indicates to a geologist the sequence of events that formed the land surface at a particular location. Starting with the basement rock, unit 1, work your way up to the recent erosion.

Geologically, an *unconformity* is a contact surface between two rock units that does not represent a continuous deposition of layers. Something occurred to break the sequence of strata at that point, such as extensive erosion.

15-16 Cro-Magnon skull. It is completely human and "modern" in every respect.

Stones of Witness

When evolutionists reject the biblical account of Creation, they also end up rejecting moral absolutes. Why?

15-17 A model of the Piltdown skull, which was declared to be a hoax

15-18 The Nebraska man was constructed from a tooth that later was discovered to have belonged to an extinct peccarylike animal.

15-19 The *superposition principle* states that a lower layer must have been deposited before higher layers in a sequence of strata and is therefore older than layers deposited above it.

15.10 Human Fossils

Bones of people who lived thousands of years ago have been preserved in the ground. Yet no fossils of "ape-men" have been found. You may have seen artists' drawings or even three-dimensional reconstructions of the faces of "cave men." The artists are relying on their imagination and preconceived notions when they make such reconstructions. The best reconstructions show that these ancient humans were so similar to modern people that, if they were dressed in modern clothes, you would not even give them a second glance on the street.

Do human bones in caves prove evolution? The Bible records people living in caves (Gen. 19:30; 1 Sam. 22:1). People in ancient times often buried their dead in caves (Gen. 23:17–20; John 11:38). Naturally, then, we find bones in caves. Jumping to the conclusion that bones in caves are from subhuman species is unscientific.

All the fossils that supposedly prove man's animal ancestry fall into one of the following categories:

1. Completely human fossils
2. Misidentified animal fossils
3. Hoaxes

Scientists have found no transitional fossil between ape and man. Evolutionists disagree about man's ancestry. They cannot even agree about man's most recent ancestor. There are almost as many proposed family trees for man as there are scientists who study the fossils.

15.11 The Geologic Column

In the 1700s, as men began using more natural resources such as coal and iron ore, scientists saw the need to identify and classify the different kinds of rock they observed in the earth. These geologists were, for the most part, interested in making their observations agree with the earth's history according to the Bible. They held to two basic principles when identifying layers in the rocks. First was the principle of *superposition*, which states that in a series of rock layers, the layers toward the bottom had to be laid first and therefore were older than layers higher up. Using this idea, the layers of rock can represent a kind of calendar. The second principle was that water deposits sedimentary layers horizontally.

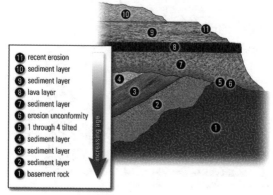

11 recent erosion
10 sediment layer
9 sediment layer
8 lava layer
7 sediment layer
6 erosion unconformity
5 1 through 4 tilted
4 sediment layer
3 sediment layer
2 sediment layer
1 basement rock

increasing age

These eighteenth-century geologists recognized three main rock groups: primary, secondary, and tertiary. The primary rocks were believed to be formed before the Flood and contained no fossils, but the secondary rocks contained fossils and were believed to have been laid in the Flood. Tertiary rocks held many fossils and were thought to have come from the erosion of secondary rocks after the Flood. Bible believers at that time had no difficulty accepting this system of rock classification.

Early in the 1800s, geologists began challenging the biblical view of the earth's history. They proposed that the earth must be millions of years old in order to account for the thicknesses of sedimentary rocks when compared to the rates at which sediments were collecting in recent times. Geologists also observed that similar fossils seemed to be found in corresponding layers of rock located very far apart. Because the geologists believed that simple creatures evolved before complex ones, they considered rocks containing simple fossils to be older than those containing more complex fossils. Furthermore, they assumed that rocks containing similar fossils must have similar ages, even if these rocks are horizontally far apart. Eventually, these fossils that seemingly linked layers of rock together to a corresponding time were called "guide fossils" or **index fossils**.

For example, a common fossil is a trilobite. Trilobites are a group of extinct marine animals that resembled crabs, lobsters, or shrimp (crustaceans). Evolutionists believe that trilobites were among the first complex creatures to evolve about 600 million years ago. They then became extinct about 250 million years ago. If evolutionists find a trilobite fossil in a rock, they assign the rock a date of between 250 and 600 million years, depending upon which species of trilobite was found. One problem with dating rocks by index fossils is how the fossils were dated—by the assumed age of the rocks in which they were found! This is a classic example of the logical fallacy called *circular reasoning.*

Geologists all over Europe published their findings of rock strata and fossil populations found in the strata. Because the geologists were looking for agreement, they found many similar vertical sequences of fossils in the layers of rock, which led them to believe that these matching sequences represented the same time period in the earth's past. By linking all of these strata sequences from different localities together, geologists created what is now called the **geologic column**, a sequence of rock units and layers that supposedly extends through time from the earliest known rocks to the recently deposited mud, gravel, and sand. No place on earth has been continuously building up rock layers since the beginning of the earth, so an undisturbed geologic column does not actually exist at any location. Some uniformitarian geologists claim that there are a number of locations across the world where remnants of all the major geologic units are stacked in their proper order, but there are serious problems with this interpretation of the data. The existence of the geologic column is the source of great controversy between young-earth Creationists and evolutionists of all kinds.

Geologists realized that, according to the uniformitarian thinking developed during the early 1800s, immense periods of time must have passed for the geologic column to exist. This gave rise to the deep-time view of the earth's history called the **geologic time scale**.

trilobite (TRY luh BITE)

crustacean (kruh STAY shun)

15-20 Trilobites are index fossils for the uniformitarian Paleozoic geologic periods.

 Additional Resource

Evolutionists seek to bolster their dates for index fossils and geologic layers by doing radiometric dating of layers of igneous rock between the sedimentary layers. They claim that this confirms their dates in a reliable fashion. However, as mentioned in Chapter 13, there are serious technical problems with the radiometric dating techniques. In addition, evolutionary scientists are biased (one could say prejudiced) to reject or reinterpret dates that do not agree with their preconceived ideas of what the dates *should* be. This problem has been thoroughly documented in John Woodmorappe's excellent book *The Mythology of Modern Dating Methods* (El Cajon, CA: Institute for Creation Research, 1999).

The subphylum Trilobita, a group of about 10,000 species, is rarely used as an index fossil since, by some accounts, it covers parts of three geologic eras. Instead, individual species of trilobites are used that supposedly cover smaller increments of the geologic time scale.

Evolutionists claim that the entire geologic column exists in several places in the world. The larger question would seem to be, Why does it not exist in most of the world? Evolutionists conjecture that erosion causes some layers to be present in one location and not in another. They also attribute varying thicknesses of the geologic layers to varying rates at which layers were laid in that location.

Visual 15-4: The Uniformitarian Geologic Column

The visual shows the geologic time scale in proportion to the amount of time supposedly involved in each time unit. According to evolutionary scientists, the period of life (Phanerozoic) consists of only about 12 percent of the entire existence of the earth. The Holocene epoch, which comprises the last 10,000 years or so and supposedly is characterized by the appearance of modern humans, is not even the thickness of the line at the top of the right-hand column!

By 1854, the geologic column was believed to be complete enough that the geologic time scale was published in nearly its modern form. Minor changes continued to be made to the time scale, up to as recently as 1981. Geologic time is subdivided into eras, periods, epochs, and ages. Each time unit has a corresponding rock stratum or group of strata. Table 15-1 shows the modern geologic time scale.

15-1 GENERALIZED EVOLUTIONARY GEOLOGIC TIME SCALE

Era	Period	Epoch	Life form—first appearance	Time (millions of years ago)
Cenozoic	Quaternary	Recent / Pleistocene	man	
	Tertiary	Pliocene / Miocene / Oligocene / Eocene / Paleocene		1
Mesozoic ("age of reptiles")	Cretaceous / Jurassic / Triassic		birds, mammals / dinosaurs	70
Paleozoic	Permian / Carboniferous	Pennsylvanian / Mississippian	reptiles	240
	Devonian		insects / seed plants / amphibians	
	Silurian / Ordovician / Cambrian		fish / land plants / trilobites	
Precambrian			one-celled organisms	600

Most Creationists believe that both the fossils and the rocks they are in are only thousands of years old. Many interesting fossil finds contradict the geologic time scale and show that its ages are greatly inflated. Since 1992, both evolutionary and creationary scientists have discovered unfossilized dinosaur bones containing what appear to be red blood cells and muscle ligaments attached to bones. It is virtually impossible based on observed rates of tissue decay for any sort of cellular tissue to have survived for 65 million years, which is the accepted time in the past when dinosaurs became extinct. These findings are much more consistent with bones that are only a few thousand years old.

15.12 Polystrate Fossils

In Germany, France, the British Isles, Nova Scotia, California, and several eastern states, fossils that extend through several layers of sedimentary rock have been found. These are called **polystrate fossils**. They are usually tree trunks in an upright or somewhat slanted position. Polystrate fossils furnish clear-cut evidence that sediment was deposited rapidly, as in a flood. If the rock layers surrounding the fossils had formed at the slow rate that evolutionists assumed as they constructed the geologic time scale, the trees would have decayed or fallen rather than fossilized. Evolutionary geologists agree that many of these fossils were buried rapidly, but they claim that local floods were responsible.

One type of polystrate fossil in California is especially interesting. Near Santa Barbara, fish fossils extend through several layers of algae fossils. Evolutionists calculate that each algae layer took hundreds or thousands of years to form. That would mean that the head and tail of the same fish were buried several thousands of years apart! Clearly the beds must have formed around the fish rapidly, not slowly. The most remarkable find was a polystrate whale fossil extending through many layers and many thousands of years, assuming a uniformitarian time scale. These fossils show that strata form rapidly and that the layers do not represent the passage of long periods of time.

polystrate (PAHL ee STRATE): poly- (Gk. *polus*—many) + -strate (L. *stratum*—covering, layer)

15-21 Polystrate tree trunks in Bouddi National Park, Australia. The longer trunk is nearly 3 m tall.
credit: Simon Taylor

15-22 This canyon was formed in about a day near Mount St. Helens (left). Layers can form very rapidly from water-borne volcanic debris (right).

The term *polystrate fossil* is peculiar to the Creationist literature. Evolutionary geologists disparage it as a Creationist concept. According to evolutionists, fossils, by definition, cannot exist simultaneously in strata representing different intervals of depositional history.

Teachers are reminded that we are emphasizing the evidences that clearly support the young-earth creationary model of the earth's history. There are many other evidences that *seem* to present difficulties that creationary scientists must account for within a biblical framework. For example, the existence of insects trapped in amber does not seem to be compatible with a Flood scenario, and fossilized worm burrows found deep in layers of sedimentary rock could not have formed during a period of rapid Flood sedimentation. This does not say that the biblical model is problematic, only that creationary scientists are far fewer in number and have been working on the problem for less time than their evolutionary counterparts. Many of these problematic claims have not been investigated from a scientific perspective that would consider the creationary evidence.

We hold to an inerrant and literal interpretation of Scripture as the basis by which we interpret observations of nature. Since we are attempting to mold a particular worldview, we believe it is better to not introduce these seemingly contradictory evidences that could confuse the issue. We can be confident that these apparently problematic evidences will yield a reasonable interpretation when examined by an authority who starts with biblical presuppositions.

Additional Resources

See the videocassettes featuring the 1980 Mount St. Helens eruption produced by ICR for more on tree trunks in Spirit Lake. These videos include other topics related to the geologic repercussions of the Mount St. Helens eruption and the support that they offer for a young earth. The titles of these videos are *Voice of the Volcano*, *Footprints in the Ash*, and *Mount St. Helens: Explosive Evidence for Catastrophe*.

Spirit Lake's Logs

The aftermath of the 1980 eruption of Mount St. Helens provided striking evidence for how some polystrate fossils may have been deposited. Spirit Lake, which is near the base of the volcanic mountain, received volcanic ash, mud flows, and debris produced by the eruption. Much of the material settled out of the water quickly, creating sediment deposits up to 183 m (600 ft) deep in some places. However, some debris, such as thousands of trunks from trees leveled by the blast, washed into the lake and remained floating on the surface.

Five years after the catastrophe, some trunks were still floating, but many had become waterlogged and sank to the bottom. What is peculiar about this was the way in which they sank. Many trunks that were previously floating prone on the surface had sunk to the bottom in an upright position. The root ends were down, buried in the lake bottom, while the top ends were pointing upward. The bases of some of these upright trunks had been buried in as much as 1 m (3 ft) of sediment, while others appeared to have been just recently submerged.

The significance of these observations is that this could have been how many polystrate tree fossils were deposited and rapidly buried as a result of the Flood. Following the Mount St. Helens catastrophe, the logs that ended up in a water environment became oriented upright on the bottom rather quickly and began to be buried in that position by layers of waterborne sediment. In the years following the Flood, similar tree trunks could have been completely buried and fossilized, forming polystrate fossils.

Two views of Spirit Lake's upright logs: an artist's rendering of conditions below the surface (top), and a photo of the tips of submerged logs still visible above the surface.

15B-2 Section Review

1. Explain why a chicken bone buried in a landfill dump is not a fossil.

2. What aspect of the fossil record fails to support the continuous evolution of biological life from simpler to more complex forms over millions of years?

3. The fossils classified as *Australopithecus* and nicknamed "Lucy" probably belonged to what kind of organism?

4. State two principles that have always been accepted when describing the geologic column.

5. How is the geologic time scale related to the geologic column?

6. Explain why most polystrate fossils are a problem for uniformitarian evolutionists. What is a better explanation for these fossils?

7. (True or False) According to evolutionists' geologic time scale, the only form of life that existed at any time during the Precambrian era was that of simple one-celled plants or animals.

Box Summary: Spirit Lake's Logs

This box discusses a possible mechanism for the formation of polystrate tree trunk fossils. There are no vocabulary terms in this box.

Answers to 15B-2 Section Review Questions

1. A chicken bone in a landfill dump has not been mineralized or otherwise preserved. It could still decompose. Therefore, it does not qualify as a fossil. (§15.7)

2. For the vast majority of fossil species, there is a lack of any fossils of intermediate forms, or missing links, that appear to show evolutionary transition between simpler organisms and more complex ones. (§15.8)

3. The *Australopithecus* fossils, including Lucy, were probably from a tree-dwelling ape. (Facet, p. 392)

4. Those who study the geologic column assume that the oldest strata are lower in the column (principle of superposition) and that water always deposits sediment in (nearly) horizontal layers. (§15.11, 15.4)

5. For each time period in the geologic time scale as defined by fossil characteristics, there are corresponding layers of rock in a hypothetical column of rock somewhere in the world. (§15.11)

6. Polystrate fossils are fossils that extend through different layers of sediment that uniformitarians say took thousands to millions of years to form. No biological organism could remain intact long enough to be buried and fossilized under those conditions. These fossils are evidence of rapid burial, such as in the Genesis Flood. (§15.12)

7. True. (§15.11, Table 15-1)

15.13 Fossil Fuels

No one knows for sure when man discovered that certain dark, rocklike materials burned. Now known as coal, its first documented use was for smelting copper ores in China around 1000 BC. For many centuries, coal usage was sporadic and limited to locations where the rock was exposed in seams on the earth's surface. Oil seeping from formations of rock on the earth's surface was probably discovered nearly as long ago. Natural gas usage was reported by Confucius nearly 2700 years ago. These natural solid, liquid, and gas materials are now known together as **fossil fuels** because they appear to come from the fossilized remains of plants and animals.

15.14 Coal

Coal is sedimentary rock that appears to have been laid down by water. However, some geologists consider it to be a metamorphic rock because heat and pressure have changed it. There are three types of coal: lignite, bituminous, and anthracite. Each successive type is harder and contains more carbon and therefore stores more energy. Coal is believed to have formed from the remains of land plants and trees. Creationists and evolutionists disagree about how these plants came to be deposited in layers and changed to coal.

Most uniformitarian geologists believe plant debris that collected in swampy areas 286 million to 360 million years ago became covered with sediment whose weight, over long periods of time, caused the chemical and physical changes that converted the plant material to coal. This theory has problems. First, radiocarbon dates show that coal is only thousands, not millions of years old. Second, rocks and large boulders have been found in some coal deposits. In addition, large rootless tree trunks have been found buried at odd angles in the coal layers. Both of these factors indicate swift-moving currents, not flat, stagnant swamps. There are many other factors noted by creationist scientists about coal beds that indicate coal was rapidly deposited under large quantities of flowing water, not that it formed slowly in quiet, swampy environments over millions of years.

Most Creationists believe that coal formed as a result of the Flood. The sudden deep burial of pre-Flood plant life during the Flood could generate the heat and pressure needed to change the material to coal. Experiments in which artificial coal was produced have shown that little time is needed for coal to form. At high enough temperatures and pressures, coal-like materials can form in less than a day.

15.15 Oil

Oil (or petroleum) is the liquid fossil fuel. Creationists and evolutionists agree that oil was formed from ocean-dwelling creatures such as fish and algae. When found, oil is usually associated with sedimentary rocks of marine origin (fossils of only sea-living creatures are found in them). Again, evolutionists believe that oil formed over millions of years, but Creationists believe that it formed quickly during or shortly after the Flood.

lignite (LIG NITE)

bituminous (bih TOO muh nus)

anthracite (AN thruh SITE)

15-23 An unusual rock specimen that has both coal and petrified wood

15-24 Automatic oil-well pumps extract crude oil from underground supplies.

Web Resource: Contaminated Coal Deposits

Some coal deposits have been dated far in excess of the 4500–5000 years expected by the creationary Flood model. There are a variety of technical reasons that can account for the lower than expected ratio of C-14 to C-12 in coal deposits. Visit the BJU Press Online Resources/*Space and Earth Science* webpage. Under Chapter 15, click on the link *Radiocarbon Dating*.

Often, tree trunks are found embedded in the coal, which is evidence that they were deposited by swift-moving currents. For an excellent article discussing these evidences, visit the BJU Press Online Resources/*Space and Earth Science* webpage. Under Chapter 15, click on the link *Rapid Coal*.

Oil shale and tar are also fossil fuels. If you choose to discuss them, they can be categorized as oil, since they yield petroleum and are believed to have formed from marine organisms, although other sources are possible. See the margin note on the next page.

This textbook presents the conventional theory for the origin of petroleum—that marine organisms trapped beneath thick layers of sediment were converted through the agencies of heat and pressure into organic liquids and gases. This theory of petrochemical origins is consistent with both naturalistic and creationary worldviews, albeit on vastly different time scales.

However, there is another theory worth mentioning—*nonorganic petroleum*. As early as the late nineteenth century, the famous Russian chemist Mendeleev suggested that petroleum originates from the reactions of inorganic metal carbides with hydrothermal fluids deep in the earth. These reactions form simple hydrocarbons that are then polymerized into the more complex hydrocarbons found in petroleum. The petroleums gradually ooze upward through fractures in tectonically active areas until they collect under impermeable rock layers or eventually leak out at the earth's surface (in spots known as seeps). This process is ongoing.

The theory, if proven true, has staggering implications for the availability of oil for the future as well as the price of oil. If oil is being continually produced within the earth, then there is no limit to its availability and no justification for keeping prices high. Also, oil exploration could expand to investigate other areas of the world that have not been considered because their geology does not conform to conventional theories of oil-basin structure.

Objectives—Section 15C

Upon completing this section, students should be able to

- distinguish magma from lava.
- compare and contrast intrusive and extrusive igneous formations.
- categorize samples of igneous rock as extrusive or intrusive.

igneous: (L. *igne*—of fire)

magma (MAG muh): (Gk. *magma*—thick paste)

15.16 Natural Gas

Natural gas, the gaseous fossil fuel, is often found with oil. One theory is that gas is a by-product of the oil formation process. Natural gas consists mostly of the organic gas methane. Since gas is less dense than liquid, natural gas is found on top of oil deposits. The high pressure of the gas often assists in pumping oil to the surface or even causing "gushers." Historically, the first documented use of natural gas was by the Chinese, who collected it from shallow wells and transported the gas through hollowed bamboo pipes to be used as a fuel for evaporating brine solutions to obtain salt.

15B-3 Section Review

1. List the three fossil fuels. Why are they given this name?
2. Scientists believe coal was formed from what formerly living material?
3. What types of rocks usually trap oil? What is believed to be the original source of oil?
4. What fossil fuel is often found on top of oil deposits? Give two reasons why this is the case.
5. (True or False) Evolutionary and creationary scientists agree on the materials that formed fossil fuels but disagree only on the age of these fossil materials.

15C IGNEOUS ROCKS

15.17 Introduction

Rocks that appear to have been molten in the past are called igneous rocks. Molten rock has two names depending on where it is located. **Magma** is molten rock found anywhere beneath the earth's surface. Molten rock that flows out onto the earth's surface is called **lava**.

Igneous rocks are of two types according to where they are formed. **Extrusive rocks** form when lava solidifies above the earth's surface. **Intrusive rocks** form when magma solidifies after squeezing into other rocks, intruding into them. These are always formed at various depths beneath the earth's surface. Intrusive igneous rocks may eventually appear at the earth's surface because of erosion.

15.18 Texture and Composition

Intrusive and extrusive rocks differ mainly in the average sizes of their mineral crystals, which is referred to as their **texture**. Rocks with larger crystals are called coarse-textured rocks. Small crystals give rocks a fine texture. The absence of crystals makes a rock look glassy. Intrusive igneous rocks tend to have textures that are coarse to fine because conditions deep underground encourage relatively large crystal formation. Factors that determine crystal size include the number of foreign particles present around which crystal accretion can begin (nucleation sites), the concentration of the various elements in the melted rock, temperature, pressure, and the rate of

Answers to 15B-3 Section Review Questions

1. The three fossil fuels are *coal*, *oil*, and *natural gas*. Fossil fuels are materials that seem to have come from the fossilized remains of plants and animals. (§15.13)

2. Scientists believe coal was formed from land plants and trees. (§15.14)

3. Oil is usually found in marine sedimentary rocks. The original source of oil is believed to have been ocean-dwelling creatures (although nonorganic processes may be replenishing oil reserves). (§15.15)

4. Natural gas is often found on top of liquid oil because (1) it is less dense than the oil, and (2) it is believed to be a byproduct of oil formation. (§15.16)

5. True. (§15.14–15.15)

15-25 A coarse-textured igneous rock like granite (left) contains large, distinct crystals of different minerals as shown in this close-up. A fine-textured rock like basalt (right) has tiny, even microscopic, crystals.

crystallization. Unexpectedly, few nucleation sites combined with high pressure and rapid crystallization (rapid cooling) produce large crystals. Extrusive rocks tend to have fine to glassy textures.

Both extrusive and intrusive igneous rocks can contain many different minerals, depending on the composition of the molten rock from which they solidify. Magmas and lavas that contain much silica are called *felsic*. They solidify into rocks that are mostly light-colored silicates such as orthoclase feldspars and quartz. *Mafic* magmas and lavas have much less silica and are rich in iron and magnesium. Mafic rocks are formed from mostly dark-colored minerals such as plagioclase feldspar, hornblende, augite, olivine, and biotite mica. Igneous rock types may fall anywhere between these two extremes, and there are other ways to classify rocks by their composition.

15.19 Igneous Intrusions

Igneous rock can be found in many distinctive formations. Underground, magma creates *intrusions* or intrusive structures. The largest intrusion is called a *batholith*, which can extend over an area of hundreds of square kilometers horizontally and can be several thousands of meters thick. Many mountain ranges are built on batholiths. A *stock* is a batholith that covers less than 100 km². Any intrusive rock formation formed deep in the earth can be referred to as a **pluton**.

When magma intrudes in such a way that it pushes overlying strata into a dome or arch-shaped rise, the solidified formation is

15-26 Felsic magmas produce light-colored igneous rocks such as granite (top), and mafic magmas produce dark-colored rocks such as diorite (bottom) and basalt.

batholith: batho- (Gk. *bathos*—depth) + -lith (Gk. *lithos*—rock)

pluton (L. *Pluton*—Pluto, Roman god of the underworld)

Orthoclase feldspars, also called K-feldspars, are potassium-rich and form monoclinic crystals. Plagioclase feldspars substitute varying amounts of sodium and calcium instead of potassium in the aluminum silicate crystal lattice to form triclinic crystals.

 Visuals 15-5A, B: Intrusive Igneous Formations: Batholith, Laccolith, and Stock; Sills and Dikes

Refer to these visuals as you discuss the various intrusive igneous formations. See also Visual 17-6, "Volcano Anatomy."

called a *laccolith*. The existence of multiple laccoliths is often indicated by groups of low, rounded hills in an area.

Magma may force its way between layers of existing rock to form sheets called **sills**. Since the sheet of rock is parallel to the surrounding strata, sills may be tilted along with the other rock layers. Sills can vary from centimeters to many meters in thickness and can extend for kilometers. Magma that intrudes into cracks that cut through existing layers of rock hardens to form **dikes**. Dikes do not lie parallel to the surrounding strata. They are often associated with volcanic activity.

15.20 Intrusive Igneous Rocks

Granite is coarse-grained and is the most common intrusive igneous rock. The word *granite* means "containing grains." Granite is a felsic rock, so quartz, feldspar, and only small mica crystals make up most granite. You can usually distinguish these minerals by color: feldspar, pink; quartz, white; mica, black. When granite breaks, the feldspar crystals break along cleavage planes that are smooth enough to reflect light. The mica also breaks along smooth planes that reflect light. In contrast, the quartz crystals exhibit a rough fracture. Because it withstands the forces of weathering for centuries, granite is an excellent building material and a favorite stone for monuments. Most creationary geologists believe that granite was the material God used to form the original crust of the earth.

Other intrusive igneous rocks include *gabbro*, which is a darker mafic rock of the basalt chemical family, and *diorite*, which is an intrusive rock with a chemical composition midway between basalt and granite. These all have coarse textures.

Some intrusive igneous rocks contain crystals of different sizes—large crystals embedded in a mass of smaller crystals. Such rock probably formed in two different stages of cooling. In the first stage, the minerals crystallized rapidly, using up certain elements in the melted rock. Later, different minerals formed at lower temperatures from the remaining elements. The resulting crystals were smaller. Rock containing large crystals embedded in a matrix of much smaller crystals is called *porphyry*.

15.21 Extrusive Structures

Magma that extrudes onto the earth's surface is called a *lava flow*. We will study the different kinds of lava flows in Chapter 17. In some places, lava flowed out of long cracks in the earth's surface. It flooded all the surrounding land features for hundreds of square kilometers, covering hills and filling in valleys. The resulting thick rock formation is called a **lava plateau**.

When a volcano becomes dormant, the lava within it usually solidifies. If erosion eventually removes the overlying volcanic debris, all that remains is a vertical column-like formation called a **volcanic neck**. Often, dikes radiate out from these dramatic structures like spokes in a wheel. Shiprock in New Mexico is a famous example of a volcanic neck with dikes.

15-27 Stone Mountain, Georgia, is a solid granite pluton. Confederate personalities have been carved on it.

15-28 This specimen is called "leopardite" because of its spots. It is a type of quartz porphyry.

porphyry (POHR fuh ree): (Gk. *porphurites*—a valuable purple porphyry rock quarried in Egypt)

Visual 15-6: Volcanic Igneous Features

This visual illustrates some of the extrusive igneous features discussed in the text.

Note the typical basaltic pillar structures in the volcanic neck and within the lava plateau.

15.22 Extrusive Igneous Rocks

Rocks of this group are sometimes called "lava rocks" because they solidify from molten lava. Dark, mafic extrusive rock with a fine crystal texture is called *basalt*. This family of rock is abundant throughout the world and ranges in color from dark greenish gray to black. It is often found in formations that rapidly solidified near the earth's surface or in the neck of a volcano. In many cases, the stress of cooling created patterns of long fractures in the rock mass that give the exposed rock the appearance of multisided columns (see Figure 15-30). *Felsite* is like basalt but is lighter in color because it contains more light-colored silicates. *Scoria* forms from mafic lava that is frothy with dissolved gases. It cools so rapidly that many gas bubbles are trapped inside. It looks like dark cinders. Pieces of scoria are often mistaken for meteorites. Felsic extrusive rocks include fine-grained *ryolite*, which is chemically very similar to granite. *Pumice* is similar to scoria but is a light-colored rock. It often contains so many trapped bubbles that it can float in water. *Obsidian*, sometimes called "natural glass," is also of the granite family, but it forms when degasified lava cools rapidly at near-atmospheric pressures. Like glass, obsidian has no crystals. It occurs in several colors, most commonly black, brown, and red, and it has a glasslike conchoidal fracture.

basalt (buh SAWLT)

scoria (SKOHR ee uh)

15-29 Shiprock, New Mexico, is an exposed volcanic neck (background, center). Visible in this photo is a dike extending toward you from the volcanic neck.

pumice (PUM iss)

obsidian (ahb SID ee un)

15-30 This columnar basalt is located at Devils Post Pile National Volcanic Monument in California (left). Scoria, which forms from rapidly cooled lava containing gases, is an extrusive igneous rock (top right). Pumice is a very porous and lightweight rock (bottom right).

Review: Porosity and Permeability

Pumice is an example of a rock with high porosity but almost zero permeability. Show your students Visual 15-2 again. Because of its strength, light weight, rigid structure, and fire resistance, pumice is useful as a building material. The Romans included it in structures like the Pantheon.

Objectives—Section 15D

Upon completing this section, students should be able to

- explain how metamorphism fits with a creationary view of the earth's history.
- describe the processes that produced local and regional metamorphism.
- recognize samples of rock as metamorphic in nature and categorize them as foliated or nonfoliated.

Hot liquids and gases, especially water and carbon dioxide, moving through rocks promote a form of metamorphism called *chemical metamorphism* that can occur even in the absence of extreme heat and pressure.

15C   Section Review

1. What does the word *igneous* mean? How does the term relate to rock formation?
2. What is molten rock beneath the earth's surface called? What kind of solid igneous rock formations result from molten rock within the earth?
3. What is the main property you should examine in order to distinguish between intrusive rocks and extrusive rocks?
4. What are two terms used to describe the general chemical composition of magma? What are the main chemical differences between these two kinds of magma?
5. List the intrusive formations *batholiths*, *laccoliths*, and *stocks* in order of increasing size. What are all of these formations together called?
6. What does the name *granite* mean? From a creationary science standpoint, what is significant about granite?
7. Basalts are usually found as what kind of igneous rock? Answer the same question for granites.
8. What type of igneous formation is Stone Mountain in Georgia?
9. (True or False) The texture of a rock sample is not a conclusive way of determining where the rock was formed.

15D   METAMORPHIC ROCKS

15.23   Metamorphism

metamorphic: meta- (Gk. *meta*—change of nature) + -morphic (Gk. *morphos*—form or shape)

15-31 Pressure and heat from magma will change sedimentary rock (shaded area) to metamorphic rock.

Metamorphic rocks are those that appear to have changed in their structure or chemical composition since their creation or formation. Metamorphic rocks were originally sedimentary or igneous rocks but were altered by heat, pressure, or exposure to hot fluids circulating in the earth's crust. Two kinds of metamorphic processes are recognized by geologists.

Intrusive or extrusive magma can heat and compress the surrounding rock materials, altering their crystal structure and chemical composition. This kind of metamorphism is called **local metamorphism** because the volume of changed rocks due to specific processes is relatively small. Local metamorphism is presently occurring in volcanically active regions and along active faults. Geologists recognize a number of subcategories of local metamorphism according to the processes involved.

Geologists have found evidence that in the past, immense forces were at work folding great tracts of sedimentary rock, lifting mountains, and pushing plates of the earth's crust together (see Section 16C). These events caused changes in rocks over large areas; thus, this kind of metamorphism is called **regional metamorphism**.

Creationary geologists believe that most metamorphism occurred rapidly during or shortly after the Flood. There seems to be little regional metamorphism occurring today, except perhaps along the edges of colliding plates. Evolutionary geologists, on the other

Answers to 15C Section Review Questions

1. *Igneous* comes from a Latin word having to do with fire. Igneous rocks were originally so hot that they were molten. (§15.17)

2. Molten rock beneath the earth's surface is called *magma*. Magma forms igneous intrusions (plutons). (§15.17, 15.19)

3. Intrusive igneous rocks usually have a coarser texture (they contain larger crystals) than extrusive igneous rocks. (§15.18)

4. The two kinds of magma are called *felsic* and *mafic* magma. Felsic magma is rich in silica compared to other magmas. Mafic magma has much less silica and is rich in iron and magnesium. (§15.18)

5. In order of increasing size, these formations are laccoliths, stocks, and batholiths. Together, they are called *plutons*. (§15.19)

6. The name *granite* means "containing grains." Most creationary geologists believe the earth's crust was originally made of granite. (§15.20)

7. Basalt is usually found as an extrusive rock. Granite is usually an intrusive rock. (§15.20, 15.22)

8. Stone Mountain is a magmatic intrusion, or pluton, of nonvolcanic origin exposed by erosion of overlying strata. (§15.20, 15.21)

9. True. (§15.18)

hand, believe that regional metamorphism is continuing at a very slow rate in most mountainous regions as well as along crust-plate boundaries.

15.24 Classifying Metamorphic Rocks

Metamorphic rocks are classified as **foliated** or **nonfoliated**. Foliated rock contains flattened mineral crystals aligned in parallel layers, often giving a banded appearance. The rock may break easily along these layers. Nonfoliated rocks are not banded or layered and tend to break into sharp, angular pieces.

foliated (FOH lee ATE ud): foliate (L. *folium*—leaf)

15.25 Foliated Rocks

Common foliated rocks are slate, schist, and gneiss. Slate is the metamorphosed sedimentary rock shale. Shale is composed of plate-like clay particles. Slate has a fine texture. It easily splits into broad, thin sheets. In the past, slate was used as roofing tiles and for school-room blackboards. Slate comes in various colors including black, gray, purple, red, and green.

Geologists believe that *schists* were formed when slate (a metamorphic form of shale) was deeply buried and then exposed to even greater pressures and temperatures that produced schist's flakey layering characteristics. In mica schists, the chemical components of the clay minerals became separated into minerals that form at higher temperatures, such as quartz and mica. Using a fingernail, you can easily separate schist into thin flakes of mica. Schist is recognized by its many thin layers, often highly folded. The surfaces of the layers typically have a silky sheen to them. Note that the layering in schist is *not* normally in the same direction as the original sedimentary strata but depends on the direction of metamorphic pressures. Mica schist is one of several types of metamorphic rocks that can be formed from shale. Schist also forms from the mineral talc and some igneous rocks.

schist (SHIST): (L. *schistos*—readily split)

15-32 Schist (left) has a high mica content, which makes it split easily into thin flakes. This sample of gneiss has the typical banded appearance of foliated metamorphic rock (right).

Under even greater metamorphic stresses, the same minerals found in slates as well as granites formed dense, foliated, coarsely textured rocks with distinct bands of different minerals called *gneiss*. The bands result from light-colored minerals, such as quartz and feldspar, alternating with darker materials, such as biotite mica. A wide variety of sedimentary or igneous rocks can be transformed into this metamorphic rock. *Granite gneiss*, *diorite gneiss*, and *hornblende gneiss* are just a few examples.

gneiss (NICE): (old Ger. *gneisto*—spark)

Schists often have beautiful dodecahedral or trapezohedral garnet crystals embedded within the flaky layers of the rocks. These rocks are called *garnet schists*.

15.26 Nonfoliated Rocks

Common nonfoliated metamorphic rocks include *marble* and *quartzite*. Marble is metamorphosed limestone composed of crystals of calcite and sometimes dolomite. In many specimens the crystals are so small that they cannot be seen without a microscope, while in others they may be coarse and show calcite cleavage. Limestone often contains fossils. In marble, fossils can be highly distorted or even completely obliterated by the processes of metamorphism. Marble, like limestone, will fizz when hydrochloric acid is applied to it. "Pure" marble is white, but impurities give it a wide range of colors such as red-brown, green, or black. Because marble takes a high polish, it is used in decorative tabletops, gravestones, monuments, and buildings.

Quartzite is metamorphosed quartz sandstone. Intense heat and pressure have restructured the quartz crystals so that they interlock, completely eliminating the spaces between sand grains. Silica has filled the remaining pores between the crystals, producing a rock so durable that it has been used to make millstones to grind grain.

15-33 Above are two common uses of marble. The term *marbling* comes from the colorful streaks of impurities in marble.

15-34 The Lincoln Memorial (left) is sculpted from marble. A close-up (right) shows marble's interesting texture.

Quartzite may be red, white, brown, or gray and is usually the same color as the sandstone from which it formed.

Rocks not only are useful but also testify to God's power. After learning about rocks, we can understand more fully why the Lord Jesus is called "the Rock" in Scripture. The person who builds his life on Him is wise. "*Therefore whosoever heareth these sayings of mine, and doeth them, I will liken him unto a wise man, which built his house upon a rock: And the rain descended, and the floods came, and the winds blew, and beat upon that house; and it fell not: for it was founded upon a rock*" (Matt. 7:24–25).

15D Section Review

1. What does the word *metamorphic* mean? What makes metamorphic rocks different from the other categories of rocks?

2. What kind of metamorphism takes place as magma flows through a volcanic pipe?

3. Under what conditions do metamorphic rocks form?

4. A dense, coarsely textured rock with alternating layers of light and dark crystallized minerals would be placed in which category of metamorphic rock?

5. What is metamorphosed sandstone called? What category of metamorphic rock does this rock fall into?

6. What category of rock became marble after it was metamorphosed?

7. (True or False) Foliated rock contains flattened mineral crystals in parallel layers, often with pronounced leaf-like flaking.

Answers to 15D Section Review Questions

1. The word *metamorphic* means "changed in form or shape." In metamorphic rock, some change in the structure or chemical composition of the original rock has occurred. (§15.23)

2. Metamorphism due to magma flowing through a volcanic pipe is localized to the rocks immediately around the pipe and therefore is called *local metamorphism*. (§15.23)

3. Metamorphic rocks form by actions of heat, pressure, and hot circulating fluids. (§15.23)

4. Such a rock would be considered a *foliated metamorphic rock*. (§15.25)

5. Metamorphosed sandstone is called *quartzite*. Quartzite is a *nonfoliated metamorphic rock*. (§15.26)

6. Before it was metamorphosed, marble was a sedimentary rock (limestone). (§15.26)

7. True. (§15.24–15.25)

Answers to Chapter Review Questions

What Did You Learn?

1. Sedimentary rocks consist of particles that have settled out of water (or wind) and have been compacted together. Igneous rocks are formed directly from cooling molten rock. Metamorphic rocks are igneous or sedimentary rocks that have been altered by some means involving heat and pressure, and in some cases hot fluids. (§15.2)

2. Although some igneous rocks are forming, and there is a lot of erosion occurring, the consolidation of sedimentary rocks is relatively limited. The rate at which the crustal plates are returning to be melted in the mantle is much too slow to replenish the rocks that are wearing away in the time since the creation of the earth. In a true cycle, all parts of the process occur at about the same rate, returning the system to its original condition. (§15.3)

3. Water-deposited strata were originally nearly horizontal, and then they were tilted. (§15.4)

4. The clasts were compacted by pressure and bonded by natural materials. (§15.5)

5. Young-earth Creationists believe that the majority of the sedimentary rock fossils were formed during or after the Flood, about 5000 years ago (in round numbers), according to biblical dating methods. (§15.8)

6. Index fossils are fossils that evolutionists use to determine the age of rock strata. Index fossils were chosen because they were found in rocks that were in about the same order in the geologic sequence and thus were assumed to be the same age. This is an example of the logical fallacy called *circular reasoning*. (§15.11)

7. Polystrate fossils are fossils such as tree trunks that extend through several layers of sedimentary rock. They indicate that the sediments accumulated rapidly enough that the organisms did not have time to decay before they were buried. (§15.12)

8. If coal were formed millions of years ago in swamps, it would contain undetectable amounts of radiocarbon (Chap. 13). Actual radiocarbon levels indicate that coal is only thousands of years old. Also, rocks, boulders, and rootless tree trunks buried at various angles have been found in coal beds; rapidly moving water was needed to move large stones and dead tree trunks to the site of the coal formation. (§15.14)

9. No. For example, magma in the ground that is building a volcano becomes lava when it comes out of the ground. These materials have essentially the same chemical composition. They are just in different locations. (§15.17)

10. New igneous rocks can be found in recent lava flows. (§15.2, 15.21)

In Terms of Geology

rock	385
petrology	385
sedimentary rock	386
igneous rock	386
metamorphic rock	386
rock cycle	387
stratum/strata	388
clastic	388
nonclastic	388
conglomerate	388
breccia	389
matrix	389
porosity	389
permeable	389
impermeable	389
precipitate	390
evaporite	390
salt dome	390
fossil	391
paleontology	391
index fossils	397
geologic column	397
geologic time scale	397
polystrate fossil	399
fossil fuel	401
magma	402
lava	402
extrusive rock	402
intrusive rock	402
texture	402
pluton	403
sill	404
dike	404
lava plateau	404
volcanic neck	404
local metamorphism	406
regional metamorphism	406
foliated rock	407
nonfoliated rock	407

Chapter Summary

- Rocks are natural solid materials containing minerals or organic matter that form the earth's crust.

- There are three main kinds of rocks: sedimentary, igneous, and metamorphic.

- Uniformitarian geologists believe that the rock materials in the crust are recycled. Beginning as magma, rocks may take any of several paths through the various rock types. Eventually, most rocks are remelted. Young-earth Creationists do not believe enough time has elapsed since Creation for even one cycle to have taken place at the rates of existing processes.

- Sedimentary rocks can be classified as clastic or nonclastic rocks. Clastic rocks contain eroded fragments of other rocks. Nonclastic rocks result from chemical processes.

- Fossils are traces or remains of living organisms that have been preserved by natural means.

- Fossils can tell us much about living things as they used to be.

- The vast majority of fossils that exist were probably formed during a single event at a single point in the earth's history.

- Naturalistic, uniformitarian geologists have constructed a sequence of rock units that supposedly document the geologic history of the earth. The sequence is called the geologic column.

- The history of the earth has been subdivided into eras, periods, epochs, and ages that correspond to the various units of the geologic column. This geologic time scale accounts for all 4.5 billion years of the earth's history, according to uniformitarian geologists. Scientific evidence, such as polystrate fossils, falsifies this time scale.

- There are three kinds of fossil fuels formed from the matter of former organisms: coal, oil, and natural gas.

- Igneous rocks originate from magma or lava. They can be classified into two groups, extrusive and intrusive igneous rocks, according to their texture and where they formed.

- Metamorphic rocks result from chemical or structural changes in pre-existing rocks.

- The mineral grain patterns in metamorphic rocks allow us to categorize them as foliated or nonfoliated metamorphic rocks.

11. Coal could be considered metamorphic rock because heat and pressure were required to change its original materials. Students may object to this statement because the original material was not a rock. (§15.14, 15.23)

12. There does not seem to be any place on the earth where large amounts of new igneous or sedimentary rocks are being subjected to pressure, temperature, or hot fluids. Obviously, these conditions exist near active volcanoes and along active faults, but these local processes are very limited compared to the large deposits of metamorphic rocks seen throughout the earth today that speak of regional metamorphism in the past. (§15.23)

True or False

13. False. Rocks are the sources of metal ores, chemicals, fuels, and decorative materials, to name just a few of their uses. (§15.1)

14. True. (§15.4)

15. True. (§15.5)

16. False. The much smaller spaces between particles in siltstone retard the flow of fluids through it compared to the rate of flow through sandstone. (§15.5)

17. True.

18. True. If your students could do their own research on the matter, they would find that there is very little agreement on the characteristics of the so-called hominid species. Essentially all "ancestral human" fossil specimens

What Did You Learn?

1. Describe the main differences between sedimentary, igneous, and metamorphic rocks.

2. Discuss why the uniformitarian rock cycle does not appear to be a true cycle.

3. How could parallel sedimentary strata that is visibly at an angle to the ground be deposited by water?

4. Describe how the clasts of sedimentary rocks are held together.

5. Why do most young-earth Creationists believe that the majority of fossils found in sedimentary rocks are less than 5000 years old?

6. What are index fossils? How were such fossils selected by evolutionists? What logical fallacy does this kind of reasoning represent?

7. What are polystrate fossils? What do they indicate about the sedimentary environment in which they were formed?

8. Explain why the Flood model of coal formation is superior to the swamp model.

9. Is it necessary that magma and lava from the same source be chemically different? Explain.

10. Where can *new* igneous rocks be collected?

11. Why could coal be considered a metamorphic rock?

12. Why does it seem that relatively little metamorphic rock is forming today?

True or False

13. Rocks are not useful for anything other than building materials.

14. Sedimentary rocks form the majority of exposed rocks on the earth's surface.

15. When people talk about "natural concrete," they mean conglomerate.

16. The permeability of siltstone is nearly as good as that of sandstone because the two have nearly the same porosities.

17. The reason few human (and land vertebrate) fossils exist is probably that these organisms were able to avoid being buried during the initial stages of the Flood by fleeing the rising waters.

18. There is no scientific evidence in the fossil record to show that humans have evolved from apelike creatures.

19. The geologic column could be a record of the stages of the pre-Flood, Flood, and post-Flood rock formation at a given location.

20. According to evolutionists, fish appeared during the Mesozoic era.

21. The first use of natural gas as a fuel occurred in the 1700s.

22. Magma that flows out onto the earth's surface without losing dissolved gases can produce frothy, sponge-like rocks.

23. Mafic rocks contain relatively little silica.

24. *Gneiss* means "easily split."

25. The most common foliated metamorphic rocks are slate, schist, and gneiss.

What Do You Think?

1. Other than body parts, what traces of organisms could be fossils?

2. What are some characteristics of "human-ness" that would make a human fossil distinct from a similar but nonhuman animal?

3. Why are dinosaur fossils found in Antarctica?

4. What are some uses of sedimentary rocks, igneous rocks, and metamorphic rocks?

5. How do evolutionists explain the fact that the thicknesses of the different layers of the geologic column tend to differ with location?

6. Why do even some evolutionary scientists question the theory that the extinction of the dinosaurs was caused by an asteroid impact?

My Review Checklist

- ☐ I have carefully read the entire chapter.
- ☐ I have reviewed all of the photographs, illustrations, and graphs.
- ☐ I have reviewed all of my notes in the margins.
- ☐ I have reviewed and corrected the quizzes on this chapter.
- ☐ I have studied all of the vocabulary terms.
- ☐ I have had all of my questions answered.

or ceremonial burial, and so forth). The presence of thickened bones (eye ridges, long bones, etc.) is not, by itself, a sub-human trait, since many modern human populations living under rigorous conditions have thickened bones.

3. The region that became Antarctica may have been warmer during the climate of the pre-Flood era, thus permitting dinosaurs to live there. According to some Flood theories, the earth's crust broke apart and the continental plates were displaced large distances. The Antarctic plate may have moved south from a more temperate latitude, carrying its fossils with it (see Chapter 16).

4. There are many possible answers. A few are as follows:

   sedimentary—glass from sandstone, cement from limestone, limestone building blocks

   igneous—granite for building materials, gem stones

   metamorphic—marble for monuments, slate for roofing and paving stones

5. Evolutionists conjecture that the sediments were deposited at different rates in different locations, just as snow or rain accumulations differ in different parts of the world.

6. Even the uniformitarian fossil record indicates that the extinction of the dinosaurs was a gradual process. The types of animals that should have been affected by the impact but remain to the present are strong evidence that an asteroid impact did not cause the dinosaurs to become extinct. Many scientists question whether the Chicxulub crater is an actual meteorite impact crater. If we look at the influence of large historical volcanic eruptions around the globe, we do not see temperatures or climatic conditions changing drastically enough to cause animal species to become extinct. Therefore, it is not likely that even a large meteorite impact would have such an effect. (See *The Great Dinosaur Extinction Controversy* by Charles Officer and Jake Page [Helix Books: 1996].)

are better interpreted as apelike animals, if not outright hoaxes. (Facet, p. 392, §15.10)

19. True. (§15.11)

20. False. Fish appeared during the Paleozoic era according to evolutionists. (§15.11, Table 15-1)

21. False. Early Chinese used natural gas to evaporate brine for salt. (§15.16)

22. True. (§15.22)

23. True. (§15.20)

24. False. *Schist* means *easily split. Gneiss* means *spark.* (§15.25)

25. True. (§15.25)

What Do You Think?

1. There are many ways that an organism can leave evidence of its existence. These include fossilized shed skin or exoskeletons, tracks, trails, imprints, burrows, feces, nests, and eggs.

2. Answers will vary. Students should find this to be an interesting question. Examples include the skeletal features of walking erect (location of skull-neck joint, shape and angle of pelvis, relative lengths of limbs, lordic shape of spine), opposable thumb, large cranial capacity, hyoid bone (speech), and the shape of the jaw and teeth. Also consider cultural indicators (the presence of tools, weapons, art and musical objects, other manufactured objects, evidence of a purposeful

Overview

Chapter 16 first introduces the idea of mountains and high hills, then describes the various types of mountains and the processes that seemed to have formed them. Finally, students will review the evidence for the plate tectonics theory and examine a creationary model that better accounts for the evidence in a manner consistent with the Bible. Students will also enjoy learning to draw relief maps and read topographic maps through the investigations in this chapter.

Section 16A gives a physical description of mountains. The term *mountain* cannot be defined objectively. Whether a physical feature is called a mountain or a hill is a matter of local custom. The differences between elevation, actual height, and relief are explained.

Section 16B categorizes mountains according to the processes by which they are thought to have formed. Types of depositional mountains are covered. Erosional or residual mountains are described as being a consequence of the Flood. Fold and fault-block mountains seem to be the result of tectonic orogeny.

Section 16C deals with the controversial plate tectonics theory, outlining the historical course of its development as evidence accumulated. The creationary catastrophic plate tectonics model is discussed as a better description of the observational and experimental evidence.

Schedule Summary

Section 16A: 2 periods

Section 16B: 2 periods

Section 16C: 2–3 periods

Investigation Summary

16E "Making a Model and Relief Map of a Mountain"

16F "Making a Profile Map of a Mountain"

16G "Topographic Maps"

16H "Mountains"

 Bulletin Board Ideas

1. Use photographs of various mountain ranges labeled with the type of mountains to provide a simple teaching board.

2. Post topographical maps of your area to catch students' interest.

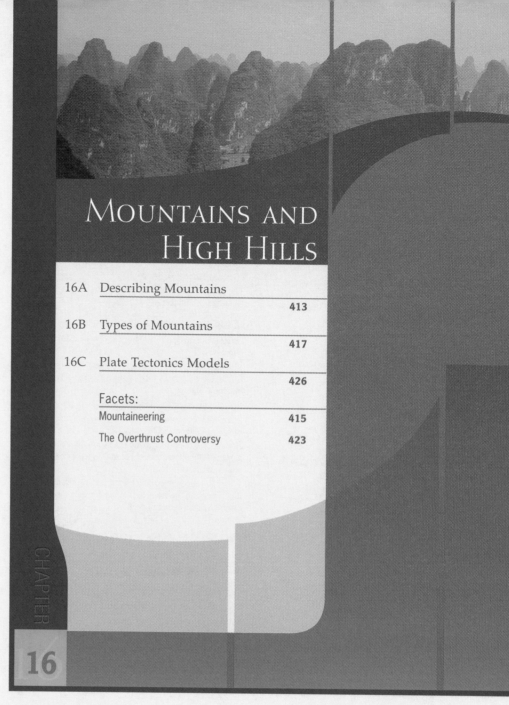

MOUNTAINS AND HIGH HILLS

CHAPTER

16

SUGGESTED TEACHING SCHEDULE

DAY 0

Assignment

Reading: Section 16A, "Describing Mountains"

DAY 1

Discuss the ambiguity of the terms *mountain* and *hill*. Explain the terms *elevation*, *actual height*, and *relief*, and discuss how they apply even if a mountain lies partially or completely under water. Distinguish between mountain ranges and mountain systems. Emphasize that the most extensive mountain system on Earth is the Mid-Atlantic Ridge. Begin familiarizing students with reading and interpreting contour relief maps.

Assignment

Complete: 16A Section Review Questions

Applications 16A, "Elevation, Actual Height, and Relief"

Reading: Investigation 16E, "Making a Model and Relief Map of a Mountain"

Investigation 16F, "Making a Profile Map of a Mountain"

DAY 2

Do Investigations 16E, "Making a Model and Relief Map of a Mountain," and if time permits, 16F, "Making a Profile Map of a Mountain."

Assignment

Complete: 16F, "Making a Profile Map of a Mountain," if not done in class

Reading: Section 16B, "Types of Mountains"

DAY 3

Quiz—Section 16A, "Describing Mountains"

Discuss the different depositional mountains and the processes that formed them. Cover erosional mountains from the perspective of Flood geology. Describe the various kinds of geologic folds and the mountains resulting

16A DESCRIBING MOUNTAINS

16.1 What Is a Mountain?

You have probably heard the saying "Don't make a mountain out of a molehill," with the intended meaning of "don't make a big problem out of a small problem." The difference between a mountain and a molehill seems obvious, but can you accurately describe the difference? Your explanation would probably include your definition of *height*.

We can define a mountain as "a natural elevation of the earth's surface rising more or less abruptly to a summit." This definition applies equally well to a hill. The difference between mountains and hills is mostly in height. What height distinguishes mountains from hills? There is no standard. Usually we think of mountains as landforms with heights of thousands of meters. Yet, in flat terrain even a small rise of land is considered a mountain. A mountain in New Jersey may be a mere foothill in Colorado. The Watchung Mountains near New York City, for example, are a series of ridges only 90 to 120 m (300 to 400 ft) high. Since the distinction between a mountain and a hill is based strictly on local interpretation, we must go along with whatever custom has been established in an area.

16.2 Elevation and Height

An important characteristic of a mountain is its height. Where do we begin to measure height? For example, the highest mountain on the earth's surface is Mount Everest, at 8848 m (29,028 ft). Is that 8848 m above its base, or above the lowest land on the earth, or above sea level, or above the lowest point on the ocean bottom? The height of Mount Everest, and that of other mountains, is usually given in meters or feet above sea level. This measurement is also called the mountain's **elevation**.

Although Mount Everest has the highest elevation, it does not look especially impressive. The mountains around it are nearly as high, and its base is about 5200 m (17,000 ft) above sea level. Thus the height of Everest's peak above its base, its **actual height**, is only about 3600 m (12,000 ft). The actual height of a mountain is the height of its summit above the surrounding terrain. Other mountains have greater actual heights. Mauna Kea, which forms a large part of the island of Hawaii, has the greatest actual height of any mountain on Earth: over 10,000 m (33,000 ft) from its submerged base, or nearly three times that of Everest. Mauna Kea's elevation, however, is only 4200 m (14,000 ft), less than half that of Everest because most of Mauna Kea's actual height is below the ocean's surface.

Watchung (WAH chung)

Mauna Kea (Mow nuh KAY uh)

16-1 Elevation is measured from sea level, and actual height is measured from the base of the mountain. Mauna Kea has a greater actual height than Mt. Everest.

3. Obtain a large USGS digital elevation map of the world showing the tectonic plates, earthquake zones, and volcano belts.

 Field Trip Ideas

1. Using a topographical map of a geologically interesting area near your school, take your students on a day trip to identify the features on the map and find them on the ground. This would relate topographical map reading to an actual hiking experience.

2. If your school is located in a hilly region containing many road cuts through folded strata, take your students to a road cut that illustrates anticlines and synclines particularly clearly. If you are familiar with the concepts, measure the strike and dip of the strata at various points in the road cut.

Objectives—Section 16A

After completing this section, students should be able to

- distinguish between elevation, actual height, and relief; and when given appropriate data, calculate each for a given mountain or region.

- name the highest mountains of the earth, North America, and the continental United States (and specify their locations).

- demonstrate a basic proficiency in interpreting contour relief maps, determining elevation on a map, and identifying points of steep and flat terrain.

- describe groups of mountains and name and locate the largest mountain system on the earth.

 Concepts Students Find Difficult

Figure 16-1 may be a little confusing to students until they spend some time studying it. The data and sea level on the left side of the figure relate only to Mount Everest, which is in the foreground. The data and sea level on the right side apply only to the Mauna Kea silhouette in the background. We have attempted to combine these two well-known mountains to relate the concepts of mountain base, sea level, elevation, and actual height. Note that the profile for Mauna Kea represents that of shield volcanoes, which are immense compared to other kinds of mountains (see Chapter 17).

---

from them. Illustrate the four kinds of faults and how mountains can develop from a series of normal fault blocks. Two days may be required to adequately cover this material.

Assignment

Complete: 16B Section Review Questions

Applications 16B, "Types of Mountains," and 16C, "Describing Mountains"

Reading: Investigation 16G, "Topographic Maps"

DAY 4

Do Investigation 16G, "Topographic Maps."

Assignment

Complete: Investigation 16H, "Mountains"

Applications 16D, "Formation of Mountains (Orogeny)"

Reading: Section 16C, "Plate Tectonics Models"

DAY 5

Quiz—Section 16B, "Types of Mountains"

Discuss the development of the contemporary uniformitarian plate tectonics model. Begin with the inadequate geosyncline theory; then progress through Wegener's initial proposal of the continental drift theory. Show how accumulated data led to the sea-floor spreading theory and the identification of continental plates. Discuss the uniformitarian mechanism for plate tectonics and the evidence that is used to support this theory. Then present the creationary catastrophic plate tectonics (CPT) theory and contrast it with uniformitarian plate tectonics.

Assignment

Complete: 16C Section Review Questions

Selected Chapter Review Questions

(schedule continued on p. 414)

Visual 16-1: Elevation, Actual Height, and Relief

Point out that although Mauna Kea and Mount Whitney have approximately the same elevation, Mauna Kea's actual height is greater because its base lies so far beneath the ocean's surface.

Visual 16-2: Topographic Map of a Mountainous Region

Use this visual in conjunction with the map in the box to illustrate the various features of topographic relief maps. Point out to your students some features like mountains, rivers, and ridges. Show them locations with steep slopes and others with gentle slopes. Note that contour lines form Vs in stream valleys, and the "V" points upstream. Demonstrate how to determine contour interval by counting contour lines between index contours. Note peak elevation markers, streams and bodies of water, glaciers, and other physical features. Differentiate between map grid lines and political boundaries. Refer to Appendix B7 for common topographic map symbols.

Demonstration: Local Relief Maps

Allow your students time to study geological survey or aerial survey maps to learn about the geological formations in your area. Local maps may be purchased from map stores in your area or from the online USGS Map Store. Visit the BJU Press Online Resources/*SPACE AND EARTH SCIENCE* webpage. Under Chapter 16, click on the link *USGS Map Store*.

Investigation 16E, "Making a Model and Relief Map of a Mountain," is an excellent exercise for students to do in groups during class or individually as an out-of-class project.

16-2 Mount McKinley, Alaska, is the highest peak in North America.

Noteworthy mountains in North America include Mount McKinley in Alaska (the highest mountain in North America, with an elevation of 6194 m or 20,320 ft), Mount Whitney in California (the highest mountain in the forty-eight adjoining states at 4418 m or 14,494 ft), and Mount Mitchell in North Carolina (the highest mountain in the eastern United States, with an elevation of 2037 m or 6684 ft).

A measure of elevation differences in a region is **relief**, the difference in height between the region's highest and lowest points relative to sea level. For example, in California the highest mountain, Mount Whitney, is 4418 m (14,494 ft) above sea level; the lowest point, in Death Valley, is 86 m (282 ft) below sea level. The relief of the state of California is thus about 4504 m (14,776 ft). Mountainous areas have high relief, but plains and plateaus have low relief.

Relief Maps

A map that shows altitude either by a three-dimensional model or by color, shading, or some other device, is a *relief map*. One type of relief map uses *contour lines*, lines joining points of equal elevation. The elevation of each line is either labeled or can be determined from labeled lines nearby. A mountain is shown by closed curves of increasing elevation that enclose successively smaller areas toward the summit. Closely spaced contour lines indicate a steep slope, while widely spaced lines show a gentle slope.

Relief maps that contain contour lines are also called contour or topographic maps.

Quiz—Section 16C, "Plate Tectonics Models"

Review for a chapter test.

Assignment

Study for a chapter test.

DAY 7

Test—Chapter 16

Assignment

Reading: Section 17A-1 (§17.1–17.6), characteristics of earthquakes and earthquake hazards

Box Summary: Relief Maps

This box introduces students to reading topographic maps and using the terms *relief map* and *contour line*. Spend some time going over the features of this map.

MOUNTAINEERING

More than 175 people have died attempting to reach the summit of Mount Everest, the tallest mountain in the world. The first eight teams to try failed to climb its northern slope. Finally, a British team that included Edmund Hillary, a beekeeper from New Zealand, and Tenzing Norgay, his Sherpa guide, reached the "roof of the world" on May 29, 1953. They chose a route from the south.

Since then more than 1555 people have reached the summit. The first American, Jim Whitaker, reached it in 1963. Once the peak was scaled, the challenge became to find new, "impossible" routes or ways. For instance, in 1971 an international team scaled the harsh southwest face of Everest, which had previously been assumed unclimbable. In 2001 a blind American, Erik Weihenmayer, assisted by Sherpa guides, successfully summitted. In 2003 Gary Guller, an amputee, managed to summit with only one arm. The list of others who have completed this challenging feat includes a sixteen-year-old boy, a 64-year-old man, and many women.

Mountain climbing is an elite sport. There are no more than half a million true mountaineers. Yet their ranks are worldwide, for mountains occur on every continent. Mountaineers usually acquire their interest while hiking on the hills and mountains near their home. Few thrills compare to that of climbing the rocky heights above the timber line. Popular hiking trails crisscross the mountain ranges of the United States. Hiking, an enjoyable sport in itself, is an integral part of all advanced mountain climbing. Even the ascent of Mount Everest begins with long walks at the mountain's base, which take up the greater part of the climb while the mountaineer becomes acclimated.

Mountains have been important throughout history as more than just ground for adventure. In early times people revered the mountains as the home of the gods. (In fact, climbers of the world's third highest mountain, Kanchenjunga (KUN chun JUNG guh), stop

Sir Edmund Hillary
John Pascoe Collection, Alexander Turnbull Library, Wellington, N.Z.

Junko Tabei of Japan was the first woman to climb Mount Everest, in 1975.

Rappelling down a mountain

a few meters short of the actual summit because the Sikkimese (SEEK uh MEEZ) consider it sacred.) Moses received the law on top of Mount Sinai, and many scholars believe that Jesus' transfiguration took place on top of Mount Hermon. Generals and pioneers have explored mountains to find passes to the lands on

Facet Summary: Mountaineering

This Facet discusses the motivation behind mountaineering and the history of some of man's boldest conquests. Notable climbers are identified. Some practical aspects of the sport are covered, such as required personal qualities, basic equipment, common dangers, and some climbing techniques. There are no vocabulary terms in this Facet.

the other side. Hannibal's failed attempt to cross the Alps with a herd of elephants to invade Rome shows that mountains can affect military strategy and success.

Mountaineering became a serious sport about one hundred fifty years ago. Eighteenth-century scientist-climbers aroused a new scientific interest in the mountains. European scientists first turned their attention to the Alps on the border of Italy and Switzerland. In rapid succession, skilled mountaineers conquered the high peaks of this range. Mountaineers then looked abroad for new challenges, the last of which was the forbidding Himalayas in Asia. Here on "the roof of the world" were the highest peaks, including the "grandfather" of them all, Mount Everest.

Why do these sportsmen risk their lives to climb mountains? "Because they are there" is the answer Edmund Hillary once gave, and that has become the traditional response. Mountaineering is one of the most demanding sports of all. A rugged mountain is fraught with risks that test the mountaineer's courage, skill, resourcefulness, strength, and stamina. The mountaineer has the pleasure of overcoming some of nature's greatest obstacles and witnessing scenery beheld by few people.

Above all, mountain climbing is a team sport in which leadership is one of the most prized abilities. Only the most experienced climbers take the lead and draw up the rear. The leader must think ahead to find the easiest route, and he must take into account the ever-changing weather conditions. The lead man presses forward, and the rest of the team catches up with him one at a time.

Mountaineers require years to become skillful with their equipment. Each surface—rocks, snow, and ice—demands different skills. The most important "equipment" is the body. The climber tries to keep at least three parts of his body in contact with the climbing surface at all times, usually his feet and hands. He almost never jumps. He relies on his legs to push himself upward. His hands are mainly for balance, except when climbing major overhangs. The pitons and ropes are primarily safeguards in case of a fall, not for pulling upward.

Climbing down a mountain is actually more difficult than climbing up because the mountaineer is blind to the handholds beneath him. However, his descent is much easier if he has ropes. He can then *rappel* (ra PEL). In rappelling, he lets both ends of his rope hang from a piton that is driven into the rock. He then slides down the rope. He retrieves the rope simply by pulling it through the piton. An expert climber has a steady rhythm as he climbs and descends the mountain. An expert in action is an impressive sight.

The United States has many mountain ranges popular with climbers. In the winter a low mountain can offer the same challenges as a high one. Major U.S. clubs include the American Alpine Club, the Appalachian Mountain Club, the Colorado Mountain Club, and the Sierra Club.

Mountain climbing is much less dangerous if you know what you are doing. More deaths occur on hills than on high mountaintops because the greatest dangers are foolhardiness and inexperience. A good leader has learned the virtue of patience, and that the safety of the group is more important than the success of the climb. The leader must avoid the "point of no return," when supplies are too short, the weather is too bad, or the team is too fatigued to make it back safely. It is not enough to know whether you can make it to the top; you must provide for the descent as well.

Common dangers	Basic equipment
• mountain sickness (caused by little oxygen in the thin air) • fatigue • frozen extremities • bad weather • avalanches • falling rocks, snow, and ice • deep crevasses hidden by snow • fragile snow shelves • short supplies • broken equipment • poor quality of equipment	• boots • rope • pitons (spikes with an eye hole, driven into rock) • carabiner (ring that clips to the piton and holds the rope) • crampons (spikes that attach to boots for gripping ice) • ice ax (for balance, probing, and cutting footholds in ice)

16.3 Groups of Mountains

Mountains exist either singly or in groups. A series of mountain peaks is called a **mountain range**. A group of mountain ranges is a **mountain system**. The highest mountain system is the Himalaya-Karakoram, which includes 96 of the 109 peaks of the world that are higher than 7300 m (24,000 ft). The most extensive mountain system lies under the Atlantic Ocean. The Mid-Atlantic Ridge extends for

16,000 km (10,000 mi) down the middle of the ocean. A few of its peaks are high enough to appear above the surface of the water; the highest of these is Pico Mountain in the Azores. Its elevation is 2351 m (7713 ft).

16A Section Review

1. What is the difference between a mountain and a hill?

2. What is the altitude of a mountain's summit above sea level called?

3. What is the name of the world's highest mountain? How high is it?

4. What is the highest mountain in North America? Where is it? How high is it?

5. Where is the most extensive mountain system in the world located?

6. What is a map that shows relative differences in elevation called?

7. (True or False) The relief and elevation of an island volcano are the same thing.

16B TYPES OF MOUNTAINS

16.4 Introduction

Mountains come in many forms. Some are high; others are low. Some are steep; others have gentle slopes. Some are volcanoes; others contain mostly sedimentary rocks. Some have layers that are crumpled; others have flat layers. Geologists have divided mountains into groups based on how they think the mountains formed.

Mountains in the Bible

The Bible refers to mountains more than three hundred times. Noah's ark rested on the mountains of Ararat (or Urartu, in present-day Armenia and Turkey). Moses received the Law on Mount Sinai. Abraham offered his son Isaac on Mount Moriah. Elijah retreated to Mount Horeb after a great victory over the prophets of Baal on Mount Carmel. The city of Jerusalem stretches across several mountaintops; its average elevation is 760 m (2500 ft) above sea level. Jesus often spoke from a mountainside, as in the Sermon on the Mount. On one occasion the Lord allowed Peter, James, and John to catch a glimpse of His glory on the Mount of Transfiguration. Later, after His resurrection, He left this earth from the Mount of Olives, with a promise that He shall someday return to that mountain when He begins His reign on Earth. In Revelation, the apostate church is described as a woman who sits on a beast with seven heads (Rev. 17:9, 18). These are then identified as the seven mountains of a royal city that many interpret to be Rome, which is also known as the "City of Seven Hills."

Pico (PEE koh)

Azores (AY zohrz)

Mid-Atlantic Ridge

16-3 The longest mountain system in the world is the Mid-Atlantic Ridge, which is part of an extensive mid-ocean ridge system that extends almost from pole to pole.

The Mid-Atlantic Ridge was named before geologists realized that it is continuous with the other mid-ocean ridge systems in the Pacific and Indian Oceans. Had they known this they might have found a better name for it, one that reflects its universality. The mid-ocean ridge system wraps around the earth like the seams on a baseball.

Visual App-5A: Digital Elevation Map of the Continental United States (Appendix B6)

Visual App-5B: Landform Regions of the Continental United States (Appendix B6)

You should refer to these visuals and appendices as you discuss the various mountain types and mountain ranges, as well as in later studies of glacial and erosional features. These are wonderful resources that warrant close study. For example, one can just imagine immense quantities of water flowing south off the north central portion of the map, forming the subtle erosional features seen there.

Objectives—Section 16B

After completing this section, students should be able to

- list and describe the four processes by which mountains were formed or in some cases are forming today.

- explain the features of various types of depositional and erosional mountains.

- describe the common types of folds and faults.

Many people down through history have claimed to have seen the remains of the ark exposed in the glaciers on Mt. Ararat, a high volcano in Turkey. However, it is possible, even likely, that the ark did not land on Mt. Ararat. The reference to the "mountains of Ararat" in the Bible (Gen. 8:4) indicates that the ark may have come to rest in what became the Kingdom of Urartu that encompassed portions of eastern Turkey, Iran, and Armenia. There are even local traditions that the mountain called Cudi Dagh in southeastern Turkey is the actual landing spot of the ark. Much information and disinformation on this subject can be found on the Internet by searching with keywords such as *Noah, ark, Ararat, Urartu,* and *Cudi Dagh.*

Box Summary: Mountains in the Bible

This box discusses notable mountains in the Bible in connection with events that occurred (or are prophesied to occur) on them or to their theological significance. There are no vocabulary terms in this box.

Answers to 16A Section Review Questions

1. Mountains are higher than hills, but the distinction is arbitrary and determined by local custom. (§16.1)

2. The altitude of a mountain's summit above sea level is called its *elevation*. (§16.2)

3. The world's highest mountain is Mount Everest, at 8847 m (29,028 ft). (§16.2)

4. The highest mountain in North America is Mount McKinley. It is in Alaska and is 6193 m (20,320 ft) high. (§16.2)

5. The most extensive mountain system in the world is located mostly underwater in the Atlantic Ocean and is called the *Mid-Atlantic Ridge*. (§16.3)

6. A map that shows relative differences in elevation is called a *relief map*. (box, p. 414)

7. True. (§16.2)

This visual incorporates Figures 16-4 and 16-5. Use this visual in your discussion of depositional mountains. The glacial kame in the lower photo is the tree-covered hill just to the right of the road. Kames are large piles of unstratified glacial till that were dropped in place as the glacier melted and retreated.

Volcano types are covered thoroughly in Chapter 17, and glacial features are described in Chapter 20.

Stones of Witness

Acts 17:26–27 states that God has appointed the "bounds of their [the nations'] habitation" so that they might "seek the Lord." These verses explain that God uses various geologic structures (including remnants of His judgment, like mountains) to force men to face their own profound limitations and to search for the only One who can give true meaning to life.

Depositional mountains are discussed in more detail in Chapters 17, 18, and 20.

Parícutin (pah REE koo TEEN)

Krakatoa (KRAH kuh TOH uh)

Stones of Witness

Since most of the mountains we see today are probably the result of the Flood, it is easy for Christians to see how mountains can be testimonies to God's judgment on sin. But did you know that these same geologic formations testify to God's desire to redeem the world to Himself? Read Acts 17:26–27, and see if you can determine how mountains are testimonies to divine redemption.

16.5 Depositional Mountains

Depositional mountains form by the accumulation of rocks on the earth's surface. These materials may be volcanic or carried by wind or glaciers.

Volcanoes build up in height when lava emerging from a central vent or break in the earth's surface hardens into rock and cinders. They can form quickly, like Parícutin, which erupted in a farmer's field in Mexico and within a year accumulated a cinder cone over

16-4 Mount Fuji in Japan is a depositional mountain formed from volcanic matter.

330 m (1100 ft) above the surrounding area. Volcanoes also can change or destroy themselves quickly. When Mount Ararat in Turkey exploded in 1840, it blew out a large gorge on its northeastern side. The volcano on the island of Krakatoa in Indonesia destroyed two-thirds of the island when it erupted in 1883. Molten rock from underground sometimes replaces that which is blown away, but generally the structure of the mountain is considerably different after an explosive eruption.

Sand dunes are wind-deposited hills of sand. Although we tend to think of sand dunes as insignificant hills, those in the Sahara Desert in Algeria may be as high as 430 m (1400 ft) and may cover several square kilometers.

16-5 Hongoryn Els dunes in the southern Gobi Desert of Mongolia. They are also known as the Singing Sand Dunes for the sound of the sand in high winds.

Glacial deposits produce several types of hills: *moraines*, *eskers*, *kames*, and *drumlins*. A moraine is a ridge of rock debris that was carried or pushed along by a glacier. When the glacier melted, it left piles of debris that appear as long continuous ridges. The moraines left by the leading edges of the huge continental glaciers that were present during the Ice Age may be over a hundred meters high and hundreds of kilometers long. Good examples of such *terminal moraines* include the Harbor Hill and the Ronkonkoma moraines, which extend nearly the entire length of Long Island, New York.

moraine (muh RAYN)
drumlin (DRUM lun)
Ronkonkoma (rahng KAHNG kuh muh)

Eskers are low, snaking, ridge-like deposits that remained after glaciers melted away or retreated. They are the sediment beds of melt-water streams that flowed through ice tunnels carved by the running water near the margins of glaciers. Kames were formed when glacial debris washed into depressions in the ice. When the glacier melted, the rubble formed small, isolated, steep-sided hills. Drumlins are smooth elliptical hills, 6 to 60 m (20 to 200 ft) in height and 0.5 to 1 km (0.3 to 0.6 mi) long, that glaciers deposited as they moved along. They usually occur in groups rather than singly, all parallel to the direction the glacier traveled. In the United States, drumlins occur from New England to Minnesota, with an unusually high concentration in New York. Boston's Bunker Hill, of Revolutionary War fame, is a drumlin.

16-6 A terminal moraine is a ridge of rock debris that a glacier piled up at its leading edge.

plateau (pla TOH)

16.6 Erosional Mountains

Erosional mountains, or **residual mountains**, are mountains that were carved out by extensive erosion, usually from a plateau. A *plateau* is a region of flat rock structure having a high elevation. Plateaus usually consist of mostly sedimentary rock.

As erosion dissected (cut apart) a plateau, some parts of the plateau remained intact. The intact parts of the plateau often contained minerals that strengthened it. In other cases, the remnants were just parts of the larger plateau that were located in such a way that they avoided being washed away with the rest of the plateau. In the western U.S., broad, flat-topped hills remaining from the dissection

16-7 This esker is located in Wisconsin.

16-8 Erosion dissects a plateau to form erosional mountains.

16-9 Aerial view of a small drumlin in Sodus, NY

  Visual 16-4: Erosional Mountains

This visual incorporates Figure 16-8. Use this visual in your discussion of erosional mountains. The right-hand photo is of Stone Mountain near Atlanta, Georgia. It is a form of erosional mountain called a *monadnock*, where an intrusion of magma solidified, then the overlying rock eroded away to expose the pluton.

In southeastern Venezuela, several towering mesas called *tepuys* (*tepuy* is the local Indian word for mountain) rise above the surrounding tropical forests and savannahs. These tablelands contain eerie rock formations, canyons, carnivorous plants, and an abundance of water. Angel Falls, the highest waterfall in the world, cascades out of Auyan Tepuy (Mountain of Evil), falling a distance of 0.9 km (0.6 mi).

Stones of Witness

God has left scarred but beautiful structures like these on the earth so that we will be reminded not only of His judgment on sin and provision for redemption but also of His glorious nature and love of beauty. These things remind us to give due praise to a worthy God.

mesa (MAY suh)
butte (BYOOT)

monadnock (muh NAD nahk)

16-10 Erosional mountains: Fossil Butte National Park, Wyoming (above), and Monument Valley, Arizona (right). Severe erosion often leaves just tall spires called pinnacles (below)).

Stones of Witness

Since God has given us the record of the Flood and its consequences, how should we respond to the strange beauty of the mountains of Monument Valley and Bryce Canyon?

process are called *mesas*; smaller flat-topped hills are *buttes*. Both mesas and buttes have steep sides. The Catskills of southeastern New York and the mountains of the Allegheny Plateau of West Virginia are erosional. Sometimes only one area of the higher ground survives to form a single mountain. A *monadnock* is an isolated mountain that was resistant to erosion while the area around it was eroded to a flat plain. Mount Monadnock in New Hampshire and Stone Mountain in Georgia are monadnocks.

The uniformitarian explanation for erosional features such as those shown in the figures is that long ago, during a wetter climate, the land was being pushed upward as the rivers were cutting downward into the rock, eroding the material away. This model has a number of problems. From the perspective of time, it assumes that climatic conditions remained the same for hundreds of millions of

years to allow for river erosion to take place. The vertical sides and flat tops of buttes and mesas could not have been preserved over such a long period without erosion rounding down the edges.

From a wider perspective, the geologic evidence from over a large area of the American West points to rapid erosion on a continental scale. The only conceivable source for this much water is the Flood. Places where the Flood in its early stages deposited extensive sedimentary strata probably experienced much erosion near the end of the Flood and shortly after it. These sedimentary rocks had not yet hardened fully, so the water running off them could easily erode them. There was no shortage of water. It had covered the tops of the mountains and now had to "return from off the earth" as God caused the continents to rise and the ocean basins to subside. Thus, the water cut deep gorges and dissected plateaus to form erosional mountains, riverbeds, valleys, and canyons. The sedimentary remnants of this erosion are evident all over the Southwest, deposited by rapidly flowing water. Shortly after the Flood, the natural cements solidified and the soft sedimentary material became rock.

16.7 Fold Mountains

Solid rocks can fold or bend in a short period of time if a force is applied to them under the proper combination of temperature and pressure. Even under normal environmental conditions, rock will slowly "creep." Limestone benches in old gardens, for example, have sagged under the influence of gravity after two or three centuries. Softer, unsolidified materials, such as clays and moist sand, can easily bend under compression. You can demonstrate this yourself by pushing on the ends of a strip of clay.

Most major mountain ranges contain some folded rocks. The Rockies, the Appalachians, the Alps, and the Himalayas all show evidence of folding. In some mountains the folding of the rocks seems to have formed the mountains; these are **fold mountains**. Other mountains contain evidence of other processes working with folding.

Because water has deposited most sedimentary rocks, we know that they generally begin as horizontal or nearly horizontal strata. Where we find slanted or upturned strata, forces in the ground have usually been at work to tilt or bend the rock. These forces may be vertical, horizontal, or at an angle. In many places the bending seems to have happened while the rock was still soft, because there is no evidence of the rock fracturing in the tight folding that can be seen. The rapid folding of deposited flood strata, the concept held by Creationists, better explains this appearance than the gradual processes envisioned by uniformitarian geologists.

16.8 Kinds of Fold Mountains

Different types of folds appear on the earth's surface. Erosion has exposed some of them; others are discovered during mining operations, road cuts, and other excavations. Certain kinds of folds seem to have been caused by horizontal forces. An **anticline** is an arch of rock layers. Forces acting toward each other bend the layers of rock into an upward fold. A **syncline** is a trough or downward fold

16-11 The eroded remnants of tightly folded anticlines (top and bottom) and a broad syncline fold (middle) produce spectacular fold-mountain topography. The Gosses Bluff meteorite impact structure is in the center.

anticline (AN tih kline): anti- (Gk. *anti*—against, opposite to [gravity]) + -cline (Gk. *klinein*—to lean)

syncline (SIN kline): syn- (Gk. *syn*—together, same) + -cline

16-12 This formation near Dorset, England, is an example of an adjacent anticline and syncline.

In geology, the technical term for soft, unsolidified sedimentary rock is *unconsolidated*. As sediments accumulated and were heated by compaction and magmatic intrusions, water was driven from between the particles and chemical reactions bonded the particles together. These *consolidated* sediments form the layered rock units we see today.

 Demonstration: Geologic Folding

Put a flat layer of clay on a piece of wax paper on a table. Place several other flattened layers of clay of different colors on top of the first layer. Trim the sides so that a nice cross section of the layers is visible, and cut the ends square. Take two blocks of wood and place one at each end of the layered clay. Push the blocks toward each other. The clay will fold in one or more anticlines and synclines. This works best if the layers are relatively thin compared to the length of the strips of clay.

Visual 16-5: Geologic Folding

This visual is a reproduction of Figure 16-13. These images show idealized mountain formations resulting from the erosion of the underlying folded structures in the rocks. The answer to the question in the visual is that soft, unconsolidated sedimentary strata could be easily folded without fracturing.

The words "youngest" and "oldest" are in quotation marks to indicate the typical evolutionary interpretation of these layers. More correctly, the terms indicate the order in which sedimentary layers were deposited. According to the theory of superposition, the "older" layers had to be laid down first, followed by the "younger" layers.

If the pressures creating the folds were exerted after the rock were completely hardened, the rock would have fractured and become pulverized rather than folded.

Students may point out that the folded rock in Figure 16-14 is fractured. If one looks closely, one can see that the joints cut across the layers of rock, which are otherwise distinct, meaning the stresses that caused the fractures occurred after the folded layers had hardened.

monocline (MAHN uh KLINE): mono- (Gk. *monos*— single, alone) + -cline

monocline

syncline

anticline

dome

basin

16-13 Five major types of folds are diagrammed above. Arrows show forces that appear to have caused the folds.

of rock strata formed in a similar way. These kinds of folds rarely occur by themselves. Usually, they alternate in a repeated wavy pattern that eventually dies out. Anticlines and synclines can vary in size from just a few meters across to structures many kilometers in size.

Vertical forces may have also created folds in rock strata. Perhaps the simplest is the **monocline**, a fold that occurs when one part of a rock layer is lifted relative to another along a fault, forming what looks like a rounded step. An upward vertical force in a single location could have formed a **dome**. A dome is a structure in which the sedimentary strata arch upward like an inverted bowl. On a geologic map, a dome is a roughly circular or oval pattern formed by strata exposed by erosion. The inner exposed strata were laid down before the outer rings. In South Dakota, the Black Hills are the remnants of a geologic dome. Domes are often associated with the intrusion of magma below layers of sedimentary rock. A **basin** is the opposite of a dome. On maps, eroded basins are identified by the outer rings of exposed strata that are below, or "older" than, the layers forming the inner rings. The Michigan peninsula is almost entirely a basin structure. Basins could have formed when magma drained away from reservoirs beneath sedimentary strata, allowing gravity to cause the layers to sag.

16-14 Folded rock strata at a road cut near Newfoundland, New Jersey

THE OVERTHRUST CONTROVERSY

Mountains often become battlegrounds between creationary and evolutionary scientists, since fossils are most easily found on mountain cliffs and rocky slopes. You probably know that evolutionists claim that fossils are one of the best proofs of their theory. Evolutionists say that the fossils in bottom strata obviously formed first and that the fossil record shows that animals and plants became more complex through time. In some places, however, the fossils are in the wrong order—the more complex or "more recent" fossils are on the bottom, and the simpler "older" fossils are on the top. How do evolutionists explain these fossils?

The main assumption of rock dating and superposition in evolutionary circles is that more complex fossils are younger than simple fossils. Thus, any layer of rock that contains complex fossils, such as mammals, must be younger than a layer of rock containing simpler fossils, such as trilobites. Regardless of the arrangement of the rocks, the complex fossils are younger. According to the evolutionary uniformitarian model, even in places where rocks containing simple fossils appear above rocks containing more complex fossils, the upper rocks have to be older. Evolutionists say that the older rocks somehow moved above the younger rocks.

How can old rocks appear on top of young rocks? The evolutionists' answer is an **overthrust**. This begins with a reverse fault with a slant of less than 45° (a thrust fault).

When the fault is active, rocks on the upper side of the fault are pushed over the rocks on the lower side of the fault.

Chief Mountain in Montana is an example of an alleged overthrust.

fault develops in sedimentary strata

strata on left rides up over right side

erosion removes much of overlapping material

Then the upper layers of the overthrusted rock erode, leaving only the older rocks in the lower part of the overthrusted rock exposed.

Overthrusting has been observed on a small scale, so at first the theory seems reasonable. However, the scale required to explain several "reversed" fossil layers is not small. For example, Chief Mountain in Glacier National Park shows a strata sequence "reversal." Uniformitarian geologists believe that a block of sedimentary rock 25 to 50 km (15 to 30 mi) wide, 560 km (350 mi) long, and 3000 m (10,000 ft) thick slid over the surface of the ground for about 55 km (35 mi)! Even if such an immense force were available to move these trillions of tons of rock, the rock would likely shatter long before it had traveled the required distance.

Furthermore, the rocks at Chief Mountain show no signs of motion. The boundary between the "younger" rock and the "older" rock has no rock fragments or powder or grooves that would occur if rock surfaces scraped against each other. In fact, the boundary consists of several layers of "older" rock interspersed with "younger" rock. One mass of rock sliding over another does not produce interleaved layers.

Several other large fossil areas show more simple fossils on top of more complex fossils. The Swiss Alps show a "reversed" sequence of three layers. To

account for this order, evolutionists postulate two overthrusts. But no overthrust on this scale is believable. A more reasonable alternative is that the rocks were formed in the order that they appear. Most Creationists believe that the Flood formed most sedimentary rocks and fossils. In a standard fossil sequence, the waters of the Flood buried the bottom-dwelling, fixed marine organisms first, followed by larger and more mobile organisms. It is logical that the larger vertebrate animals such as dinosaurs, birds, and mammals were the last to be drowned and buried. In the case of an "overthrust" fossil sequence, it is possible and even likely, that massive currents carried bottom-dwelling organisms and washed them in over sediments from earlier stages of the Flood that contained more complex organisms. Thus, all the layers of fossils are about the same age and cannot show evolution.

Permian ("oldest")

Jurassic

Tertiary ("youngest")

Two "miraculous" separate overthrusts are suggested to explain this order of strata in the Swiss Alps.

Facet Summary: The Overthrust Controversy

This Facet refutes the uniformitarian overthrust theory which claims that in some places "older" rocks were supposedly thrust over "younger" rocks along a low-angle reverse fault. Be sure to cover the vocabulary word *overthrust* if you intend to include it on a test.

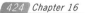
Visual 16-6: Major Faults in the Contiguous United States

This visual is a reproduction of Figure 16-15. The map shows the major faults that are *visible at the earth's surface*. Overlying material often buries faults for many miles. Students should note that most of the faulting is associated with mountain ranges in both the western and eastern United States. This map shows that earthquakes, which are often associated with movements along faults, could occur in most states in the country, except perhaps in the central plains. The state of Kentucky, not one that is normally associated with earthquakes, experienced a major earthquake on December 16, 1811.

16.9 Fault-Block Mountains

Some mountains formed when large sections of the crust moved along cracks in the rock. A **joint** is a large crack in a rock along which no movement (slippage) has occurred. A crack along which there has been slippage is a **fault**. A fault was caused by a force applied against a rock that caused stress the rock could not relieve by bending; thus, the rock cracked and moved in order to relieve the stress.

16-15 Major faults in the continental United States

The hanging wall of a fault is the wall on the upper side of the sloping fault line. The footwall is on the underside of the fault. The rock units may move in almost any direction relative to each other across the face of the fault.

16.10 Kinds of Geologic Faults

Geologists have identified several kinds of faults that describe the relative movement of the bodies of rock on either side of the fault. Assume that the tilt of the fault plane, or its *dip*, is not vertical, as in Figure 16-16. If the body of rock under the fault rises in relation to the rock above the fault (which could actually have dropped), then the fault is called a **normal fault** (figure A). If the opposite motion occurs, so that the body of rock above the fault rises in relation to the other body, then the fault is called a **reverse fault** (figure B). This is particularly true if the fault's angle is more than 45° from the horizontal. If the reverse fault's angle is less than 45°, it is called a **thrust fault**. Finally, if the only motion along the fault is horizontal, then the fault is called a **strike-slip fault** (figure C). The *strike* of a fault is the direction of a horizontal line drawn on the face of the fault. The famous San Andreas fault is a strike-slip fault.

16-16 A normal fault (A), a reverse fault (B), and a strike-slip or transform fault (C)

Visual 16-7: Types of Faults

This visual is a reproduction of Figure 16-16. To help students remember which wall is the hanging wall of an inclined fault and which is the footwall, imagine a reverse fault where the hanging wall is above the surrounding terrain. In this case, an observer would look up and see the face of the fault inclined above, or hanging, over his head. Similarly, in a normal fault, the footwall would be inclined away from the observer so he could rest his foot on it.

A. Normal fault

B. Reverse fault

C. Strike-slip (transform) fault

Faulting plays an important role in the **fault-block mountain**, a mountain bounded by one or more normal faults. The Sierra Nevada in California is a classic example of this type. It shows a normal fault in which the surface on the west side of the fault has risen above the level of the surrounding country. This raised block of material is enormous, measuring about 120 km (75 mi) from west to east and about 640 km (400 mi) from north to south. The eastern end has been pushed upward about 3 km (2 mi). Various forces have acted to cut the block into separate mountains having gentle western slopes and steep cliffs on the east. California's highest peak, Mount Whitney, is part of this range.

normal faults

16-17 The Sierra Nevada (left) is made of fault-block mountains. Fault-block mountains are bounded by at least one fault. A landmass on one side of the fault rises above the landmass on the other side (right). It is by no means necessary that the process took millions of years.

 Visual 16-8: Fault-Block Mountains

This visual is a reproduction of the right-hand illustration in Figure 16-17. Use this visual when discussing fault-block mountains. Refer also to Visuals App-5A and B. Note that in geological diagrams, the half arrows on either side of a fault line indicate relative motion across the fault. This image depicts a series of normal faults. The elevated footwall sections become eroded as water flows along the fault lines between the blocks, forming these distinctive mountains.

16-1 NOTABLE MOUNTAINS

Mountain	Location	Height (m)	Year climbed	Notes of interest
Mt. Everest	Nepal/Tibet	8848	1953	highest mountain in the world
Aconcagua	Argentina	6962	1897	tallest mountain in the Western Hemisphere
Mount McKinley	Alaska	6194	1913	tallest mountain in North America
Mount Logan	Yukon Territory	5959	1925	tallest mountain in Canada; one of the most massive mountains in the world, still growing
Kilimanjaro	Tanzania	5895	1889	highest mountain in Africa, formerly snow-capped year round despite proximity to the equator
Mount Elbrus	Republic of Georgia	5642	1874	highest mountain in Europe, extinct volcano
Ararat	Turkey	5165	1829	first major modern climb; a possible site of Noah's ark
Vinson Massif	Antarctica	4897	1966	highest mountain in Antarctica
Matterhorn	Switzerland/Italy	4478	1865	major climb of its sheer cliffs ended the golden age of mountaineering in the Alps
Mount Whitney	California	4418	1873	highest mountain in the lower 48 states
Fuji	Japan	3776	663 (by tradition)	highest mountain in Japan; Shinto and Buddhist religions consider it sacred
Olympus	Greece	2917	1913 (first recorded)	highest mountain in Greece; legendary home of the Greek gods
Sinai	Egypt	2637	Early	name of the peak where Moses received the Law
Mont Kosciuszko	Australia	2228	1834	highest mountain in Australia

16-18 The Black Mountains near Death Valley, California, are part of a range of fault-block mountains.

The Great Basin and Range Province of Nevada and Utah has many fault-block mountains. In this region a complex system of faults has cut the earth's crust into thousands of blocks, forming many valley basins and mountain ranges. The Wasatch Range that borders the Colorado Plateau is well known in this area.

Wasatch (WAH SATCH)

16B   Section Review

1. How is a depositional mountain different from an erosional mountain?
2. What type of mountain is the Matterhorn, which was formed when a glacier carved away the surrounding rock?
3. What happens to the rocks, sand, and silt carried by a glacier?
4. What is the difference between a mesa and a butte? What type of mountain are they?
5. What determines what type of fold will be present in a fold mountain?
6. What type of mountain consists of a raised section of material bounded by one or more normal faults?
7. (True or False) The vertical forces at work in basins are usually caused by fault movement.

16C   PLATE TECTONICS MODELS

16.11   Introduction

In Section 16B we discussed four major kinds of mountains—depositional, erosional, fold, and fault-block mountains. We also briefly described the processes that could produce each of these mountain types. Depositional mountains are actively forming today. Volcanoes erupt, sand dunes form and migrate across deserts, and glaciers melt, leaving behind their piles of glacial till and sediment. What about the other types of mountains? Are mountains being carved out of deep sedimentary rocks by flowing water? Are rock layers being folded? Are blocks of rock rising or dropping to form fault-block mountains? The answers to these questions are all "yes," but these processes are occurring so slowly that only by careful measurements can one observe anything happening at all. These extremely slow rates of activity are used by uniformitarian geologists to justify the need for hundreds of millions of years for mountain formation. However, there is much evidence that some mountains formed rapidly and recently—something that "old-earth" geologists have difficulty explaining.

16-19 What forces caused the wrinkles in the earth's crust that we call mountains?

Objectives—Section 16C

After completing this section, students should be able to

- trace the history of the development of the contemporary plate tectonics theory held by most geologists.
- describe the evidence for the existence of tectonic plates.
- describe geologic features associated with sea-floor spreading and plate subduction.
- discuss how one creationary plate tectonics theory consistent with the Bible accounts for the observed features better than the uniformitarian theory.

Neo-Darwinism and its overarching theory of biological evolution is the foundational paradigm by which nearly all biological research is being conducted today. In a similar way, the uniformitarian plate tectonics theory is considered by geologists all over the world to be the fundamental cause of nearly every geological feature and process in existence. This theory accounts for the formation of immense mountain ranges, the melting of the rock that becomes volcanic lava, the energy that causes earthquakes, and the shapes of the continents.

By learning the material in this section, students will become familiar with topics on standardized tests derived from the uniformitarian theories of the earth's history. After completing this chapter, students will understand the faulty reasoning of the plate tectonics theory and related topics, but they will also have the knowledge they'll need to "correctly" answer standardized test questions in order to maximize their test scores.

Answers to 16B Section Review Questions

1. A depositional mountain is a geologic feature formed by the accumulation of rock or sediment transported by some means to a location. An erosional mountain is formed when rock is eroded from a preexisting geologic feature. (§16.5–16.6)

2. The Matterhorn is an *erosional* or *residual mountain.* (§16.6)

3. When the glacier melts, they are deposited as hills in the form of moraines, eskers, kames, and drumlins. (§16.5)

4. A mesa is a large erosional remnant of a plateau, and a butte is a much smaller, isolated erosional remnant. Both are *erosional* or *residual mountains.* (§16.6)

5. The direction of the forces that were exerted on the unconsolidated rock determined the different types of folds that were produced. (§16.8)

6. A mountain consisting of a raised block of material bounded by one or more normal faults is called a *fault-block mountain.* (§16.9)

7. False. Faults are the *results* of vertical movements caused by forces. The vertical forces at work in a basin are derived from gravity acting on the remaining rock after magma beneath has drained away. (§16.8)

In this section, we will study the development of the various uniformitarian theories that were and are used to explain the origin of mountains, also called **orogeny** by geologists. We will then present the best creationary interpretation of the evidence in contrast to these theories, that most mountains existing today are probably the result of the Genesis Flood.

16.12 The Geosyncline Theory

Both evolutionists and Creationists look at mountains and suspect that they were raised by titanic forces sometime in the past. Where did these forces come from?

One theory about these forces that was accepted during the nineteenth century and through the mid-twentieth century is the **geosyncline theory**. According to this model, in various places around the world immense trough-like synclines, or *geosynclines*, many hundreds or thousands of kilometers in width and length, were gradually filled with sediments from surrounding terrain. The weight of the sediments caused the geosyncline to subside or sink, allowing more sediment to collect and solidify into rock. Later, an uplifting force pushed the sediments upward, folding and fracturing them into mountains.

The geosyncline theory was very poor in explaining how fold and fault-block mountains came into being. It gave no explanation for the source of the uplifting force, and the horizontal forces generated by the uplift could not have produced the folding seen in mountain ranges around the world. Many geologists suspected that there had to be a better explanation for their observations.

16.13 Continental Drift

As early as 1620, Francis Bacon noted on newly printed maps of his day that the coasts of Europe and Africa seemed to parallel the coasts of North and South America. More than a century later, Benjamin Franklin, in a leap of imagination, noted that the shapes of the African, South American, and North American continents fit together like the broken pieces of an eggshell. He suggested that the earth's surface was a solid shell floating on a liquid interior and that sometime in the past the turbulence of the liquid interior ripped the earth's shell apart and moved the continents to their current locations. This was the beginning of what came to be known in the 1800s as the **continental drift theory**.

The theory gained more prominence in the 1920s when Alfred Wegener published several papers on his *continental displacement theory*. He suggested that all the modern continents had started as a single large continent called **Pangaea**, which was surrounded by a single global ocean called the **Panthalassa Ocean**. The continents were somehow wrenched apart and moved over the earth's surface to their current locations. For support of his idea, he pointed out the similar fit of the continental shorelines, similar geologic

16-20 The geosyncline theory could not explain how mountains could be folded or lifted upward.

Francis Bacon (1561–1626) was an English philosopher who was best known for developing the philosophical basis for science in Western cultures.

Alfred Wegener (1880–1930) was a German meteorologist and geophysicist who is best known for first describing the continental drift theory in a scientific paper. He died during a climatological expedition to Greenland.

16-21 Wegener proposed that the world's continents began as a single continent called Pangaea surrounded by a single sea called the Panthalassa Ocean.

We do not know when the idea of continental drift originated, but it predates Francis Bacon. The Dutch mapmaker Abraham Ortelius suggested in 1596 that the Americas were torn from the European and African continents. By the mid-1800s, many people were proposing that the continents might have moved. Some thought they might still be moving, only very slowly. A few, such as the geographer Antonio Snider-Pellegrini, associated this movement with the Creation narrative and the devastation of Noah's Flood. However, the rise of the uniformitarianism of James Hutton and Charles Lyell relegated the Genesis Flood to insignificance in the eyes of the mainstream geologists, and evidence for continental drift was ignored.

Historical geologists believe that the breakup of Pangaea occurred in stages. First, it began to separate into two sections. The northernmost section called *Laurasia*, contained what are today the North American and Eurasian continents. The southern section contained the South American, African, Indian, Australian, and Antarctic continents, called *Gondwanaland*.

Ensure that students do not come away from this section with the idea that the so-called magnetic banding adjacent to the Mid-Atlantic Ridge is clear-cut evidence for slow sea-floor spreading. To the contrary, the field data indicates that during the formation of these magnetic signatures, conditions in the local geomagnetic fields were chaotic, consistent with the upheaval associated with a global Flood. For a discussion of this evidence visit the BJU Press Online Resources/*SPACE AND EARTH SCIENCE* webpage. Under Chapter 16, click on the link *Magnetic Banding*.

 Visual 16-9: Sea-floor Spreading Theory

This visual is a reproduction of Figure 16-22. Rift zones form what geologists call *divergent plate boundaries*, where sea-floor spreading takes place. The lithosphere consists of the crust and upper mantle but is shown as a single unit here to clarify the movement mechanism. Recall that the arrows adjacent to the faults show relative movement. Blocks of rock near the center of the rift developed faults and fell downward as they moved away from the rift to make room for newer material.

One of many long transform faults in the fracture zone is shown in the background. A better understanding of the relationship between transform faults and mid-ocean ridges can be seen in Figure 16-23 on page 429. These fractures are believed to have relieved stresses in the crust that built up due to unequal rates of sea-floor spreading.

features in regions of the modern continents that were adjacent to each other in the beginning, and the existence of similar kinds of fossils in these regions. He and his supporters also noted that where continents seem to have collided, great mountain ranges had appeared.

During Wegener's lifetime, most scientists disregarded his theory because he could not provide a means by which immensely massive continents could plow many hundreds of kilometers across the earth's crust. His suggestions of centrifugal force or the gravitational pulls of the sun and moon were quickly shown to be incapable of producing such continental motion.

16.14 Sea-Floor Spreading

For more than a decade following Wegener's death, relatively few scientists agreed with the continental drift theory. But data began to accumulate from various sources, forcing scientists to take another look at the idea. During World War II, navy ships using echo sounders to hunt enemy submarines discovered mid-ocean ridges, deep ocean trenches, and, in some places, wide continental shelves that extended the margins of continents many kilometers out to sea.

Early in the twentieth century, geologists discovered that in many lava flows around the world, magnetic minerals locked in the hardened rock were oriented in the opposite direction to the earth's modern magnetic field. In addition, some lava fields around old volcanoes contained minerals having opposite magnetic orientations in different locations in the field. These opposing magnetic orientations recorded in sequential lava flows implied to geologists that the earth's magnetic field must have reversed many times during its history.

During the 1960s and '70s, evidence for magnetic reversals was observed in the cores of the deep ocean drilling projects mentioned in Chapter 13. Geologists discovered alternating bands of magnetic minerals on both sides of the mid-ocean ridges. They interpreted this data to mean hot magma had oozed up through a crack, or **rift**, in the ocean floor crust. Something pulled the rift apart allowing more magma to well up and solidify. Thus, the newest rock was at the center of the ridge corresponding to the location of the rift, with older rock farther away from the rift. The hardened rocks preserved the earth's reversing magnetic field through time, just like the volcanic eruptions on land. Geologists concluded that the ocean crusts were spreading away from the mid-ocean ridges, carrying the continents with them. This process became known as **sea-floor spreading**.

Geologists were quick to propose a mechanism for sea-floor spreading. They suggested that hot, lower-density rock deep in the mantle rose in *thermal plumes*, which collided with the underside of the lithosphere. The plume then split and moved sideways, pulling the lithosphere apart in two directions (see Figure 16-22). This convection process is similar to what we saw in thunderstorms and in the sun's interior. Recall from Chapter 13 that the lithosphere rests on top of a layer of rock, called the asthenos-

The magnetic banding surrounding mid-ocean ridges is not as clear and supportive of regular magnetic reversals as geologists would like to believe. Additionally, analysis shows that magnetic reversals occur vertically as well as horizontally in ocean bottom cores, complicating the interpretation of the data.

16-22 Sea-floor spreading is believed to be slowly taking place because of convection within the mantle rock beneath the ocean lithosphere.

phere, that is very close to melting. The asthenosphere is believed to be easily deformed, which allows the lithosphere to slide over the rest of the mantle.

16.15 Tectonic Plates

Geologists have discovered distinct segments of the earth's crust that seem to be slowly moving, called **tectonic plates**. They can be classified as either *continental plates* (those that contain mostly continental land masses) or *oceanic plates* (those that form a portion of the ocean bottom). There are nine major plates and six minor plates. The major tectonic plates are the:

African Plate (continental)

Antarctic Plate (continental)

Indo-Australian Plate (continental and oceanic)

Eurasian Plate (continental)

Nazca Plate (oceanic; west of South America)

North American Plate (continental)

Pacific Plate (oceanic)

Philippine Plate (oceanic)

South American Plate (continental)

The minor tectonic plates are the:

Anatolian Plate (continental; Turkey)

Arabian Plate (continental; Saudi Arabia)

Cocos Plate (oceanic; west of California and Baja California)

Juan de Fuca Plate (oceanic; west of Washington and British Columbia; consists of three parts: the northern Explorer Plate, the Strait of Juan de Fuca Plate, and the southern Gorda Plate).

16-23 The tectonic plates of the world. Edges of the plates are marked with yellow lines.

The tectonic plates on this list represent the major plates that are distinct from the others. However, geologists recognize smaller sections of these plates that have tectonically active boundaries. For example, the plate that moved to cause the devastating Indian Ocean tsunami in December 2004 is called the Burma microplate. It is sandwiched between the India Plate to the north and west, the Australian Plate to the south (both parts of the Indo-Australian Plate), and the Sunda Plate to the east (part of the Eurasian Plate).

 Visual 16-10: Tectonic Plates

This visual is a reproduction of Figure 16-23. Point out to students the tectonic plate boundaries, the mid-ocean ridges, the relationship of transform faults in the fracture zones to the rifts, and the distribution of earthquakes compared to the plate boundaries. Use the key provided in the visual to identify the various features.

Visual 16-11: Oceanic Plate Subduction

This visual is a reproduction of Figure 16-24. Seismic data has revealed the structure of subduction zones in which thin, denser oceanic crust appears to be sinking beneath less-dense continental crust. Such a structure occurs at what are called *convergent plate boundaries*. Features associated with a convergent boundary often include a trench in the ocean bottom and a fringe of volcanoes produced by plumes of molten material rising from the melting ocean crust on the continental side of the trench. Emphasize that this illustration is a snapshot of a process that seems to have occurred in the past but now has all but stopped. The very slight movements seen today could not reasonably have produced the tectonic features present at most convergent boundaries within a young-earth model.

Visual 16-12: Island Arcs and Deep Ocean Trenches

This visual is a reproduction of Figure 16-25. Note how the entire Pacific Plate seems to be shoved in under the adjacent plates to the north, west, and south, forming trenches at the convergent boundaries. Adjacent to each trench there is a string of volcanic islands or volcanic mountain ranges. Similar features occur along much of the eastern margin as well.

Figure 16-23 is a world map showing the locations of the tectonic plates. Note that the margins of the continents often extend far beyond their natural shorelines. The close fit between the African, South American, and North American plates is even more dramatic when we consider the actual continental margins. All the major oceans have mid-ocean ridges where geologists believe sea-floor spreading is taking place.

What happens to the extra ocean crust in the sea-floor spreading model? It seems that the earth's surface would be completely wrinkled from all the new crust material piling up against the existing crust after supposedly millions of years of crust formation. Geologists have noted that many deep trenches exist in the ocean basins along continent margins and along strings of islands called **island arcs** (see Figure 16-23). They believe that as the relatively thin and denser oceanic lithosphere collides with a more massive but less dense continental crust, it bends downward and slides under the continental crust hundreds of kilometers into the mantle in a process called **subduction** (see Figure 16-24). Seismologists have recorded numerous earthquakes deep under the continental margins and island arcs where these subducting oceanic plates are thought to be melting in the mantle. The island arcs consist of strings of volcanoes that result from the newly melted magma, and many volcanoes exist near the continental margins where crust is believed to be subducting.

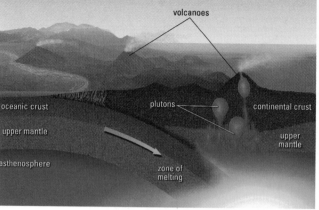

16-24 Subduction of an oceanic plate beneath a continental plate

16-25 The collision of the western edge of the Pacific Plate with other plates seems to be the cause for the existence of numerous volcanic islands and trenches in the Western Pacific Ocean basin.

In recent years, seismologists have used earthquake waves to produce three-dimensional images of the earth's interior, using a process similar to those for three-dimensional brain scans. They have discovered large, cooler masses of rock within the mantle below the places where the crust is believed to be subducting. These masses could be the remnants of subducted oceanic lithosphere. Warmer masses in the mantle that appear to be convection plumes below many of the mid-ocean ridges are believed to explain the sea-floor spreading in those regions.

16.16 Uniformitarian Plate Tectonics

With all this data now available, most geologists are in general agreement that Wegener was correct in his overall continental drift theory. They also now have a naturalistic, uniformitarian explanation for how the continents drifted and are continuing to drift today. This explanation is called the **plate tectonics** theory. Uniformitarian geologists believe that plate tectonics provide the forces that have formed and are forming the mountains and other features on the earth's surface. Because it supposedly explains so many geologic features and processes, plate tectonics has grown to become the underlying evolutionary theory of most physical geology today.

From Figure 16-23, you can see that the extensive mid-ocean ridge mountain system encircles most of the world, like the seams on a baseball. According to plate tectonics, these are regions of sea-floor spreading. Along the western coasts of North and South America, the Pacific, Nazca, and Juan de Fuca oceanic plates are subducting. Note that there are coastal fold mountain ranges all along the American west coasts, apparently due to the impact of these ocean plates moving against and under the continental plates. In addition, there are numerous volcanoes and faults extending the length of the western portions of the Americas caused by the stresses of these plate collisions. Elsewhere, the collision of the Indo-Australian Plate with the Eurasian Plate apparently raised the Himalayan mountain system. Nearly anywhere you look on the earth's surface where there are tall, jagged, volcanic, or folded mountains, there is usually a tectonic plate collision or subduction boundary nearby. In fact, nearly the entire rim of the Pacific consists of subduction zones that have produced numerous active volcanoes and major earthquakes. You will study these evidences of titanic forces at work in the next chapter.

Measured rates of plate movements vary from less than a centimeter per year up to more than 50 cm/y. Based on these rates, uniformitarian geologists estimate that Wegener's Pangaea broke up about 200 million years ago, which would account for the width of the Atlantic Ocean, which was formed entirely by sea-floor spreading. Major mountainous features such as the Rocky Mountains in western North America are thought to have begun forming 50–70 million years ago, while the Himalayan mountains supposedly formed relatively recently—around 40–50 million years ago. But are these ages reasonable? Even from a uniformitarian viewpoint, modern erosion rates exceed mountain building rates by a significant amount. Except where mountains are still growing, most mountains should have eroded to sea level long ago. Is there a more reasonable explanation for the origin of mountains and the other major features of the earth?

16-26 Large cool masses in the mantle may be remnants of subducted crust. Uniformitarian geologists believe the warm masses in the mantle may be causing sea-floor spreading.

Seismic tomography is the process of analyzing earthquake waves received by many seismic stations to produce three-dimensional images of the earth's interior.

Processes (physical, biological, chemical, social, or ecological) have inputs and outputs. Quite often the results of a process can affect what is coming into the process. If the process output slows down what is coming into the process, then a *negative feedback* situation exists, and eventually the process will stop. If, however, the output of the process increases the input to the process, the process accelerates and will continue to do so until something breaks or something else occurs to reduce or interrupt the input. This is called *positive feedback*. Such a situation is suggested for the runaway subduction process.

John R. Baumgardner (1944–) is an American physicist with the Theoretical Division of the Los Alamos National Laboratory in New Mexico. He specializes in supercomputer modeling of atmospheric and geophysical processes.

16-27 John Baumgardner, a creationary physicist who developed a biblically-based model for the origin of today's continents and ocean basins

You should realize that computer simulations cannot prove anything, no matter how good they are. A computer simulation is only as good as the programmer's ability to create a program that can mimic observed phenomena. In the case of historical geology, a simulation can only give a person more confidence that a particular process *could* have occurred in the past.

16.17 Creationary Plate Tectonics

Plate tectonics as a process for describing historical geology has been accepted by most uniformitarian geologists since only the early 1970s. Some creationary geologists agree with uniformitarians that there is ample geologic evidence for tectonic plates, subduction, and the existence of mountains and other features that seem to be associated with plate tectonics. They disagree on the time frame, the rate, and the underlying processes that produced the modern-day continents. The event and the conditions that must have occurred were nothing less than devastating to the earth—a catastrophe of unimaginable proportions, such as the Genesis Flood.

One physical process that could support such a biblically sound alternative to conventional plate tectonics has been studied and tested by a few creationary scientists since the early 1990s. It is known as "**runaway subduction**." This process involves a rapid slipping of oceanic crust under adjacent plates, moving at speeds of many kilometers per hour rather than just a few centimeters per year. The Creationist John Baumgardner is a pioneer in this field, having conducted modeling of the process using powerful supercomputers.

Baumgardner has proposed that the continents were created as essentially a large single land mass, similar to Wegener's Pangaea. He suggests that nearly the entire original ocean floor surrounding the continent was rapidly subducted as continents moved outward to replace it. Data collected by the Deep Sea Drilling Program indicates that most of today's ocean crust consists of rock from the Mesozoic and more recent parts of the uniformitarian geologic column (see Chapter 15). This means that, according to evolutionists, the existing sea floor is much younger than the oldest parts of the continental plates, which are believed to be from the Precambrian.

However, it seems best for a Creationist to interpret the Mesozoic and more recent parts of the geologic column in terms of sediment deposits that followed a massive amount of sea-floor spreading. Thus, according to the Flood model, most of the present ocean floor did not exist before the Flood. As noted earlier, three-dimensional images of the mantle obtained from analysis of earthquake data indicate immense cooler masses at great depth within the mantle, which may be remnants of the subducted ocean crust.

16.18 A Model for Catastrophic Plate Tectonics

How could the ocean floor be subducted rapidly? A volume of rock in the lithosphere that is relatively cool, but has a higher density than the mantle below it, could start to sink. As it sinks, friction heats the edges of the surrounding material through which the rock is moving. This heating causes the strength of the mantle material to decrease so that it begins to act like a lubricant, further increasing the rate of sinking. An increase in the rate of sinking causes further heating, and the rate of sinking soon becomes very rapid. This is called *thermal runaway*. Laboratory tests have confirmed that silicate rocks found in the crust react this way under extremes of temperature and pressure. Baumgardner has performed numerous computer simulations showing this sinking is possible. His model also shows that the apparent movements of the continents could have occurred within the one-year timeframe of the Genesis Flood.

16-28 An artist's conception of the Atlantic Ocean according to catastrophic plate tectonics a few days after the beginning of the Flood

Baumgardner's computer program modeling begins before the Flood, with the continents assembled in a pattern similar to Figure 16-21. To do the calculation, the computer must be supplied with the temperatures and other conditions of the plates at all the points. According to the computer simulation, when the ocean plates began to sink, huge rifts ripped through the original supercontinent. Baumgardner believes that the breaking up of the fountains of the deep mentioned in Genesis 7 represents fracturing of the crust and the start of runaway subduction. The individual continental plates pulled apart and began to move away from each other. At the center of the Atlantic Ocean basin and elsewhere, spreading zones and mid-ocean ridges developed. When the spreading was most active, these ridges were elevated in the spreading zone by the upwelling mantle. Some portions of the ridges may have briefly appeared above sea level. The global sea level was raised and caused the continents to be flooded. At the same time, the continental surfaces next to subduction zones dropped in elevation and were probably covered over with sediments. The whole physical arrangement of the earth was disrupted and changed in a short period of time as the continents spread apart. Thus Baumgardner calls his model **catastrophic plate tectonics**.

16.19 Problems with the Models

One difficulty that appears with both plate tectonics models concerns the locations of the subduction zones and ridge systems. For instance, the African Plate is bounded on the west by the Atlantic Ocean and the Mid-Atlantic Ridge and on the east by the Indian Ocean. There is no subduction zone on either side of Africa. To reach subduction zones, one must travel to the west coast of South America and, in the other direction, to the east of New Zealand. On the west coast of South America, the oceanic Nazca Plate is pushed toward and beneath the South American Plate. In the southwest Pacific, the Pacific Plate subducts under the Australian Plate.

It is impossible to effectively illustrate the initial events of the Flood based on the catastrophic plate tectonics theory. In this figure, we show from the vantage point of low-Earth orbit the Atlantic Ocean forming as the great fissure at its center is spewing lava, superheated steam, and volcanic ash into the atmosphere. The South American Plate is in the foreground and the African plate is in the distance. The steam billowing from the rent in the earth is quickly condensing. Some creationary scientists believe that the precipitation from the mid-Atlantic rift and other "fountains of the great deep" around the globe could have produced the rain that the Bible says lasted for nearly six weeks.

 Concepts Students Find Difficult

For a long time, Genesis 10:25 has puzzled some Bible students. It says that in the days of Peleg the earth was divided. In the early years of the Creation Science movement, it was popular to assume that Moses was talking about the continents drifting apart. That view lacks credibility if the Bible is studied carefully. The Hebrew word for *Earth* (*erets*) can mean the planet Earth, a landmass, or the people who inhabit the earth. Larry Pierce, a writer for AiG's *Creation Magazine*, has pointed out that Peleg was born in 2247 BC (Ussher's chronology). This date was about 100 years after the Flood. The Babylonian Empire was founded when Peleg was 13 years old, the Egyptian Empire when he was 60 years old, and the Grecian Empire when he was 160 years old. Peleg lived 239 years. This provides good reason to conclude that Genesis 10:25 means that the *people* of the earth were divided in Peleg's time. Don't fail to notice how these events tie together to confirm the genealogies of the Bible.

 Web Resource

Visit the BJU Press Online Resources/*SPACE AND EARTH SCIENCE* webpage. Under Chapter 16, click on the links *Peleg—AiG* or *Peleg—ICR* to go to sites that will give you more information about the breakup of the continents.

Dr. Walt Brown has noted that an ice age immediately following the Flood would have lowered mean sea level drastically. People would have been able to walk from continent to continent on dry land. During Peleg's life span, the Ice Age may have peaked and the glaciers may have begun to recede. Melting ice may have caused sea levels to begin rising to levels near what we see today. Thus, the continents would have been divided by the rising ocean waters, which could be another meaning of the Genesis 10 reference.

Hypotheses for secondary causes of the Flood have been proposed by D. Russell Humphreys and Robert Herrmann that involve a rapid expansion of space during the Genesis Flood and the associated cooling of the matter within it. These hypotheses could not only solve the cooling problem for CPT, they also could provide the supernatural trigger that initiated the runaway subduction process in the first place. Such hypotheses provide the bases for further investigation and computer modeling.

16-29 One model of catastrophic plate tectonics involves the entire Atlantic Ocean spreading away from Africa.

Thus, the African Plate's situation is difficult to picture. Many textbooks (including this one) show the thermal plume of mantle traveling vertically upward and spreading both east and west in a symmetric fashion at the Mid-Atlantic Ridge (see Figure 16-22). This is an oversimplification. The model contradicts the measured plate movements across the world. One proposal is that the plate east of the Mid-Atlantic Ridge is building westward at a given speed, half the rate at which the plate west of the ridge expands westward. Thus, new sea floor is still being produced near the ridge as the two plates separate due to their relative speed difference, but both plates are moving westward. Keep in mind that in standard plate tectonics theory the speeds of the plates are only centimeters or millimeters per year, while in catastrophic plate tectonics these speeds would have been much greater during the Flood.

A second problem specific to catastrophic plate tectonics, but not to slow plate tectonics, is the heat generated by the process. If the continents move rapidly, then frictional heat is expected to be generated rapidly as well. The seeming problem of heat generation is not insurmountable. Scientists have tested the strength of silicate rocks in the laboratory under widely varying conditions of heat and stress. They found that the strength of these rocks can be reduced by as much as a billion times. Such weakening in the lithospheric and asthenospheric rocks during runaway subduction could dramatically reduce the heat produced from friction. However, much heat would still be formed. Baumgardner and his assistants have calculated that the heat could have been removed by the boiling off of ocean water as superheated steam. In addition to cooling the newly formed crust, the resulting curtains of steam jets at the mid-ocean rifts could have blown water into the atmosphere sufficient to produce the rain of the Genesis Flood. The Bible mentions first that "the fountains of the great deep" were broken up, and then the rains began to fall (Gen. 7:11).

16.20 Conclusion

In *operational science* that deals with phenomena that happen today, valid hypotheses must be capable of being falsified. If we are investigating unrepeatable events occurring only in the past, then we are dealing not with laboratory science but with a branch of so-called "science" that attempts to describe how things began—*origins science*. We cannot repeat the creation of the universe in the laboratory. Therefore, operational science is incapable of distinguishing valid alternatives for the origins of things.

Historical geology reveals evidence in the earth's strata and structures that indicates certain things occurred, but the evidence is incomplete and it supports more than one possible origin. Biblical creationary scientists hold that it is impossible to arrive at proper conclusions about origins unless one accepts the scriptural account of Creation. If conventional geology denies this basic principle, it is doomed to failure from the start. Wrong assumptions lead to wrong conclusions. Frameworks that ignore the inspired Scriptures will never be complete, and they will also often be incorrect.

16C   Section Review

1. What is the geologic term for mountain building? What aspect of mountain building did geologists have trouble explaining?

2. What theory was originally accepted as the description of how mountains formed? What were its major problems?

3. List two kinds of scientific evidence that indicate to geologists that the present-day continents were once part of a large single continent before they drifted apart.

4. How many tectonic plates have been identified? Look at Figure 16-23 and then examine a globe. Identify the largest tectonic plate.

5. What is the modern uniformitarian model that explains continental drift? How long do uniformitarian geologists believe this process took?

6. What is one creationary model that accounts for continental drift? How long do creationary scientists say the process took? What evidence do creationary scientists have for this theory?

7. (True or False) According to the catastrophic plate tectonics model, nearly the entire original sea floor was subducted during the year of the Flood.

Here is another example of positive feedback. Wrong assumptions lead to wrong conclusions, which accelerate the production of more wrong assumptions and more wrong conclusions, resulting in the runaway deceit and wickedness the Bible predicts for the last days (2 Thess. 2:3–12). These effects are held in check (negative feedback) even now only by the Holy Spirit, through the preaching of the cross and the witness of born-again Christians.

Answers to 16C Section Review Questions

1. The geologic term for mountain building is *orogeny*. Early geologists had difficulty identifying the forces that caused fold and fault-block mountains to form. (§16.11–16.12)

2. The *geosyncline theory* was believed to be the process by which mountains formed. It could not adequately account for the necessary vertical and horizontal forces that uplifted and folded sedimentary layers. (§16.12)

3. Answers will vary. The text mentions the interlocking shapes of the continental margins, similar unique fossils found in widely separated continents that would have been adjacent in the proposed single continent, similar geologic features in formerly adjacent regions, and great mountain ranges that exist where continents collided. (§16.13)

4. Geologists have identified about fifteen principal tectonic plates. The Pacific Plate is the largest. (§16.15)

5. The modern model for continental drift is called *plate tectonics*. Uniformitarian geologists believe the process took place over at least the past 200 million years. (§16.16)

6. One creationary model for continental drift is called *catastrophic plate tectonics*. Creationary scientists believe that most of the motion took place during the year of the Genesis Flood. In addition to considering the continental shapes, fossils, and geologic features, these scientists look to the Bible as placing an upper limit on the amount of time available and to laboratory experiments that show runaway subduction is feasible. (§16.17–16.18)

7. True. (§16.17)

In Terms of Geology

Chapter Summary

- A mountain is a natural elevation of the earth's surface rising more or less abruptly from its surroundings to a summit.

- The difference between a mountain and a hill is determined by local custom.

- A mountain's height may be given by its elevation or its actual height.

- A set of associated mountains is called a mountain range; a set of associated mountain ranges is a mountain system.

- Mountains can be formed in four different ways: by deposition, erosion, folding, or faulting (or a combination of these processes).

- Volcanoes, sand dunes, moraines, and drumlins are all examples of depositional mountains.

- Erosional or residual mountains appear to have been cut by erosion from a plateau. Examples of erosional mountains are mesas, buttes, and monadnocks.

- Most fold mountains seem to have formed from mostly unhardened sediments. Fold mountains can be monoclines, synclines, anticlines, basins, or domes.

- Vertical movements of blocks of rock along faults produce fault-block mountains.

- Titanic forces are required to form fold and fault-block mountains. The apparent breakup, movement, and collision of continents in the past seems to be the most logical source for such forces. Several models have been proposed that explain mountain formation. The model that best explains most of the observed geologic formations in the crust is the plate tectonics theory.

- The uniformitarian theory of plate tectonics is based on the very slow rates of continental drift measured today. The theory requires at least 200 million years for the continents to have drifted to their current locations.

- A young-earth creationary model of plate tectonics, called catastrophic plate tectonics, accounts for the observed effects of plate tectonics rapidly taking place within the biblical timeframe of the Genesis Flood.

Answers to Chapter Review Questions

What Did You Learn?

1. The mountain's base is 3048 m − 2194 m = 854 m above sea level (10,000 ft − 7200 ft = 2800 ft). (§16.2)

2. The relief of the county is the difference between its maximum and minimum elevations: 688 m − 252 m = 436 m (2257 ft − 827 ft = 1430 ft) (§16.2).

3. Mount Everest does not look as impressive as some lesser mountains because its actual height is less than some other mountains, and because the mountains around it are nearly as high. (§16.2)

4. The largest mountain system in the world is the Mid-Atlantic Ridge. It is associated with

What Did You Learn?

1. The summit of a certain mountain is 3048 m (10,000 ft) above sea level. Its actual height is 2194 m (7200 ft). How high is its base above sea level?

2. The highest point in a certain county is 688 m (2257 ft) above sea level. The lowest point is 252 m (827 ft) above sea level. Find the relief of the county.

3. Why does Mount Everest not look as impressive as some lesser mountains?

4. What is the world's largest mountain system? What geologic feature is it associated with?

5. Who was the first to reach the top of Mount Everest? When was this accomplished?

6. What agent is believed to have formed Bunker Hill near Boston, Massachusetts? A 465 m high sand dune in Algeria?

7. What kinds of mountains show evidence for the operation of both upward and downward vertical forces in rock strata?

8. What was the first piece of evidence that indicated that modern-day continents might have been closer together in the past?

9. What is the term that describes the sinking of relatively dense oceanic crust below less dense continental plates? What theory is this process associated with?

10. What laboratory evidence convinced some creationary scientists that catastrophic plate tectonics was feasible?

True or False

11. Mountains on other planets and moons are called mountains because their discoverers think they are more mountain than hill.

12. Because of the volcano Mauna Kea, the island Hawaii has the greatest relief of any place on Earth.

13. Mount Ararat is a depositional mountain.

14. Rocks can bend slightly if a large, unopposed force is applied continuously over a long period of time.

15. Since rocks will fracture or crumble if a strong enough compressive force is applied, whether opposed or not opposed, massive overthrusts are probably impossible.

16. The land surrounding the San Andreas Fault in California is a good example of fault-block mountains.

17. Where uniformitarian geologists claim significant overthrusting of older rocks over younger has occurred, such as at Chief Mountain in Montana and the Matterhorn in Switzerland, the old and young strata in contact do not show any evidence of having been dragged across each other for hundreds of kilometers.

18. According to creationary scientists, mountains were formed during or shortly after the Flood and are now just wearing away.

19. Creationists should not depend on a theory such as uniformitarian plate tectonics to explain the features of the earth today.

What Do You Think?

1. Do valleys cause mountains, or are valleys a result of mountains?

2. How would you determine the actual height of an underwater mountain?

3. Why do drumlins occur in groups?

4. How did glaciers play a role in the American Revolutionary War?

5. For which human activities are mountain locations preferred over those in valleys or on flat land?

My Review Checklist

☐ I have carefully read the entire chapter.
☐ I have reviewed all of the photographs, illustrations, and graphs.
☐ I have reviewed all of my notes in the margins.
☐ I have reviewed and corrected the quizzes on this chapter.
☐ I have studied all of the vocabulary terms.
☐ I have had all of my questions answered.

---

the mid-Atlantic rift that was the source of spreading between the combined North and South American plates and the combined Eurasian and African Plates. (§16.3, 16.14)

5. Sir Edmund Hillary was the first person to reach the top of Mount Everest, on May 29, 1953. (Facet, p. 415)

6. Bunker Hill is a drumlin, which is a landform deposited by glaciers. The sand dune in Algeria is formed by the wind. (§16.5)

7. Certain types of fold mountains and fault-block mountains show the operation of vertical forces. (§16.7–16.9)

8. Several centuries ago, maps indicated to thoughtful men that the west coastlines of Europe and Africa seemed to correspond to the east coastlines of the Americas. (§16.13)

9. The movement of oceanic crust under continental crust is called *subduction*. Crustal plate subduction is associated with the plate tectonics theory. (§16.15)

10. Scientists discovered that the strength of silicate rocks decreased by a factor of a billion or more when subjected to the right combination of heat and stress. (§16.19)

True or False

11. True. (§16.1)

12. False. The relief of a region is the difference between the highest and lowest points within the region relative to sea level. While Mauna Kea is the world's tallest mountain as measured from its base, its base is well outside of the geographical limits of the island of Hawaii (marked by its shoreline). (§16.2)

13. True. (§16.5)

14. True. (§16.7–16.8)

15. True. (Facet, p. 423)

16. False. The San Andreas Fault is a strike-slip fault. Little vertical movement is associated with this fault. (§16.10)

17. True. (Facet, p. 423)

18. False. Careful GPS measurements at many mountains all over the world show that they are still growing. For example, nearly the entire Himalayan range is still rising, and Mount Logan in the Yukon seems to be growing slowly. Many volcanic mountains are continuing to deposit materials that add to their height. (§16.11)

19. True. No uniformitarian theory will be adequate to describe the origins of the geologic features observed today. However, the evidence that the theory attempts to account for can be interpreted from a biblical framework to support theories that are consistent with Scripture, such as catastrophic plate tectonics. (§16.20)

What Do You Think?

1. Some valleys have been formed by the removal of material by massive water erosion and glacial action. Many existing river valleys were formed this way. The surrounding higher elevations that remain may be classified as mountains. On the other hand, mountains that are raised by tectonic forces or by deposition will produce valleys between their elevated peaks.

2. The actual height is the difference in elevation between the mountain's peak and base. If it is assumed that elevations below sea level are negative, the difference will yield a positive actual height. Other answers are possible.

3. Drumlins formed under glaciers from the debris the glaciers picked up and carried along. Since advancing continental glaciers moved over great distances, the broad glaciers formed many drumlins.

4. Bunker Hill is a drumlin that was deposited by a glacier.

5. Answers will vary. Mountains are the preferred location for communication antennas. Mountains are also ideal for recreation such as climbing and downhill skiing. Mountains are used as cool vacation retreats during hot summers. Some mountains are good sites for wind-driven electricity generators.

Overview

Both earthquakes and volcanoes are phenomena that make humans feel insignificant and powerless against the irresistible forces of nature. Chapter 17 explores the tectonic processes that unleash the raw energy of the earth. It is a comfort to remember that God is sovereign over the universe He created and is in control of all of the events on the earth. It is humbling to realize that God in His sovereignty is the Author of calamities as well as blessings.

Section 17A introduces earthquakes as a direct consequence of the tectonic activity in the earth. Earthquake hazards are for the most part due to the inadequacy of human engineering and technology to deal with the effects of earthquakes. Earthquake locations can be pinpointed and their intensities can be measured, but accurate predictions of impending quakes still elude seismologists.

Volcano anatomy, emissions, and classifications are the focus of Section 17B. Volcanoes can be classified by their structure, activity, explosivity, and location.

Section 17C investigates the less dramatic but important processes involving heated groundwater. Geothermally heated groundwater produces hot springs and geysers and is becoming an increasingly important source of energy for man's use.

Schedule Summary

Section 17A: 2–3 periods

Section 17B: 2–3 periods

Section 17C: 1–2 periods

Investigation Summary

17G "Seismoscope"

17H "Finding the Epicenter of an Earthquake"

17I "Types of Volcanoes"

 Bulletin Board Ideas

1. Title your bulletin board "Volcanoes and Earthquakes." Put the *V* in *Volcanoes* upside down, and use orange or red tissue paper behind the letter to simulate an exploding volcano. Put the letters in the word *Earthquake* in a haphazard fashion. Fill out the bulletin board with appropriate pictures or news articles.

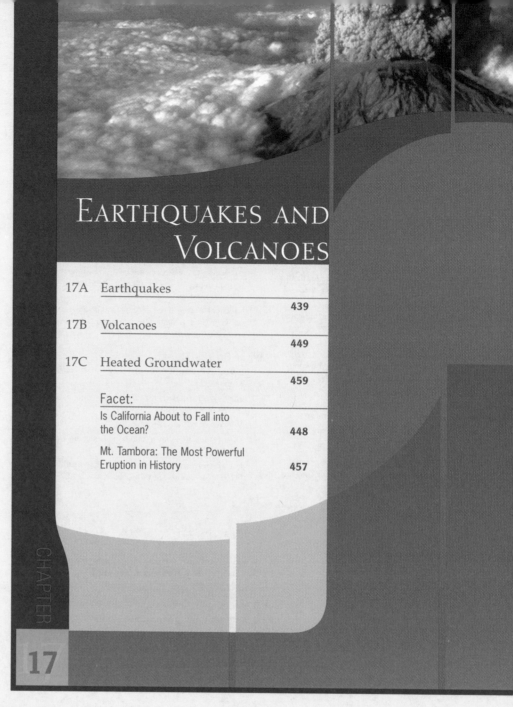

EARTHQUAKES AND VOLCANOES

CHAPTER **17**

SUGGESTED TEACHING SCHEDULE

DAY 0

Assignment

Reading: Section 17A-1 (§17.1–17.6), characteristics and hazards of earthquakes

DAY 1

Describe the forces that generate earthquakes. Compare and contrast an earthquake's magnitude and intensity. Illustrate how to locate an earthquake. Discuss the hazards of earthquakes and how to minimize them.

Assignment

Complete: 17A-1 Section Review Questions
Applications 17A, "Earthquake Effects"

Reading: Section 17A-2 (§17.7–17.9), earth waves and earthquake prediction

DAY 2

Describe the three types of earth waves. Examine how seismologists analyze earth waves to pinpoint the epicenter and focus of an earthquake and endeavor to predict future earthquakes. Discuss how certain preparations reduce the hazards of earthquakes.

Assignment

Complete: 17A-2 Section Review Questions
Applications 17B, "Earth Waves"

Reading: Investigation 17G, "Seismoscope"
Investigation 17H, "Finding the Epicenter of an Earthquake"

17A EARTHQUAKES

17.1 What Is an Earthquake?

Earthquakes and volcanism are geological events that occur mostly in the same regions, and both are currently thought to be related to plate tectonics. Both types of events indicate the instability of the earth's structure. People like to think of the earth they stand on as secure and solid. Those who have experienced a severe earthquake or have been near an erupting volcano may have second thoughts about the earth's stability.

An **earthquake** consists of a series of shock waves traveling through the earth. Some of these waves travel along the surface and others through the interior of the earth. Most earthquakes are too slight for a person to feel. Still, a few earthquakes each year shake the ground enough to frighten people nearby, and occasionally a strong earthquake near a city causes great destruction.

17.2 Locations and Causes of Earthquakes

As we discussed in Chapter 16, the plate tectonics theory states that the earth's crust is made of many large pieces called *plates*. Most plates are the size of a continent or larger. The plates are in motion; their speeds have been measured by sensitive instruments using lasers and mirrored satellites. Today, the plates are moving very slowly—from just a few millimeters per year to 50 centimeters per year. Some plates carry continents with them. The plates collide at their margins (edges), and the margin of one grinds past or slides under the other. The shock waves caused by sections of the plates colliding and subducting are most likely the major source of earthquakes. Fold and fault-block mountains (Chapter 16) are, in theory, a result of colliding plates, and a large portion of the earth's volcanoes are found along the margins of the plates as well.

17-1 Map showing the major earthquake belts of the world. Yellow lines represent plate boundaries, dots specify earthquake epicenters of varying depths, and black lines indicate transform faults.

The stresses of colliding plates produce cracks in the rocks of the crust called faults. If the blocks of rock on either side of the fault do not move, the fault is "locked." Moving tectonic plates continue to apply stress to the fault. The rocks will flex slightly, but as long as no slippage occurs the fault remains locked. Eventually, because of the excessive stresses, the rocks along the fault surface fracture like a stiff rubber band and the fault slips. As the rocks shift to their unstressed positions, the movement, called **elastic rebound**, produces waves of motion similar to sound waves in the earth that radiate from the point of slippage. Often, slippage in one location of the fault increases the strain on other locked portions of the fault, causing those sections to slip sometime later. These secondary earthquakes are called *aftershocks*.

2. Put a world map on a bulletin board and use straight pins to locate specific volcanoes or the epicenters of significant earthquakes. See Table 17-2 (p. 443) and Table 17-4 (p. 453) for more information. Post a picture or a news article related to that specific volcano or earthquake next to its location on the map.

3. Print out or update daily a map of your area with current earthquake data from the USGS National Earthquake Information Center. Use different-sized circles to indicate the magnitude of the quakes plotted on the map.

 Field Trip Ideas

1. Visit a local seismic station if there is one in your area, or contact the USGS to have a seismologist speak in your classroom.

2. If you live in the vicinity of a lava field or one of the extinct volcanoes in the U.S. West or Southwest, you can inspect lava dikes, sills, tephra, ash, and the various forms of solidified lava in these locales.

Objectives—Section 17A

Upon completing this section, students should be able to

- relate tectonic plate movement to earthquake and volcanic activity.
- compare earthquake intensity with Richter magnitude.
- relate the focus and epicenter of an earthquake.
- describe hazards caused by earthquakes.
- describe the characteristics of the three types of earth waves.
- analyze the possibilities of earthquake prediction.

 Review: Tectonic Plates

Figure 17-1 can be projected as an overhead image using Visual 16-10. Review the oceanic and continental plate features. Note the tectonic activity most evident at the margins of the convergent tectonic plates and along the mid-ocean ridges.

Since fold and fault-block mountains are a result of tectonic activity, these mountains can actually get higher. For example, Mt. Everest's height increases by about 6.1 cm (2.4 inches) per year.

DAY 3

Quiz—Section 17A, "Earthquakes"

Do Investigation 17G, "Seismoscope." Review with your students the instructions for Investigation 17H, "Finding the Epicenter of an Earthquake." They will complete this investigation as homework.

Assignment

Complete: Investigation 17H, "Finding the Epicenter of an Earthquake"

Reading: Section 17B-1 (§17.10–17.13), volcano anatomy and emissions

DAY 4

Illustrate the parts of a volcano and describe its gaseous, liquid, and solid emissions.

Assignment

Complete: 17B-1 Section Review Questions
Applications 17C, "Volcano Structure"

Reading: Section 17B-2 (§17.14–17.17), classifying volcanoes

DAY 5

Discuss four different ways volcanoes can be classified—by structure, activity, explosivity, and location.

Assignment

Complete: 17B-2 Section Review Questions
Applications 17D, "Volcano Activity"

Reading: Investigation 17I, "Types of Volcanoes"

DAY 6

Do Investigation 17I, "Types of Volcanoes."

Assignment

Complete: Applications 17E, "Famous Volcanoes"

Reading: Section 17C, "Heated Groundwater"

(schedule continued on p. 440)

Review: Inertia

We suggest that you review the concept of inertia discussed in §2.12 to describe how the flexibly supported mass of a seismic sensor would not move while the earth around it does.

Concepts Students Find Difficult

There may be some confusion encountered when researching earthquake intensity and the Richter scale on the Internet. Many websites state that each number in the scale is an increase of 10 in earthquake *strength*. This is incorrect. Actually, the *amplitude* of the earthquake waves increases by a factor of 10 with each Richter number. However, the energy of an earthquake wave increases by a factor of about 31.6 for each increase in Richter number.

A magnitude 10 earthquake releases as much energy as the entire population of the United States consumes in one year.

Review: Exponential Rates

Remind your students of other scientific concepts that change at an exponential rate, such as stellar magnitude (Chap. 3) and radioactive decay (Chap. 13).

Visual 17-1: Method for Determining Relative Earthquake Magnitude

Use this visual to demonstrate a graphical way of determining earthquake magnitude. Students may wonder why the time-distance and amplitude scales are not evenly divided. These are logarithmic scales that permit making interpolation evaluations such as this.

Modern seismic stations use computer algorithms that take into account the direction from which the waves arrived and the location of the epicenter to repeatedly refine the magnitude value. For example, the magnitude of the great Sumatra earthquake of December 2004 was revised downward and upward several times in the months following the quake as these and other factors were evaluated.

---

seismologist (size MAHL uh jist): seismo- (Gk. *seismos*—earthquake) + -logist (Gk. *logistes*—one who calculates)

Charles F. Richter (RIKH tur) (1900–1985) was an American seismologist who in 1935 first proposed the earthquake intensity scale that bears his name.

17-2 A seismograph of earthquake waves (top). A seismologist interprets the seismograph and prepares a report for distribution (bottom).

17.3 Earthquake Magnitude

In Chapter 13, we introduced earthquake scientists, called seismologists. They use special instruments called **seismographs** to detect and measure earthquake waves. The early seismographs consisted of a large mass attached to a flexible supporting system. A light beam reflecting off mirrors attached to the mass traced a line on a rotating drum covered by photographic paper. If the earth moved, the recording drum and support moved but the mass did not. The line on the paper thus became zigzagged instead of straight. The height of the "zigs" or "zags" showed the strength of the earthquake waves. A seismographic recording is called a *seismogram*. Modern seismographs still use large masses, but the instruments sense and display the motions of the earth using electronic and digital components, including personal computers. Data is transmitted over the Internet.

For many years seismologists have rated earthquakes by the **Richter scale**, named for Charles Richter. The scale was based on the height of the seismographic trace produced on Richter's recording drum. The scale indicates the energy released, or the **magnitude**, of the earthquake. The Richter scale is not a linear scale; that is, an earthquake of magnitude 4 does not have twice the energy of an earthquake of magnitude 2. Instead, each change of one on the scale multiplies the energy released by about 31.6. Thus, an earthquake of magnitude 3 has 31.6 times as much energy as a magnitude 2 earthquake. An earthquake of magnitude 4 has 31.6 times as much energy as a magnitude 3 earthquake and 31.6×31.6, or almost 1000, times as much energy as a magnitude 2 earthquake. Modern instruments record earthquakes using different magnitude scales that are keyed to the type of wave received. Because the news media and the public have become accustomed to hearing earthquakes rated on the Richter scale, seismologists will convert the readings back to the Richter scale format before giving a public report. They will also average the readings from several stations to get the final figure.

The Richter scale covers a wide range of earthquakes. An earthquake with a magnitude just over 0 barely registers on a sensitive seismograph. People can feel quakes with a rating of 3 or more. A magnitude of 6 or more is potentially destructive; a quake whose magnitude is more than 7 is a "major earthquake." A "great earthquake"

17-1	EARTHQUAKE RICHTER MAGNITUDES
<2.0	recorded; generally not felt
2.0–2.9	possibly felt by people
3.0–3.9	felt by some people
4.0–4.9	felt by most people
5.0–5.9	damage to poorly built structures
6.0–6.9	damage to well-built buildings
7.0–7.9	major earthquake; serious damage
8.0–8.9	great earthquake; extensive destruction near epicenter
>9.0	massive earthquake; regional destruction

DAY 7

Quiz—Section 17B, "Volcanoes"

Show how groundwater is heated and describe some geological features formed by groundwater that is heated by geothermal activity. Discuss the advantages and disadvantages of harnessing geothermal energy.

Assignment

Complete: 17C Section Review Questions
  Applications 17F, "Heated Groundwater"
  Selected Chapter Review Questions

DAY 8

Quiz—Section 17C, "Heated Groundwater"

Review for a chapter test.

Assignment

Study for a chapter test.

DAY 10

Test—Chapter 17

Assignment

Reading: Section 18A, "Weathering"

has a magnitude of 8.0 or more. The Richter scale is not just a 1 to 10 scale but is open-ended. The most destructive quakes usually have had magnitudes between 8 and 9. Calculations show that if an earthquake with a magnitude of 10 occurred anywhere on the earth, people around the world would feel the shaking.

17.4 Earthquake Intensity

An earthquake's destructiveness is indicated by its **intensity**. An earthquake's intensity depends not only on its energy but also on other factors such as its location underground, its distance, its duration, and the size and quality of nearby structures. Duration can make a great difference in damage. Some buildings can withstand a few seconds of violent shaking but fall apart after a minute or two. Earthquakes can last anywhere from a few seconds to several minutes, but most earthquakes last less than a minute. The 1994 Northridge, California, earthquake lasted 15 seconds. One earthquake in China in 1556, the deadliest in all recorded history, is said to have had shocks and major aftershocks that lasted two hours.

Disaster relief organizations and engineers are often more interested in how destructive an earthquake is in terms of its effect on human population centers. Therefore, a separate scale was developed similar to the Fujita-Pearson scale for tornado destructiveness (see page 243). The earthquake damage scale, called the Modified Mercalli Intensity (MMI) scale, is expressed in roman numerals from I to XII (see Appendix B8). An earthquake that leaves no visible damage receives a rating of one (I). The Northridge earthquake, which was rated only 6.7 on the Richter scale, was a ten (X) on the MMI scale. Because the Northridge earthquake occurred in a highly populated area, it did much more damage than many earthquakes with more energy as measured by the Richter scale, such as the 1964 "Great Alaskan Earthquake" (see Table 17-2), which was rated a nine (IX) on the MMI scale.

17.5 The Focus and Epicenter

The location of an earthquake is an important factor in how much damage it causes. The center of an earthquake's activity is called its **focus**. The focus is usually several kilometers underground, and it may be as much as 670 km (420 mi) below the earth's surface. The closer the focus is to the surface, the greater the damage the earthquake causes. The place on the earth's surface that is directly above the focus is called the **epicenter**. Although an earthquake is normally most severe at its epicenter, a strong earthquake may cause damage hundreds of kilometers from the epicenter. Deep rock formations and surface topography can sometimes focus and amplify seismic waves to produce greater localized damage.

17-3 Earthquake damage in Charleston, SC, in 1886 (top) and in San Francisco in 1906 (bottom)

epicenter (EP ih SEN tur): epi- (Gk: *epi*—upon) + -center

17-4 Diagram showing the relationship of the epicenter to the focus

Most likely, the aftershocks of the 1556 Chinese quake came so soon after the main quake that those who survived thought it was a single long earthquake.

A portion of the landmass of Tarzana, CA, experienced the highest accelerations ever recorded (1.78 Gs). The Northridge earthquake caused great damage up to 6 mi away.

Visual 17-2: Earthquake Focus and Epicenter

This visual is a reproduction of Figure 17-4. Note that shockwaves emanate in all directions from an earthquake. These are the waves that eventually pass through the earth to be received by sensors on the opposite side of the planet.

17.6 Earthquake Hazards

A hazard is defined as a source of danger; a risk is a possibility of injury or death to people and damage to property. Scientists and engineers cannot change an earthquake hazard, but when they thoroughly understand the hazards, there is much that can be done to reduce or even eliminate the risks.

Most earthquake deaths occur when a strong earthquake's epicenter is near a city. Two factors explain this. First, because people are concentrated in cities, more people are exposed to the earthquake's effects. Second, most earthquake-related deaths occur when manmade things fail, such as when buildings collapse or utilities are destroyed. Earthquakes seldom cause deaths directly. Thus, if an earthquake strikes a city, especially in a poor country where buildings may not be well constructed, the death toll is high. In contrast, if an earthquake strikes a modern city that enforces strict building codes and has well-designed and strongly built structures, there are fewer deaths.

17-5 The high death toll and great human suffering from the 2003 earthquake in Bam, Iran, was due to the lack of earthquake resistance in the building construction and materials.

In December 2003 an earthquake registering 6.6 on the Richter scale struck several cities in the southeast region of Iran. In well-built cities, the intensity of such a quake would be "potentially destructive." However, the buildings in the historic city of Bam were made of clay bricks cemented with clay and mud. The residential sector of over 200,000 houses was 80–90 percent destroyed. The 500-year-old Silk Road citadel of Arg-de-Bam was severely damaged. Nearly 40,000 people were killed; most were buried in the rubble or died of exposure in the winter cold following the disaster. The toll of deaths and injuries was directly attributed to the poor construction of the buildings. Today, architects have learned how to design buildings that can withstand earthquakes up to 8.0 on the Richter scale. For older buildings, they have learned how to reinforce structures that were not built to the highest earthquake resistance standards.

Another significant earthquake hazard in populated areas is fire. Earthquakes do not produce fire directly. However, the shaking and vibration breaks electrical wires in buildings and in underground and aboveground wires. Electrical arcing can easily ignite flammable materials. The most significant fire hazard comes from broken natural gas supply pipes in the ground and in buildings. The combination of leaking gas and arcing electrical wires can be explosive. To make the fire problem more difficult, broken water supply pipes in the ground can prevent fire fighters from quickly dousing fires. The greatest earthquake disaster in the U.S. occurred on April 18, 1906, when a section of the San Andreas Fault slipped up to 10 m (30 ft). The main earthquake lasted about one minute. However, the fires that resulted leveled the city of San Francisco, causing more than 3000 deaths and costing over $400 million in 1906 dollars.

Earthquakes, even distant ones, can be especially hazardous for people who live near the seashore. Earthquakes can trigger devastating waves called **tsunamis**. Tsunamis can travel as fast as 835 km/h

Stones of Witness

Shortly after the devastating earthquake in Bam, Iran, one American made the following observation:

> In the long term, we can help the people of Iran to live under a more responsive government, and we can help them build a 21st century economy—the kind of economy that produces enough wealth to allow them to build safer buildings.

Should a Christian agree or disagree with this statement? Why? (Quotation from *World Magazine,* January 10, 2004, p. 11)

tsunami (tsoo NAH mee): tsu- (Jap. *tsu*—harbor) + -nami (Jap. *nami*—wave) Tsunamis were once called *tidal waves*—but they have nothing to do with the tide.

Stones of Witness

A Christian should agree that loving one's neighbor as himself (Mark 12:29–31) involves maximizing the usefulness of God's world so that one's neighbor's life becomes safer, more meaningful, and more fulfilling. Such use of geologic knowledge and technology need not compromise the preaching of the gospel. Rather, it gives the believer a chance to share the gospel in a compelling way with people who otherwise might not listen.

(520 mi/h). In the open sea they are only about one meter high, but when they approach the shore, the shallower bottom lifts the waves much higher. Tsunamis can carry large ships moored in a harbor hundreds of meters inland. Following earthquakes in or near the ocean, tsunamis often claim more lives than other earthquake hazards. For example, following the 2004 Indian Ocean earthquake near the island of Sumatra in Indonesia, all of the more than 200,000 victims died directly or indirectly as a result of the numerous tsunami waves the quake generated. It is not known if any were killed by other earthquake hazards. Tsunamis also carry devastation far from the epicenter of the earthquake. One tsunami from the 1964 Alaska earthquake killed people as far away as California.

Earthquakes can also cause landslides and mudslides. These are particularly dangerous in mountainous regions, where sliding rock and debris can gain great speeds on steep slopes and then plow through villages and dwellings.

17-6 Tsunami flooding in Maddampegama, Sri Lanka, following an earthquake near the island of Sumatra in 2004

17-2			NOTABLE EARTHQUAKES	
Year	Location	Magnitude	Deaths	Interesting facts
526	Turkey		250,000	destroyed Antioch
1556	China	~8	830,000	deadliest earthquake in recorded history; said to have had shocks and aftershocks that lasted two hours
1692	Jamaica		2000+	Most of Port Royal vanished beneath the sea.
1755	Portugal	8.7	70,000	One fourth of Lisbon's population died. Quake was felt throughout Europe; first systematic scientific study of an earthquake
1811	New Madrid, Missouri	~8.1	(not reported)	A series of earthquakes hit a sparsely populated area of Missouri with no surface evidence of faults and shook more than $2/3$ of the country; formed Reelfoot Lake in TN; Mississippi River flowed backwards for several minutes near Memphis
1906	San Francisco, California	7.8	3000+	great destruction; broken gas and water lines hindered efforts to put out fires
1908	Sicily/Italy	7.2	70,000	worst of many earthquakes in this area; Hundreds of convicts escaped jail and terrorized Messina.
1920	China	8.6	200,000	destroyed 10 cities
1923	Japan	7.9	143,000	destroyed $3/4$ of Tokyo; Fires and broken gas lines ignited wood and paper homes. Oil tanks spilled into the harbor, causing an inferno. A rare "fire" tornado, created by rising hot air, swept through the city. The sea bottom in Sagami Bay dropped 1310 ft.
1939	Turkey	7.8	32,700	followed by floods and blizzards
1946	Japan	8.1	1330	generated 6 tsunamis; damaged 155,000 sq. km
1952	Kamchatka, Russia	9.0	None	about $1,000,000 in property damage from 13 m tsunamis
1960	Chile	9.5	5700	largest magnitude earthquake ever recorded

Death tolls for earthquakes and volcanoes are only estimates. These natural disasters often bring floods, disease, and starvation. Deaths due to loss of housing, income, and mental and physical hardships continue long after the event is over.

This table is provided for interest only. It is not necessary for students to memorize this information.

This table is provided for interest only. It is not necessary for students to memorize this information.

17-2 NOTABLE EARTHQUAKES (CONTINUED)

Year	Location	Magnitude	Deaths	Interesting facts
1964	Prince William Sound, Alaska.	8.3	131	largest magnitude recorded in U.S.; lasted nearly 4 minutes; generated 5 tsunamis—main one 67 m (220 ft) high; MMI IX
1970	Peru	7.9	66,794	quake-induced rock and snow avalanche swept 16.5 km, burying two towns
1976	China	7.5	255,000	deadliest earthquake in modern times; leveled city of Tangshan
1985	Mexico	8.0	9500	hit a large region, including Mexico City
1988	Armenia (USSR)	6.8	25,000	extensive destruction due to poorly constructed buildings
1989	Prieta Loma, California	6.9	64	hit San Francisco during the World Series; largest quake on the San Andreas fault since 1906
1990	Iran	7.7	40,000	destroyed 700 villages in Northwestern Iran
1994	Northridge, California	6.7	51	Portions of 11 major roads into Los Angeles had to be closed. Costliest natural disaster in U.S. history: $44 billion. MMI X
1995	Japan	6.9	5502	Epicenter occurred directly underneath the densely populated city of Kobe.
2001	India	7.7	20,103	severely damaged the state of Gujarat; over $5.5 billion in damage to buildings and infrastructure; many towns leveled
2003	Iran	6.6	40,000+	In the town of Bam, 90% of the buildings were destroyed.
2004	Sumatra/Indian Ocean	9.0	200,000+	The epicenter was about 50 kilometers from the nearest land. No known deaths from the earthquake directly; the deaths occurred in 12 nations surrounding the Indian Ocean as a result of the numerous tsunamis generated by the quake and the follow-on disease and famine.

17-3 EARTHQUAKES IN THE BIBLE

Occasion	Reference	Interesting facts
Ten Commandments	Exod. 19:18	Mt. Sinai quaked.
Judgment of Korah	Num. 16:31–33	The earth opened, swallowed the rebel Korah, his followers, and their families, and then closed again.
Battle of Gibeah	1 Sam. 14:15	A huge Philistine army fled in panic while the earth shook.
Elijah fled from Jezebel	1 Kings 19:11	Mt. Horeb trembled as the Lord passed by the prophet.
Reign of Uzziah	Amos 1:1 Zech. 14:5	Israel was hit by an immense earthquake, still famous approximately 300 years later.
Crucifixion	Matt. 27:51	The earth quaked, and the veil of the temple split in two.
Resurrection	Matt. 28:2	An angel descended from heaven and rolled the stone away from Christ's grave.
Philippian jail	Acts 16:26	A great earthquake shook the foundation of Paul's prison and loosed his chains.
Tribulation	Rev. 16:17–18	The greatest earthquake of all time will shake the world.

17A-1 Section Review

1. How large are tectonic plates?

2. What kind of instrument is used to measure earthquakes? How do scientists describe the energy and destructiveness of earthquakes?

3. What is the center of an earthquake's activity called? In what kind of geological structure is this center usually located?

4. What is the place on the earth's surface that is directly above the focus of an earthquake's activity called?

5. Name three hazards associated with earthquakes.

6. (True or False) Most deaths blamed on earthquakes are caused by people falling into cracks in the earth's crust opened by the earthquake.

17.7 Earth Waves

An earthquake sends out vibrations or waves in all directions from its focus. Seismographs in various parts of the world detect these earthquake waves. As with all waves, earthquake waves have *amplitude* and *wavelength*. These properties are used to describe the waves.

Some earthquake waves pass directly through the interior of the earth. Such waves are called *body waves*. The first body waves to be received at a seismic station are called **P waves**, where *P* stands for the Latin word *primus*, meaning *first*. P waves have relatively small amplitudes and short wavelengths. They travel quickly through the earth's interior and can penetrate solid and liquid rock. Therefore, P waves can travel through both the inner and outer core of the earth as well as the mantle and crust.

S waves are the *second* waves (Latin: *secundus*) to arrive at a seismic station. Secondary waves have a much larger amplitude compared to P waves. Thus, they are both stronger and slower than P waves. Like P waves, they travel through the earth's interior, so they are also body waves. However, seismologists discovered that S waves cannot pass through the core but are detected only in the lithosphere and the mantle. This makes geologists believe that at least the outer portion of the core is liquid.

The last waves to reach a seismic station are *surface* or *long waves* (also called **L waves**). They travel along the earth's surface rather than through its interior. L waves are the slowest but most destructive waves of an earthquake.

After studying waves from many earthquakes, seismologists realized that they can find the distance to an earthquake by examining the time between the arrival of P waves and S waves. The farther the station is from the epicenter, the longer the interval between the P and S waves. A single station can tell the distance to the earthquake's epicenter but cannot tell its location. Three stations recording the same earthquake can pinpoint its epicenter. Although computers determine epicenters now, a seismologist could draw a circle for each station with the center of the circle at the station and the radius being the distance from the epicenter of the earthquake. The point at which the three circles intersect is the epicenter. By studying the arrival times of all three types of waves, seismologists can calculate the depth of the focus from the epicenter.

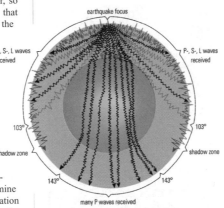

17-7 The wavelength of a wave is the distance between two sequential crests; its amplitude is the amount the earth is displaced from its rest position.

17-8 Earthquake waves and the direct paths they travel. The "shadow zones" are locations where no S or P waves are received by direct transmission through the earth.

P waves are longitudinal waves. The particles in the wave vibrate parallel to the direction of wave propagation.

P waves

S waves are transverse or shear waves. The particles in the wave vibrate perpendicular to the direction of wave propagation. Transverse waves are transmitted through elastic materials by the periodic vibration of the particles. Nonelastic materials, such as liquids and gases, cannot transmit transverse waves because their particles cannot vibrate back and forth in place as in an elastic solid. Early seismologists noted that S waves were not received from earthquakes on the opposite side of the earth within a certain number of degrees of the direction to the earth's center. As the model of the earth's interior was refined, seismologists suggested that the earth's core is at least partly liquid or has liquid-like properties, which would explain why S waves cannot be detected from those directions.

S waves

L waves propagate in a way similar to water waves. Particles move in a circular path perpendicular or parallel to the surface of the earth. The circular paths are largest at the surface and diminish in size deeper into the earth. This results in a rolling motion that can quickly break up roads and buildings. The vertical wavy motions are known as *Rayleigh waves* (named for the British physicist John William Strutt, Lord Rayleigh, who predicted the existence of this kind of wave in 1885). The horizontal wave motions are known as *Love waves* (named after A. E. H. Love, a British mathematician who developed the mathematical model for this kind of wave in 1911). Love waves are the fastest surface waves.

Rayleigh waves

Love waves

Visual 17-3: Paths of Earthquake Waves in the Earth

This visual is a reproduction of Figure 17-8. Point out that P waves are refracted through the core and change direction at the boundary of the core and mantle. The S waves are blocked by the core. These two effects produce the body-wave shadow zone that exists between 103° and 143° from the focus of the earthquake.

Answers to 17A-1 Section Review Questions

1. Tectonic plates vary in size. Some are as big as continents or even larger. (§17.2)

2. The instrument called a *seismograph* is used to measure earthquakes. The energy of an earthquake is described by the Richter magnitude scale. An earthquake's destructiveness is indicated on the Modified Mercalli Intensity scale. (§17.3–17.4)

3. The center of an earthquake's activity is called the *focus*. The focus is usually located in a *fault*. (§17.2, 17.5)

4. The place on the earth's surface directly above the focus of an earthquake is called the *epicenter*. (§17.5)

5. Answers will vary. The text mentions falling buildings and debris, electrocution, fires, and tsunamis. (§17.6)

6. False. Most deaths are caused by buildings that collapse, fires, ruptured gas mains, breaks in electric wires, and tsunamis. (§17.6)

Use a metal Slinky to demonstrate P and S waves. If you compress one end of the Slinky's coils, the compression travels down the length of wire, creating a longitudinal (P) wave. If you move your hand up and down, the wave travels perpendicular to the particles in the Slinky, creating a transverse (S) wave.

 Visual 17-4: Earthquake Wave Time-Delay Graph

This visual is a reproduction of Figure 17-9 (left). The trace is an example of how a seismograph can be used to determine distance to the earthquake's epicenter. The trace is assumed to start at the bottom of the graph when the earthquake starts. At 4 s the P waves arrive at the station, at 7.5 s the S waves are received, and at 9.5 s the L waves arrive. These times are matched to their corresponding curves, which produces a unique *surface* distance to the epicenter.

 Visual 17-5: Triangulation to Find an Earthquake Epicenter

This visual is a reproduction of Figure 17-9 (right). For any given station, all that can be determined is the distance to an earthquake. Therefore, a minimum of three stations must receive the earthquake signal in order for seismologists to unambiguously determine the epicenter.

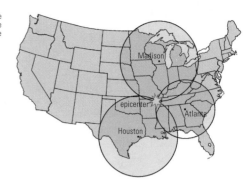

17-9 The length of time between the arrival of S and P waves is used to calculate the distance between a seismic station and the epicenter (above). The epicenter of an earthquake is determined by using observations from at least three seismic stations (right).

Long strike-slip faults between tectonic plates or between sections of the same plate are also called *transform faults*. While such faults may be visible on the surfaces of continents, they are most numerous deep in the oceans where they cross mid–ocean ridge mountain systems.

17-10 Aerial view of the San Andreas Fault in the Carrizo Plain area of central California

17.8 Faults and Earthquakes

Faults are a feature of the earth's surface often associated with earthquakes. A fault, as described in Chapter 16, is a crack in rock where the rock has moved. Some faults are only a few centimeters long; others are hundreds of kilometers long. Scientists of the nineteenth century thought that faults somehow caused earthquakes. Later seismologists thought that earthquakes caused faults. Today they believe that neither is the cause of the other because both are caused by the movement of tectonic plates.

The majority of felt earthquakes occur within 70 km (45 mi) of the earth's surface. These earthquakes often occur along faults that are visible on the surface. The most famous surface fault is the San Andreas Fault in the western portion of southern California. It is a strike-slip fault between the Pacific and North American tectonic plates. Earthquakes that are deeper than 70 km cannot usually be felt but are measured by seismographs. These medium and deep earthquakes are believed to occur along the margins of a tectonic plate that is in the process of subducting under another plate.

17.9 Earthquake Prediction

Seismologists are trying to develop accurate methods for predicting earthquakes. A few days' or hours' notice would do little to save buildings, but it does dramatically reduce the number of fatalities and injuries in a major quake. Intensive research throughout the world has gone into reaching this goal. Seismic hazard mapping has identified most of the faults in earthquake-prone areas. Instrumentation records seismic activity in many places, giving seismologists the opportunity to analyze patterns and learn what they mean. A great deal is learned each time there is an earthquake in an instrumented area, but reliable forecasting of earthquakes is probably years away.

An ideal prediction of an earthquake would specify where, when, and with what magnitude an earthquake will occur. Seismologists know what areas are most likely to have earthquakes. Interestingly, almost nine-tenths of all earthquakes occur in the Circum-Pacific and Alpine-Himalayan volcano belts. The remaining one-tenth of earthquakes may occur anywhere on the earth. These two natural disasters—earthquakes and volcanoes—seem to be related; in fact, erupting volcanoes often trigger earthquakes, and earthquakes sometimes precede volcanic eruptions.

To give crude predictions of earthquakes, seismologists study the history of areas with faults. For example, they have discovered that a major earthquake strikes San Francisco about every 150 years. The city's last major earthquake was in 1906 and had an estimated magnitude of 7.9–8.3. Although there was an earthquake registering 6.9 in 1989 with an epicenter near San Francisco, it was not strong enough to be the expected major quake. However, this kind of prediction is imprecise and unreliable. Earthquakes do not follow schedules rigidly; they may be "early" or "late." Furthermore, a city cannot evacuate for an earthquake when seismologists do not know for sure even what year it will occur.

17-11 Collapsed overpasses of Interstate 5 in California as a result of the Northridge earthquake in 1994

Another way of predicting earthquakes from the history of a fault is to notice what areas have not had an earthquake recently. If major earthquakes have occurred all along a fault except in one area, this seismically inactive part of an active fault, or *seismic gap*, may be due for an earthquake. However, the seismic gap may be less earthquake-prone than its surroundings. So, again, prediction is imprecise and unreliable.

The major difficulty in predicting earthquakes is that seismologists do not fully understand their cause. Plate tectonics may help to explain why volcanoes and earthquakes occur and where they are likely, but so far it does not help to predict when they will occur. Such prediction requires more than the current knowledge of rocks a few kilometers into the lithosphere. With our current knowledge we cannot even be sure that the accepted theories concerning earthquakes are correct.

Because the prediction of earthquakes continues to be a difficult problem, more emphasis is being given to preparation for earthquakes. Geologists have produced maps showing locations of seismic gaps. It is thought that these fault zones may be storing up energy that may be released suddenly in a large quake. Planners are encouraged to place important facilities such as hospitals, fire departments, and schools far away from land and soil formations that can amplify the effects of earthquakes. Strict building standards are developed and followed for buildings that must be built within potential quake areas. Where the ground is seismically unstable, building is prohibited. Through these and many other ways, man uses the wisdom God has given him to avoid hurt to his fellow creatures and thus demonstrates yet another way to fulfill the Creation Mandate.

 Concepts Students Find Difficult

Students should understand the following two things: (1) Earthquakes can happen in regions where no fault is visible on the surface of the earth. Tectonic plates are relatively thin membranes of rock moving under the influences of innumerable forces imposed from all sides of the plate and from underneath. Present and past stresses that routinely cause rents and buckles build up within the plates themselves far from the plate boundaries. This is the source of mid-plate earthquakes. (2) The fact that a moderate earthquake takes place in a certain region does not mean that a violent earthquake cannot happen in the same location.

Certain land formations and conditions can magnify the effects of an earthquake. For instance, unconsolidated landmasses, such as deposits of glacial debris or even fill emplaced by humans, can turn into a mass that shakes like Jell-O or flows like a liquid when exposed to continuous shaking for a short period of time. This behavior is called *liquefaction*. Land deposits such as these are not good sites on which to erect a building. Much of the damage caused by the 1989 Loma Prieta earthquake near San Francisco was due to liquefaction of fill soil under many structures.

FACETS OF GEOLOGY

Is California About to Fall into the Ocean?

California, known as a rich land of opportunity, is built on what is probably the most earthquake-prone land in America. A system of fractures over 1300 km (800 mi) long, including the famous San Andreas Fault, slices through the state, showing evidence of past and possibly imminent movement. Ignoring the signs of potential danger, many millions of people have built their homes along this and many other faults in California. Hospitals, schools, dams, highways, bridges, and other structures of modern civilization are located along both sides of the San Andreas Fault and the faults associated with it.

This system of faults separates a sliver of southern California from the rest of America. That sliver of California, attached to the Pacific Plate, is moving northward at more than 5 cm a year relative to the North American Plate that contains the rest of California. The potential hazards of this fault movement arise not so much from where the fault slips but where it *doesn't* slip. There are segments of the fault that appear to be locked, which could indicate that the fault is building significant stresses that

may be released only in the form of a large earthquake in the future. Pressure has been building for more than a decade at two specific points along the fault, near the populous cities of San Francisco (last hit in 1989) and Los Angeles (last major quake in 1994).

Damage from such a quake may be greater along the coast, where unstable cliffs have already caused landslides. Housing developments have been built right up to the edge of some cliffs. A major earthquake could break off huge chunks of these cliffs and send them and the houses tumbling into the ocean.

The people on both sides of the fault experience over a thousand tremors each year, but no one knows exactly when the "big one" will strike. Modern efforts to understand and predict earthquakes are more than an academic interest to Californians. Hundreds of sensitive instruments operate around the clock in pits, tunnels, and holes near the fault. They attempt to measure surface changes that indicate the build-up of tension, changes in gravity and magnetism, or creeping land and tilting earth. Sophisticated lasers measure minute bulges in the

earth's surface, as little as 2 mm over a 16 km distance. In 2004, a drilling project was begun in Parkfield, California to investigate the materials and deep structure of the San Andreas fault system.

Geological studies indicate that the "big ones" near Los Angeles and San Francisco have occurred on an average of once every 150 years. Yet no one knows when God will allow another. Past major quakes near Los Angeles have occurred as much as 275 years apart. Nor do we have any solid evidence that earthquakes have repeating cycles. Perhaps one will never hit again. Modern instruments have measured a tremendous build-up of tension, only to see that tension in a fault can suddenly subside without an earthquake.

So, is California about to fall into the ocean? This question is a somewhat humorous acknowledgment that the area is unquestionably prone to major quakes. From our understanding of the underlying plate tectonics, it seems highly unlikely that anything as drastic as California falling will occur, since the ocean floor is only a little deeper than the surrounding land.

Facet Summary: Is California About to Fall into the Ocean?

This Facet highlights the extensive fault system in California that has seismologists expecting a "big one" in that area. Use this opportunity to discuss experiences students have had with earthquakes. There are no vocabulary terms in this Facet.

17A-2 Section Review

1. List the types of shock waves that are produced by an earthquake.

2. Which structure inside the earth does not transmit S waves? What does this imply about the nature of at least part of this structure?

3. What kind of fault is the San Andreas Fault?

4. Why is it difficult to predict earthquakes? How do seismologists determine which locations have the greatest likelihood of earthquakes?

5. What tectonic activity occurring around the rim of the Pacific Ocean could contribute to numerous earthquakes in this region?

6. What human activity is more effective than prediction in reducing the number of deaths due to earthquakes? Give two kinds of actions that this may involve.

7. (True or False) P waves are the most damaging because they are the primary earthquake waves.

17B VOLCANOES

17.10 What Is a Volcano?

Almost everyone has heard of volcanoes—the mountains that erupt. Our English word *volcano* comes from Vulcano Island, a now-dormant volcano in the Mediterranean Sea. This island was named for Vulcan, the Roman god of fire. A **volcano** is a landform built up by solidified molten rock that has come to the earth's surface through a vent from a source of magma deep in the earth.

Volcanologists (volcano geologists) believe that most volcanoes are associated with the movement and heating of tectonic plates by the mantle beneath. As mentioned in Chapter 16, sea-floor spreading allows hot material from the mantle to come to the top of the oceanic crust in long oceanic rift zones. Many volcanoes can be found in these zones. The crust at the subducting edges of the plates is believed to be carried downward and remelted. The resulting plumes of magma rise to form volcano systems that parallel boundaries where plates collide. Other volcanoes seem to be associated with extremely hot mantle plumes that remained relatively stationary as tectonic plates moved over them. These volcanoes are found as strings of islands across an otherwise intact area in the middle of an oceanic tectonic plate. The Hawaiian Islands are an example of such a chain.

When molten rock from deep within the crust near the Moho melts, it works its way upward through faults and joints in the overlying rocks. The magma can be hot enough to melt out large spaces called *magma chambers* in the rock as deep as 50 km (30 mi), although they are often much closer to the surface. Once the magma forces its way through the surface rocks, it quickly widens the hole and forms a **vent**. The magma flows through the vent onto the earth's surface, where it is then called **lava**. Ejected lava may solidify in many ways during eruptions as it accumulates around the vent, thus

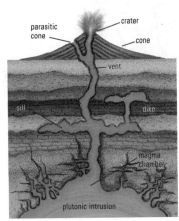

17-12 Sectional view of a volcano

Labels: parasitic cone, crater, cone, vent, sill, dike, magma chamber, plutonic intrusion

Objectives—Section 17B

Upon completing this section, students should be able to

- illustrate the anatomy of a volcano.
- categorize liquid, solid, and gaseous volcanic emissions.
- classify volcanoes based on the structure of their cones.
- compare active, dormant, and extinct volcanoes and state why these categories are not distinct.
- explain how a volcano's explosivity is assessed.
- classify volcanoes based on their location.

 Additional Resources

Check your local library for videos or DVDs on volcanoes. Videos by National Geographic, NOVA, and Nature generate interest and are helpful for showing your students footage of erupting volcanoes. You should scan programs from these sources first for objectionable content.

 Visual 17-6: Volcano Anatomy

This visual of the cross-section of a composite volcano illustrates most of the volcanic features described in this section. Note that high-pressure magma tends to force its way into adjacent strata of sedimentary rocks to form sills and dikes.

Answers to 17A-2 Section Review Questions

1. An earthquake produces three kinds of waves—P (primary) waves, S (secondary) waves, and L (long or surface) waves. (§17.7)

2. S waves do not pass through the *core*. This seems to indicate that at least part of the core is liquid. (§17.7)

3. The San Andreas Fault is a *strike-slip* (or *transform*) *fault*. (§17.8)

4. It is difficult to predict earthquakes because their causes are not fully understood. Seismologists plot the epicenters of earthquakes on maps. With time, they can see patterns of epicenters that reveal the locations along faults where earthquakes have not occurred and may be building up stress (seismic gaps). (§17.9)

5. The Pacific Plate is slowly subducting under other plates surrounding the Pacific basin, which produces numerous earthquakes. (§17.8, 17.2, Chap. 16)

6. Preparing for earthquakes is more effective than predicting them. Preparing can involve identifying where earthquakes occur and measuring their frequencies and strengths, avoiding building important facilities in quake-prone areas, increasing building-code standards for structures in quake zones, and avoiding building in areas that have unstable soils or features that otherwise increase the effects of earthquakes. (§17.9)

7. False. L (surface) waves are the most damaging because of the wavelike motion that these waves give to the earth's surface. (§17.7)

caldera (kal DEHR uh)

17-13 Night eruption of the stratovolcano Longuimay in Chile. Notice the glowing avalanches, bombs, cinders, ash, and lava ejected.

17-14 Glowing avalanches or pyroclastic flow on Parícutin

Vesuvius (vuh SOO vee us)

Montserrat (MOH sehr AH)

Pyroclastic flows are also called *nuée ardente*, which is French for "fiery cloud."

lahar (lah HAR): (Indonesian. *lahar*—a mud-flow of volcanic ash mixed with water)

fumarole (FYOO muh ROHL): (L. *fumarium*—smoke chamber)

building a **volcanic cone**. An especially tall or active volcano may develop one or more *parasitic vents* and cones in the side of the main cone or beside it.

At the top of the volcanic cone is a depression called a **crater**. Craters may be of varying sizes, depending on the violence of the eruptions. Sometimes an immense explosion blows away the upper portion of the cone, or it collapses into the emptied magma chamber beneath the cone. Either event can form a huge depression called a **caldera**, which can be many kilometers in diameter. Often the caldera fills with water, especially if the volcano is an island. Crater Lake, Oregon, is an example of a water-filled caldera.

VOLCANIC EMISSIONS

17.11 Gaseous Emissions

While volcanoes are known for their emission of lava, they emit a variety of other materials as well. These materials include gases, liquids, and solids. All these materials come from the magma within the earth.

Magma contains many gases dissolved in the molten rock. These gases separate from the magma due to the reduction in pressure as the magma approaches the surface or emerges from the earth—much like a bottle of soft drink fizzes when the cap is removed. Often the first sign of a volcano's eruption is the emission of gases.

Sometimes a volcano emits a mixture of hot solid particles suspended in water vapor or other gases. This hot mixture, called a **glowing avalanche**, is so heavy that it flows rapidly down the volcano's slope instead of rising into the air. Also called a *pyroclastic flow*, it can move at speeds up to 150 km/h (93 mi/h) and contain gases at temperatures from 100–800 °C (212–1472 °F). It suffocates or incinerates everything in its path. This type of eruption from Mount Vesuvius destroyed the cities of Herculaneum and Pompeii in Italy in AD 79. More recently, 20 people were killed in a glowing avalanche from the Soufriere Hills volcano on the island of Montserrat in the Caribbean in 1997. Such flows are called glowing avalanches because at night the entire flow glows a dull red.

Volcanoes emit large quantities of superheated water vapor. Although these emissions are usually harmless, they can have tragic consequences on a snow-capped volcano. The 1985 eruption of Nevado del Ruiz in Colombia was mostly steam, but it melted some of the snow. This melted snow caused a volcanic mudslide, called a **lahar**, that buried an estimated 23,000 people. A lahar is often compared to a flow of mixed concrete and can contain large boulders and rocks of various sizes. Lahars can also result from heavy rain on a hillside deposit of uncompacted volcanic ash, or when the wall of a crater lake fails, releasing the water down the slope.

Fumaroles are vents in the ground where steam and other gases from volcanic activity escape. Carbon dioxide escaping from fumaroles can be dangerous. Since it is a dense gas (about 1.5 times as dense as air), carbon dioxide can collect in depressions in the ground and form a deep layer that displaces atmospheric oxygen. Death Gulch in Yellowstone National Park is such a place where carbon dioxide collects. On especially calm days, grizzly bears and other animals have suffocated there.

17-15 These fumaroles in the East Rift Zone of Hawaii are active.

17.12 Liquid Emissions

When most people think of a volcano, they picture red-hot lava flowing down the mountain's side. Most volcanoes emit lava at one time or another. The type of magma that supplies the volcano determines what percentage of its emissions will be lava. Thin, runny magma is more likely than thick magma to remain fluid enough to flow as lava. Although lava is frightening, it causes fewer deaths than other types of volcanic emissions. Since lava seldom flows faster than a fleeing person can walk, it is easy to avoid.

Lava solidifies in a variety of ways, depending on its composition and where it cools. Basaltic lavas that have low silica content tend to be runny and flow great distances at speeds up to 30 km/h (19 mi/h) near the vent. As this kind of lava cools, it forms a skin that wrinkles as the still-molten lava within continues to flow. The wrinkled, ropey surface that forms is called a *pahoehoe* flow. Another kind of basaltic lava flow moves very slowly, forming a splintered, sharply fractured surface as the flow moves downhill. This kind of lava produces an *'a'a* flow. Gases released from the thick 'a'a lava often form large bubble-like voids and sharp edges. High-silica-content (felsic) lavas tend to be lighter in color and very thick in consistency. They flow like cold molasses, with speeds measured in meters per day.

If lava erupts under water, the exterior of the flow cools immediately and forms a shell. Then the molten lava inside the flow bursts through the shell, forming a new shell. This process is repeated,

pahoehoe (pah HOY hoy): (Hawaiian) Pahoehoe is a fast-flowing lava that, when it hardens, has a shiny surface and an appearance similar to twisted rope.

'a'a (AH AH): (Hawaiian) 'A'a is a slow-flowing lava that, when it hardens, has a rough broken surface with sharp pieces of rock projecting from the flow.

17-16 An advancing lava flow, called pahoehoe (top); an 'a'a lava flow slowly advances, displaying the rough, broken texture of such lava (middle); mafic (balsatic) lavas tend to be thin and runny (bottom)

The Ol Doinyo Lengai volcano in Tanzania has a very unusual type of lava—*natrocarbonatite* lava. This lava has extremely low silica content, and its viscosity is similar to that of water. Its unusual content allows it to be a liquid at much lower temperatures. In the daytime the lava appears black, and at nighttime the lava appears dull red. Rain turns the lava white as the result of a chemical reaction between the lava and water.

17-17 Pillow lava forming under water (top). Shiprock is the remnant of a volcano neck after the overlying tephra and other pyroclastic materials eroded away (top right). Cinders and ash darken the snow atom Mt. Ngauruhoe in New Zealand (bottom).

forming a flow that looks like a stack of pillows. Consequently, flows that form under water are called *pillow lava*. Because it occurs only under water, historical geologists can use pillow lava to identify where ancient volcanoes erupted under water.

17.13 Solid Emissions

When volcanoes erupt explosively, they emit ash, cinders, bombs, and sometimes large chunks of rock. These forms of solidified lava are together called **pyroclastic materials**. They can range in size from microscopic dust particles to chunks weighing several tons.

When gas-laden lava explodes in the vent of a volcano, the fine mist of solid lava particles falls as **ash**. Volcanic ash is made up of tiny angular glassy fragments and somewhat resembles the dusty ash that comes from burning wood. The size of these particles is between microscopic dust and about 2 mm. An accumulation of loose ash is called **tephra**. Most of the people who died in the 1980 eruption of Mount St. Helens were suffocated by volcanic ash. This is a common cause of death from volcanoes.

Cinders are like ash but are larger, from 2 to 64 mm (0.1 to 2.5 in.) in diameter. Larger blobs of lava fall as blocks that can vary from baseball-size to the size of a house. **Bombs** are blocks of lava that solidify in a streamlined shape as they fly through the air. They usually fall within 3 km (2 mi) of the volcano's vent, but the other kinds of pyroclastics can travel much farther. Clouds of ash can travel all the way around the world and pose a significant hazard to aircraft that fly through them.

Explosive volcanoes are more dangerous than volcanoes that allow lava to seep out because their emissions travel faster and are less predictable. They also often destroy the volcano. Mount St. Helens lost nearly 400 m (1300 ft) of its height in its 1980 explosion; volcanic islands often disappear beneath the ocean as a result of large explosive eruptions. Volcanic explosions can also be extremely loud. The 1883 destruction of Krakatoa, Indonesia, by a volcanic explosion was heard as far as 4600 km (2900 mi) away.

17-4	NOTABLE VOLCANIC ERUPTIONS			
Date	**Name**	**Location**	**Deaths**	**Interesting facts**
1650 BC	Santorini	Aegean Sea	Unknown	estimated to be five times more powerful than any eruption on record; possibly destroyed the Minoan civilization on the island of Crete
AD 79	Mt. Vesuvius	Italy	3360	buried the Roman "pleasure cities" of Pompeii and Herculaneum; archeologists found the ancient cities frozen in time
1669	Mt. Etna	Sicily	Unknown	explosive eruption that damaged several towns; over 150 eruptions (most not explosive) since ancient times
1783–84	Mt. Laki	Iceland	10,000	a fissure 24 km long appeared and erupted for 8 months; lava flow covered 580 km² (226 mi²); poisonous gases killed livestock and caused crop failure; one-forth of the population died of starvation
1815	Mt. Tambora	Indonesia	92,000	deadliest volcanic explosion on record; 10,000 direct deaths and 82,000 deaths from starvation and disease; ash in the atmosphere turned 1816 into the world's first "year without summer"
1873–74	Mauna Loa	Hawaii	None	world's largest active volcano; this eruption lasted 1.5 years; noted for beautiful fountains of lava flows
1877	Cotopaxi	Ecuador	1000	one of the tallest active volcanoes; melted snow on one slope caused a deadly lahar that streamed 100 km (60 mi)
1883	Krakatoa (also Krakatau)	Indonesia	36,000	²/₃ of its island disappeared; ash and smoke were blown 80 km (50 mi) high; sound was heard over 4600 km (2900 mi) away; most deaths caused by tsunamis
1902	Mt. Pelée	Martinique, West Indies	29,000	city of St. Pierre destroyed by a glowing avalanche; only two people survived (a prisoner in a thick-walled cell and a merchant barricaded in his store)
1943–52	Parícutin	Mexico	3	within only a year a farmer's cornfield turned into a mountain 336 m (1100 ft) high; 3 people killed by lightning caused by the pyroclastic eruption
1963	Surtsey	Iceland	None	formed a new island within weeks; lagoon, sand beaches, and white cliffs formed within a year
1980	Mt. Saint Helens	Washington	57	North America's greatest recorded eruption; the lateral blast had a velocity of 482 km/h (300 mi/h); minor eruptions continued in 2004
1985	Nevado del Ruiz	Colombia	23,000	lahars caused by melting of the snowcap devastated river valleys; 75% of the people in the town of Armero were killed
1991	Mt. Pinatubo	Luzon Is., Philippines	338	explosive eruption 95 km (60 mi) from Manila; closed two U.S. military bases
–2004	Stromboli	Italy	none	longest continuously erupting volcano known; has been erupting with low intensity since before Roman times; called the "lighthouse of the Mediterranean"

This table is provided for interest only. It is not necessary for students to memorize this information.

Visual 17-7: Types of Volcanoes

This visual is a reproduction of Figure 17-18 on page 455. The diagrams give some idea of the general profile of the three types of volcanoes. Their heights are not in proportion to their breadths, and their sizes are not in proportion to each other. Dimensions given are typical.

17-18 Types of volcanoes: Surtsey (above) is a shield volcano off the coast of Iceland. Mount Ranier (below left) is an example of a composite volcano. A cinder cone in Lassen National Park, California (below right). Sample profiles of shield, composite, and cinder cones are shown on the opposite page.

17B-1 Section Review

1. How does a volcano differ from other kinds of depositional mountains?

2. Sketch a typical volcano, the earth's surface, and the magma reservoir. Label its features.

3. What are the two types of nonlava flows caused by volcanic activity that can be very destructive? How are they different? How are they similar?

4. Besides lava in the liquid form, what else may be emitted by a volcano?

5. What are vents in the ground where steam and other gases escape called?

6. What are two common types of solidified lava found around volcanoes erupting on land? Which type of lava is found only with underwater eruptions?

7. Where and when was the largest known volcanic explosion within historical times?

8. (True or False) The most significant hazard from most volcanoes is the flow of lava down its slopes.

CLASSIFYING VOLCANOES

17.14 Classified by Structure

To study volcanoes, volcanologists group similar volcanoes together. Three major ways to classify volcanoes are by *structure*, by *activity*, and by *explosivity*.

A volcano's shape and composition depend on the type of material it emits. Some volcanoes emit mostly lava, some emit mostly ash and cinders, and others emit lava and ash in alternating eruptions.

Volcanoes that discharge mainly runny lava in relatively quiet eruptions are called **shield volcanoes**. Like a shield, they are dome shaped and have relatively flat slopes. The Hawaiian Islands are classic examples of shield volcanoes. Mauna Loa has a greater area within its base on the sea floor than any other volcano in the world. Nearby Mauna Kea holds the world's record for actual height for any mountain. From its underwater base it stands over 10,000 m (33,000 ft)

Answers to 17B-1 Section Review Questions

1. A volcano grows from the emission of various forms of lava that are deposited around a vent in the surface rock connected to a source of magma deep under ground. Other depositional mountains are formed from clastic materials already on the surface of the earth. (§17.10)

2. See Figure 17-12 on page 449.

3. The two types of nonlava flows are *glowing avalanches* and *lahars*. Glowing avalanches are volcanic debris carried along by extremely hot volcanic gases. Lahars occur when water carries along volcanic debris in a mud- and rock-laden flow. Both can move

very fast depending on the slope of the volcano. Both destroy by sliding debris and smothering. (§17.11)

4. Besides liquid lava, volcanoes also emit various gases, including steam, finely divided solid lava as ash and cinders, and blocks and bombs. (§17.11, 17.13)

5. Vents in the ground where steam and other gases escape are called *fumaroles*. (§17.11)

6. Two common types of lava flows are *pahoehoe* lava and *'a'a* lava. *Pillow lava* formations are found only in association with underwater eruptions. (§17.12)

7. The largest known volcanic explosion was in the Aegean Sea in 1650 BC. (Table 17-4, p. 453)

8. False. Lava is usually the least hazardous emission associated with volcanoes. Pyroclastic flows, poisonous gas emissions, and lahars have been responsible for more deaths than lava. Volcanoes may explode with the devastation of numerous atomic bombs. Exploding volcanic islands can cause tsunamis that affect lands thousands of miles away. (§17.11–17.13)

high. Surtsey, a shield volcano located south of Iceland, formed a new island in 1963. Today, the island supports plant life, and animals have migrated to the island. This is proof that islands do not take vast spans of time to form. The largest volcano known in the solar system, Olympus Mons on Mars, also has the profile of a shield volcano.

Volcanoes that explosively eject mostly pyroclastic materials (ashes, cinders, and bombs) produce **cinder cones**. These cones consist primarily of gravel-size bits of solidified lava. They typically have relatively steep slopes because the cinders tend to interlock with each other, preventing motion downhill until the slope exceeds a certain angle, called the *angle of repose* for the cinders. These volcanoes usually result from a single relatively short eruptive period. Therefore, they are typically small volcanoes. One famous cinder cone volcano is Parícutin, a Mexican volcano that first erupted in 1943.

Volcanoes that eject lava and pyroclastic materials in alternating episodes are called **composite cones** or **stratovolcanoes**. These names refer to the layered or stratified appearance of the material forming the cones. The lava layers result from relatively quiet eruptions. The pyroclastic layers come from explosive eruptions. These cones have a shape that is somewhere between the broad shield volcano and the steep-sided cinder volcano. They are larger than cinder cones and have the symmetrical cone shape that most people associate with volcanoes. Most volcanoes are composite volcanoes. Fuji in Japan, Mount Etna in Sicily, Mounts Rainier and St. Helens in Washington, Mount Vesuvius in Italy, and Mount Mayon in the Philippines are all composite volcanoes.

17.15 Classified by Historical Activity

A volcano's activity is difficult to define, and there are widely varying opinions among volcanologists about what determines the activity of a particular volcano. Things to consider when classifying a volcano by activity are the time since its last actual eruption, earthquake activity associated with the volcano, hot water springs flowing from the volcano's vicinity (see Section 17C), and changes in elevation within the volcano's crater or caldera. Most geologists would agree with the following definitions of activity.

An **active volcano** is one that has erupted within historical times or shows signs that it could erupt at any time. The historical time

Surtsey (SURT SAY)

The *angle of repose* of a pile of material is related to many factors. Particle size, shape, density, and the "stickiness" of the materials all affect how steep the sides of a pile can be.

shield cone — 9 km — 150 km

composite cone — 3 km — 15 km

cinder cone — 0.3 km — 1.5 km

 Demonstration: Angle of Repose

Angle of repose is determined mainly by the particle size, roughness, angularity, and surface adhesiveness, as well as by the humidity and temperature of the atmosphere. You can demonstrate the differences in angle of repose by comparing equal-sized piles of sand, flour, M&Ms, ping-pong balls, and so forth. Such an investigation would make an excellent science fair project.

Volcano activity classifications are by nature subjective and may change without notice. Volcanoes that are classified as active give clear indications of recent or incipient activity. Volcanoes that are definitely extinct show extensive erosion and essentially no seismic activity beneath them. The dormant classification is the hardest to assign accurately.

period differs from place to place because not all locations in the world have been populated or even explored for the same amount of time. Examples of active volcanoes are Mauna Loa in Hawaii, Vesuvius in Italy, and Mount St. Helens in Washington. A *continuous volcano* has small eruptions every few hours, days, or weeks and has been having them for a long time. Mount Stromboli in the Aeolian Islands of Italy has been erupting as often as several times each hour for at least 2000 years.

A **dormant volcano** has not erupted in historical times but could erupt based on seismic indications of tectonic activity beneath the volcano. Mount Shasta in California and Mount Rainier in Washington are both dormant volcanoes. Geologists classify Mauna Kea in Hawaii as dormant. Astronomers are so confident that the volcano is unlikely to have a significant eruption that they have built their largest and most expensive telescopes on its summit. An **extinct volcano** has no historical record of eruption, gives evidence for long periods of inactivity based on erosion patterns, and has no significant seismic activity in the earth beneath it.

Although the terms *active, dormant,* and *extinct* help scientists in their study of volcanoes, they can be misleading. The uninformed may believe that dormant or extinct volcanoes are not dangerous. However, occasionally a volcano formerly classed as dormant or extinct erupts disastrously. Mount Vesuvius had not erupted for over 3500 years before its eruption in AD 79 and was considered extinct by those who knew that it was a volcano. Two cities built near its base were wiped out because their citizens reasonably assumed that it posed no danger they needed to take seriously. Similarly, Mount St. Helens had not erupted for over a hundred years before its 1980 eruption. Nearly any volcano may erupt at any time. Active volcanoes are simply more likely to erupt based on their recent history. A volcano cannot be classified as truly extinct until the magma chamber has been exposed by erosion.

17.16 Classified by Explosivity

Scientists try to classify natural catastrophes by their destructiveness—how much energy they produce and how they affect human populations. We have seen such rating scales for tornadoes, hurricanes, and earthquakes. Volcanoes are no exception. Probably the best indicator of the destructiveness of a particular volcano is its *Volcanic Explosivity Index,* or VEI. This index, a scale from 1 to 8, is an estimate of the explosive power in a volcanic eruption. Of the more powerful eruptions worldwide in the last 1000 years, there have been 184 rated a category 4, 38 rated a category 5, 7 rated a category 6, 1 rated a category 7, and none rated a category 8. The one VEI category 7 eruption was Mt. Tambora in Indonesia in 1815 (see the Facet on the facing page). Geologists believe that there was at least one VEI category 8 explosion in the past—the explosion that formed the Yellowstone Caldera in Yellowstone National Park. They have found evidence that in a single blast 1000 km³ of rocks and pyroclastic materials were released, creating a crater nearly 40 km by 70 km (25 mi by 45 mi) over a kilometer deep. The explosion is estimated to have been 800 times more powerful than that of Mount St. Helens.

The Volcanic Explosivity Index (VEI) was devised by Christopher Newhall of the U.S. Geological Survey and Stephen Self at the University of Hawaii in 1982 to provide a relative measure of the magnitude of a volcanic eruption. This scale is analogous to the Fujita-Pearson tornado intensity scale and the MMI scale for earthquakes. It is an indirect measure of the energy liberated in the volcano explosion, obtained by estimating the destructiveness of the blast.

17-19 Oregon's Crater Lake—this lake is set in the crater of an extinct volcano, Mt. Mazama. Wizard Island (center of photograph) apparently formed after the cone collapsed to form the caldera.

17-20 Mount St. Helens, which erupted in 1980, is an active volcano.

17-21 The Yellowstone Caldera is the remnant of one of the largest volcanic explosions ever.

MT. TAMBORA: THE MOST POWERFUL ERUPTION IN HISTORY

Nearly two hundred years ago, 140,000 natives and European colonists lived on the island of Sumbawa in the East Indian archipelago of what is now called Indonesia. On a peninsula of this island there was a 4000 m (13,000 ft) volcano named Mt. Tambora that had not erupted for perhaps a thousand years. The 12,000 people living at the foot of this huge mountain felt secure. Within the previous 50 years, three volcanoes on nearby islands had erupted very explosively. The people knew what devastation an erupting volcano could bring, but Mt. Tambora remained quiet. However, in the spring of 1814 their volcano began coming alive. A few mild bursts of volcanic ash were noticed. Then all was quiet for a few months.

In February 1815 Mt. Tambora sent out several more spurts of volcanic ash. Then, on April 5, a new vent opened on the north side at the summit, spewing a huge spray of ash and cinders out over the Flores Sea. A series of earthquakes sent shocks throughout the group of islands. Two hundred miles to the north, the captain of a British East India Company warship, the *Benares*, heard the commotion and thought it was a naval battle, perhaps between pirates and British shipping vessels just over the horizon. He was ordered to go investigate. The ship found nothing, of course.

Over the next several days, ash in the sky reduced the daylight to a gray overcast. The Europeans on Java to the west and in a settlement on the east coast of Sumbawa became concerned that a major volcanic event was taking place, but they believed it was one of the other volcanoes that had recently erupted. Starting on the evening of April 10 and continuing through the early morning hours of April 12, a 2500 mi length of the East Indian island chain was rocked by heavy repetitive shocks. Mt. Tambora erupted in a series of mighty blasts that produced immense pyroclastic flows, destroying the villages on its flanks. A column of ash and cinders rose over 28 miles and covered the islands to the west. Volcanic bombs

ranging in size from walnuts to double fists rained down on the village of Sangir, less than 25 mi from the volcano and in sight of the summit. As the peak collapsed, it produced ocean surges that swamped Sangir with walls of water more than 12 feet high. Later, blasts of air leveled trees and buildings in the battered village. As the second day progressed, the few surviving people witnessed a darkness that was like night, caused by the ash that filled the sky. The volcano continued emitting sharp, huge explosions that finally abated during the night of the eleventh. The next day, floating pumice up to two feet thick choked the ocean for miles to the west of the island, making sea travel difficult.

In studying this eruption, volcanologists estimated that Mt. Tambora lost more than 1000 m (3300 ft) of height through explosion and collapse. A caldera 6 km (4 mi) in diameter formed where the summit had been. Ash up to two feet thick settled on houses and other buildings for miles around, crushing them and their occupants. By the morning of April 12, some 10,000 people had died as a direct result of the eruption. Survivors included only about 50 inhabitants who stayed on the peninsula or fled by canoe after the eruptions began. In the weeks and months that followed, buried crops caused famine that took thousands of lives on Sumbawa and an estimated

37,000 lives on Lombok Island to the west of Sumbawa. Mt. Tambora's eruption took more than 87,000 lives in all.

Wind currents distributed the ash and aerosols around the world, reducing the amount of solar radiation that reached the Northern Hemisphere. As a result, the winter of 1815–16 was bitterly cold. In 1816 there was a very short to nonexistent summer growing season throughout the Northern Hemisphere. Food supplies were soon exhausted, and thousands of additional people died of disease and starvation around the world. Terrible winterlike storms raged all year long. One particular storm so impressed novelist Mary Godwin (soon to become Mary Shelley) at Lake Geneva, Switzerland, that her description of it became the "dark and stormy night" setting for her novel *Frankenstein: The Modern Prometheus*.

Mt. Tambora's 1815 eruption was rated a 7 on the VEI scale. It is one of only four eruptions in recorded history of this intensity. Other eruptions such as the 1883 explosion of Mt. Krakatoa or the 1980 eruption of Mt. St. Helens are more famous, but none match or exceed Mt. Tambora for sheer suddenness, shortness of duration, and destruction. Yet, as awe-inspiring as that event was, it cannot compare to the cataclysms that unleashed the Flood of Noah's day.

The explosion of Mt. Tambora is believed to be the largest volcanic explosion to be documented by observers. The Santorini Plinian explosion in the Aegean Sea occurred within historical times, but it was not observed by any who survived to pass on eyewitness documentation of the eruption. The magnitude of that explosion is conjecture based on its secondary effects.

Facet Summary: Mt. Tambora: The Most Powerful Eruption in History

This Facet focuses on some of the details of the explosive eruption of Mt. Tambora in 1815, the largest volcanic eruption ever observed and recorded. There are no vocabulary terms in this Facet.

According to the catastrophic plate tectonics theory based on the Flood narrative from Scripture, thousands of now-extinct volcanoes could have erupted during the year-long Flood when the tectonic plates were rapidly moving over the surface of the earth. As the tectonic activity subsided, the majority of the volcanoes went extinct. The active volcanoes remaining today reflect the low level of current tectonic action compared to the time of the Flood.

Stones of Witness

State a hypothesis based on a biblical worldview of geologic history that could explain why there are so many more extinct volcanoes than active ones.

Kamchatka (kam CHAT kuh)

Aleutian (uh LOO shun)

A seamount is an isolated mountain, usually a volcano, on the floor of the ocean.

17-22 The majority of the world's active volcanoes are located in two major belts, the Pacific "Ring of Fire" and the Alpine-Himalayan belt.

17.17 Classified by Location

More than 1511 volcanoes on land are considered active. One creationary geologist estimated that 70% of the world's volcanic mountains are extinct. That would place the total number of volcanic mountains at more than 5000. There are also approximately 20,000 submarine (underwater) volcanoes in the Pacific Ocean alone. Some geologists estimate that there could be more than 100,000 active and extinct volcanoes on the earth's surface. Most active volcanoes are located in two volcano belts, the Alpine-Himalayan and the Circum-Pacific belts.

One belt surrounds the Pacific Ocean and corresponds to the zone where the Pacific tectonic plate is subducting beneath adjacent plates. This **Circum-Pacific belt** is sometimes called the "Ring of Fire." It includes the volcanoes in New Zealand, New Guinea, the Philippines, Japan, the Kamchatka Peninsula of Russia, the Aleutian Islands, Alaska, the western margin of the United States, Central America, the western margin of South America, and numerous volcanic Pacific islands scattered between these bodies of land.

The **Alpine-Himalayan belt** reveals the collision of the African and Indo-Australian plates with the southern margin of the Eurasian Plate. This belt extends from the Mediterranean area eastward through Turkey and the Middle East, north of India and on into the Indonesian islands. It contains the volcanoes of Sicily, Italy, the Aegean Sea, Asia Minor, the Indian Ocean, Southeast Asia, and Indonesia.

Active volcanoes can be associated with tectonic activity in other locations of the world as well. The mid-ocean rift zones where sea-floor spreading is taking place contain numerous submarine volcanoes and volcanic islands. Iceland and the Azores are volcanic islands of the Mid-Atlantic Ridge mountain system. Easter Island in the eastern Pacific Ocean sits on top of a mid-ocean ridge system there. Other volcanic islands seem to rise from locations in the middle of tectonic plates. The Hawaiian Islands and Emperor Seamounts form a long system of volcanoes in the northwest portion of the Pacific Plate.

legend
● volcanoes
■ subduction zones
■ tectonic plate margins

17B-2 Section Review

1. List the three types of volcanic mountains. What determines which kind of cone a volcano will form?

2. Where is the largest known volcano?

3. Why does a composite volcano form?

4. Can any volcano be considered extinct with complete confidence? Explain your answer.

5. How do volcanologists describe the destructiveness of a volcano? Into which category do the majority of the more powerful volcano eruptions from the past 1000 years fall?

6. What are the zones called where most of the active volcanoes on the earth are found?

7. (True or False) The last eruption of a supposedly extinct volcano could have occurred as recently as 200 years ago if it is located in a more recently populated area of the world.

17C   HEATED GROUNDWATER

17.18   How Is Groundwater Heated?

Long ago, miners working in deep mines found that the earth's temperature naturally increases with depth. Deep drill holes have confirmed that temperature rises continuously into the crust. The rate of temperature change varies with location, but geologists have found that the temperature rises between 15 °C and 50 °C per kilometer of depth (97–200 °F/mi) into the crust. This rate of temperature change with depth is the **geothermal gradient**. The temperature gradient exists because the core of the earth has a temperature of approximately 5000 °C, while the earth's surface temperature is about 30 °C. Therefore, temperature must increase between the surface and the core in a more or less continuous if not constant rate.

Water in reservoirs deep within the earth, and water that descends to great depths along fractures in rock, is heated because of the geothermal gradient. The hot, lower-density water then tends to rise as it is replaced by cooler, denser water from closer to the earth's surface.

Another source of heat for groundwater is magma intrusions. As magma forces its way upward into the crust, groundwater near the magma becomes hot. Because the geothermal gradient is steeper in the vicinity of large magma intrusions, groundwater tends to circulate much more readily by convection through rock joints. Water heated because of the thermal gradient or by magma intrusions can reach the surface and produce a variety of interesting features that are often associated with tectonic activity.

Based on the maximum value for the geothermal gradient, what would be the temperature at a depth of 5 km (3.1 mi) into the earth? Is this hot enough to boil water?

The gradient of a measurable quantity is the change of that quantity with distance. We first discussed the pressure gradient in the atmosphere in Chapter 11, which is the change of atmospheric pressure with distance.

geothermal: geo- (Gk. *geo*—earth) + -thermal (Gk. *therme*—heat)

17-23 The geothermal gradient exists because the earth's core is far hotter than its surface, and the temperature increases steadily as depth increases. A magma intrusion can increase the temperature close to the earth's surface, increasing the gradient.

Heated groundwater is responsible for interesting and important mineral deposits that are found in many rocks. Any geologic process that is associated with heated groundwater is called a *hydrothermal* process. Many common minerals such as calcites, quartzes, and pyrites, and even gold and silver deposits, are often associated with hydrothermal activity.

Objectives—Section 17C

Upon completing this section, students should be able to

- compare and contrast two ways groundwater is heated.

- describe how surface features caused by heated groundwater are formed.

- discuss the advantages and difficulties of collecting and using geothermal energy.

Visual 17-8: Sources of Heated Groundwater

This visual is a reproduction of Figure 17-23. The thermal gradient is a measure of how fast the temperature rises as depth into the earth increases. To illustrate this in a way that may be more familiar to students, rotate the visual so that the top is to the left. Ask students which graph has the steeper slope. The steeper the temperature-distance graph, the greater the geothermal gradient. In the center of continental masses, where the crust is thickest, the gradient is lowest. In the presence of magmatic intrusions or in the thin oceanic crust, the thermal gradient is the highest. On the right side of the visual, point out how surface water trickles down through joints in the rocks to be heated.

Answers to 17B-2 Section Review Questions

1. The three types of volcanoes are the *shield volcano*, the *cinder cone*, and the *composite cone* or *stratovolcano*. The violence of the volcano's eruptions throughout its existence determines what kind of cone it will form. Quiet eruptions slowly emit runny lava flows and produce broad shield volcanoes; violent eruptions eject cinders and produce cinder cones; and alternating forms of eruptions produce alternating layers of cinders and lava, resulting in composite volcanoes. (§17.14)

2. The largest known volcano is Olympus Mons on Mars. (§17.14)

3. A composite volcano forms when relatively explosive eruptions of ash and cinders are interspersed between relatively quiet eruptions of lava. (§17.14)

4. No. Almost any supposedly extinct volcano has the potential to erupt again if the original conditions of the crust and mantle recur. Mt. Vesuvius is a good example of this. (§17.15)

5. Volcanologists use the Volcano Explosivity Index (VEI) scale to describe the destructiveness of a volcano. The majority of powerful eruptions fall into the VEI 4 category. (§17.16)

6. One zone is called the Circum-Pacific belt (or the "Ring of Fire") and the other is called the Alpine-Himalayan belt. (§17.17)

7. True. For example, Mount Rainier, a volcano in Washington State, has not erupted since it was discovered within the last three hundred years. This does not preclude an eruption within, say, the last 500 years. (§17.15)

The Japanese macaque lives at the most northern latitude of all of the primates. Also known as snow monkeys, these primates take advantage of local hot springs warmed by volcanic activity to survive during the harsh cold seasons. At Jigokudani Wild Monkey Park (*Jigokudani Yaen-Koen*), located at the base of the mountain Shiga Kogen in the Japanese Alps, visitors can observe these monkeys bathing in the hot springs.

 Visual 17-9: Model of Geyser Activity

This visual is a reproduction of Figure 17-25. Note how the tortuous path of the subterranean steam and water chambers controls the action of the geyser.

 Demonstration: Geyser Eruptions

You can model a geyser erupting using some simple lab ware. Outfit a 500 mL Erlenmeyer flask with a rubber stopper drilled to snugly hold a titration burette inserted into it. The burette needs to extend to within 2–3 cm of the bottom of the flask. Add 150–200 mL of water to the flask so that the tip of the burette is covered. Place the Erlenmeyer flask on a hot plate, and then clamp the entire apparatus in place with a burette clamp. Ensure that all observers are wearing wraparound safety glasses. This demonstration idea was taken from "Modeling Geyser Eruptions in the Classroom," *Science Scope*, April/May 2005, 42–45. See the article for ideas on observation and discussion questions.

17-24 Travertine terraces at Mammoth Hot Springs, Yellowstone National Park

travertine (TRAV ur TEEN)

17-25 Geyser "plumbing": Long twisted chambers filled with groundwater extend down into areas near hot magma. As steam forms, it develops enough pressure to overcome the weight of the water above and forces some water out the upper chambers. Groundwater refills the chambers, and the process starts over.

geyser (GY zur)

17-26 Geyserite around the opening of the Lone Star Geyser in Yellowstone National Park

17.19 Hot Springs

An area where heated water simply rises to the surface in a liquid state is called a **hot spring**. The spring at Warm Springs, Georgia, has a temperature of 31 °C (88 °F) and is heated by the thermal gradient by descending about 1 km (0.6 mi) into the crust. Hot springs in the western United States are heated by magma that has worked its way close to the surface of the earth. A famous hot spring is Mammoth Hot Springs in Yellowstone National Park in Wyoming. Here the water flows out of the ground through a series of fissures in the side of a hill.

Heated groundwater is much more effective in dissolving minerals and chemical compounds than cool water. It is then not surprising that the water in hot springs usually has a very high mineral content. Hot springs often produce stepped rock formations called *terraces*. These are composed of a form of calcium carbonate called *travertine*, which is precipitated by the cooling water. Algae and bacteria, which grow in the heated water, may assist in the formation of travertine deposits. They are also responsible for coloring the travertine terraces red, blue, and brown.

Hot springs that come to the surface in volcanic ash and cinder fields suspend the tephra particles, forming muddy, bubbling springs called **mud pots**. Steam bubbles break at the surface of these pools of mud, sending splatters of mud into the air as the bubbles burst.

17.20 Geysers

A thermal spring that ejects its water from the ground at intervals is a **geyser**. Though scientists do not completely understand geysers, they think that nearby magma heats the water in a long, twisting chamber. The twisted chamber prevents the hot water from immediately approaching the surface. The *superheated* water rises until the pressure can no longer hold it in a liquid state. It suddenly flashes to steam and the steam cloud expands, forcing the entire column of water out of the ground. The chamber then refills with groundwater, and the heating process begins again.

Geyser openings are often surrounded by a whitish deposit called *geyserite*. This resembles travertine but is not made of calcium carbonate. Instead it consists of silica dissolved from the igneous rock through which the water has passed.

17.21 Harnessing Geothermal Energy

The geothermal gradient and magma intrusions can produce nearly endless quantities of hot water and steam in some localities. Using his God-given imagination, man has long recognized the potential usefulness of heated groundwater as an energy source, which we call **geothermal energy**. As early as 863 BC, the Celts in England recognized the healing and cleansing effect of the hot mineral springs at a place that one day would be called Bath, England. In AD 50 the Romans built extensive public bath facilities in Bath. Several of these ornate structures and their hot springs remain today.

Modern resorts around the world also use hot springs for bathing and swimming. But geothermal energy can heat more than bath water. Hundreds of projects around the world involve the use of heated groundwater and geothermal steam for heating homes and businesses, supplying fish and algae farms (aquaculture), feeding and watering livestock, heating greenhouses, supplying industrial chemical plants, and most significantly, generating electricity. More than 85% of the homes in Iceland are heated directly by geothermal steam.

In 1904 engineers at Larderello, Italy, began experimenting with the use of geothermal energy to generate electricity by using geothermal steam to power turbine generators. Today, the United States is the largest producer of geothermally generated electricity, exceeding 2700 MWh of electrical capacity. This is enough electricity to continuously supply 130,000 houses. Although geothermal power plants provide less than 3% of the electricity generated by nuclear power plants (and only 0.4% of all electrical power sources) in the U.S., the potential hazards of and environmentalist opposition to nuclear plants makes the use of geothermal energy a safe and environmentally clean alternative. All industrialized nations located in tectonically active regions of the world are now building geothermal power plants.

The few projects that tap geothermal energy have been encouraging. Still, not many places have heat close enough to the surface to be accessible. Also, the financial risk associated with exploration to find efficient sources of geothermal steam discourages more widespread use of this resource. For now at least, geothermal energy is only a minor source of energy. Perhaps in the future we will learn how to tap more deeply into the earth to make more of this energy available.

17-27 A geothermal plant in Iceland

17-28 Lake County, California, geothermal plant

17C Section Review

1. Identify the two ways by which groundwater can be heated.
2. What do geologists call heated groundwater that rises directly to the surface and forms pools? What is formed if this heated water mixes with volcanic ash deposits as it works its way to the surface?
3. What is the scientific term used to refer to heat or temperature within the earth?
4. How do travertine and geyserite form? How are travertine and geyserite different?
5. How is the source of a geyser different from that of a hot spring?
6. What are three kinds of activities that may use geothermal energy?
7. (True or False) Properly designed geothermal power plants are virtually nonpolluting and use a renewable source of energy, making them much more cost effective, cleaner, and safer than either nuclear or fossil-fuel power plants.

Students Sometimes Ask

Is geothermal electricity cheaper than other types of energy? The costs to establish a geothermal electricity generating plant are high, involving purchasing a 1000- to 1500-acre site above a high-quality geothermal reservoir—a huge capital investment—as well as equipment to deal with hazardous emissions. But geothermal energy has greater than 90% availability (other types have 75% or less), and operating costs may be as little as $0.03 to $0.10 per kWh.

Students Sometimes Ask

How do geothermal power plants affect the environment? Geothermal plants have subterranean gas emissions, such as carbon dioxide and hydrogen sulfide, that pollute the atmosphere, but only 5–20% as much as an equivalent fossil-fuel-powered plant. There are sludges to be disposed of, the potential for increased seismic activity, and often land subsidence if the waste water is not reinjected into the landmass.

Answers to 17C Section Review Questions

1. Groundwater can be heated because of the geothermal gradient and by proximity to magma intrusions. (§17.18)

2. When hot groundwater simply rises to the surface, it creates a *hot spring*. Heated groundwater containing volcanic ash forms a thick muddy spring called a *mud pot*. (§17.19)

3. The term that refers to topics involving heat or temperature within the earth is *geothermal*. (§17.18)

4. Both travertine and geyserite are deposits formed from geothermally heated water; however, they are formed differently and have different compositions. Travertine precipitates when hot mineral-laden water cools. Travertine is a form of calcium carbonate or limestone. Geyserite is formed from the precipitation of silica that was dissolved as water passed through silicate rocks. (§17.19–17.20)

5. A geyser is heated groundwater that emits from the earth's surface in periodic eruptions of liquid water and steam. These eruptions are believed to be due to the tortuous nature of the water and steam passages leading to the surface. A hot spring is a relatively quiet flow of hot water that pools on the surface. (§17.19–17.20)

6. Answers will vary. The textbook mentions heating homes and businesses, aquaculture, feeding and watering livestock, heating greenhouses, supplying industrial chemical plants, and generating electricity. (§17.21)

7. True. The words *properly designed* are important. Very early geothermal power plants discharged waste hot water into local brooks, killing the fish and disrupting the local environment. This is one of the complaints that environmentalists have against geothermal plants in general. (§17.21)

In Terms of Geology

Chapter Summary

- The best current model for explaining earthquakes, volcanoes, and geothermal activity is provided by the plate tectonics theory.
- Earthquakes are believed to result from the elastic rebound of rocks as they slip along a fault.
- The intensity of an earthquake, or the energy it produces, is measured on the Richter scale; the damage that an earthquake produces in populated areas is measured by the Modified Mercalli Index (MMI) scale.
- The greatest hazards from earthquakes are indirect rather than direct, due to destruction of man-made structures and utilities. Secondary effects such as rockslides, mudslides, and tsunamis often accompany earthquakes.
- Earthquakes produce three kinds of shock waves (P, S, and L). These waves are similar to sound waves, travel along various paths through the earth, and are detected by special sensors.
- The ability to predict earthquakes remains elusive. Preparation for earthquakes using earthquake-resistant building codes and not building in known earthquake-prone locations minimizes losses.
- A volcano is a landform built up by molten rock that has come to the earth's surface through a vent.
- Volcanoes can emit gases, liquids, and solids in the form of steam, poisonous gases, lava, ash, cinders, and bombs.
- Volcanoes can be classified according to their structure, historical activity, and explosivity.
- Volcano hazards may be direct, from explosions and emissions, or indirect, from lahars, tsunamis, and effects on weather.
- Most active volcanoes are found in the Circum-Pacific or the Alpine-Himalayan volcano belts. These belts are associated with the collision of tectonic plates.
- Hot springs, fumaroles, and geysers are indicators of sources for potentially useful geothermal energy.

What Did You Learn?

1. How do geologists believe earthquakes occur? What theory describes the overall cause for earthquakes?

2. How much more energy is released in an earthquake registering 6 on the Richter scale than in one registering 3?

3. Discuss two reasons why a weaker earthquake in one area might do more damage than a stronger earthquake in another area.

4. Explain how P and S waves are used to determine how far away an earthquake occurred.

5. Why are at least three seismic stations needed to determine the focus of an earthquake?

Answers to Chapter Review Questions
What Did You Learn?

1. Geologists believe that immense stresses build up in the rocks of the crust, causing them to deform slightly. Eventually, the rocks fracture suddenly, releasing accumulated stress as the blocks slip along a fault in a process called elastic rebound. The plate tectonics theory accounts for the forces and locations of most earthquakes. (§17.2)

2. Each whole-number interval on the Richter scale is 31.6 times as powerful as the preceding number. An earthquake registering 6 would have $31.6^3 \approx 31,600$ times more energy than an earthquake registering 3. (§17.3)

3. Answers will vary. A weak quake in an urban area could cause more damage than a stronger quake in a rural area. If buildings are poorly constructed in an area, even a weak earthquake could cause severe damage. If a weaker quake occurred near or in the ocean, a tsunami could result, whereas a stronger quake inland would not produce a tsunami. A weak quake that lasted several minutes could do more damage than a strong quake that lasted only a few seconds. A weak quake whose waves were focused by geological formations could be far more damaging than a stronger one in a stable area. (§17.4, 17.6)

4. The time interval between the arrival of P and S waves at a seismic station gives information that can be used to indicate the distance to the earthquake's focus. (§17.7)

5. A single seismic station can tell only the distance to an earthquake's focus, not its location. The distance to the earthquake is represented by a circle on a map. Two stations can usually identify the distance to the focus and two possible locations based on where the two range circles intersect. A range circle from a third station will not only identify the epicenter but will also locate the focus. (§17.7)

6. An active volcano is one that has erupted in historical times or is exhibiting strong seismic activity that indicates it could erupt at any time. A dormant volcano has not erupted in historical times, but seismic activity in the area indicates that an eruption might be possible. Volcanologists often must rely on secondary seismic and hydrothermal indicators to tell the difference between the two types. We do not understand the processes that cause eruptions well enough to reliably classify volcanoes by their activity. (§17.15)

7. If the geothermal gradient is as high as 50 °C/km, the temperature could be (4 °C) + (2 km)(50 °C/km) = 104 °C. (§17.18)

8. The geothermal gradient is a number that describes how fast the temperature changes with depth into the crust. Geothermal energy is the heat available in the crust as it flows from the core to the surface of the earth. (§17.18, 17.21)

6. What is the difference between an active and a dormant volcano? What is often the only way that volcanologists can tell the difference? Is this method completely reliable?

7. If water at the surface of the earth with a temperature of 4 °C trickled downward 2 km into the earth, how hot could the water become without the presence of a magma intrusion?

8. What is the difference between the geothermal gradient and geothermal energy?

9. How can geothermal energy be used to generate electricity?

True or False

10. The height of the zigs and zags on a seismogram tells us how much energy is in the earthquake that produced them.

11. A magnitude 5 earthquake on the Richter scale has 999 times as much energy as a magnitude 3 earthquake.

12. Iran was the location of the deadliest earthquake in history.

13. The most destructive waves produced by an earthquake are the L waves.

14. Faults can exist only where tectonic plates meet.

15. The use of lasers and satellites to map the movements of tectonic plates enables seismologists to reliably predict when an earthquake will occur.

16. Volcanoes form from vent pipes connected directly to the molten mantle rocks.

17. Historically, pyroclastic flows and lahars have caused more deaths than flowing lava from volcanic eruptions.

18. The MMI scale rates the destructiveness of a volcano.

19. Volcanoes are not found in the middle of oceanic or continental plates. They are found only along the edges of plates where they collide with other plates.

20. Heated groundwater transfers geothermal energy mainly by conduction.

21. Geysers occur because of the shape and constrictions in the path of heated groundwater to the surface.

22. More geothermal energy sources could be developed if energy companies would accept the risks and explore for suitable locations to build plants.

What Do You Think?

1. Do you think Mars has "marsquakes"?

2. Do earthquakes cause faults, or do faults cause earthquakes? Or is there some other explanation?

3. How would an earthquake magnitude scale compare to the Richter scale if it reported earthquake energy directly?

4. If you were a ship captain planning to enter port within the next 3 hours, and you received a report that a large earthquake occurred along a sea coast 3000 km away on the opposite side of the ocean, how would respond to this information?

5. Why do people continue to live near volcanoes that have repeatedly erupted throughout history with deadly results?

6. Why would an aircraft flying through a cloud of volcanic ash have problems?

7. What problems do you think are encountered in harnessing and using geothermal energy?

My Review Checklist

☐ I have carefully read the entire chapter.

☐ I have reviewed all of the photographs, illustrations, and graphs.

☐ I have reviewed all of my notes in the margins.

☐ I have reviewed and corrected the quizzes on this chapter.

☐ I have studied all of the vocabulary terms.

☐ I have had all of my questions answered.

---

20. False. Heated groundwater flows through the rocks mainly by convection. Hot water deep in the ground rises as it is replaced by cooler water from shallower depths. (§17.18)

21. True. (§17.20)

22. True. (§17.21)

What Do You Think?

1. Mars has volcanoes and faults, so earthquakes on Mars, or "marsquakes," would seem likely.

2. Earthquakes occur due to motion along existing or new faults, but a fault by itself does not cause earthquakes. According to the plate tectonics model, both are caused by stresses in the crust that are created by the motions of tectonic plates.

3. The energy magnitudes for small earthquakes would be small, but the energy magnitudes for larger earthquakes would be very large with many digits. For example, assuming an earthquake rated 1 on the Richter scale has an energy of 1 unit, then an earthquake rated 8 on the Richter scale would have 994,252,429,700 energy units.

4. The captain would probably turn his ship around and head back out to sea to find the deepest water possible, knowing that any tsunamis created by the quake would be barely felt in deep water. If he chose to continue into port, his ship and crew could be trapped and destroyed by a large tsunami within 4 to 6 hours of the earthquake.

5. Volcanic soils are very fertile, so farming on the flanks of a volcano is highly profitable. Farmers are willing to accept the risk of a possible eruption, hoping that they will have enough warning to escape with their lives. It is the unexpected catastrophic explosion, pyroclastic flow, or lahar that increases the danger of living near a volcano.

6. The airborne ash is very abrasive since it is finely divided volcanic rock. The windows of a rapidly moving aircraft could quickly be sandblasted, and the grit sucked into jet and propeller engines would destroy the smooth machined surfaces causing the engines to choke. Such incidents have caused aircraft engines to fail, requiring expensive repairs and endangering lives.

7. If geothermal activity is not visible on the earth's surface, then a suitable source of heat must be located by drilling many holes (an expensive process). Once a heat source is found, the decision must be made about how to use the energy. The method for disposing of hot water must be decided (cooling towers? pump the water back into the ground?). As the water cools, dissolved minerals may precipitate to clog pipes, so the water must be demineralized somehow before it can be used. The tectonic history of the area may not support building a large, expensive plant where the possibility of an earthquake and/or a volcanic eruption is high.

---

9. Wells pipe high-pressure steam from hydrothermal reservoirs deep in the earth to steam turbine generators that produce electricity. (§17.21)

True or False

10. True. (§17.3)

11. True. (§17.3)

12. False. The deadliest earthquake in history happened in China in AD 1556. (Table 17-2, p. 443)

13. True. (§17.7)

14. False. Faults can exist between different sections of the same tectonic plate. (§17.8)

15. False. Reliable earthquake prediction has so far eluded seismologists, even with sophisticated modern technology. (§17.9)

16. False. Volcanoes are supplied from magma chambers that form within the crust. (§17.10)

17. True. (§17.11–17.12)

18. False. The volcano explosivity index (VEI) rates the destructiveness of a volcano. The MMI scale rates the destructiveness of an earthquake. (§17.4, 17.16)

19. False. Thousands of extinct volcanoes are found scattered over the middle of oceanic plates as seamounts and especially along mid-ocean ridge systems. (§17.17)

Overview

Chapter 18 presents weathering, mass wasting, and stream erosion as examples of the degeneration of the earth, which occurs as a consequence of the Curse. These processes are good examples of the effects of the second law of thermodynamics. Erosion is slowly removing tillable soils from the continents. Even though the Flood probably eliminated the original soils from Creation, God through His providence has established weathering processes to replenish soil.

Section 18A begins by explaining the processes of chemical and mechanical weathering. Soil structure, fertility, and formation are also discussed. We show that, depending on climate and the source of soil raw materials, soil formation is not always as slow as is usually believed.

Section 18B addresses the movements of large amounts of rock and soil under the influence of gravity. Creep and rock glaciers are examples of slow mass wasting. Landslides and other examples of rapid mass wasting are also discussed.

Section 18C outlines the structure of a typical stream, from its headwaters to its mouth. Stream profiles may exist between the extremes of high and low gradients, depending on the topography. Erosion by streams is responsible for removing and redistributing soils and for reshaping the land topography.

Schedule Summary

Section 18A: 3 periods

Section 18B: 1 period

Section 18C: 3 periods

Investigation Summary

18F "Soil Composition"

18G "Erosion"

Bulletin Board Ideas

1. Title the board "EROSION: A Degenerative Process." Use a yellow background. For the word "EROSION," use two sets of letters, yellow and brown. Layer the brown letters directly on top of the yellow letters. The first 'E' should be all brown, but subsequent letters should have some of the brown letter torn off, revealing the yellow letter underneath. The effect is that the word

WEATHERING, MASS WASTING, AND EROSION

CHAPTER

18

SUGGESTED TEACHING SCHEDULE

DAY 0

Assignment

Reading: Section 18A-1 (§18.1–18.3), chemical and mechanical weathering

DAY 1

Explain chemical weathering as a chemical change in rock caused by weak acids generated from carbon dioxide or organic materials and from oxidation. Discuss mechanical weathering caused by plants, freezing water, and wind.

Assignment

Complete: 18A-1 Section Review Questions
Applications 18A, "A Degenerating Earth"
Applications 18B, "Chemical and Mechanical Weathering"
Reading: Section 18A-2 (§18.4–18.6), soil structure and formation

DAY 2

Introduce soil as a combination of weathered rock and organic material. Discuss soil horizons, emphasizing that soil composition depends on the kinds of rocks in the region, the climate, and the vegetation. Explain soil fertility factors. Finish by explaining that soil formation is not always a slow process, and give examples from the text.

Assignment

Complete: 18A-2 Section Review Questions
Applications 18C, "Soil Science"
Reading: Investigation 18F, "Soil Composition"

DAY 3

Do Investigation 18F, "Soil Composition."

Assignment

Reading: Section 18B, "Mass Wasting"

18A WEATHERING

18.1 Introduction

Hebrews 1:11 says that the heavens and Earth "shall wax old as doth a garment." The heavens are indeed wearing out. Stars exhaust their fuel and become supernovas; comets vaporize and break up into fragments, some of which burn up in the earth's atmosphere as meteors; and the earth itself rotates more slowly every day. Similarly, the earth's surface shows signs of wear. These things are a reminder to us that if the earth were a creature, it would groan in pain because of its cursed state, waiting for Christ to bring the fullness of redemption to His world (Rom. 8:22). Christ, the second Adam, will bring not only forgiveness and spiritual wholeness but also a healing of the natural effects of the Curse.

Three ways that the earth's surface "wears out" are *weathering*, which disintegrates rocks; *mass wasting*, which lowers hills and mountains; and *erosion* by flowing water, which moves tons of soil every year. In this section you will study two types of weathering—*chemical* and *mechanical*.

18.2 Chemical Weathering

Chemical weathering disintegrates rocks by changing their chemical composition. You may remember from the discussion of minerals in Chapter 14 that some rocks react with acids. For example, a small piece of limestone will completely dissolve in a beaker of hydrochloric acid. Natural acids are important agents of chemical weathering. Gaseous carbon dioxide dissolves in water to form *carbonic acid*, the weak acid present in carbonated beverages. Decayed plants produce a mixture of weak acids called *humic acid*, and lichens produce acids as well. These acids can dissolve the minerals in rocks. Because the acids are weak, however, they take a long time to dissolve the stone. Weathering agents can also change some minerals without dissolving them. For example, carbonic acid weathers feldspar to form a solid matter called clay. Oxygen and other chemicals also cause chemical weathering. Chemical weathering is indicated by differences in color, texture, and hardness of the rock compared to the appearance of a freshly broken surface.

Several factors influence the speed at which chemical weathering proceeds. The mineral itself is the most important of these. Whereas calcite (limestone) weathers relatively rapidly, silica (quartz) resists weathering remarkably. Climate is also important. Warmth and moisture promote chemical weathering by speeding up the reaction between the acid and the mineral. Gentle slopes and abundant vegetation, which retain rainwater longer, hasten the process. Another significant factor is the amount of rock surface exposed to the weathering agents. The greater the area, the more chemical weathering takes place. When rocks break apart, new surfaces become exposed to the chemical agents. Similarly, the burrowing of earthworms, moles, gophers, and other small animals constantly mixes the soil particles and makes them more susceptible to chemical weathering.

18.3 Mechanical Weathering

Mechanical weathering breaks up large, angular rocks into smaller, rounder pieces by physical forces. Unlike chemical weathering, mechanical weathering does not change the composition of the

Decayed plant material is called *humus*, and the acid produced as it decays is called *humic acid*. "Rich" soil contains much humus and is usually darker in color than the same type of soil with less humus.

18-1 Weather pits formed by naturally acidified water

"EROSION" is actually eroding away. Complete the board with pictures of erosion activity from newspapers, magazines, or the Internet.

2. Display color photos of landslides, rockslides, avalanches, or other examples of rapid mass wasting.

 Field Trip Idea

Visit a canyon if one exists in your area. Ask your students if the profile of the current stream is a high or low gradient. Look at the strata that form the walls of the canyon. Ask students what factors would determine how rapidly flowing water erodes downward through the rocks. Then ask them if there is any way of estimating the time it would take to erode downward through, for example, 20 m of rock.

Objectives—Section 18A

Upon completing this section, students should be able to

- distinguish between chemical and mechanical weathering.
- list some weathering agents and describe their actions.
- discuss the components of soil.
- describe the three soil horizons in a complete soil profile.
- explain steps farmers can take to increase soil fertility.

Demonstration: Chemical Weathering

Weigh three pieces of limestone of approximately the same size and place each in a beaker. To the first beaker add 10 mL of dilute hydrochloric acid. To the second add 10 drops of the dilute acid and 10 mL of water. Add only water to the third beaker. Let the beakers stand for several days. Remove the rocks, allow them to dry overnight, and then weigh them. State the final weights as a percentage of the original weights.

DAY 4

Quiz—Section 18A, "Weathering"

Define mass wasting as the movement of soil or rocks under the influence of gravity. Give examples of both slow and rapid mass wasting. Do Applications 18D, "Mass Wasting."

Assignment

Complete: 18B Section Review Questions

Reading: Section 18C, "Stream Erosion"

DAY 5

Quiz—Section 18B, "Mass Wasting"

Describe the structure of streams. Discuss the characteristics of both low-gradient and high-gradient streams.

Assignment

Reading: Investigation 18G, "Erosion"

DAY 6

Discuss the effects of streams—erosion, solution, and deposition. Note the differences between deltas and alluvial fans. Do Investigation 18G, "Erosion."

Assignment

Complete: Applications 18E, "Stream Erosion"

18C Section Review Questions

Selected Chapter Review Questions

DAY 7

Quiz—Section 18C, "Stream Erosion"

Review for a chapter test.

Assignment

Study for a chapter test

(schedule continued on p. 466)

Demonstration: Mechanical Weathering—Frost Wedging

Fill a discarded small glass jar completely with water. Tightly cap the jar, place it in a zippered plastic bag, and place the bag in a freezer. Observe the jar after several hours, or during the next class period. The expansion of the ice should fracture the jar. Point out to the students that this is the process that causes cracks in sidewalks and roads. It illustrates why roads in northern climates need constant repair.

 Visual 18-1: Frost Wedging

This visual is a reproduction of Figure 18-2. The photo on the right is an example of granitic rock dissected by frost wedging.

Water pipes often burst when they freeze in the winter because of water's property of expanding when it freezes.

18-2 Water in cracks and pores expands as it freezes, creating enough force to split rock apart (above); boulders raised by frost heaving (middle); potholes from mechanical weathering by stream sediments (right)

rocks. Plant roots and germinating seeds are effective agents in enlarging cracks in rocks because they exert pressure on anything confining them. Perhaps you have seen a sidewalk heaved or cracked by tree roots. Even small weeds can damage an asphalt driveway or parking lot by enlarging the small openings into which the seeds originally fell.

Water that freezes in cracks and pores of rocks is another forceful mechanical weathering agent called **frost wedging**. Water expands about 9 percent when it freezes, and it can exert tremendous pressure against the surfaces it touches. Each time the ice thaws and the water refreezes, it has new opportunities to splinter off small fragments and to extend the cracks farther into the rock. In dry climates, a similar process involving salt solutions in joints occurs, called *salt wedging*. As the water evaporates, the precipitating salt crystals force the joints apart.

A second way freezing water causes mechanical weathering is by **frost heaving**. Ice below the surface of the ground pushes surface material upward as much as 45 cm (18 in.) in a season. This upward push breaks up fine-grained rocks. Because of frost heaving, farmers in frost-prone zones often encounter new rocks in their plowing each spring. Water expands as it freezes and forces the rocks upward. As the ice melts, soil sifts below the rocks and supports them in the higher position. This freezing and thawing occurs repeatedly, winter after winter, with each cycle pushing the rocks still higher.

Wind erosion is another form of mechanical weathering. It is most obvious in desert regions that have loose sand. Wind-driven sand is an effective abrasive agent that erodes rocks such as sandstone and other clastic rocks. Its action is like sandblasting, a method used for cleaning stone buildings and rusted metal parts. Many unusual rock formations in the western United States were formed by wind erosion.

DAY 8

Test—Chapter 18

Assignment

   Reading: Section 19A, "Description of the Oceans"

Wind often carries away the loose material from a desert area, leaving an excavated basin called a **blowout**. When all the sand and other loose materials have blown away, only pebbles and cobbles remain. The surface is then called a **desert pavement**. Sand that the wind moves from one area is deposited elsewhere in mounds and ridges called **sand dunes**. A dune forms when the wind's speed slows and the wind is unable to carry its load. Once established, the dune itself becomes an obstacle that slows the wind even more, causing additional sand to accumulate. This is how the dune grows.

Another method of mechanical weathering is **exfoliation**, a process that removes thin slabs or flakes of rock from large rounded outcroppings or boulders. It can weather even durable granite. Geologists believe that exfoliation is due to both chemical and mechanical weathering. They suggest that initially chemical reactions occur in the joints of the rock (chemical weathering). Because the products of these chemical reactions occupy more space than the

exfoliation (eks foh lee AY shun): ex- (L. *ex*—off) + -foliation (L. *folium*—leaf)
Sheetlike exfoliation is also called *spalling*.

Joints in rock may have formed from tectonic stresses after the rock solidified. These joints or joint systems tend to extend deep into the interior of a mass of rock. Joints caused by uneven heating of the rock surface typically do not extend very far into the rock. Either kind of joint can be the entry point for water, salt, or plant roots that result in wedging activity.

18-3 Spectacular rock formations eroded by wind and water in the Claron Rock formation in Bryce Canyon National Park, Utah (left); desert pavement in Death Valley, California (middle); sand dunes in Namibia, Africa (right)

original rock, the weathered material in the rock expands outward, pushing away the outer rock layers (mechanical weathering). Joints may form and expand due to uneven heating and cooling by day and night. Surfaces of solidified igneous intrusions exposed by erosion will often produce exfoliation layers like an onion as the weight of the overlying rock layers is removed.

A visible result of mechanical weathering is the accumulation of rock debris at the base of a cliff. This debris, called **talus**, forms as rock fragments weather and fall from the cliff. Because these fragments have sharp corners and often are large, they can interlock with each other to form a steep slope with an angle of repose of 34–37° to the horizontal.

talus (TAY lus)

18-4 Exfoliation is a type of mechanical weathering that may form talus. This solid rock in Yosemite National Park is undergoing exfoliation (above). Talus at the base of cliffs in Banff National Park, Alberta, Canada (left).

It is interesting to conjecture about how familiar aspects of creation may have appeared before the effects of the Curse and the Flood. Take soil, for example. From our vantage point on this side of the Flood, we believe that soils take hundreds of years to form and that they are the products of gradual weathering and deposition. The original soils were not produced in this way. Therefore, there is no reason to believe that they appeared as today's soils do.

Have your students consider other natural features that we intuitively believe take long periods of time to form, and then consider what they may have looked like at the end of Creation week. Some features, like canyons, rocky sea shores, sand bars, deltas, and the like may not have existed at all in the earliest days of the earth. This is a profitable exercise to break young minds out of the prevalent uniformitarian mindset.

 Visual 18-2: Soil Profile

This visual is a reproduction of Figure 18-6 on page 469. Refer to this image when you are discussing soil horizons.

Some soils form from the deposits of volcanoes. These soils are the result of the weathering of volcanic debris.

uniform mixture of sand, clay, bedrock particles, and organic matter

granite bedrock

18-5 We don't know what the soil composition at Creation looked like, but we can be fairly certain that it was not made up of the products of erosion and decomposition since these processes had not occurred yet.

pedologist (pee DAHL uh jist)

18A-1 Section Review

1. State three ways the landmasses of the earth degenerate.
2. What are the two types of weathering? How are they different?
3. What factors can influence the rate of chemical weathering?
4. How much does water expand when it freezes? How does this affect the weathering of rock and soils?
5. What is the accumulation of rock debris at the base of a cliff called? What type of weathering produces this debris?
6. (True or False) Weathering reduces the orderliness of the materials in the original rock.

18.4 Result of Weathering—Soil

What happens to weathered rock? Large particles become gravel, medium-size particles become sand, and small particles may become clay or, if water carries them away, silt. When sand, silt, or clay mix with organic material, they become **soil**. Many soils form as the result of sedimentation, where water or wind action transports these weathered materials.

Not all soil has come from the weathering of rock. Sometime during the second or third day of Creation, perfect soils were created by God for the purpose of supporting and nourishing the plants that appeared on the third day. This original soil was not the result of weathering but rather from a supernatural creative act. It is possible that this soil didn't even look like present-day soils. Following the Fall until the Flood, the rate of soil depletion from plant growth, erosion, and farming may have exceeded the natural means to replenish it that God had created. During this time, people probably discovered many of the organic or artificial methods used to replenish the soil today. By action of the Flood, the original soil materials were lost as they became completely mixed with other sediments. God in His providence provided the process of weathering to replenish parts of the soil.

18.5 Soil Structure and Composition

Most soils contain three layers, which *pedologists*, or soil scientists, call **horizons**. The lowest horizon, the C-horizon, rests on bedrock. It consists of weathered pieces of bedrock fragments. The next layer, the B-horizon or subsoil, contains thoroughly weathered minerals from the C-horizon as well as minerals and other materials that have descended from the A-horizon. The A-horizon, or topsoil, is the most fertile part of the soil. It contains **humus**, decayed organic material, which provides many nutrients for plants and increases the ability of the soil to hold water. Rainwater carries some of the nutrients down to the B-horizon.

The composition of a soil depends on the kind of rocks in the region in which it forms, the climate, and the vegetation. Soils contain various amounts of sand, silt, and clay. If the region has mostly quartz rocks, its soils may be sandy. If the rocks contain mica, feldspar, or similar materials, the rocks are more likely to form clay.

Answers to 18A-1 Section Review Questions

1. Three ways by which Earth's landmasses show degeneration are *weathering*, *mass wasting*, and *erosion*. (§18.1)

2. The two types of weathering are *chemical* and *mechanical*. Chemical weathering involves various physical and biological agents that change the chemical makeup of the minerals in a rock. Mechanical weathering involves different physical and biological agents that break rock into smaller pieces without altering its chemical makeup. (§18.2–18.3)

3. The factors that can influence the rate of chemical weathering include the kinds of minerals in the rocks, the climate, temperature, moisture, amount of exposed surface, and the effect of mechanical weathering agents such as small burrowing animals that expose fresh surfaces to chemical influences. (§18.2)

4. When water freezes it expands 9 percent. When water expands as it freezes in joints, it breaks rocks into smaller pieces and can cause frost heaving in soils that exposes rocks to additional weathering. (§18.3)

5. The rock debris at the base of a cliff is called *talus*. Talus is usually caused by mechanical weathering. (§18.3)

6. True. You may want to point out that weathering is an excellent example of the second law of thermodynamics mentioned in Chapter 1. (§18.3)

If the soil is near a flooding river or a dried-up lake, it may contain silt. **Loam**, an especially fertile soil, contains about equal parts of sand and silt and about half as much clay. To be fertile, however, it also must contain humus.

Soils that receive plenty of rain differ from desert soils. Too much rain can remove most of the nutrients from the topsoil and reduce the amount of oxygen available to the roots of plants and to microorganisms. These factors make it difficult for most plants with shallow roots to grow and stay healthy. Soil in rainy climates also tends to be acidic. Roses and pine trees grow well in acidic soils, but crops such as alfalfa do not. Farmers in rainy climates may add lime (produced by heating limestone) to their soil to neutralize the acid and "sweeten" the soil.

The eastern United States has mostly acidic soils as a result of rainy climates. Soils in dry climates, on the other hand, tend to have plenty of nutrients in the topsoil. These soils often need only water to make them productive farmland. Farmers in southern California take advantage of the fertile desert soil by extensive irrigation. Much of the western United States has similar dry, but otherwise fertile, soil.

Organic matter is necessary for a fertile soil. Plants need the nutrients in humus in order to grow. Areas that are not disturbed by man receive a steady supply of humus as plants die and decay. In farmed areas, on the other hand, farmers often remove all their crops so that only small amounts of dead plant matter enter the soil. Thus, soils that have been farmed for several years may become infertile. To avoid this, farmers fertilize their fields. They may add chemical fertilizers to replace the missing nutrients, or they may use a kind of organic fertilizer. For example, farmers whose main crops are pasture and grain crops for their animals may use manure as a fertilizer. Another way to replace the nutrients is to grow a crop that will be plowed under rather than harvested. This is called green manure. If the soil is to continue to be fertile, the nutrients that are removed by plants and erosion must be replaced.

Another way to maintain fertility was sometimes practiced by ancient farmers when they let their fields lie fallow, or uncultivated, one year out of every six or seven. Today some farmers follow a similar practice of planting a "fallow crop" such as clover every six or seven years. This allows the soil to accumulate moisture and nitrogen, and then the crop is plowed under to build humus before it is farmed again.

18-6 Changes in the soil's shade or color mark the soil horizons in this soil profile in Southland, New Zealand (left). A typical soil profile (below) has three main layers (called horizons) above the bedrock.

A horizon

B horizon

C horizon

bedrock

loam (LOME)

18-7 Furrow irrigation of a cotton farm in California

Stones of Witness

Read Leviticus 25–26. What was the significance of God's commandment to let all fields and orchards lie fallow (observe their Sabbaths) every seventh year? How did the Israelites (and how do we today) benefit in a more general way from this principle? What happens when this principle is not followed?

Your students may find it interesting to test a local soil sample using a soil test kit, which can be purchased at a gardening store.

Stones of Witness

God desires to teach His people to place their trust ultimately in Him—not in their resources and not in their technology or skills. He encourages all His people toward this trust through various means. One very important way is how He has designed His world. Every aspect of the natural order needs regular periods of rest: the human body, the animals we use to help us work, and the soil that meets our needs. We should not attempt to ignore this need for rest for the sake of increased productivity. Instead, we should accept the need for rest as an opportunity to reflect on God and our dependence on Him. Labor without rest and reflection does not lead to greater productivity. It leads instead to barrenness and waste. As God told His people long ago: *"Man doth not live by bread only, but by every word that proceedeth out of the mouth of the Lord doth man live"* (Deut. 8:3).

18-8 Plants spring up in a lava flow in Volcano National Park, Hawaii.

18.6 Rate of Soil Formation

Rates of soil formation vary enormously, depending on a number of factors such as native bedrock type, temperature, amount of precipitation, seasonal changes, and ground slope. On some steep, exposed rock surfaces, soil has not formed at all; in other sites, soil formation is very slow and has apparently taken thousands of years. In some places, however, weathering and soil formation are more rapid, such as in the tropics. The combination of abundant rain and high temperatures produce very rapid chemical weathering of the underlying bedrock. Poor soils many meters thick may form over just a few years. Volcanic debris often can support plant growth only a few years after an eruption. For example, on the slopes of the volcano Krakatoa, about 50 cm (20 in.) of soil formed from volcanic ash within forty-five years after its eruption in 1883.

Soil can also develop rapidly along the edges of retreating glaciers. About 35 cm (14 in.) of soil formed in Glacier Bay National Park in less than two hundred fifty years following the glaciers' retreat. Thus, under favorable conditions, soil can form rapidly. According to the biblical model of the earth's history, all the soils of the world must have come into existence since the Flood, which means they must have formed in much less than 4500 years.

18A-2 Section Review

1. List the possible components of soil. Where do soil scientists believe these components come from?
2. What is another name for a soil scientist? Using an encyclopedia or the Internet as a reference, describe what aspects of soils these scientists might study.
3. What are the layers of soil called? Which layer has the most humus and why?
4. What are some evidences that soils do not require thousands of years to form?
5. (True or False) The newly created soil in the Garden of Eden must have contained A-, B-, and C-horizons over the bedrock.

18B MASS WASTING

18.7 Introduction

Mass wasting is the downhill movement of large masses of soil or rocks under the influence of gravity. It may be either slow or rapid. The occurrence and speed of mass wasting depends on the slope, the vegetation, and the amount of water in a plot of ground. Steep slopes are more likely to experience mass wasting than are gentle slopes because gravity acts more effectively on a steep slope. Plant roots tend to stabilize the soil; thus, land with heavy vegetation is less likely to experience mass wasting than land with sparse or no vegetation. Excessive water acts as a lubricant for mass wasting. Therefore, rapid mass wasting is more likely to occur after heavy rains.

Objectives—Section 18B

Upon completing this section, students should be able to

- define *mass wasting*.
- describe both slow and rapid mass wasting processes.
- state the factors that contribute to mass wasting.

Answers to 18A-2 Section Review Questions

1. The possible components of soil include sand, silt, or clay combined with decayed organic material (humus). Sand may come from weathered quartz-bearing native bedrock deeper underground or from sediment deposited in place. Silt consists of extremely fine particles that have been deposited as sediment. Clay may come from the weathering of feldspar and mica-bearing bedrock or from sedimentation. Organic material comes from dead plant and animal matter that has decayed. (§18.4–18.5)

2. Another name for a soil scientist is a *pedologist*. Answers will vary. Soil scientists study the chemistry and structure of soils, how soils are produced, soil conservation and restoration, and the mechanical properties of soil. (§18.5, outside sources)

3. The layers of soil are called *horizons*. The A-horizon has the most humus because it is located at the top of the soil profile where plants and other organisms grow. (§18.5)

4. Scientists have shown that soil can form in just a few years following a volcanic eruption or the retreat of a glacier. According to the biblical model of the earth's history, all the soils of the world must have formed within the past 4500 years. (§18.6)

5. False. The first soils were not produced from weathering but were supernaturally created "very good." There does not seem to be any fundamental requirement for horizons to exist other than as the end result of a natural weathering process, so soil horizons were not necessarily present at Creation. (§18.4–18.5)

18.8 Slow Mass Wasting

One type of slow mass wasting is **creep**, the almost imperceptible downhill motion of soil. It occurs at a rate of a few centimeters each year—so slowly that it does not break the cover of vegetation. Although we cannot see creep happening, we can see its accumulated results. Evidences of creep include slanted fence posts, leaning stone walls, tilted telephone poles, and ripples in sod.

Building contractors know that creep can be a serious problem. A house on a slope built solely on soil and not anchored to bedrock can be carried downhill along with the soil. Seldom does a house stay level as it moves. Floors and walls often become noticeably crooked a few years after the process of creep has begun. Eventually, the house is considered too unsafe to occupy.

On the other hand, a house anchored to bedrock will collect soil against its upper side. In such cases, builders may dig a level yard into the hill slope above the house and build a thick retaining wall to keep back the advancing soil. Some specially designed buildings may be anchored in the bedrock on the slope so that the creeping soil "flows" around the building. For large building projects, removing the creeping soil may be the best solution.

Rock glaciers furnish another example of slow mass wasting. These are "rivers" of rocks found extending down the valleys in certain mountainous regions of Alaska, Colorado, and other places where the mountainsides are steep and the ground remains frozen most of the year. Because spaces between the rocks are filled with ice, rock glaciers move slowly. The ice moves much as it does in an ordinary glacier, carrying the rocks with it down the valley.

18.9 Rapid Mass Wasting

A more dramatic type of mass wasting is the **landslide**. This general term describes any rapid mass movement downhill. If the mass includes detached bedrock, its specific name is **rockslide**. If it includes only loose surface material, the movement is a **debris slide**.

A rockslide is a sudden catastrophic slippage caused by weakness between layers of bedrock. A famous rockslide occurred in Wyoming in 1925. An estimated 38.5 million m³ (50 million yd³) of rock and soil slid down the side of Sheep Mountain, across the Gros Ventre River, and 110 m (360 ft) up the other side of the river valley. This slide created a dam that backed up the water for 8 km (5 mi). The dam held for two years. Then, during the spring flooding of 1927, the dam broke, and six people downstream drowned.

Weak materials—a layer of sandstone resting on a layer of clay—caused the Gros Ventre rockslide. The steep slope was another factor. Melting winter snow and heavy spring rains weakened the adhesion between the sandstone and the clay, and the rock was pulled down by gravity. Human intervention did not cause this slide because the slide occurred in an undeveloped area. On the other hand, human intervention probably could not have prevented it. Rockslides are the most devastating kind of landslide. They are uncontrollable and seldom give any warning.

18-9 Ripples in the soil are evidence of creep (top). Other evidences of creep are tilted fence posts and telephone poles, and trees with roots that point uphill (bottom).

18-10 A rock glacier near San Juan, Colorado. The mountain peak on the left is Emery Peak.

Gros Ventre (GROH VAHNT)

18-11 The Gros Ventre rockslide in Wyoming

Rock glaciers around the world have been categorized into three types based on their activity and ice content. *Active* glaciers contain abundant ice mixed with their rock content and may move several meters per year. *Inactive* rock glaciers contain less ice and show no signs of movement. *Fossil* rock glaciers contain no ice but display the classic transverse furrowing and ridges of a rock glacier.

Scientists are not sure how rock glaciers form. Some suggest that they are normal glaciers that have gradually exchanged ice for rock content. Others believe rock glaciers are essentially permafrost in loose rocky debris moving downhill.

18-12 A huge landslide scars the San Juan Mountains in Colorado.

18-13 Aerial view of a debris slide in the Tien Shan Mountains of Kyrgyzstan

erode: e- (L. *ex*—off) + -rode (L. *rodere*—to gnaw)

Earthquakes sometimes trigger rockslides. In 1959 Madison Canyon in Montana was near the epicenter of an earthquake measuring 7.5 on the Richter scale. Eighty million tons of rock slid into the Madison River, creating a lake nearly as large as the one formed by the Gros Ventre slide. So violent was the slide that the winds it created could be felt miles away. Other earthquake-triggered landslides—at least seventy-eight of them—occurred during and after the 1964 Alaska earthquake, which was rated 9.2 on the Richter scale. Many of these landslides were under water in the ocean, triggering some deadly tsunamis.

Debris slides include earthflows, mudflows, and avalanches. In an *earthflow*, a portion of earth slides away from its original location and moves downhill as a flexible solid. In a *mudflow*, a mixture of earth, water, and rock flows down a slope as a semi-liquid. Its consistency is similar to that of newly mixed concrete. If the debris is volcanic, such a mudflow is called a *lahar*. An *avalanche* of ice and snow often includes much rock and dirt.

18B Section Review

1. What is the downhill movement of large masses of soil or rock under the influence of gravity called? What factors can lead to this kind of earth movement?

2. What kind of evidence indicates that creep is occurring? What are two ways to prevent damage to a building due to creep?

3. What is rapid mass wasting that involves detached pieces of bedrock called?

4. List three kinds of debris slides. What is one common cause of debris slides?

5. (True or False) Rock glaciers occur only in areas where the soil remains frozen most of the year.

18C STREAM EROSION

18.10 Introduction

A significant force in the wearing down of the earth's surface is running water. Water can **erode** soil and rocks. The most consistent water erosion comes from streams.

18.11 Definition of Stream

A **stream** is a confined body of water that flows either continuously or seasonally on the earth's surface or underground. The term can be applied correctly to the smallest creek or the mightiest river. The highest point of a stream is its **headwaters** or **source**. The Mississippi River, for example, has several sources in high mountainous regions. Near its source, a stream may be merely a trickle. Typically, the headwaters of a stream have a high **gradient**, or change in height for each horizontal meter of distance it flows. This means streams are generally steeper near their sources.

Objectives—Section 18C

Upon completing this section, students should be able to

- describe the anatomy of a stream from source to mouth.
- contrast high- and low-gradient streams.
- describe the features of stream basins and the divides between them.
- list the two types of eroded materials that a stream may carry.
- describe three types of stream depositional features.

Answers to 18B Section Review Questions

1. The downhill movement of large masses of soil or rock under the influence of gravity is called *mass wasting*. The slope of the land, the vegetation of the area, and the presence of water all influence the rate of mass wasting. (§18.7)

2. Creep is indicated by telephone poles, stone walls, buildings, or fence posts on a slope becoming tilted after a period of time. Answers may vary, but protecting a building from soil creep may include building a retaining wall upslope, anchoring the building in bedrock and allowing the soil to flow around it, or removing the creeping soil completely. (§18.8)

3. The rapid mass wasting that involves bedrock is called a *rockslide*. (§18.9)

4. Three kinds of debris slides are *earthflows*, *mudflows*, and *avalanches*. Causes vary but may include earthquakes and heavy precipitation. (§18.9)

5. True. (§18.8)

18-1	NOTABLE RIVERS		
Name	Location	Length (km)†	Interesting facts
Nile	Africa	6650	world's longest river; passes through desert; waters used for extensive irrigation; birthplace of ancient Egypt
Amazon	South America	6400	world's largest river basin; ⅕ of the world's discharge of water; over 1000 tributaries; floods 350,000 sq km (135,000 sq mi) of forest each year; home to the largest freshwater fish, largest snake, and "man-eating" piranha
Yangtze	Asia	6300	irrigates the "rice bowl" of China
Mississippi-Missouri	North America	6020	although the Mississippi River flows from northern Minnesota to the Gulf of Mexico, the Missouri River (a tributary) is longer; third largest river basin in the world
Hwang Ho	Asia	5464	muddiest river in the world; has changed its course 26 times; birthplace of China; more people killed by flooding than with any other river; called "China's sorrow" for that reason
Ob-Irtysh	Asia	5410	flows into the Arctic Ocean; passes through peat bogs and frozen tundra; frozen about half the year
Amur	Asia	4416	longest river in Siberia; forms border between China and Russia
Lena	Asia	4400	flows into Arctic Ocean; its mouth is frozen most of the year; may freeze completely solid, contains the second largest delta in the world
Congo	Africa	4373	rapids and waterfall near its mouth; second in volume only to the Amazon
Mackenzie	North America	4241	flows into the Arctic Ocean; frozen $2/3$ of the year; ice bridges for truck traffic are built across it in the winter at Fort Providence
Mekong	Asia	4183	a major international border in Southeast Asia
Niger	Africa	4180	source is only 240 km (150 mi) from the coast; flows inland and north-east from its source and southeast at its mouth
Yenisey	Asia	4092	empties into the Arctic Ocean through a delta that is frozen $3/4$ of the year; radioactively contaminated by a Cold War–era plutonium reactor
Paraná	South America	3998	basin extends from southern Brazil to northern Argentina
Murray-Darling	Australia	3717	only major river on the continent
Volga	Europe	3690	Europe's longest river; Moscow, Russia's capital, was built on its banks
Yukon	North America	3185	frozen $3/4$ of the year; site of the longest canoe and kayak race in the world annually; origin of the Klondike gold rush
Rio Grande	North America	3034	border between U.S. and Mexico; shifts in the river's course have led to border disputes; swift currents often lead to the deaths of illegal immigrants
Ganges-Brahmaputra	Asia	2897	one of the dirtiest rivers in the world; holy river to the Hindus
Indus	Asia	2896	gave India its name; elevation at source is 5500 m (18,000 ft) in the Himalayan Mountains of Tibet
Danube	Europe	2850	flows through 13 countries; Vienna, Austria's capital, was built on its banks; empties into the Black Sea
Tigris-Euphrates	Asia	2800	"the cradle of civilization;" Babylon and Assyria were built on its banks; watered Abraham's homeland, Ur of the Chaldees
Zambezi	Africa	2736	contains Victoria Falls, a natural wonder of the world

†Estimates of lengths vary depending on the reference and the location chosen as the river's source.

This table is provided for interest only. It is not necessary for students to memorize this information.

The base level of the Jordan River is the Dead Sea.

 Visual 18-3: River Basin

A river's drainage basin includes all the area drained by its tributaries between its headwaters and its mouth.

Pause for a moment to consider the idea that most large lakes in the world are of relatively recent origin according to the Flood geology model. This is a reasonable conclusion based on the presupposition that the entire earth's surface was covered by the floodwaters according to the Bible and reshaped by massive movement of sediments. It is possible that many lakes today, especially in the higher latitudes, are a direct result of glaciation in the Ice Age following the Flood.

 Visual 18-4: Stream Gradient

This visual is an annotated reproduction of Figure 18-14. The purpose of this visual is to illustrate how stream gradient is determined. If your students are familiar with the mathematical concept of slope, explain that a stream's gradient is similar to the slope of a linear graph. A graph's slope is found by dividing the change in the graph's ordinate (Δy) by the change in its abscissa (Δx). Similarly, the stream gradient is found by dividing the stream's vertical change in height by the horizontal distance it flows. Both graphical slope and gradient indicate the steepness of their respective systems. The stream gradient is mathematically equal to the tangent of the stream's angle of descent from the horizontal.

 Visual 18-5: Drainage Basin Divides of the Contiguous United States

This visual is a reproduction of Figure 18-16 (right). Note that there are three principal drainage basins within the contiguous United States. They drain into four bodies of water—the Pacific, the Atlantic, the Gulf of Mexico, and the Gulf of California.

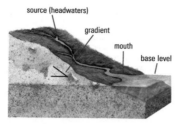

18-14 Profile of a typical stream

tributary (TRIB you TEHR ee)

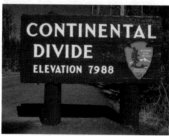

18-15 Many tributaries drain this drainage basin near New Plymouth, New Zealand.

CONTINENTAL DIVIDE
ELEVATION 7988

18-16 This sign (above) is at the south entrance of Yellowstone National Park in Wyoming. The North American continental divide (right) is found in the Rocky Mountains. The eastern continental divide separates drainage basins but technically is not a "continental" divide.

The point at which a stream flows into another body of water is its **mouth**. The mouth may be in an ocean, a lake, or another river. The mouth of the Amazon is in the Atlantic Ocean. The mouth of the Jordan River is in the Dead Sea. The mouth of the Missouri River, in contrast, is in the Mississippi River. The lowest level to which a stream can flow is called its **base level**. For many streams this is the level of the lakes into which they flow, but the ultimate base level for most streams is sea level. Exceptions occur, however. The Jordan River has a base level more than 400 m (1360 ft) *below* sea level.

From a uniformitarian view, if the present processes of erosion were to continue long enough, most lakes would fill in with sediment carried by the stream, becoming part of the stream bed as the stream continued its way down toward its ultimate base level. Uniformitarian geologists consider the base level the lowest point to which a stream can erode. Therefore they believe lakes are only temporary base levels for streams. Within a creationary model, however, lakes that exist today came into existence immediately following the Flood or, in more recent years, because of glacier retreats or human efforts. Slow sedimentation rates for most large deep lakes indicate that they will be around for many thousands of years to come.

Streams are fed by other, usually smaller, streams called **tributaries**. Tributaries flow into the main stream. A stream and its tributaries are a *stream system*. Seen from above, a river system often resembles the veins in a leaf. The land drained by a system is the main stream's **drainage basin**. The size of the drainage basin differs for different streams. For a small stream, it may be only a few hundred square kilometers; for the Amazon, it is more than 7.1 million km^2 (2.7 million mi^2)—a third of South America. A ridge separating one stream's drainage basin from another's is called a **divide**. The Rocky Mountains form the Continental Divide of the United States. The land east of the Rockies is drained largely by the Mississippi River system and others whose waters flow into the Gulf of Mexico and Atlantic Ocean. The land west of the Rockies is drained by several river systems whose waters flow into the Pacific Ocean or the Gulf of California.

18.12 High-Gradient Streams

The stream's gradient determines its appearance. *High-gradient streams* tend to be energetic and turbulent. Such streams, found in mountainous or hilly regions, are characterized by steep sides and deep channels of water that occupy almost all the lower parts of the narrow valleys. These streams often have waterfalls and rapids. High-gradient streams also tend to vigorously erode their beds downward. Their steep-sided valleys tend to experience mass wasting.

Waterfalls form in several ways: by faulting, by the bulldozing action of glaciers, and by the unequal erosion of rocks. A classic example of the last method is Niagara Falls, where the water flows over the lip of the sturdy dolomite rock ledge that forms the riverbed and erodes the underlying softer shale more rapidly. The erosion undercuts the dolomite, creating a steep cliff over which the water falls.

Rapids are places where the slope is steep and the rocks in the streambed are irregular. The flow of the water is turbulent, with many small eddy currents. The rockiness and the shallowness of most rapids make them dangerous or unnavigable with even a small boat. Rapids can form from a waterfall that has degenerated by extensive erosion.

Lakes frequently form connecting links between high-gradient streams. A lake usually has a stream that feeds its upper end and another stream that drains its lower end. Because the water flows from the upper to the lower end, the lake does not stagnate. The continuous drainage at the lower end keeps dissolved minerals from accumulating in the water, and the lake stays fresh instead of becoming salty. Not all lakes have outlet streams. The Great Salt Lake of Utah, the Salton Sea of California, and the Dead Sea in the Middle East are well-known examples. They have become salty because they receive minerals dissolved in the streams that feed them, but they lose water only by evaporation, which traps and concentrates the minerals in the lake.

18.13 Low-Gradient Streams

Low-gradient streams have less energy than high-gradient streams because the water flow is slower. Water energy is dependent mostly on the speed of flow. These streams wind back and forth on a rather flat area known as a **floodplain**, which is covered with water when the stream floods. Falls and rapids are rare on floodplains, and stream erosion occurs mostly sideways against the stream banks. Ridges of soil, called **levees**, are often present on both sides of these streams. These are the deposits of sediment formed when the stream floods.

A typical low-gradient stream consists of many snaking curves called **meanders**. The water erodes soil from the outside of each meander and deposits sand and soil on the inside. During a flood the stream water may cut across the narrow part of a meander (the *neck*) and establish a new route called a **neck cutoff**. The meander that is bypassed may dry up, or it may retain some water to become an **oxbow lake**.

18-17 A high-gradient stream in Yosemite National Park

levee (LEV ee)

meander (mee AN dur)

18-19 Characteristic features of a low-gradient stream

18-18 Oxbow Lake on the Wairau River near Blenheim, New Zealand

The Hwang He (also called the Hwang Ho or the Yellow River) in China derives its name and its color from the silt it removes from the Loess Plateau. It carries so much silt that during its frequent floods its channel is reshaped, which changes the river's course and sometimes takes it through villages and cities. This problem causes so many drowning deaths that the river has acquired the nickname "China's Sorrow."

Streams often form the boundaries for counties, states, countries, and private properties. Therefore, it is frequently important to stop the sideways erosion of low-gradient streams as they meander. The means most often employed to do this are artificial levees. *Mainline* levees generally parallel the main channel or its tributaries. *Ring* levees encircle an area to protect it from flood damage. *Spur* levees are projections from mainline levees that deflect currents so as to prevent erosion of the mainline levee. *Setback* levees provide backup in the event the mainline levee fails. *Sublevees* are subterranean barriers to seepage under mainline or ring levees. Artificial levees reduce the erosion problems where used but may increase erosion and flooding problems downstream.

FACETS OF GEOLOGY

THE GRAND CANYON

Most people in the United States at one time or another hear evolutionary propaganda about the Grand Canyon. It may be in the classroom, on television, or in newspapers, books, or magazines. It could come from the lips of a tour guide speaking to a group of awestruck viewers touring the natural wonder.

The Grand Canyon is nothing if not awe inspiring; it is 350 km (217 mi) long, 1.6 km (1 mi) at its deepest point, and from 6.4 km (4 mi) to 29 km (18 mi) in width. To a Christian, it declares the power of God and the truth of the Genesis record; but evolutionists see it differently. They say that the exposed sedimentary strata in the canyon represent hundreds of millions of years of deposition followed by millions of years of erosion.

The fossils in the strata, they say, tell the story of how life developed on the earth. This differs in every respect from what God's Word tells us.

One creationary explanation of the Grand Canyon is that most of the exposed strata of the canyon represent sediment deposited during the Genesis Flood. Much of the erosion may have happened shortly after the Flood, when the material was still soft and unconsolidated (not compacted and cemented), and large amounts of water were moving from the continents to the oceans. Rivers undoubtedly carried much more water soon after the Flood than they do now. As the strata of the canyon hardened and the volume of water in the river decreased, erosion became slower and less extensive. Photographs show that the most recent erosion, at the bottom of the canyon, has been confined to a narrow region on either side of the river.

Creationary scientists have conducted several research projects to gain additional insight into the history of the Grand Canyon. One of these investigated the discovery of pollen grains of gymnosperm and angiosperm plants in the lowest strata of the canyon. According to evolutionists, those plants did not exist until several million years after they think these strata formed. Another project investigated a thick layer of sand-stone visible in the canyon walls that most geologists agreed represented sand dunes deposited in a desert over millions of years. Following experimentation, a creationary researcher demonstrated that the sand must have been deposited under deep flowing waters. Steven Austin, a sedimentary geologist with the Institute for Creation Research, has used uniformitarian radioactive dating techniques to show that solidified lava layers near the top of the canyon, which actually flowed over the rim, were dated to be older than lava rocks buried deeply under the lowest strata. This finding is contrary to the principle of superposition and thus invalidates the billion or more years evolutionary geologists give for the deposition of the rocks forming the Grand Canyon. Much other evidence is accumulating that the rocks forming the Grand Canyon, as well as the canyon itself, came into existence during a recent catastrophic flood. Additional dedicated creationary geologists are needed to push forward this kind of research to refute the claims of evolutionary, naturalistic geologists and proclaim the truth and reasonableness of God's Word.

★ denotes pollen find

Triassic
Permian
Carboniferous
Cambrian
Precambrian
Precambrian
Colorado River

Cutaway view of the Grand Canyon showing where fossil pollen has been found—evolutionists claim the pollen should not be found below the stratum marked with the arrow.

A group of Creationists studying the Grand Canyon

Facet Summary: The Grand Canyon

This Facet presents evidence that the Grand Canyon was formed as the consequence of the relatively recent Flood rather than over millions of years. Ongoing creationary research in the canyon is presented. There are no vocabulary terms in this Facet.

18.14 Effects of Streams

Stream erosion moves topsoil from the continents and deposits it in the oceans. The amount of material transported by this process is staggering. Several billion metric tons of dissolved minerals flow into the oceans each year, never to be recovered. Another 24 million metric tons of topsoil are lost the same way. In the United States alone, erosion amounts to an estimated topsoil loss of more than 11 cm (4 in.) every thousand years.

The story of erosion begins on mountain slopes and hillsides as rain falls. Raindrops striking the ground splash soil particles in all directions. On the average, the particles move farther downhill than uphill; hence, the overall motion is downward. At the same time, rainwater moving downhill carries soil with it. The greatest erosion occurs when a stream is at flood stage. It usually reaches flood stage in the spring when the stream is moving a large amount of snowmelt rapidly.

Another process of erosion on hillsides, called **solution**, occurs when moving water dissolves minerals from the soil and carries them away. The rainwater from the slopes flows into small streams, which in turn join larger streams. Most stream water eventually reaches an ocean.

Stream water carries two kinds of eroded materials: suspended particles, which are carried along by the water's motion, and dissolved substances. The amount of suspended material a stream can carry depends on the speed of the stream. A fast-moving stream can carry more and larger particles than a slow-moving stream. Eventually, however, the water in a fast stream slows down because of friction with its stream bed and the drag within the water itself. When it does, the stream drops some of its suspended load as sediment. *Deposition*, the depositing of transported materials, occurs in an orderly fashion, with larger particles falling out first as the stream slows. The progression continues as smaller and smaller particles settle out. The finest particles—silt—do not settle until the water becomes almost stationary.

What do stream deposits look like? You have probably seen such deposits, although you may not have recognized them. Floodplains form from stream sediment deposited during floods. Another type of stream deposit is the **delta**. A delta forms where a stream enters a lake, an ocean, a gulf, or other large body of water. Where a high-gradient stream flows out from a mountain valley onto a level plain, its

Stones of Witness

May a Christian properly devote his life to managing soil erosion along the Mississippi River? Why or why not?

18-20 A flooding stream can carry a large amount of eroded soil.

18-21 Delta of the Nile River in Egypt—the branching channels in a delta are called distributaries.

Stones of Witness

We trust that by this point in the course, the students will answer with an enthusiastic *yes*! To defend their response, perhaps they will cite Genesis 1:28, which states that humans are to "subdue" the earth. Managing soil erosion is an aspect of attempting to "subdue" the destructive forces of the earth. Students may also cite Genesis 2:15, which states that God placed Adam in the garden "to dress it and to keep it." Humans today may be engaged in a similarly honorable task when they attempt to preserve useful farmland. As with any attempt to obey the Creation Mandate, this task should be motivated by love for God and love for one's fellow man (Mark 12:29–31).

By preserving the earth from destruction, we show our Maker that we value the good things He has given us. By maximizing the usefulness of our land's resources, we show our fellow humans that we value their well-being. The gospel is not lost in such an endeavor. By valuing for divine reasons the very things that unbelievers value for selfish reasons, we open the door to many profound opportunities to share the gospel.

Demonstration: Suspended Sediment

Have a student who lives near a fast-moving stream bring in a sample of water taken from near the bottom of the stream (without actually scraping the bottom). Let the sediments in the water settle, and examine the jar to see how much soil is at the bottom. This is soil that has been moved by the action of the stream.

Demonstration: Ordered Deposition

Add several inches of various kinds of sediment to a large jar—small pebbles, fine silt, coarse sand, gravel, and so on. Fill the jar with water and shake it. Set the jar upright quickly. The sediment will fall fast. Note how the sediment settles in layers, with the bigger pieces at the bottom and the smaller pieces nearer the top. This demonstrates a stream's orderly deposition, called *sorting* by hydrologists. The sorting process can be seen even more clearly if the agitation of the water is reduced gradually over several minutes. Distinct layers of sediments sorted by particle sizes will emerge.

Visual 18-6: Deltas and an Alluvial Fan

The alluvial fan is on the bottom left of this visual. Point out that an alluvial fan looks like a delta but is on land, usually in arid climates, instead of at the stream's mouth. Deltas are so named because of the triangular shape, resembling the Greek letter delta (Δ). The branched distributary channels of a delta form when the sluggish stream deposits so much sediment that the bottom builds up, diverting the stream in several directions. The Mississippi delta is a classic example, showing multiple distributaries.

FACETS OF GEOLOGY

CONTROLLING EROSION

Pedologists (soil scientists) believe that before the settlement of Jamestown, the United States had an average of about 20 cm (8 in.) of topsoil. Today that depth is only 15 cm (6 in.). Scientists still do not know of an economical way to make more topsoil. Therefore, we must learn to conserve what we have.

Several methods can help control soil erosion. A simple way is to plant vegetation in areas likely to erode. Plant roots hold soil in place well. Because worn-out soil produces only scattered, weak plants that are sometimes unable to hold back erosion, restoring the productivity of the soil is important. Crop rotation with soil-building plants is one of several important preventive measures.

Gravity acts directly on water flowing downhill to cause soil erosion. Through contour plowing and planting, farmers arrange crop rows at right angles to the direction the water flows. This arrangement forms many small dams that check the flow of water. No-till agriculture limits erosion by planting without plowing or breaking up the soil surface; thus, it is not as open to erosion. Strip-cropping, the practice of interspersing strips of row crops such as corn with strips of cover crops such as grass and alfalfa, also helps prevent erosion. Cover crops are plants that have many small roots close to the surface of the soil. To further slow erosion, property owners may terrace a slope by grading it into nearly level areas with walls around the steep sides.

Flooding is a major problem in some parts of the United States. Not only do floods cause the loss of life and property,

but they also rapidly displace large amounts of valuable soil. Although this soil may settle downstream in a useful location, it is more likely to settle in the bottom of a river or lake where it can no longer grow crops.

Artificial levees, or walls, on either side of the river are one solution to this problem. These work reasonably well in some areas but prove inadequate in others. Their flaw is that they confine the sediment that normally spreads out over the river's entire floodplain to the river channel. As sediment is deposited in the channel, the stream becomes shallower, causing the water to rise higher the next year. In order to contain floods, the levees must be built progressively higher or moved out farther from the river, or both. Though dredging the sediment from the channel is possible, it is costly.

Another approach to the problem of flooding is to build temporary reservoirs along the course of a river. At flood stage, these reservoirs take much of the overflow and store it until the river recedes. The reservoirs then slowly discharge the water back into the river.

Soil is one of our most valuable resources. We need soil to raise crops to feed ourselves and our livestock and to grow fruit trees and trees that we can use for lumber and paper products. Soil is just one more essential component in the complex world God created. Without soil, life on land would not be possible. In order to properly fulfill the Creation Mandate (Gen. 1:28), a good citizen will do his part to help his fellow humans in the effort to conserve soil.

Strip-cropping (top) and terracing (middle) can control erosion. Soil erosion damage (below, both).

Facet Summary: Controlling Erosion

This Facet presents the need for erosion control as well as several techniques for accomplishing it. The role of flooding and flood control in soil conservation is also discussed. There are no vocabulary terms in this Facet.

The Badwater alluvial fan is relatively small compared to others. The largest alluvial fan in the United States is the Cedar Creek alluvial fan to the east of Ennis, Montana. The stream flows west from a valley in the Madison Mountains and spreads out over a fan of sediment that extends more than four miles to the north, west, and south. The Cedar Creek fan is considered to be one of the world's classic alluvial fans.

18-22 The Badwater alluvial fan in Death Valley, California (left). The contour map (right) shows the fanlike distribution of the stream sediment.

speed is suddenly reduced, and an **alluvial fan** may form. The alluvial fan looks like a delta spreading out from a mountain pass, but it is on land, usually in arid climates, instead of at the stream's mouth. Floodplains and deltas are built from topsoil eroded farther upstream and thus contain some of the most fertile soils and are among the most agriculturally productive areas on the earth.

> alluvial (uh LOO vee ul); from *alluvium*—material deposited by a stream or river on the floor of its valley.

18C   Section Review

1. What is the rate of drop of a stream called? How does this characteristic affect the amount of sediment a stream can carry?

2. What is the ultimate base level for most streams? Can a stream flow below this ultimate base level? Explain.

3. What are smaller streams that flow into larger streams called? What are streams that result from the subdivision of a larger stream called?

4. What is the main difference in energy contained in high-gradient and low-gradient streams?

5. What is a looping bend in the path of a low-gradient stream called? What often occurs to these bends with time?

6. What form of erosion occurs when water dissolves minerals and removes them from the soil?

7. Compare alluvial fans with deltas.

8. (True or False) From the North American continental divide, streams flow west into the Pacific Ocean or Gulf of California or east to the Gulf of Mexico or the Atlantic Ocean.

9. (True or False) Evolutionists believe the Grand Canyon was formed slowly by erosion over millions of years, but Creationists believe it formed quickly as the waters flowed off the continent after Noah's Flood or as a result of a great inland lake emptying some years after the Flood.

Answers to 18C Section Review Questions

1. The rate of drop of a stream (the change in height for each horizontal meter of distance that it flows) is its *gradient*. (§18.11) Higher-gradient streams can carry more sediment because they move faster and are more turbulent. (§18.14)

2. The ultimate base level for most streams is *sea level*. Streams can flow below sea level if they are flowing into a depression that lies below sea level. Examples of this include the Jordan River and rivers in the Netherlands and Djibouti. (§18.11)

3. Smaller streams that flow into larger streams are called *tributaries*. Smaller streams that are subdivisions of a larger stream are called *distributaries*. (§18.11, 18.14)

4. A high-gradient stream has more energy than a low-gradient stream because its water is flowing faster (more kinetic energy). (§18.12–18.13)

5. A looping bend in a low-gradient stream is called a *meander*. The river often cuts off a meander, forming a neck cutoff or an oxbow lake. (§18.13)

6. The erosion that occurs when water dissolves minerals and removes them from the soil is called *solution erosion*. (§18.14)

7. An alluvial fan is created when a high-gradient stream flows onto a level plain and deposits its load of sediment in a fanlike formation. A delta is similar to an alluvial fan but is formed at a river's mouth, where the river enters a large body of water, such as the ocean. (§18.14)

8. True. Note that this statement applies to the United States. In Canada, streams may also flow north into Hudson Bay or the Arctic Ocean. (§18.11)

9. True. (Facet, p. 476)

CHAPTER REVIEW

In Terms of Geology

Chapter Summary

- The earth's surface is worn down by weathering, mass wasting, and erosion.

- Weathering changes the shape, size, and composition of rocks through mechanical and/or chemical processes. The ultimate result of weathering is that massive rocks are reduced to fine particles that form new soil.

- Chemical weathering often occurs because of carbonic acid or biological acids from plants and lichens (as well as other chemicals, such as oxygen).

- Mechanical weathering may involve biological agents such as plant roots, frost and salt wedging, expansion and contraction due to temperature changes, and abrasion by wind- or water-borne particles.

- Weathering produces the raw materials of soil. Fertile soil is the proper combination of sand, clay, silt, and decayed organic matter (humus). Soil may form slowly or rapidly, depending on factors that encourage the weathering and deposition of soil-forming materials in a given location.

- Mass wasting is the downhill movement of large quantities of soil and/or rocks under the influence of gravity. Mass wasting may be a slow or rapid process. In populated areas, mass wasting can have significant impact on structures and the lives of residents.

- A stream is any confined body of water that flows continuously or seasonally on the earth's surface or underground. The rate of flow depends on the gradient of the streambed.

- High-gradient streams are energetic and rapidly erode their stream beds downward. They can carry relatively large quantities of debris, and the particle sizes tend to be larger than in low-gradient streams.

- Low-gradient streams have low energy and flow relatively slowly. They can carry large amounts of finely divided sediment but not large particles or rocks. They erode sideways and form meanders, levees, floodplains, and oxbow lakes.

- Stream erosion removes immense quantities of topsoil annually. Sediment can form alluvial fans and deltas where a stream deposits its sediment load at a base level. This eroded topsoil is replaced upstream through the weathering process.

Answers to Chapter Review Questions

What Did You Learn?

1. Humic acid from decaying plants and acid from lichens can chemically weather rocks. Roots and germinating seeds can mechanically weather rocks by enlarging cracks and splitting the rocks. (§18.2–18.3)

2. Weathered rock is more rounded, pitted, and discolored compared to the native unweathered rock. (§18.2–18.3)

3. The A-horizon is the most fertile because it has the most organic material, oxygen, and water. (§18.5)

4. Answers will vary. Factors mentioned in the text include steepness of slope, weak materials or layers of material that do not stick well to each other, heavy precipitation or water saturation that lubricates the layers of debris, and earthquakes. (§18.9)

5. Answers will vary depending on location. Locate the largest river, creek, or brook on a map and follow it until it enters another stream or a large body of water. (§18.11)

6. A boat on a low-gradient stream might travel extra distance because stream meanders increase the actual distance traveled between two locations compared to the direct, point-to-point distance. (§18.13)

7. Six methods for controlling soil erosion are planting vegetation (cover crops), crop rotation, contour plowing, no-till agriculture, strip-cropping, and terracing. (Facet, p. 478)

True or False

8. True. (§18.2)

9. True. (§18.3)

10. False. If the implications of the Bible's description of the Flood are understood, it is without question that the original soils were lost when they were completely mixed with other sediments or buried during the Flood. (§18.4)

11. False. Most deserts are teeming with both plant and animal species that thrive in desert climates.

12. True. (§18.6)

13. False. Rock glaciers are essentially normal glaciers containing much more rock than ice. (§18.8)

What Did You Learn?

1. How do plants weather rocks?

2. How can you tell that a piece of rock has been weathered?

3. Which soil horizon is most fertile? Why?

4. What three factors can increase the likelihood of a rock or debris slide?

5. What is the base level for the largest stream that flows near your school?

6. Why might a boat have to travel 2 or 3 miles on a low-gradient stream to travel between two towns that are 1 mile apart?

7. List six methods for controlling soil erosion.

True or False

8. Chemical weathering can result in both a change of composition and a change in shape.

9. In general, a lack of talus at the base of a rock cliff indicates that the rock is resistant to mechanical weathering.

10. God preserved the original, very good soils for our use today.

11. Deserts are vast areas of hot sand dunes where nothing living can survive.

12. Soils can form relatively quickly (in a matter of months or a few years).

13. Rock glaciers occur only in the tropics where it is too warm for true glaciers to exist.

14. Just like the pressure gradient we discussed in Chapter 11, the stream gradient represents a change in something compared to horizontal distance over ground.

What Do You Think?

1. You are considering going into business manufacturing artificial topsoil to replace soil eroded off farmland. What questions must you answer to ensure that your business will be as profitable as possible?

2. Are soil and dirt the same thing?

3. Two building sites are offered to you. One is on a hillside fenced in with a row of picturesque, tilted old fence posts covered with beautiful rose bushes. The other is on a hillside as well, but it has a row of unsightly, weathered, vertical telephone poles covered with kudzu vines. On which site would you choose to build your house? Why?

4. Should soil from deltas or dredged rivers be transported back to eroded farmland?

5. Should people be allowed to live on floodplains? Consider legal, practical, and responsibility aspects.

6. Why can we not use the amount of talus to determine the age of a cliff?

My Review Checklist

☐ I have carefully read the entire chapter.

☐ I have reviewed all of the photographs, illustrations, and graphs.

☐ I have reviewed all of my notes in the margins.

☐ I have reviewed and corrected the quizzes on this chapter.

☐ I have studied all of the vocabulary terms.

☐ I have had all of my questions answered.

14. True. The pressure gradient is the change of atmospheric pressure with distance over ground. Stream gradient is the change of height with distance over ground, expressed as a decimal. (§18.11)

What Do You Think?

1. Answers will vary. The questions would include the following: Who would buy artificial topsoil? How much would they be willing to pay for it? Where could you find sufficiently large and cheap quantities of the raw materials (sand, silt, clay, and humus)? How would you mix them? What would mixing cost? What would the packaging and transportation costs be? What would the profit be? What volume of business would you need to make a decent living?

2. While soil has a scientific definition, dirt has a less distinct definition and connotations that can mean anything from soil to filth. A pedologist might view calling soil "dirt" the same way a gemologist would view calling a precious cut diamond a "rock."

3. The site with the telephone poles would be the better choice. Both the rose bushes and kudzu vines tell you the fence and the telephone poles have not been replaced recently, and the weathered condition of both implies they have been in place for many years. The site with the tilted fence posts is experiencing soil creep while the site with the vertical telephone poles is not.

4. There is no easy answer to this question. It would seem to be logical that you could just scoop up the sedimentary mud and redistribute it to the farmlands from where it came. However, there are many problems with this idea. First, dredging up the mud, transporting it somewhere to dry out, then transporting it back to farms upstream is a huge and expensive logistical problem. Add to that the fact that the sediment is mixed with all kinds of natural and man-made debris, such as tree trunks, construction materials, and other refuse purposely or accidentally discarded into the stream, all of which needs to be removed. Finally, scientists know that physical processes and bacterial activity in sediments can concentrate toxins and other adverse chemicals in the sediments that would then be transferred to farmland if such a soil replenishment program was implemented. Overall, it is much more economical (and safer) to build up soil and limit soil erosion at the source than to dredge deltas and streams to recover eroded soil.

5. There are three elements to this question: what is legal, what is practical, and what is responsible. In the United States, people believe in having the freedom to live wherever they want to live if they can afford it and it is not otherwise prohibited. Most people who live within a floodplain do so because of economic reasons that often outweigh the risks of infrequent floods. These reasons may include the fact that farming is more productive in floodplains, a city's commerce is dependent on a riverfront, or a person prefers to have a short commute to work. These practical considerations will often dictate that a person resides within a floodplain. However, the associated risks of flooding may make residing in certain locations unreasonable. Insurance companies will not insure buildings located too close to a river known to flood often or will require such high premiums that a person cannot afford to build in that location. The costs to the community that result when a residential area is flooded are very high. For this reason, zoning boards will limit or prohibit construction in certain locations to limit losses during floods. So, ultimately, what is responsible and practical is often limited by what is legal.

6. As with any other uniformitarian model, the rate of accumulation cannot be used to scientifically determine the age of a cliff that was not observed as it formed. Assumptions that would have to be made include establishing the original size and shape of the cliff, the uniformity of weathering processes, the rate at which talus was removed by additional weathering forces, and the uniformity of the cliff materials. If any of these factors are known to be non-uniform, then additional assumptions would have to be made to account for their effects.

Emil Silvestru was born in 1954 in a small town in the Transylvania province of Romania. This was a time of severe Communist repression, secret-police domination, and fear. At the age of twelve he became fascinated with the caves and other karst features of this region. In 1979 he was awarded a master's degree in geology from the state university in Cluj, the capital of Transylvania province. His graduate studies were then interrupted for 10 years because the Communist dictator Nicolae Ceausescu had put his wife Elena in charge of deciding what courses of study the state university could offer, and she ruled against a doctoral program in geology.

Mr. Silvestru spent seven years in geological explorations in northern Romania, finding deposits of lead and zinc ores. He also published several research papers on karstology. In 1986 he began working as a researcher at the Emil Racovitza Speleological Institute in Cluj, where he became the head scientist. As an associate professor, he also taught geology subjects at the university, and he earned his PhD there after the 1989 overthrow of the Communist government made it possible. His renown as an authority on karst geology is worldwide.

Dr. Silvestru's wife, Flory, was a Baptist believer. She was living dangerously in a Communist country: she read her Bible regularly and attended secret meetings where Christian movies were shown. Most of the movies were American made, and Flory arranged for her husband to go with her to translate the English for the other seekers. Eventually this, along with several miraculous escapes from near-fatal accidents and his wife's faithful secret prayers for him, brought Dr. Silvestru to a saving knowledge of Jesus Christ. He quickly realized that there was a conflict between his scientific "knowledge" and the scriptural account of the Creation and the Flood. One by one he examined his evolutionist, uniformitarian doctrines and found that they were based upon wild assumptions and not on fact. In 2002 Dr. Silvestru and his wife and two daughters moved to Canada, where he is working as a lecturer and full-time researcher for Answers in Genesis, a creationary science and evangelistic organization.

THE HYDROSPHERE
unit 5

Emil Silvestru: Hydrogeologist

The present is not the key to the past! More than 75% of all known rocks are sedimentary, most of which are believed to have been formed in the oceans. Over 90% of the rocks formed in the oceans were laid in shallow oceans. But only 10% of present-day oceans are shallow. The sediments the oceans hold are insignificant compared to the millions of tons of sedimentary rock. These facts clearly show that present processes of sedimentary rock formation are not the key to rock formation in the past!

My personal passion is speleology (the science of caves and their geology). I have concluded that most caves formed toward the end of the Flood, created by hot and very aggressive fluids called hydrothermal solutions that ate away the limestone in a matter of months. Modern caves have been re-shaped by carbon dioxide-rich waters that infiltrate cracks and joints in the limestone to form unique and beautiful formations.

God flooded the world with a global ocean which covered and eroded the continents. This is by far the most logical source of rock-forming and rock-eroding processes. Deep canyons cut miles below the ocean surface by forces not present today are scars bearing witness to the monumental forces present during the Flood.

This is why studying the oceans is crucial if you want to understand geologic history and appreciate the extent and uniqueness of God's judgment on the fallen world.

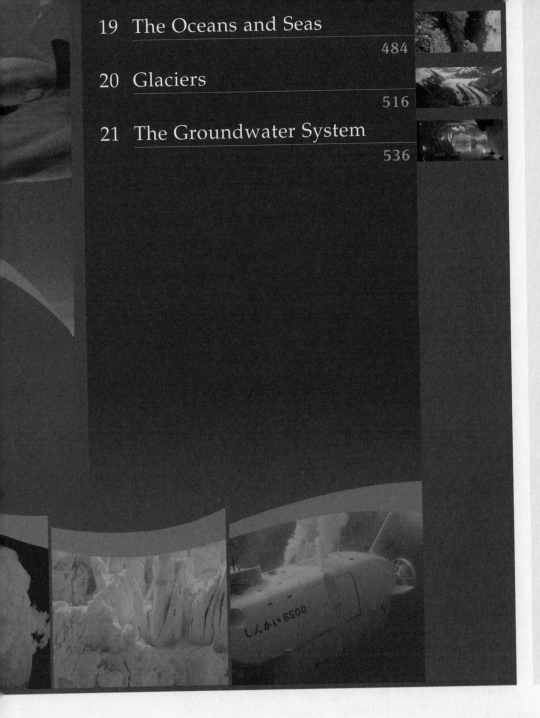

Overview

As the first chapter in the unit dealing with the hydrosphere—the waters of the earth—Chapter 19 logically introduces the fascinating arena of science called *physical oceanography*. Rather than being a distinct scientific discipline, oceanography is an assemblage of nearly every scientific area as it applies to the study of the oceans. This chapter can barely scratch the surface of such a vast body of knowledge, but it is certain that most of your students will become enthralled with what they will learn.

Section 19A identifies the four major oceans as well as general submarine and tectonic features of ocean basins. Coral reefs are introduced as biological structures that contribute to the features of ocean basins.

Section 19B describes the various chemical components of seawater as well as the processes by which minerals are added to and removed from the oceans. Water itself is the most valuable component of seawater, and we discuss two methods of desalinizing it.

Section 19C explores the tidal motions of the oceans, the wave action that erodes and modifies the shapes of shorelines, and the currents that transport waters all over the world.

Section 19D presents a brief history of scientific ocean exploration and describes some of the essential instruments used to explore the oceans.

Schedule Summary

Section 19A: 1–2 periods

Section 19B: 1–2 periods

Section 19C: 2–3 periods

Section 19D: 1–2 periods

Investigation Summary

19I "Desalting Seawater"

19J "Examining Density Currents"

 Bulletin Board Ideas

1. Display a large poster map of the world showing the topography of the ocean basins. Nearby, display a photographic view of the entire world without cloud cover to illustrate the difference between the ocean coastlines and the continental margins.

CHAPTER

19

THE OCEANS AND SEAS

SUGGESTED TEACHING SCHEDULE

DAY 0

Assignment

Reading: Section 19A, "Description of the Oceans"

DAY 1

Describe the physical arrangement and general features of the ocean bottom. Discuss the methods used in the past and present to measure the depths and shapes of the ocean basins. Note that the existence of numerous seamounts, trenches, and island arcs gives evidence for a geologically active past. Describe the biological contributions to ocean topography in the form of coral reefs. Do Applications 19F, "Ocean Basins."

This information may require two days to cover.

Assignment

Complete: 19A Section Review Questions
Applications 19E, "Ocean Topography"
Applications 19G, "Coral Reefs"

Reading: Section 19B, "Composition of Seawater"

DAY 2

Quiz—Section 19A, "Description of the Oceans"

Discuss several theories of the origin of salty oceans from a creationary viewpoint, showing that the current levels of salinity are consistent with a recent Creation and global Flood. Describe how minerals enter and leave the ocean waters to maintain a nearly constant salt concentration. Emphasize that among all the valuable substances present in the ocean, the fresh water it contains is the most precious resource. Discuss the methods for extracting potable water from seawater. Note the presence of gases dissolved in seawater and their distribution in the water column.

19A DESCRIPTION OF THE OCEANS

19.1 Introduction

The importance of the oceans cannot be overemphasized. The oceans cover about 71 percent of the earth's surface. The Pacific Ocean alone covers more area than all the landmasses put together. The oceans contain almost all of the earth's water—more than 97 percent. If the earth's crust were level, this immense quantity of water would cover it to a depth of 2.7 km (1.7 mi).

Oceanographers are scientists and engineers from almost every field who are striving to better understand and use the oceans. Marine biologists investigate the plant and animal life at different depths. Meteorologists study the influence of the oceans on weather and climate. Chemists analyze the distribution of various elements and compounds in the oceans and how those chemicals affect ocean processes. Physicists model the distribution of energy in the oceans and how the great currents move over the earth's surface. Engineers find ways to work and live on and in the oceans. They also develop methods to harness the energy of the ocean to generate electricity and find economical ways to produce drinking water from seawater. Studying the oceans improves our understanding of the earth. It also has practical benefits as we improve weather forecasts, find new sources of food, minerals, and energy, and discover safer means of transportation and recreation on the oceans.

Compared to land, the surface of the ocean appears flat and featureless. Perhaps that is why early scientists tended to ignore the ocean. Modern scientists have found that the ocean is far from featureless, though the features are not readily apparent to the eye, and that it has many interesting aspects to study. Its basins and its composition are among the topics that oceanographers study.

19.2 The Oceans

The oceans of the earth surround the landmasses. Because all oceans are connected, oceanographers sometimes say that the earth has only one ocean. For convenience, however, they usually divide the world ocean into three or four major parts: the Atlantic, Indian, Arctic, and Pacific oceans. Parts of these oceans are mostly surrounded by land and are called **seas**. For example, the Mediterranean Sea and the Caribbean Sea are usually considered branches of the Atlantic Ocean. Because knowledge of these oceans and seas was important for the development of international trade during the age of sailing ships, explorers studied and mapped the ocean as they mapped the land. Thus, the surface of the ocean and its boundaries are its best-known parts.

19-1 Major oceans and seas of the earth. Is the surface of the earth mostly land or mostly water?

Whether a body of water is called an ocean or a sea is not a matter of formal definition but rather of common usage. In general:

Oceans are the largest bodies of water, separating the continents.

Seas are small-to-large bodies of seawater, usually partially or almost completely surrounded by land.

Gulfs are defined in the same way as seas, but they tend to be smaller than seas.

2. Have students design underwater colonies along the same lines as the NASA Ames Space Colony competition, and post artistic illustrations of their designs on a bulletin board.

🜋 Field Trip Ideas

1. Visit a major aquarium near you. Make it a point to study the exhibits that deal with the local geology and physical environmental features of your locale (the biological exhibits are always interesting, but they should be saved for the end of your visit as you have time). Have students note and then write about any evolutionary or uniformitarian biases that they notice in the exhibits.

2. If you live near a coastline that exhibits several of the coastal features mentioned in the text, take a trip to inspect them. You could incorporate some simple experiments into the trip, including measuring longshore current speed and performing percolation tests of the beach sand at various distances away from the water.

Objectives—Section 19A

Upon completing this section, students should be able to

- state the location and names of the world's major oceans and seas.

- describe the general ocean basin topography from the continental shelves to the abyssal plains and the methods used to determine the profiles of these features.

- detail notable structures in each zone of an ocean basin.

- describe various kinds of coral reef formations and the significance of atolls.

🖳 Visual 19-1: World Maps of Oceans and Seas

Use this visual when introducing the concept that the earth is a water-covered planet. These images and those in Figure 19-1 are rendered in perspective in order to better illustrate how much of the earth's surface is covered by water.

Some authorities claim that the waters surrounding Antarctica south of Africa, South America, and Australia constitute a fifth major ocean called the *Southern Ocean*. This region has distinctive currents, wind patterns, climate, and biological communities that justify such a designation.

Assignment

Complete: 19B Section Review Questions

Reading: Section 19C-1 (§19.11–19.14), tides and mean sea level
Investigation 19I, "Desalting Seawater"

DAY 3

Quiz—Section 19B, "Composition of Seawater"

Do the preparatory steps of Investigation 19I, "Desalting Seawater," and start the boiling process. This investigation could be done as a demonstration while you are teaching the material for this period. Complete the investigation before the end of class.

Discuss the causes of ocean tides and their effects. Note that the periodicity of the tides is due to the earth's rotation beneath the tidal bulges in the oceans. Discuss the existence of exceptional tides due to special circumstances. Explain the difficulty in defining the reference sea level at any point on the earth's surface.

Assignment

Complete: 19C-1 Section Review Questions

Reading: Section 19C-2 (§19.15–19.17), wave structure and formation, wave action along shorelines, wave erosion

DAY 4

Discuss how waves are formed by wind action. Describe the basic structure and nomenclature of water waves. Illustrate how waves refract when they approach a shoreline and why they form breakers. Describe the currents formed by breaking waves. Note how waves erode and reshape coastlines through sediment deposition. Do Applications 19B, "Wave Motions," as a review exercise.

Assignment

Complete: 19C-2 Section Review Questions
Applications 19A, "Wave Structure"
Applications 19C, "Wave Erosion and Deposition"

Reading: Section 19C-3 (§19.18–19.19), surface and subsurface ocean currents

(schedule continued on p. 486)

The *Challenger* expedition is discussed in more detail in Section 19D.

A lead line consisted of a large lead weight attached to a rope that was marked in fathoms (6 ft intervals) or other units of distance. Water depth was measured by "taking a sounding." This involved stopping the vessel, dropping the weight over the side, and lowering the rope until it was felt to go slack. The depth mark on the rope was noted, and the weight was then reeled back in. For deep waters, this process was very laborious and often inaccurate if subsurface currents were present. Figure 19-36 on page 508 shows a ship taking a sounding with a lead line.

Sounding leads often included a blob of tallow or wax pressed into the end of the lead weight. When the lead hit bottom and was hauled back on board, the navigator examined the material sticking to the tallow and compared it to the description of the bottom conditions given in navigational guides. In this way, the materials (such as sand, pebbles, or broken shells) helped the navigator determine his ship's position. Oceanographic sailing ships recorded this data for the purpose of evaluating the biology and geology of the ocean bottom.

 Visual 19-2: Features of the Ocean Floor

This visual is a reproduction of Figure 19-3. Use the visual as you discuss the various topographical features in an ocean basin.

The Antarctic continental shelf differs from the average continental shelf in that it descends to a depth of about 350 m (2200 ft) before dropping off into the abyss.

 Visual 19-3: Ocean Basin Topography of the World

This map will place the individual features described in this section in the context of their actual occurrence. Point out the continent margins that have broad continental shelves and those that plunge steeply into trenches. Note the numerous individual seamounts in the Western Pacific and the way the mid-ocean ridge system encircles the world. Alert students that the sizes and shapes of the landmasses are greatly distorted toward the poles in this map projection.

Sonar is an acronym for sound navigation and ranging.

bathymetric: bathy- (Gk. *bathus*—deep) + -metric (Gk. *metrikos*—to measure)

19-2 Echo sounding is used to map the topography of the ocean floor.

19-3 Generalized topography of the ocean floor

19.3 Exploring the Ocean Basins

Until the late nineteenth century, most scientists assumed that the ocean's floor was as flat as its surface. Because they had no way to study the deep ocean floor, they could not test their assumption. Then, in 1872, the British warship HMS *Challenger* began a four-year expedition to study the ocean. One of its tasks was to determine the ocean's depth in various places. As the scientists measured the depths, they realized that the ocean floor has even more features than the land. The ocean floor has deeper valleys, taller mountains, and broader plains than the land.

The *Challenger* used a long wire rope weighted with lead called a *lead line* to measure the depths of the oceans. Modern oceanographic vessels use **echo sounding** (a form of *sonar*) to measure ocean depths. In this technique, the ship sends pulses of sound to the ocean floor and records the time it takes them to return. Ships using echo sounding have now measured the depths of much of the ocean floor. Cartographers use this data to produce *bathymetric* charts, or maps of the ocean topography.

Although surface ships have discovered valuable information about the ocean floor, the best way to study a region is to visit it. The biggest obstacle to visiting the ocean floor is the great pressure of the water. It was not until the early years of the twentieth century that scientists had a manned *submersible*, or diving vehicle, capable of withstanding the pressures of great depths. Manned and unmanned underwater vehicles allow scientists to travel or send instruments with cameras to the ocean floor so that they can see the area they are studying. The oceans are so vast and the number of vehicles so few that only a fraction of the ocean floor has been studied. Satellites have been used for much of the recent mapping of the ocean floor. Section 19D contains a more detailed description of some of the vehicles and equipment used to explore the oceans.

19.4 General Bathymetric Profile

The earliest oceanographers discovered that the ocean is comparatively shallow along most margins of the continents. The bottom slopes out gently from the continents, forming a **continental shelf**. Continental shelves are submerged edges of continents and as such have the same geologic formations and topography as the adjacent land. A typical continental shelf extends 70 km (43 mi) from the seacoast to an average depth of 135 m (440 ft). In some places, the continental shelves are very narrow or nonexistent, and the coastal cliffs drop directly into deep water. In other locations, the continental shelf is broad, extending more than 1500 km (930 mi) from the shoreline. The average slope of the continental shelf is about a tenth of a degree.

Day 5

Discuss the factors that produce the global ocean surface currents and note the general current patterns. Emphasize that surface currents are responsible for modifying the climates of adjacent landmasses. Describe the various subsurface ocean currents and the physical factors that cause them.

Assignment

Complete: 19C-3 Section Review Questions
Applications 19D, "Ocean Currents"

Reading: Investigation 19J, "Examining Density Currents"

Day 6

Quiz—Section 19C, "Ocean Motions"

Do Investigation 19J, "Examining Density Currents." If time remains, begin discussing Section 19D, "Ocean Exploration."

Assignment

Reading: Section 19D, "Ocean Exploration"

Day 7

Discuss the history of scientific ocean exploration. Describe the design and use of some basic oceanographic instruments. Relate the development of manned submersible vehicles and research submarines and how they vastly increased knowledge of the ocean depths. Discuss the inherent hazards of manned deep-sea research and that unmanned submersibles are becoming more common and sophisticated.

Assignment

Complete: 19D Section Review Questions
Selected Chapter Review Questions

At the edge of each continental shelf descends a relatively steep **continental slope**. The slope is the beginning of the deep ocean basin. The top of the slope may be 1 to 5 km (0.6–3 mi) above the base of the slope that marks the bottom of the ocean basin. This topographical relief can be much greater in the presence of a tectonic plate margin, such as off the coast of Peru and Chile in South America. The angle of continental slopes varies between 1 and 25 degrees, which also depends on the amount of tectonic activity near the continental margin. For example, the west margin of the North American continent forms the edge of a tectonic plate, and the average continental slope is about 5 degrees. In the Atlantic Ocean, the east margin of the continent is hundreds of kilometers away from the plate margin and the average slope is about 2 degrees.

Often the slopes have **submarine canyons** carved into them with deltas or sediment fans at their mouths. A few of these canyons appear to be related to the mouths of large rivers, but most do not. Many are confined to the continental slope. Creationary scientists who have studied the question of how the canyons formed suggest three possibilities for their origin. Some think that sea level was perhaps much lower before the Flood than it is now, leaving the continental slopes and shelves exposed as dry land with large river valleys. The canyons could be river valleys that were inundated during the Flood. Others agree that the submarine canyons are drowned river valleys but suggest that they were formed during a period of glaciation after the Flood. Most scientists agree that sea level was at least 100 m (328 ft) lower during the Ice Age than it is today. Some propose that the canyons were carved by submarine mudslides during the final stages of the Flood as large quantities of water and sediment flowed from the continents into the ocean basins.

Beyond the continental slope is usually a gentle **continental rise**. The continental rise is built largely from sediments that have washed off the continental shelf. In this area, oceanographers have found formations similar to alluvial fans or deltas on land. The descending continental rise levels off and meets the ocean floor, which has an average depth of more than 3 km (2 mi). The flat, deep sea floors are called **abyssal plains**. These plains are the part of the ocean basin that appears closest to the old idea of a flat, featureless, ocean bottom. The ocean floors are covered by sediments that vary in thickness. Oceanographers study the floor sediments by drilling cylindrical core samples from them. Even where the abyssal plains are covered with deep sediments, the plains are not featureless. Ridges and mountains rise from the plains to give the ocean-floor topography at least as much variety as the land.

19-4 A computer-generated map of the continental slope off the California coast showing the Lajolla submarine canyon

abyssal (uh BIS ul): (Gk. *abussos*—bottomless, deep)

 Beholding the Waters
Which of the theories for the origin of the submarine canyons in the continental slopes best agrees with the catastrophic plate tectonics model?

 Beholding the Waters

The first theory is not supported by the catastrophic plate tectonics model. For a pre-Flood river valley to be eroded into a continental slope at the edge of a continental plate, the river would have had to flow into a preexisting ocean. The catastrophic plate tectonics model says that the continents were originally joined but broke apart at the beginning of the Flood. In other words, before the Flood there would have been no ocean between them for rivers to flow into. The other two theories show more promise. However, in the case of the second theory, some of the submarine canyons are cut to a depth far deeper than 100 m below the current sea level, so they cannot be explained by the lower sea level during the Ice Age alone. The third explanation is most consistent with our model of the Flood and catastrophic plate tectonics. All of these explanations run into difficulties with some of the observed submarine features, but the third model seems to fit the observed data best.

DAY 8

Quiz—Section 19D, "Ocean Exploration"

Do Applications 19H, "Oceans Review," as a review exercise. Review for a chapter test.

Assignment
Study for a chapter test.

DAY 9

Test—Chapter 19

Assignment
Reading: Section 20A, "What is a Glacier?"

Have students write reports on the locations of black smokers, their structures and appearance, and the creatures that inhabit the black smoker localities.

19.5 Features of the Abyssal Plain

Each ocean has at least one mid-ocean ridge rising from its depths. These ridges are submerged mountain ranges. The best-known ridge is the Mid-Atlantic Ridge, the longest mountain system on Earth. Each ridge is jagged and fractured with many fault-block features, indicating tectonic instability. Earthquakes often occur within the ridges, and many active submarine volcanoes have erupted along the spine of the ridge system. Recall from Chapter 16 that mid-ocean ridges are the locations of sea-floor spreading in the plate tectonics models. Within the last several decades, researchers have discovered many submarine geysers in the ridge systems that spew opaque clouds of nutrients from superheated jets of seawater called "smokers." These hydrothermal vents form islands of life where many exotic and unique organisms live in deep water.

Submerged islands, or **seamounts**, protrude from abyssal plains. Drilling data indicates that most if not all seamounts are volcanic in origin. Oceanographers estimate that there could be more than 100,000 seamounts based on satellite bathymetric data. Some seamounts have flat tops and are called **guyots**. Perhaps these seamounts were once above sea level and were eroded by waves. Their tops are now an average of 1.5 km (1 mi) below sea level.

guyot (GEE oh)

What could have produced such widespread volcanism? The various plate tectonics models suggest that seamounts and guyots were volcanoes that formed at the mid-ocean ridges and then were carried away from the crest of the ridge as the sea floor spread into deeper water. Other seamounts that exist in chains in the middle of a plate may have formed when the tectonic plate moved over a hot spot in the mantle. Evolutionary geologists believe this process took millions of years, while creationary geologists believe that these numerous mountains attest to the devastating effects of the Flood during a short period of time.

In Chapter 16 we discussed how the catastrophic plate-tectonics model suggests that rapid subduction of an oceanic plate below a continental plate could have contributed to the formation of deep ocean **trenches**. Trenches seem to be present wherever two tectonic plates come together, or converge, one plate subducting below the other, carrying the sea floor with it. Such trenches surround much of the east, west, and northern margins of the Pacific basin. The deepest ocean depths occur in trenches. The Challenger Deep, located in the Mariana Trench in the western Pacific, is the deepest point in any ocean. Trenches often are found in close association with strings of volcanic islands called **island arcs**. These arcs are long, curved chains of islands such as the Aleutians, Kurils, East Indies, Philippines, and Ryukyus (off the southern tip of Japan), which line the margin of tectonic plates. Trenches are on the side of the arc that is farthest from the continental plate. Most trenches have a steep slope on the side toward the continental plate and a gentle slope on the side toward the oceanic plate.

19-5 A digital elevation map of the world. Dark blue indicates greatest depths (trenches and abyssal plains); shallow depths (continental shelves and mid-ocean ridges) are lighter blue.

The Challenger Deep is named after the British research vessel *Challenger II*, which discovered the spot in 1951.

Mariana (MEHR ee AHN uh)

19.6 Coral Reefs

Another type of geologic feature associated with the ocean is the **coral reef**. Corals are tiny animals that live predominantly in warm tropical and subtropical waters. Most secrete a calcium carbonate structure. Some corals live together in vast colonies along with other organisms that secrete calcium carbonate skeletons. The calcium carbonate accumulates, forming a coral reef. Occasionally, these

19-6   A barrier reef surrounding the island of Fiji (left); a fringing reef surrounding a small island, one of many Great Barrier Reef islands (right)

reefs emerged above the surface as islands when the local sea level dropped or the sea bottom rose.

Reef-forming corals require light to live. Thus, coral reefs are often found in shallow water near land. Reefs that have grown right up to the beach along a coastline are called **fringing reefs**. Little water separates the land from the reef. Fringing reefs occur along the coasts of Florida and Bermuda as well as around many Pacific islands.

Barrier reefs are farther from the land, and a lagoon forms between the reef and the land. The lagoon opens to the sea through passages in the reef. The largest coral reef in the world is the Great Barrier Reef off the northern coast of Australia. It extends about 2000 km (1250 mi) and covers more area than many countries.

An **atoll** is a ring of low coral islands and reefs surrounding a central lagoon. In most cases, an atoll began as a barrier or fringing reef around a volcanic island. Geologists have two theories for the formation of atolls. First, the central volcano could have collapsed, forming a caldera below sea level, leaving the fringing ring of coral islands behind. Second, the sea level could have risen (or the sea bottom could have subsided), slowly drowning the central island. The coral reefs continued to grow upward, forming the ring of coral

19-7   A scuba diver enjoys some of the unusual color and beauty associated with the Great Barrier Reef.

atoll (AT ol *or* AY tol)

19-8   Kyangle Atoll and its lagoon in the Palau islands in the Pacific Ocean (left); Cutaway view of an atoll on the top of a volcano (right)

Inform students that a *reef* is any rocklike submarine outcrop, especially one that constitutes a navigation hazard. There are noncoral reefs along nearly all rocky coasts.

Visual 19-4: Types of Reefs

This visual incorporates the right-hand illustration of Figure 19-8. It illustrates the other types of coral reef formations that can be found on or around seamounts, as mentioned in the text.

In recent decades, marine biologists have noted that coral reefs around the world have been in decline. The colored algae—single-celled plants—that grow on the coral skeletons and provide some of the coral animal's nourishment are sensitive to warm temperatures. In many locations the sea temperatures may rise due to temporary climactic conditions, and the algae die or are expelled. If the conditions do not return to normal in a short time, the coral die too, resulting in a condition called *coral bleaching*. Biologists are concerned that coral bleaching may be an early indicator that the oceans are warming in response to the general global-warming trend. Much more research is needed to confirm this.

Objectives—Section 19B

Upon completing this section, students should be able to

- discuss various theories for the origin of salty oceans based on the Flood model.
- state that the ocean's saltiness is due to the presence of various dissolved minerals.
- describe the processes that add and remove minerals from seawater.
- state the major chemical constituents of seawater and the total concentration of dissolved solids.
- summarize various processes for recovering drinking water from seawater.

Eniwetok (EN ih WEE TAHK)

islands and reefs at the ocean surface. Several Pacific island groups are atolls, including Wake, Midway, Bikini, and Eniwetok.

Coral reefs are significant to humans for several reasons. First, they can form islands to live on. Most of the larger atolls in the Pacific Ocean are inhabited. Second, reefs can be dangerous to ships. Shallow seas where coral is common are difficult for ships to navigate. The coral reefs may not be visible from above the water but are close enough to the surface to damage a passing ship. Many of the first ships that came to the New World wrecked on coral reefs. Coral reefs are also important as a home to colorful communities of sea life, with many species of plants and animals that live only in coral reefs.

19A Section Review

1. What percentage of the earth's surface do the oceans cover? Considering the other planets in the solar system, why is this significant?
2. What kinds of scientists may be oceanographers?
3. Name the tool that *Challenger* used to measure the ocean depths. Describe how it was used.
4. Describe three characteristics of a continental shelf.
5. What is the most common type of material that forms a continental rise? Where does this material come from?
6. What are the flat deep-sea floors called?
7. What is a long submerged mountain range at the spreading margin between tectonic plates called?
8. What are long curved chains of volcanic islands called? What other submarine feature are these chains of islands usually associated with?
9. Where is the largest coral reef in the world located?
10. Describe an atoll and discuss how geologists believe atolls could have formed.
11. (True or False) The oceans have more and taller mountains and more and deeper valleys than the continents.

19B COMPOSITION OF SEAWATER

19.7 The Origin of Salty Oceans

Seawater is a complex solution of water, dissolved minerals, and dissolved gases. Its exact composition varies with local conditions. Most of the dissolved mineral content is sodium chloride—common table salt—but seawater includes other compounds and elements. Where did the ocean's dissolved minerals come from?

According to a biblical view of Earth's history, everything about our planet is the product of not only a supernatural Creation but also the effects of a global Flood. We cannot know whether God created the sea salty or fresh, nor do we know the original composition of the ocean. According to the Flood model, we can predict that the vast amount of erosion during and following the Flood could have resulted in high concentrations of dissolved minerals in the water that would have made the oceans very salty.

Answers to 19A Section Review Questions

1. The oceans cover about 71 percent of the earth's surface. Earth is the only planet known that has any quantities of liquid water on its surface. (§19.1, Chap. 13)

2. Answers will vary. Students may name nearly any scientist in a physical or biological science field that can pertain to the study of the oceans. (§19.1)

3. The *Challenger* used a weighted rope (a lead line) to measure the ocean depths. The weight was lowered from the ship until it touched bottom. The length of rope paid out indicated the depth. (§19.3)

4. A typical continental shelf includes topography similar to the adjacent land, with an average width of 70 km (43 mi), an average maximum depth of 135 m (440 ft), and an average slope of about $\frac{1}{10}$ degree. (§19.4)

5. A continental rise is usually formed of sediment that comes from the adjacent continental shelf. (§19.4)

6. Flat deep-sea floors are called *abyssal plains*. (§19.4)

7. A long submerged mountain range emerging at the spreading margin between tectonic plates is called a *mid-ocean ridge*. (§19.5)

8. Long curved chains of islands are called *island arcs*. Island arcs are usually associated with *deep-sea trenches*. (§19.5)

9. The largest coral reef in the world is the Great Barrier Reef located off the northern coast of Australia. (§19.6)

10. An atoll is a ring of low coral islands and reefs surrounding a central lagoon. Geologists suggest the following possible origins: a coral reef built up around a volcanic island that eventually collapsed into a caldera, leaving only the coral reef exposed; a coral reef surrounded a low volcanic island, which subsequently was submerged by subsidence of the ocean floor or rising sea level, leaving the living coral reef to continue building up the atoll. (§19.6)

11. True. (§19.3)

We also know that marine plants and animals exist today that can survive in salt water but not in fresh, while most freshwater organisms cannot live in salt water. Although we will never know for sure, we can logically deduce that *all* the kinds of aquatic organisms that exist today had to survive for some time in seawater during the Flood. Therefore, it would seem that the original oceans must have been at least somewhat salty. Those organisms that became trapped in bodies of salt water that later turned into freshwater lakes as the Floodwaters receded lost the ability to live in the salty oceans.

Even if the oceans were essentially fresh water following the Flood, the creationary model of earth's history can still support the development of salty oceans seen today. We know that the oceans gain and lose minerals every day. The streams that enter the ocean carry large amounts of dissolved minerals with them. Much of the ocean's salt (mineral) concentration could have accumulated in a just few thousand years from the streams.

"Of course they're safe! Confidentially, they're nothing more than sugar."

19-9

19.8 Minerals and Saltiness

If fresh stream water replenishes the ocean, why is the ocean salty while the streams are fresh? When water evaporates, it leaves almost all of its dissolved minerals behind. Thus, the ocean gains minerals and water daily but loses only water to evaporation. A net gain of minerals occurs if only stream flow and evaporation are considered. Lakes that have no outlets, such as the Dead Sea and Great Salt Lake, have become saltier than the ocean as the water continually evaporates.

How do minerals leave the ocean's water? One way is through the activities of living organisms. For example, the animals that form seashells and coral reefs absorb calcium and carbon dioxide (in the form of carbonates) from the seawater to use in building their skeletons. Microscopic diatoms similarly remove silicon from ocean water to form their skeletons of silica. In addition, minerals are removed and deposited as sea-floor sediments. Clay particles, which are covered with negative electrical charges, bind positively charged metallic ions and then settle to the ocean floor. The elements bound to the clay particles are thus removed from the water. Some substances such as carbon dioxide reach saturation and precipitate as carbonate compounds that settle to the bottom.

19-10 Microscopic diatom skeletons are made of silica. © Dr. Richard Kossel & Gene Shih/Visuals Unlimited

diatom (DY uh TAHM)

Early in the 1990s, oceanographers began studying a fine, continuous rain of particles called "marine snow" that drifts down from near the ocean's surface to deeper depths and ultimately to the bottom. This "snow" consists of tiny single-celled animals and plants, colonies of cellular organisms, sand, dust (including meteoric dust), chemical precipitates, excrement, and microscopic particles, often bonded together by bacterial colonies. It contains organisms very different from those in the waters in which it settles. Marine snow is important because it speeds up the sinking of microscopic organisms but slows the sinking of larger dead animals and waste matter. This gentle rain of particles forms the main source of food for many bottom-feeding and drifting organisms.

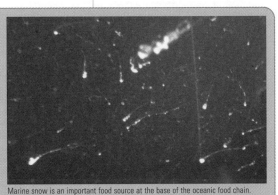

Marine snow is an important food source at the base of the oceanic food chain.

Box Summary: Marine Snow

This brief box elaborates on the concept and significance of marine snow, an additional process for transporting organic and inorganic materials between different zones in the ocean. Be sure to review this box if students will be responsible for the term *marine snow*.

19-11 Magnesium salt is removed from seawater (top). Manganese nodules on the ocean floor (bottom).

Visual 19-5: Composition of Seawater

This visual shows the mineral content of seawater as percentages of the major ions. This is more appropriate than listing the equivalent compounds since the positive and negative ions are free to bond in any possible combination.

More than 80 of the naturally occurring elements have been isolated in seawater. Physicists state that there are 88 naturally occurring elements having atomic numbers between 1 and 92, leaving out elements 43 (technetium), 61 (promethium), 85 (astatine), and 87 (francium). All isotopes of these latter four elements have such short half-lives that they quickly decay away. Although extremely small amounts of these four are created by cosmic ray interactions, their quantities are not readily measurable. All the elements beyond 92 (uranium) are called *transuranium elements* and are found on the earth only as the products of artificial nuclear reactions.

The legal issues surrounding manganese nodule mining include controversy about undersea mineral rights in international waters and environmental concerns about the disruption of bottom ecosystems caused by the current methods of nodule mining.

Fresh or drinkable water is usually referred to as *potable* (POH tuh bul) water. The word is derived from Latin, *potare*—to drink.

These processes and many more remove chemicals from solution in seawater. The average time between the entrance of an atom or molecule into the ocean and its removal by some means is called **residence time**. Residence time is different for each type of particle.

The amount of dissolved solids in seawater varies over the earth. The sea tends to have less salt in areas of high rainfall or near the discharge of large rivers because the fresh water dilutes it. Also, the ocean near the poles tends to be less salty because it evaporates slowly, and melting icebergs dilute it. In warm areas like the Mediterranean Sea, however, the ocean contains higher concentrations of salt. Evaporation is high, rainfall is low, and few large rivers flow into the Mediterranean Sea. The saltiest ocean basin is the Persian Gulf, where evaporation is highest compared to freshwater input.

The oceans contain vast amounts of commercially valuable dissolved minerals. For example, seawater contains magnesium, bromine, phosphorous, and tin. It even contains gold! Nearly every naturally occurring element has been identified in seawater. Unfortunately, most are too dilute to be recovered profitably. For example, 77,000 metric tons of seawater contain only a single gram of gold. A few compounds are concentrated enough to be obtained from seawater. On the average, if 1000 g of seawater is evaporated, 35 g of various minerals will remain. About three-fourths of this is sodium chloride (NaCl).

At the present time only plentiful ocean chemicals such as sodium chloride, magnesium, and bromine are commercially extracted from seawater. A potential mineral resource in the ocean is *manganese nodules*. These nodules range from golf ball to baseball size and are composed mostly of manganese and iron oxides, but they also contain significant amounts of nickel, copper, cobalt, lanthanum, zinc, and traces of many other minerals. Nodules can be found on more than half the sea floor, but they are most numerous in ocean depths of about 5000 m near mid-ocean ridges. Scientists agree that they are formed by at least three types of chemical reactions, but bacteria may play a part in their formation process. The rate of sedimentation in the areas where they are found exceeds the measured rate of nodule growth. Therefore, they should not even exist. Why are they there, how do they get so big, and why do they sit out in the open on the ocean bottom rather than being covered by sediment while still tiny? These questions have puzzled oceanographers for more than a century. Although manganese nodules contain many minerals, only cobalt is considered important enough to warrant research into deep-sea mining operations. Currently, legal and logistical issues make manganese-nodule mining too difficult and costly compared to land mining operations.

19.9 Water—The Most Valuable Ocean Resource

Although the many minerals dissolved in seawater are valuable, its most valuable constituent may be fresh water. In many places near the sea, fresh water is scarce. Thus, the people in these places try to **desalinate**, or remove the salt from, seawater. The most straightforward but least efficient way to desalinate water is distillation. This process boils or evaporates the water and then condenses its vapor. Only minute traces of the minerals enter the vapor, so the condensed water is fresh. This method is expensive because it requires a lot of

desalinate (dee SAL uh NATE)

fuel or another thermal energy source to boil the water. Physicists are studying other, possibly cheaper, ways to desalinate water. For example, some countries are using the waste heat from nuclear power generation to distill seawater. The seawater cools the power plant, and the waste heat evaporates some of the seawater that is then distilled. Economists also think that recovering and selling minerals from the salt removed from the seawater may reduce the price of the fresh water produced.

Probably the most economical desalinization method is a process called **reverse osmosis**. In such a process, seawater is pumped at high pressure against a special membrane that allows water molecules to pass through but prevents the salt and other particles from crossing over. The water is collected and passes through an ion exchanger to remove any remaining dissolved minerals. The result is pure drinking water. The entire process requires far less power than distillation. In fact, such a plant can be powered by photovoltaic panels, making such desalinization plants practical for underdeveloped equatorial countries.

19.10 Dissolved Gases

Besides dissolved minerals, seawater contains dissolved nitrogen, oxygen, carbon dioxide, and other gases. Because the gases dissolve at different rates in water, their proportions are different from those in the atmosphere. In addition, the solubility of a gas in water generally decreases with increasing temperature. For these reasons, nitrogen, which makes up 78 percent of the atmospheric gases, makes up a lower proportion of the dissolved gases in seawater, and the other gases proportionately more. Surface water is usually richer in oxygen than deeper water because of the nearness of the oxygen in the atmosphere and the presence of marine plants and microorganisms that produce oxygen. The oceans easily absorb carbon dioxide from the air (it is consumed by photosynthetic and carbonate-shelled organisms) and thus help to regulate the amount of carbon dioxide in the atmosphere.

19B Section Review

1. Explain why we will never know for sure how the oceans came to be salty.
2. Discuss two ways in which chemicals and minerals may be removed from solution in the ocean's waters.
3. What factors may cause the concentration of dissolved minerals in seawater to vary?
4. Name the most abundant dissolved mineral in seawater.
5. What is the average mass of the dissolved minerals in 1000 g of seawater?
6. What is the process of removing dissolved minerals from seawater called? Give two methods for accomplishing this task.
7. Why does surface water have a higher concentration of dissolved oxygen than deeper water?
8. (True or False) Seawater near the mouth of a large river will probably contain less salt but more of other minerals than seawater far from land.

19-12 A reverse osmosis plant in Dunedim, Florida, uses a sophisticated filtering process to remove salt from ocean water.

Beholding the Waters

In poor, underdeveloped countries like Bangladesh and Peru, many people die every year because of inadequate supplies of good drinking water. How could a Christian respond to this problem?

Beholding the Waters

Guide the students to an answer that connects the Creation Mandate (Gen. 1:28), the command to love one's fellow humans (Mark 12:30–31), and the commission to proclaim the gospel (Matt. 28:18–20). By helping underdeveloped countries to desalinate ocean water through reverse osmosis, we could teach them to become more skilled at fulfilling the Creation Mandate. Since we are also helping them meet a most basic physical need (and thus saving thousands of lives precious to God), we are showing love for our fellow humans. Moreover, if we use this display of love to tell such peoples of God's greater love for their eternal redemption, we are also fulfilling our calling to disciple the nations for God's glory.

Point out that many Christian mission organizations specialize in drilling wells and establishing solar-powered water purification plants throughout the world. Few efforts could be as rewarding as providing lost, thirsty people both liquid water and Living Water (John 4:6–15).

Henry's law is the physical principle that describes how gases dissolve in liquids. In general, it states that the amount of a gas that is dissolved in a solvent, such as water, is proportional to the partial pressure of the gas over the liquid. However, the amount of dissolved gas also depends on the temperature of the water (cold water holds more gases than hot water) and the kind of gas. Furthermore, the gas must not react chemically with the water (or other solvent). Some chemistry books have tables of Henry's law constants for several different gases determined for specific liquids at standard conditions.

Students Sometimes Ask

Students may wonder why oxygen and other atmospheric gases do not dissolve in equal concentration from the surface all the way to the bottom of the oceans. This would be a good point at which to discuss the concept of *diffusion*. Gas particles are in constant motion. They tend to naturally move from places of high concentration to places of low concentration. Diffusion is aided by large differences in concentrations between two points and by higher solubility of the substance that is diffusing. Because the solubility of most gases is very low in water, the concentration of gases drops off very quickly with increasing depth.

Answers to 19B Section Review Questions

1. As with other ultimate-origins questions that involve events outside recorded history, humans can only guess with their finite minds how and when the oceans became salty. The Bible says that the earth was created with an ocean, but Scripture is silent regarding the ocean's composition or how that composition changed with the Flood. (§19.7)

2. Answers will vary. The text discusses the removal of calcium carbonate and silica by animals, the bonding of metal ions to clay particles, and precipitation. Students may also mention nodules and marine snow. (§19.8)

3. Factors that can cause the concentration of dissolved minerals in seawater to vary depend on freshwater dilution and rate of evaporation. Dilution factors include all forms of precipitation, river mouth discharges, and melting ice. Evaporation tends to be less near the poles and greater in equatorial regions. Students may also mention biological effects on mineral concentration. (§19.8)

4. The most abundant mineral dissolved in seawater is sodium chloride (NaCl), or common table salt. (§19.8)

5. The average mass of dissolved minerals in 1000 g of seawater is 35 g. (§19.8)

6. To remove dissolved minerals from seawater is to desalinate it. The process is called *desalinization*. Distillation and reverse osmosis may be used to desalinate seawater. (§19.9)

7. Surface water is closer to the source of oxygen (the atmosphere), and the dissolved oxygen concentration is highest closest to the source. Also, shallow water that is within the light zone (photic zone) contains photosynthetic organisms that release oxygen into the water. (§19.10)

8. True. This is because the sediment-laden river water usually contains higher concentrations of silicates, carbonates, and clay minerals that are eventually removed in the marine environment. (§19.8)

Objectives—Section 19C

Upon completing this section, students should be able to

- describe how the lunar and solar tidal bulges are formed.
- discuss the periodicity of ocean tides and the causes of unusual tides.
- state the factors that determine mean sea level and discuss how sea level varies across the globe.
- illustrate ocean wave structure and nomenclature.
- discuss how waves refract as they approach shore and the currents associated with wave action along shorelines.
- describe the shoreline erosional and depositional features due to wave action.
- describe the global patterns of ocean surface currents and the factors that produce them.
- show how the major surface currents can modify climates of adjacent landmasses.
- describe the factors that produce subsurface ocean currents.
- trace the generalized deep thermohaline circulation currents on a world map.

The formation of the tidal bulge on the far side of the earth from the moon is often attributed to *centrifugal force*. We suggest that you avoid the concept of centrifugal force altogether. Centrifugal force is not a real physical force, such as gravity or the centripetal force, but rather is an effect of rotational inertia. Physicists often call such effects (including the Coriolis effect) *pseudo-forces* because they are imaginary forces that have to be invented in order to account for unexpected accelerations within a given frame of reference. It is best to avoid any reference to a pseudo-force in this discussion.

You may want to briefly discuss the concept of *momentum* before delving into the origin of the tidal bulges in the oceans. Momentum in physics is the product of the mass and the velocity of an object—what Sir Isaac Newton called its "quantity of motion." For a given mass, the greater the velocity, the more momentum the object has. Since the earth and moon revolve around each other at a constant angular speed (degrees per hour), the farther from the common center of revolution the ocean mass is, the faster it will be moving—thus the greater momentum it will have.

Visual 19-6A, B, C: Global Tide Demonstration

Cut out the diagrams on overlays 19-6B and C. Trim off the visual packet header and footer information. Push a thumbtack from the underside through the center mark on the globe on Visual 19-6A, then place the visual on the overhead projector. The center marks (+ mark) on overlays 1–4 should be penetrated by the tack point when they are used. Use overlay 1 when discussing the effect of the moon's gravity in producing the near-side bulge. Use overlay 2 when discussing how the inertia and radial motion of the earth forms the far-side bulge. Also note that the high-tide point is offset from the point on the opposite side of the earth from the moon

19C OCEAN MOTIONS

19.11 Perpetual Motion

The ocean is never motionless. Even when it appears calm, it is moving in *currents* or is rising or falling because of the *tide*. The wind causes most of the ocean's surface activity, but gravity and even earthquakes contribute to its motions. There is activity deep beneath the surface caused by other forces as well.

TIDES

19.12 Lunar Tides

Ocean **tides** are caused mostly by the moon's gravity, with some influence from the sun's gravity and the *momentum* of the mass of water in the oceans. On the side of the earth facing the moon, the moon's gravity attracts the ocean water, forming a bulge on that side of the earth.

On the side of the earth opposite the moon, the ocean water is

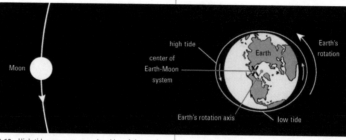

19-13 High tides occur on opposite sides of the earth because of the gravity of the moon and the rotation of the earth-moon system around a common point.

far more affected by the earth's mass than by the moon's gravity. However, an ocean bulge forms because of the mechanics of the revolving earth-moon system. As with any two celestial objects revolving around each other, the earth and the moon revolve around a point that is the center of mass of the two objects. In the case of the earth-moon system, the earth is so much more massive than the moon that the system's center of mass lies deep within the earth. This point is about 75 percent of the earth's radius from the surface on a line between the centers of the earth and moon. Therefore, the ocean on the side opposite the moon is farther from the center of revolution than the ocean on the side facing the moon. Thus, the ocean water on the far side is revolving faster and has greater momentum, so it tends to be thrown away from the center like mud off the rim of a wheel. The bulge caused by the ocean's momentum is somewhat smaller than the bulge caused by the moon's gravity.

The bulges of ocean water on the near and far sides of the earth remain stationary in relation to the moon as the earth rotates beneath them. The bulges represent sea levels higher than the average. The regions of the oceans between the two tidal bulges have to supply the water that makes up the bulges, so the sea level in these regions is lower than the average level.

The maximum sea level caused when a point on the earth's surface arrives at a bulge of water is called a *high tide*. This effect is most noticeable along a seacoast, where changes in sea level can be compared to a fixed height reference. When a point moves under the lowest sea level between bulges, a *low tide* occurs. Along most coasts there are two high tides and two low tides each day. It takes twenty-four hours and fifty minutes for a location on the earth's surface to experience two complete high-low-high tide cycles (twelve hours and twenty-five minutes to go from one high-tide bulge to the next). The high tides are not exactly twelve hours apart because as the earth has been rotating the moon has moved forward in its orbit. It takes fifty minutes more each day for a location on the earth to catch up with its previous position relative to the moon.

due to friction with the rotating earth. Overlay 3 combines the two effects to illustrate the two lunar tide bulges. Overlay 4 shows the smaller effect of the sun on the earth's tides. Rotate Visual 19-6A under the overlays to demonstrate how low and high tides occur across the world each day.

The textbook's description of the mechanics of ocean tide formation is very simplified to make it understandable at this grade level. Many factors contribute to the formation of the tidal bulges at any given location. The forces acting on the ocean's waters are a combination of the moon's gravity, the moon's distance, the earth's gravity, the geoidal surface height, the angular momentum of the water at a given latitude, and obstructions to tidal flow presented by continents, among many other factors.

19-14 High (left) and low (right) tides are caused by the rotation of the earth beneath the tidal bulges.

19.13 Solar Tides

The sun's gravity causes tides as well, but in most locations they are much smaller than those caused by the moon. The earth rotates under these smaller bulges in twenty-four hours plus a few minutes. Eventually the solar tides and the slower-traveling lunar tides coincide. Twice each month, at the new moon and full moon, the sun, moon, and earth are in a straight line. At these times, the sun's gravity works with the moon's to form a higher-than-usual tide called a **spring tide**. When the sun, the earth, and the moon form a right angle, the effects of the sun's gravity work against the moon's to form a lower-than-usual tide called a **neap tide**. Neap tides also occur twice each month, at the first and third quarter phases of the moon.

neap (NEEP) (origin unknown but possibly OE.—weak, lacking power)

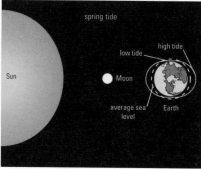

19-15 When the sun and the moon are at right angles to the earth, lower tides called *neap tides* occur (left). When the sun and the moon are in line, very high tides called *spring tides* occur (right).

19.14 Unusual Tides

The shapes of the coast and ocean basin also affect the height and time of tides. In the Mediterranean Sea, the tide seldom rises more than 30 cm (1 ft). But at the head of the Bay of Fundy in New Brunswick, the tide may rise over 16 m (52 ft). This bay is a V-shaped inlet with its narrowest parts farthest from the sea. It acts as a funnel to bring a large amount of seawater into several narrow inlets. During high tide, some of the bay's rivers run backward. Most parts of the Gulf of Mexico experience only one high tide per day because of the semi-enclosed nature of its basin.

Unusually high tides can occur with the approach of a hurricane and its storm surge. If the hurricane's arrival coincides with a spring tide, extremely high tides can occur with sea levels many meters above normal. Add to the high water level the larger-than-normal wind-driven breakers that accompany hurricanes, and the result is often total devastation to the coastal region.

19-16 A tide schedule (top); circles locate the V-shaped inlets in the Bay of Fundy (bottom) that act as funnels resulting in unusual tide heights.

19-17 Bay of Fundy at high (top) and low (bottom) tides

What Is Sea Level?

What is sea level? Does it change with each tide and wave, or is it strictly set and unchanging? **Sea level** changes with the tides, but **mean sea level (MSL)**, which is commonly referred to as just "sea level," is steadier. Mean sea level is the height about halfway between the high and low tides. Since the heights of high and low tides vary, they are measured over several years and then averaged to determine mean sea level.

Prior to the space age, cartographers (mapmakers) used mean sea level to determine the zero reference for elevation. It has been known for several centuries that the earth is flattened at the poles into a geometric figure called an *ellipsoid*, or a flattened sphere. However, detailed gravitational measurements obtained late in the last century revealed that the actual surface of the ocean does not follow a regular ellipsoid, but rather has high and low spots relative to the ellipsoid. This surface, called the *geoid*, was determined by all the points that had exactly the same gravity. Geophysicists assumed that MSL corresponded to the gravitational geoidal surface. Imagine their surprise when recent worldwide GPS measurements indicated that MSL varies from the geoid by more than 100 m in some places! MSL is now determined by corrections applied to the geoid from actual local measurements.

Not only is MSL not constant from place to place, but it is changing everywhere in the world. Overall, MSL is rising about 2.5 mm each year. This average rate was computed from satellite altimeter measurements of mean sea level since 1993. Some locations had even greater increases, and a few reported decreases in mean sea level. Most scientists attribute this increase in mean sea level to global warming, which has caused the world's glaciers to melt faster, adding water to the oceans.

The geoid surface. Departures of the geoid from a regular ellipsoid are indicated by color and are exaggerated by a factor of 15,000 to emphasize the irregularities. Differences in MSL are figured from this surface.

A datum (or map reference elevation) that is sometimes more useful than MSL is mean lower low water (MLLW). There are usually two low tides each day, one in response to the sun (a low tide) and one in response to the moon (a lower low tide). The MLLW is the average of the lower low-tide measurements, preferably over a 19-year period if there is sufficient data. This reference elevation maximizes the amount of land surface displayed on a map.

The measured variations of the geoid from the regular ellipsoid reflect variations in the thickness and density of the crust. Local MSL variations are attributed to magma intrusions, shoreline shape, ocean currents, prevailing winds, seasonal and cyclical changes in the ocean's surface, and average atmospheric pressure.

19C-1 Section Review

1. What is the primary cause of twice-daily tides around the world?

2. What effect of the earth-moon system revolution causes the water bulge on the side of the earth farthest from the moon?

3. Explain why most coastal locations on Earth experience two high tides separated by two low tides each day.

4. What name is given to the higher-than-usual tide formed when the sun's and moon's gravitational pulls work together?

5. In most locations is mean sea level rising, falling, or staying the same?

6. (True or False) During low tides, some of the rivers emptying into the Bay of Fundy run backward.

Box Summary: What Is Sea Level?

This box discusses the concept of a *reference height*, specifically the mapping elevation reference height known as *mean sea level* (MSL). Students will learn that the earth's surface is not smooth, spherical, or even regular. The problem of accurately determining mean sea level has only recently become understood, and the answer is not always arrived at easily. Be sure to review this box if students will be responsible for the vocabulary terms *sea level* and *mean sea level*.

Answers to 19C-1 Section Review Questions

1. Twice-daily tides are caused mainly by the gravity of the moon and its overall effects on the earth and its oceans. (§19.12)

2. The earth-moon system gives the ocean on the side of the earth farthest from the moon extra momentum, which flings it away from the center of revolution, forming a bulge. (§19.12)

3. As the earth rotates under the two tidal bulges caused by the moon's gravity and the ocean's momentum, the bulges and the in-between low points sweep past coastal locations, producing a high, then a low, then a high, and then a low tide in approximately a 24-hour period. (§19.12)

4. When the sun's and the moon's gravitational pulls work together, the result is a *spring tide*. (§19.13)

5. In most locations sea level is rising about 2.5 mm per year. (box, p. 497)

6. False. Rivers emptying into the Bay of Fundy run backward only at high tides because the incoming tide flow exceeds the river flow. (§19.14)

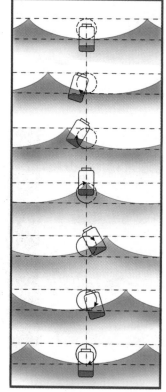

19-18 Water particles or objects in a wave follow a circular path.

Visual 19-7: Movement Within a Surface Wave

This visual is a reproduction of Figure 19-18. Note the direction of wave movement. Emphasize that waves do not result in significant horizontal movement of water. The particles remain essentially in one place, moving in circular paths.

The tallest wave ever recorded occurred during a Western Pacific typhoon in 1935. Officers aboard a U.S. Navy tanker, the USS *Ramapo*, used the dimensions of the ship as geometrical aids to calculate the wave height. From crest to trough, the waves were 34 m (112 ft) high, more than twice as high as the official U.S. Navy estimated maximum possible wave height at that time.

Concepts Students Find Difficult

Tsunamis in past decades were more likely to be called "tidal waves," especially in disaster movies and popular literature. These devastating waves have nothing to do with waves caused by tidal forces, called *tidal bores*, such as those that occur annually in the Quiantang River in China. Today, most students should be familiar with the correct name for earthquake-generated waves.

Visual 19-8: Wave Terminology

This visual is a reproduction of Figure 19-19. Key things to note are the dimensional terms *wavelength* and *wave height*. The wavelength may be measured from any corresponding points on two successive waves, not just the crests. The wave height is the distance from trough to crest. This is different from the *amplitude* of a wave, which is measured from the dashed middle line to either the crest or the trough. Observe that the sizes of the water particle orbits decrease with depth until only a slight back and forth motion remains at the wave base. This is because surface waves transmit energy primarily along the surface. Liquids do not transmit energy readily by friction, so particles below the surface have smaller motions.

WAVES

19.15 Wave Generation

The most obvious motion of the sea is its waves. Most waves are generated by wind. As the wind blows along the surface of the ocean, it drags the surface water along with it a short distance, piling it up and causing a small disturbance in the water. As innumerable disturbances add up, they form wavelets, which add together to form waves. Waves move energy from one point to the next, but the water particles themselves do not move great distances. Instead, the particles follow a circular or orbital path, remaining in essentially one place. This is clearly shown by a fishing bobber in the water. The waves pass by but the bobber just rises up and down in a small circle without moving horizontally with the wave.

Waves have several measurable characteristics. The vertical distance from the **crest** (peak) to the **trough** (lowest part) of a wave is the **wave height**. The *wavelength* is the horizontal distance from one crest to the next. Ocean waves are usually called *surface waves* because they disturb only a relatively shallow layer of the water. The **wave base**, the depth to which the wave disturbance reaches below the surface of the water, is equal to half the wavelength below the surface level if the water were still. A typical wave in the open sea may have a wave height of 1 m, a wavelength of 50 m, and a wave base of 25 m. Very large storm waves may have wavelengths of 300 m (980 ft) or more. However, at the base of these waves (150 m or 490 ft), the orbital motion of the waves is essentially gone. Military submarines will usually operate at depths well below the bases of waves in a rough sea in order to avoid excessive rolling motion.

The vast majority of ocean waves are generated by wind. Occasionally, waves are produced by earthquakes with epicenters in or near the ocean basins. These waves can be very large and are especially devastating to coastal areas in their paths. We discussed the particulars of tsunamis in Chapter 17. Following the 1967 earthquake in Alaska, which resulted in 122 tsunami-related deaths, the National Atmospheric and Oceanic Administration (NOAA) established a tsunami warning system throughout the Pacific Ocean. This system

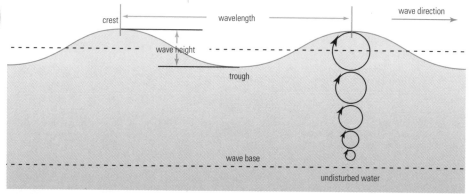

19-19 Diagram showing the common terminology used with water waves

consists of hundreds of seismic stations ringing the Pacific basin, special ocean-height monitoring buoys, and a communication system to rapidly notify affected countries of approaching tsunamis. A similar system will likely be established in the Indian Ocean as one beneficial result of the devastating series of tsunamis produced by the earthquake off the coast of Sumatra, Indonesia, in 2004.

19-20 Breakers coming ashore in North Island, New Zealand

19.16 Waves Coming Ashore

As a wave approaches the shore, it moves through shallower water. When the water's depth is less than the wave base, the wave begins to change. The bottom part of the wave slows due to friction with the sea bottom. The wave crests move closer together, reducing their wavelengths. Because the orbital motion is hindered below, the wave's energy is used to lift the wave higher, and the wave height increases. When the wave's height is more than $1/7$ (or 0.143) of its wavelength, it becomes unstable. The water at the top peaks sharply and then falls over on the forward side of the wave. Such a wave is called a breaking wave, or **breaker**.

Waves usually approach the shore at an angle. The end of the wave nearest to shore slows down due to friction with the shallow bottom. The other end of the wave continues to travel at its original speed until it too reaches the shallow water. As a result, the direction of the wave becomes nearly parallel to the shoreline. Recall from Chapter 3 that the bending of a series of waves due to a change of the material through which they are traveling is called refraction. Water waves experience refraction in a manner similar to light and sound waves.

The ratio of wave height to wave length is called *wave steepness*.

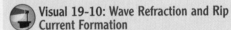

19-21 Breakers form as waves pass over shallow areas, such as near the shore. Friction with the bottom causes the wave to slow and go higher. The unstable wave that falls over is called a breaker.

19-22 The leading end of a wave slows down in shallow water, which allows the trailing end to catch up. Waves become nearly parallel near the shore.

Visual 19-9: Movement of a Wave Approaching Shore

Visual 19-10: Wave Refraction and Rip Current Formation

These visuals are reproductions of Figures 19-21, 22, and 24. Refer to them as you discuss the approach of waves toward shore. On Visual 19-9, we include the additional term *beach berm*, which refers to the upper reaches of the beach washed by waves at high tide, just below the coastal cliffs, dunes, or drift.

Visual 19-11: Longshore Currents Creating Beach Erosion

This visual is a reproduction of Figure 19-23. Note that beach sand follows a sawtooth path down the beach as successive waves wash up onto the beach at an angle, then drain straight downslope back into the ocean.

Waves are rarely exactly parallel to the shoreline. Instead, they strike the shore somewhat diagonally, moving sand, shells, and other materials onto the beach. Gravity then pulls the water and some of the shore material back into the ocean. The repeated up-and-back motion of numerous waves usually moves the sand and other debris onto and along the shore. Waves that approach the shore at an angle also produce a current that flows parallel to the shore, called a **longshore current**.

19-23 Longshore currents develop when water near the shore is deep. Little slowing of the waves occurs as they approach the shore. Longshore currents can cause a beach to drift (top).

Water that flows onto a beach will quickly return down the slope of the beach to the ocean. Occasionally water flows back from the shore in a **rip current**, a strong surface current that flows through a gap in the breakers. Rip currents occur when the breakers are large and a large amount of water must return to the ocean. A person who finds himself caught in a rip current may be carried out to deep water and quickly become fatigued trying to swim against the current. Because rip currents are narrow, the best action for a person caught in one is to swim at a right angle to it. When he is safely out of it, he can swim to shore.

19-24 Rip currents acting on a beach (top). Rip currents generally flow perpendicularly away from the beach (bottom).

Rip Currents: Swimmers Beware!

Many beachside deaths are caused by a phenomenon called "rip currents." These swift currents can knock a person standing in the water off his feet and rapidly carry him out to sea. Panicked swimmers exhaust themselves by fighting against the current and eventually drown.

Rip currents occur when high waves dump large amounts of water on the beach. As the water builds up, it rushes back out into the ocean along narrow paths. These currents usually form at low points in the breakers or hollows in the shoreline, where water tends to pile up between breakers. They can flow at 1 m/s (3 ft/s) for several minutes, racing 760 m (2500 ft) into the sea before dying out.

You can easily locate a rip current. Look for strips of water where sand is being carried out by the current, or look for slight changes in the wave patterns as they meet a rip current. If you are ever caught in a rip current, remember that rip currents are narrow. You simply need to swim *parallel* to the shore until you are free of the current. Then you can head back to shore.

Box Summary: Rip Currents: Swimmers Beware!

This box elaborates on the dangers and safety precautions associated with heavy surf and rip currents. There are no vocabulary terms in this box.

19.17 Ocean Erosion

Beaches are built from eroded materials deposited by waves. Waves, especially during storms, also can remove or erode the loosely deposited materials. Beach erosion is an expensive danger for people who build homes close to the seashore. At most locations along the mid-Atlantic coast of the United States, beach erosion is occurring at a rate of 0.5 to 1 m (2 to 3 ft) per year. In some areas, such as the outer banks of Virginia, beaches are being eroded as much as 8 m (25 ft) per year.

19-25 Problems associated with beach erosion in southern California

Beaches are not the only type of shore that the waves erode. Many coasts consist of rock cliffs. As the waves erode the cliffs, they create beaches in front of the cliffs. Occasionally a weaker part of the rock erodes away, leaving a **sea cave**. If a cave is eroded through a narrow headland, a **sea arch**, which resembles a natural bridge, is formed. A **stack** is a mass of rock that wave erosion has isolated from the shore. A stack often results from the collapse of a sea arch.

When the waves erode material, they must eventually redeposit it. When water laden with sand encounters an obstacle, it slows down and deposits some sand. This often happens near the edges of a bay. If the deposited sand forms an exposed strip of land extending from

19-26 Debris deposited inside a coastal sea cave

19-27 Landforms that are produced by incomplete beach erosion: a sea arch and stack near Quebec, Canada (left); a stack on the coast of New Brunswick (right)

 Visual 19-12: Wave-Eroded Landforms

This visual is a reproduction of Figures 19-26 and 27. Refer to these images as you discuss wave erosion.

This visual is a reproduction of Figure 19-28, showing a broader view of these images. Refer to these images as you discuss wave deposition.

19-28 Landforms that are built from eroded material and deposited by wave action: tombolo (top left), hook (bottom left), barrier islands (center), spit (right)

tombolo (TOM buh LOH)

the shore across part of a bay, it is called a **spit**. The spit may eventually extend across the bay's mouth, closing it to the sea. This is a **bay barrier**. A spit with a sharp bend is called a **hook**. When the waves deposit sand as an island parallel to the shore but the island has no connection with the mainland, the deposit is called a **barrier island**. Many of the islands of the southeast coast of the United States are barrier islands. Another wave deposit called a **tombolo** often connects islands with each other or to the mainland.

19C-2 Section Review

1. What causes most surface waves? What geologic event could cause a large surface wave?
2. An ocean wave with a wavelength of 36 m and a wave height of 0.5 m approaches the shoreline. At what water depth will the wave height begin to increase?
3. What two kinds of currents are related to the interaction of waves with the shore? How are they different?
4. What name is given to a mass of rock that has been cut off from the mainland by erosion? What sedimentary formation may connect such a rock to the shoreline?
5. (True or False) A wave with a wavelength of 25 m and a wave height of 3 m is not breaking.

Answers to 19C-2 Section Review Questions

1. The wind causes most surface waves. A submarine earthquake or debris slide could cause a large surface wave called a *tsunami*. (§19.15, Chap. 17)

2. The wave height will begin to increase when the bottom depth decreases to less than 18 m. (§19.16)

3. Waves coming onshore cause *longshore currents* and *rip currents*. Longshore currents flow parallel to the shore, but rip currents flow away from the shore. (§19.16)

4. A mass of rock that has been cut off from the mainland by erosion is called a *stack*. A stack may be connected to the shoreline by a *tombolo*. (§19.17)

5. True. The ratio of wave height to wavelength (steepness) is less than ⅐. (§19.16)

CURRENTS

19.18 Surface Currents

As described previously, longshore currents and rip currents occur only near land because they are produced by waves approaching the shore or by water returning to the sea from off a beach. There are currents in the ocean caused by other forces, which move more water and move it greater distances.

Surface currents, like waves, are caused by winds. However, surface currents last longer than wave patterns, and they transport water long distances. The surface currents of the ocean tend to follow the prevailing winds. Like the winds, the currents are affected by the rotation of the earth (Coriolis effect). Thus, in the Northern Hemisphere the currents tend to form great clockwise closed-loop flow patterns called **gyres**. In the Southern Hemisphere, the gyres tend to flow counterclockwise.

In the Pacific, Atlantic, and Indian oceans, there are narrow, east-flowing currents along the equator, dividing the north and south west-flowing equatorial currents. Called *equatorial countercurrents*, they result from the pile-up of water at the west sides of the respective basins where the equatorial currents run into land. They return surface waters to the east sides of the basins.

Ocean currents affect the weather by carrying cold or warm water far from its source. For example, the Gulf Stream and the Kuroshio (or Japan) Current are warm currents that flow north from warm areas. The Gulf Stream flows from the Gulf of Mexico toward Europe, and the Kureshio Current flows along the east coast of Asia toward North America, becoming the North Pacific and Alaskan currents. Winds blowing from the west (the prevailing westerlies) across

gyre (JIRE): (Gk. *giros*—ring, circle)

19-29 Major warm (red) and cold (blue) surface currents of the world's oceans. Desert regions are indicated by tan shading.

Visual 19-14: Major Ocean Surface Currents

This visual is a reproduction of Figure 19-29. The abbreviation "Eq." stands for "Equatorial" and the abbreviation "C." stands for "Current." Show students the relationships between the major deserts of the world and the location of cold currents to their west. Note the gyres in the Atlantic and the Pacific oceans.

these warm currents bring warm weather to northern Europe and western Canada. Because of the winds across the Gulf Stream, England is warmer than New York, even though it is farther north than New York. Similarly, western Canada is warmer than eastern Siberia as a result of the Kuroshio Current.

Cold currents flow from the polar regions toward the equator. These also affect the weather of the nearby land. Land near cold currents tends to be dry because cold air can hold less moisture. For example, the cold California Current off the coast of Baja California keeps that Mexican state's climate dry. Both the Atacama Desert in South America, where rain falls only a few times each century, and the Namib Desert in Southern Africa are coastal regions near cold currents (the Peru and the Benguela currents, respectively).

Atacama (AT uh KAM uh)

Namib (NAH MIB)

19.19 Subsurface Currents

Oceanographers have discovered the existence of currents flowing in the depths of the oceans that are much larger than surface currents. Because subsurface currents are harder to detect than surface currents, they are not as well known. Deep waters are not subject to wind currents, so other forces must cause their motions. Oceanographers have discovered that deep currents are caused by three major factors: friction with surface currents, flow away from piled-up surface waters, and density differences. Most deep currents are caused by more than one of these factors.

Many subsurface currents at relatively shallow depths are caused by friction with surface waters. Due to the Coriolis effect, these deeper currents flow in a direction that is skewed to the right of the surface current direction (in the Northern Hemisphere). In fact, as the depth increases the subsurface current becomes more deflected. This deflection of current direction with depth is called the **Ekman spiral**. Because water does not transmit frictional forces efficiently, current speed decreases with increasing depth.

Subsurface currents can develop when water piled up against a landmass by wind or surface currents tries to flow away under the influence of gravity. This pile-up of water causes locally higher-than-normal sea levels that force water downward, where it then flows along the bottom away from the pile-up. The downward flow of surface water is called *subsidence*. These currents are deflected by the Coriolis effect and often flow in a direction unrelated to the surface currents that caused them.

Gravity also drives currents created by differences in density. On the average, seawater is 1.025 times as dense as pure water because of the salt and minerals dissolved in seawater. As mentioned earlier, variations in mineral content, or **salinity** (saltiness), can change this density, but this effect is important only where freshwater dilution or evaporation is significant. Temperature is usually much more important in determining the density of seawater. Cold seawater will sink and flow under warmer water. Because of the uneven and sloped nature of the ocean basins, the cold water will flow downhill into the basins, forming deep currents that follow the bottom topography.

The most significant of the deep currents driven by density differences are the deep circulation or **thermohaline currents**—slow currents that flow far beneath most major surface currents. The deep thermohaline currents consist of cold and/or higher-salinity ocean

The Ekman spiral is named for V. Walfrid Ekman (1874–1954), a Swedish physicist and oceanographer who was the first to mathematically describe the response of ocean water to wind and currents.

19-30 A surface current driven by wind drags along subsurface water. The Coriolis effect deflects deeper water to the right (in the Northern Hemisphere), forming an Ekman spiral. (*Note:* Arrow length indicates current speed.)

thermohaline: thermo- (Gk. *therme*—heat) + -haline (Gk. *halo*—salty)

![Ekman Spiral icon] **Visual 19-15: Ekman Spiral**

This visual is a reproduction of Figure 19-30. Note the following key points:

1. Surface currents form and move most efficiently at 45° from the direction of the wind movement. The friction involved in wave formation produces a surface current.

2. Surface currents drag along the waters beneath them due to friction, but because the transfer of frictional forces in fluids is poor, current speed decreases with depth.

3. The Coriolis effect deflects the currents with increasing depth. At greater depths, the current direction can be totally unrelated to the surface current direction.

water that has subsided into the depths near the polar regions. These huge masses of water slowly circulate under the influence of gravity across the world's ocean basins in poorly understood patterns, eventually mixing with a deep current of very cold water that encircles the Antarctic continent. Thermohaline currents are much slower than surface currents, moving the same distance in a year that a surface current moves in an hour. Oceanographers estimate that this cold, deep water may reside in thermohaline currents for 1000 years or more before returning to the surface.

19-31 Deep water (thermohaline) currents of the world

Gravity also produces local subsurface currents. In some places, masses of water with different densities meet. The salinity differences in these cases affect the relative densities of the different water masses. Thus, the more saline water tends to sink, and the less-saline water tends to rise. This action produces a current called a **density current**. The Mediterranean Sea exchanges water with the Atlantic Ocean by a density current. The floor of the Mediterranean Sea is separated from the Atlantic floor by an underwater ledge where the two meet near the Straits of Gibraltar. Because the deep Mediterranean water flowing out of the straits is saltier, it tends to remain deep. The less-saline water from the Atlantic flows into the Mediterranean Sea at the surface. This flow forces some of the dense Mediterranean water over the ledge and into the Atlantic basin. Other seas separated from the main oceans by a restriction have similar circulation patterns.

19-32 A density current exchanges water between the Atlantic Ocean and the Mediterranean Sea.

Where water is denser because it carries sediment, another type of density current, called a **turbidity current**, is formed. Turbidity currents are a form of submarine mass wasting, similar to mudslides and lahars on land. The sediment-laden water flows down slope along the ocean floor, eroding it as it goes. Some of the underwater canyons in the continental slopes may have been eroded by turbidity currents.

On the western coasts of some continents, especially South America, the trade winds blow from the east strongly and persistently enough to move the top, warm layer of the ocean to the west.

turbidity (tur BID ih tee)

Visual 19-16: Global Thermohaline Circulation

This visual is a reproduction of Figure 19-31. It is a very generalized diagram of the deep thermohaline circulation. Oceanographers do not know much about this flow. The estimates of 1000-year circulation times are just guesses based on existing flow rates measured at deep depths. There is some concern expressed by certain oceanographers that the warming of the ocean surfaces may lock up the cold, deep waters and stop the upwelling that occurs in the Pacific and Atlantic oceans.

upwelling (UP wel ing)

This movement causes cold water from the bottom to move upward in a process called **upwelling**, which is the opposite of subsidence. The water from the bottom is rich in nutrients and forms the base of a food chain that supports the world's greatest fisheries. Water from the deep thermohaline currents returns to the surface by upwelling.

Maelström: A Sailor's Nightmare

The Moskoe-ström whirlpool was about a quarter of a mile dead ahead. . . . I involuntarily closed my eyes in horror. . . .

We suddenly felt the waves subside, and were enveloped in foam. The boat made a sharp half turn to larboard, and then shot off in its new direction like a thunderbolt. At the same time the roaring noise of the water was completely drowned in a kind of shrill-shriek . . . We careered round and round for perhaps an hour, flying rather than floating, getting gradually more into the middle of the surge, and then nearer and nearer to its horrible inner edge.

Edgar Allan Poe
"A Descent into the Maelström"

Norwegian legend warns of a ravaging whirlpool, called the Maelström, which appears without warning in the seas off the coast and swallows ships. Poe's short story was based on this legend.

A maelstrom does exist off Norway in the strait between two of the Lofoten Islands, but it is not quite so dramatic. It is a strong current that flows back and forth with the changing tide. The eddies that form can be dangerous. Fierce winds and underwater rocks amplify the disorder, whose din can be heard miles away.

maelström (MALE strum)

19C-3 Section Review

1. What is the main cause of the major surface currents of the world's oceans?
2. What are the great looping ocean-current patterns called?
3. Describe the difference between a surface current and a deep circulation current.
4. Name three causes for the formation of subsurface currents.
5. What kind of density current is caused by sinking muddy water? To what events on land is this kind of current similar?
6. What is cold, nutrient-rich water rising from the deep ocean bottom called? Why is it important?
7. (True or False) Water at the bottom of the ocean at any given location is always colder than the surface water at the same location.

Box Summary: Maelström: A Sailor's Nightmare

This box relates the facts behind one of the most popularized hazards in maritime fiction—the whirlpool. There are no vocabulary terms in this box.

Answers to 19C-3 Section Review Questions

1. The major ocean currents are produced by the combined action of prevailing winds and the Coriolis effect. (§19.18)

2. The great looping ocean-current patterns are called *gyres*. (§19.18)

3. A surface current is usually caused by prevailing winds and responds to the Coriolis effect, often forming great gyres around the perimeters of the ocean basins. Deep circulation currents flow under the influence of gravity due to temperature and salinity differences, moving slowly at speeds much less than the speeds of surface currents. (§19.18–19.19)

4. Three causes for subsurface currents are *friction* with surface currents, *pile-up and subsidence* of surface water by wind or surface currents, and *density differences*. (§19.19)

5. A *turbidity current* is caused by sinking, sediment-laden water. Turbidity currents are similar to mudslides and lahars on land. (§19.19)

6. Cold, nutrient-rich water rising from the ocean bottom is called an *upwelling*. Upwelling water supplies the raw materials for the world's greatest fisheries. (§19.19)

7. False. This is true only in tropical and temperate regions. In polar regions, the surface water can be colder; it may even be frozen. (See Chap. 13.)

19D OCEAN EXPLORATION

19.20 Historical Background

For centuries people assumed that the oceans were not much more than featureless expanses of water. Human knowledge of the oceans, as well as of lakes and rivers, was limited to what could be seen by a swimmer—how deep he could dive, how long he could stay under water, and the clarity of the water. Early in history, human curiosity about this inhospitable region of the world drove the invention of devices we now call *diving bells* to permit direct observation of the ocean bottom. We do not know who actually invented them or when, but Aristotle records that in 332 BC Alexander the Great had a large barrel constructed out of glass from which he is said to have observed the bottom of the Mediterranean Sea. For the following 22 centuries, men used various types of diving suits and bells for all sorts of practical underwater work.

In 1690 Sir Edmund Halley invented a means of replenishing the air in a diving bell by sending down barrels of fresh air, thus extending the time a diver could work under water. John Smeaton improved

19-34 A century ago, pearl and sponge divers wore a canvas suit topped with a bronze helmet with view ports. They were supplied air by a hose connected to a tending vessel on the surface. This system was very difficult to use and prone to accidents. Many "hard-hat" divers died or were permanently paralyzed.

upon this idea in 1788 by using a pump to continuously replenish the air through a hose to the water's surface. From this, it was an easy step to the diving helmet that "deep-sea divers" used until recent times. But through all of this time, there was little effort given to explore the ocean's bottom purely to increase human knowledge of what goes on under the surface of the seas. The old idea that the oceans were little more than featureless expanses of water was still dominant. Some even believed that most of the deep ocean bottom was lifeless.

19.21 The HMS *Challenger*

During the nineteenth century, an increasing number of scientists and other people questioned the belief that most of the ocean bottom was lifeless. Eventually, in 1870, Wyville Thompson of Edinburgh University and one of his students convinced the Royal Society and the British government to support the first-ever round-the-world oceanographic expedition using a medium-sized sail-and-steam warship named the HMS *Challenger*. Most of its guns were removed, and it was equipped with biology and chemistry laboratories and a staff of scientists. A special sounding machine (for measuring the depth of the water and taking a sample of the bottom at the same time) and bottom dredging equipment were also installed.

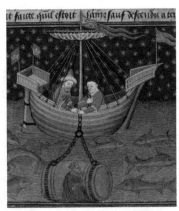

19-33 According to historical records, Alexander the Great was the first man to descend into the depths for the sole purpose of observation.

Wyville Thompson (1830–82) was a Scottish naturalist and scientist who spent more than half his career teaching at Queen's College, Belfast. During his last ten years there, he was chair of the departments of geology, mineralogy, botany, zoology, and physical geography and was recognized by the informal title "Professor of Creation."

19-35 The HMS *Challenger*

Upon completing this section, students should be able to

- present a broad historical background for the development of the scientific study of the oceans.

- describe the purpose and use of basic oceanographic instruments.

- give a general chronology of the development of man-in-sea programs and manned undersea research vehicles.

- compare and contrast the cost and effectiveness of manned and unmanned undersea research vehicles.

[?] Students Sometimes Ask

Students may wonder what kinds of accidents hardhat divers might have been subject to. In addition to the normal diving hazards of getting stuck or injured on the bottom, divers had to deal with inherent equipment design problems. The diver's air was delivered by a pump located on the vessel above through a long air hose. The air pressure in the diving suit had to be maintained equal to the external sea pressure. If the air pressure became too high, the suit would inflate like a balloon, possibly lifting the diver off the bottom. To minimize this problem, divers wore lead boots and lead weight belts. If air pressure dropped too low, sea pressure would quickly squeeze the diver, sometimes fatally. If the diver was brought back to the surface too quickly, a medical condition known as "the bends" could occur, in which gas bubbles formed in blood vessels, joints, and muscles like a soft drink fizzes when the container is opened quickly. The bends can permanently cripple or kill a diver. Many, but not all, of these problems were eliminated with the invention of scuba and saturation diving equipment.

The distance traveled by the *Challenger* expedition was equivalent to nearly three times around the world.

In 1872 the expedition began a 68,890-mile, four-year journey, charting the bottoms of the Atlantic, Pacific, and Indian oceans, analyzing water samples from the ocean bottoms and scooping up samples of marine animals and plants. The results of the expedition literally changed the course of scientific history. Among many accomplishments, the crew cataloged 4717 species of plant and animal life that were previously unknown to Western scientists.

Visual 19-17: Basic Oceanographic Instruments

Refer to this visual as you discuss some of the oceanographic tools and instruments mentioned in the text.

Most of the instruments shown in this section can be used to study lakes as well. The science of lake studies is called *limnology*, a term based on the Greek word *limne*—lake.

19-36 Depth soundings were obtained using a lead line until the invention of sonar.

lead line (LED LINE)

1 fathom = 6 ft (1.83 m)

Fridtjof Nansen (1861–1930), a Norwegian, was a Nobel Prize winning zoologist, arctic explorer, humanitarian, and statesman. His ship, the *Fram*, crossed the Arctic Ocean locked in pack ice, proving that polar ice drifts.

19-37 A rack of water sample bottles based on the Nansen bottle

19.22 Basic Oceanographic Instruments

The voyage of the HMS *Challenger* established the importance of oceanography as a separate science. The study of the ocean involves acquiring general information about sea-floor depth and topography as well as temperature, seawater composition (salinity), currents, water clarity, and biological organisms, all at various depths. In addition, scientists want to know the composition of bottom sediments or types of bedrock outcrops, if they exist, as well as the biological communities on the bottom. To obtain such information, oceanographers have developed rugged, relatively simple instruments that have changed little over the past century. As in our study of the atmosphere, we will describe several instruments that are commonly used in studies of the oceans, and freshwater lakes as well.

Prior to the invention of sonar, the lead line was used for determining water depth. Lead lines had been used for centuries by navigators to avoid running aground. When the ship was approaching shore, if the lead line did not touch bottom after several fathoms of rope were let out, the ship was considered to be in safe waters. For oceanographic purposes, a lead line was extremely difficult to use. Imagine trying to find the depth of water 10,000 m (6 mi) deep with a lead weight on a rope! Lead lines were often lowered using a motorized winch, but for deep soundings, the wire or rope often broke. Depth data was often questionable for deep soundings because currents or the ship's motion could cause large curves in the cable that added many meters to the measured sounding. Echo sounding solved most of these problems although different problems arise when interpreting echo sounding data.

Water samples at specified depths provide information such as chemical composition, temperature, density, and clarity. Fridtjof Nansen invented a simple and effective water-sampling instrument that was used for many years. The *Nansen bottle* is an open cylinder with automatic stoppers or valves at both ends. Up to twenty-four bottles may be clamped to a cable at appropriate intervals and lowered into the water. A small messenger weight is slid down the cable, which, when it strikes the first bottle mechanism, shuts the plugs and releases another messenger weight that trips the next bottle, and so on down the cable. The cable is retrieved with a winch and the bottles are removed and sent to the laboratory, where the water samples are collected and stored. Some Nansen bottles include a special thermometer that retains the temperature reading at the time the messenger weight trips the bottle. Modern researchers are depending more on computerized instruments that can measure temperature, salinity, and other characteristics directly. If water samples are required, a rack of multiple programmable bottles that open and close at specified depths are attached at the end of a cable. This modern system makes water sampling much more rapid.

Water clarity is important for photosynthetic algae and other organisms in the lighted zone of the ocean, near the surface. The density of microscopic organisms or sediments can severely reduce the amount of light reaching into deeper waters. For many years, oceanographers would lower a special disk called a Secchi disk into the water and note at what depth it was no longer visible from the surface. This disk, often painted black and white in alternating quarters, was named after its inventor, Pietro Secchi. Modern water clarity instruments use calibrated photovoltaic cells to measure the light received from a known light source. Such an instrument can be used at any depth, not just near the water's surface.

Biologists are interested in knowing what kinds of small organisms swim and float in the ocean's depths. These organisms, collectively called *plankton*, are not only interesting creatures to study, but they are important because they are food for larger organisms. Biological samples are obtained with a device called a *plankton net* that consists of a conical net made of a fine-mesh material stiffened by a

19-39 One of the many kinds of plankton nets

metal ring at its large end. At the narrow end, a collection jar is clamped to the net. The net is pulled through the water, and the small floating organisms are swept into the jar by the water flow. Weights may be added to the towline to tow the net at a selected depth.

Bottom-dwelling animals are also of interest to marine biologists. Recall that for a long time scientists believed that animals could not live at the ocean's bottom because of the extreme pressure and darkness. Devices called grab samplers were invented that collected bottom-dwelling organisms for examination. Such a sampler is basically a metal box attached to the end of a long cable that can reach the bottom. One kind of sampler has two spring-loaded clamshell-like doors that slide across the open bottom of the box to "grab" the bottom sample. After the box is lowered to the bottom, a messenger weight is dropped down the cable to trip a latch that is holding the doors open. The doors spring shut, scooping up a sample of mud, and the sampler is hauled back to the surface.

Many other instruments have been invented to help oceanographers sample and observe the depths of the world's oceans. The instruments you have studied here are just a few of the basic ones that

Pietro Angelo Secchi (SEK kee) (1818–78) was an Italian astronomer and a Jesuit priest. He is known especially for his work in stellar spectroscopy and early solar-eclipse photographs. He also published a star catalog.

19-38 The Secchi disk is used to determine water transparency near the surface.

19-40 A bottom sampler called an Ekman grab sampler

Plankton nets are used for collecting small *pelagic* organisms. Pelagic creatures are those that normally inhabit the water column, typically in open oceans, rather than the bottom.

Grab samplers are designed to collect *benthos* (*benthic* organisms). Benthic creatures and plants occupy the bottoms of lakes and oceans rather than the water column.

Visual 19-18: Advanced Oceanographic Instruments

This visual shows just two examples of a vast array of new high-tech equipment oceanographers are using to study the earth's oceans. On the left is a diagram of a tsunami monitoring system that consists of bottom water-pressure sensors and a buoy transmitter that communicates with a GOES satellite. On the right is a raw data display of a 3-D multibeam sonar system that can quickly map the topography of the ocean bottom directly, compared to the laborious process of reconstructing bottom contours from 2-D echosounder traces.

Little is known about Otis Barton other than that he was an American engineer. Some references place his birth date in 1899.

Visual 19-19: Important U.S. Research Submersibles

This visual is a reproduction of Figures 19-42 and 19-45 (left). Use this visual as you discuss bathyscaphs and deep submergence vehicles. Shown on the left is the *Trieste* in her heyday in the early 1960s. The vessel was rebuilt and designated *Trieste II* (DSV 1) in 1971. She was taken out of service in 1984. The 40-year-old *Alvin* was recently retired in October 2004 after conducting approximately 4000 dives. It is scheduled to be replaced in 2008 by a slightly roomier vehicle that will be able to explore 99 percent of the ocean bottom.

Charles William Beebe (1877–1962) was an American ornithologist (bird scientist) and the director of tropical research for the New York Zoological Society who is best known for his historic descents in the *Bathysphere*.

19-41 William Beebe and Otis Barton with the *Bathysphere*

Auguste Piccard (1884–1962) was a Swiss inventor. He applied principles learned during an early interest in hot-air ballooning to the construction of vehicles for deep ocean exploration.

bathyscaph (BATH ih SKAF): bathy- (Gk. *bathus*—deep) + -scaph (Gk. *scaphe*—boat)

19-42 The *Trieste*, the deepest-diving submersible vehicle, was a bathyscaph.

have been used for over a century in oceanography. Today, oceanographers have access to satellite imagery, bottom-profiling sonar and radar, GPS positioning and navigation, manned and unmanned submersibles (see subsections 19.25–27), and high-powered computers that model ocean processes. Even with all these advances, we still know less about some locations in the ocean depths than we do about the surface of Mars.

19.23 The *Bathysphere*

For more than 50 years, scientists studying the oceans were content to imitate the voyage of the *Challenger*, but on a smaller scale, dredging up samples from the bottom. After analyzing the lifeless and damaged organisms of some 1500 sampling nets, William Beebe thought it would be better if scientists could go down into the ocean and observe living things first hand. In the late 1920s, Beebe and the American engineer Otis Barton constructed a 1.5 m (5 ft) diameter steel ball, 3 cm (1.25 in.) thick, with three observation windows, called the *Bathysphere*.

In 1930, the *Bathysphere*, with Beebe and Barton inside, was lowered on a steel cable from a large barge into the dark waters near Nonesuch Island in the Bahamas. The two men completed a series of descents that culminated in a 923 m (3028 ft) dive. Beebe believed that each descent into regions where living things could be observed in their natural habitat yielded more information than all his sampling nets combined. Again, the impact on scientific knowledge was tremendous.

19.24 The Bathyscaphs and *Trieste*

The *Bathysphere* had two disadvantages: it couldn't go anywhere but straight down and straight up, and it couldn't collect and return with samples. In the late 1930s Auguste Piccard began developing a vehicle that would overcome these limitations. Called a *bathyscaph*, it was like a cross between a submarine and a small dirigible. A large tank containing 106,000 L (28,000 gal) of gasoline provided the needed buoyancy (gasoline is less dense than water). A hollow steel sphere with walls seven inches thick, suspended underneath the gasoline tank, provided the crew compartment. The bathyscaph was free to move near the bottom using small battery-powered propellers and had no connections to the surface.

After proving the success of the basic bathyscaph concept, Piccard built another much-improved bathyscaph, called the *Trieste*. Launched in 1953, the *Trieste* was eventually purchased by the U.S. Navy. *Trieste* conducted a series of dives, the deepest of which was 10,912 m (35,800 ft) into the Challenger Deep in the Mariana Trench. This record cannot be broken since this spot is the deepest known point in any ocean. During this 1960 dive, *Trieste* encountered the greatest pressure known to exist in the ocean—about 111,430,000 N/m^2 (17,000 lb/in^2), more than one thousand times the pressure at sea level. The vessel was equipped with a series of sampling devices, including robotic arms (with grabbers and claws) and water samplers. Deep-sea photography, using cameras and lights designed to work under the crushing pressures of deep dives, was perfected using the *Trieste*.

The *Trieste* and her sisters were instrumental in revolutionizing deep-sea research, but they still had some limitations that restricted their usefulness. They were slow and clumsy, and they could not dive for long periods of time because their battery life was just a few hours.

19.25 Manned Undersea Research

The United States and other nations of the world pursued many undersea activities following World War II. In Chapter 13 we discussed the deep drilling projects that have added to our knowledge of the earth's structure beneath the seabeds. Another direction researchers took was the development of research submarines. Although the U.S. Navy has funded 17 research submersibles throughout its history, only two were true submarines that could be equipped to conduct oceanographic research for long periods submerged over long distances. Their work has been devoted mainly to classified military undersea studies. One, the USS *Dolphin*, is a diesel-electric, deep-diving research submarine. Although a relatively small submarine, this ship can carry 12 tons of research equipment. *Dolphin* accomplished many firsts in oceanographic studies for the navy, including the deepest dive by an operational submarine.

The other submarine is called *NR 1*. She is the smallest nuclear-powered submarine in the world. Manned by a crew of five, the *NR 1* can take one or two scientists on oceanographic surveys, remaining continuously submerged for up to 35 days. She has a manipulator arm that can cut, saw, grasp, and lift massive objects of up to 900 kg (2000 lb). The submarine is also equipped with wheels for maneuvering on the bottom. It was used extensively in 1986 to recover the remains of the space shuttle *Challenger* after it exploded.

The U.S. Navy was also a leader in the Man-in-Sea program, which studied the ability of humans to work and live under water. In 1943, the Frenchmen Emille Gagnan and Jacques-Yves Cousteau designed the first self-contained underwater breathing apparatus (scuba) that permitted divers unparalleled freedom of movement under water. Both the U.S. military and sportsmen adopted the new equipment with enthusiasm. However, scuba diving was not without its restrictions. The tanks carried a limited supply of air, and deep dives required time-consuming stops on the way back to the surface for rest and to prevent injury from coming shallow too quickly. Caution was important for these excursions because they involved some danger to the diver.

In order to keep men on the bottom for longer periods, the navy built a series of experimental undersea laboratories called *Sealab* and *Tektite* that allowed divers to work at depth for up to several weeks. Cousteau himself supervised the construction of several habitats called the *Conshelf* series that housed divers for as long as a month.

19-43 The U.S. Navy's two true oceanographic submarines, USS *Dolphin* (top) and *NR 1* (bottom)

Jacques-Yves Cousteau (1910–97) was a world-renowned ocean explorer and engineer from France. He is best known for inventing the self-contained underwater breathing apparatus (scuba) and for his television specials that brought the world of oceanography into the homes of millions.

 Students Sometimes Ask

Students may ask about the differences between a submarine and a submersible. A true submarine is a larger vessel designed to operate for long periods of time at various depths and speeds and over long distances underwater. Manned submersibles are usually small and sacrifice capabilities such as speed and duration for depth of operation and the ability to perform on-the-spot sampling or to work using manipulators. Typically, submarines have fairly large crews (tens of people), while submersibles are limited to a pilot and a few passengers.

19-44 *Aquarius*, the only active U.S. undersea laboratory habitat, is moored off the Florida Keys.

Most of these Man-in-Sea programs were discontinued because of the expense, difficulty, and danger of maintaining human divers continuously at working depths. NOAA maintains the last U.S. undersea laboratory habitat, the *Aquarius*, located in the Florida Keys. Teams reside in *Aquarius* for ten days, carrying out research in varied areas that include coral reef biology as well as training and biomedical research by NASA that may help in future space flights. A number of private companies have built or are planning recreational undersea habitats for sport divers and vacationers.

19.26 Manned Submersibles

As with the space program, the public is most interested in the risk, adventure, and technology of placing humans in a foreign environment, in spite of the costs. Most scientists agree that having a human on the spot allows split-second decisions and better observations than by any other means. Many advances in manned research

19-45 The *Alvin* (above) was the first maneuverable deep submergence vehicle (DSV). The *Shinkai 6500* is a Japanese research submarine (right).

submersibles have improved their mobility and safety, making them much more useful for studying the oceans. It has been estimated that there are more than 200 manned undersea submersible vehicles worldwide. Because they have limited space for human passengers and have limited operating ranges, they require support ships to take them to and from the dive site and to restock such things as fuel, batteries, oxygen, and food, as well as to provide maintenance and repair facilities. These submersibles are the technological descendants of *Trieste*.

19.27 Unmanned Submersibles

Even with the advantages of direct observation and control, placing humans in environments for which they were not created has always been hazardous and expensive. With recent improvements in ocean engineering and computerized technology, unmanned submersibles have come into use all over the world. These robots began as instrumented sleds that were towed behind a tender or support vessel. Modern tethered submersibles are called *remotely operated vehicles (ROV)*. Connected to surface ships by power and control cables, they are capable of nearly unlimited operation and maneuvering, controlled by relay teams of pilots and scientists in the mother ship on the surface. Commercial ROVs are routinely used by oil drilling companies to perform deep-water seabed surveys and maintenance on wellheads.

 Visual 19-20: Other Modern Submersibles

This visual illustrates some other modern submersible vessels. The *Johnson Sea-Link* is a venerable research and exploration submersible that has been much improved over the years. The middle photograph is of a U.S. Navy Deep Submergence Rescue Vehicle—not a research submersible, but a submersible life boat that is sent to sunken military submarines to rescue their crews. The bottom photo is of a new generation of very small submersibles that permit one person to work and explore at deep depths at normal atmospheric pressure.

Beholding the Waters

Students should recall a similar question in Chapter 8 regarding manned space exploration. We are commanded to study and investigate all aspects of God's creation for His glory and for the benefit of humans (the Creation Mandate), and we are created with an innate curiosity about our world. Human life must be protected to the limits of human ingenuity, but no submersible will be perfectly safe, and no exploration will be completely without risk. This is the consequence of living in a fallen and cursed world. However, it is worth facing reasonable hazards with appropriate precautions to discover new creatures and other aspects of the world God created for us. Job 38:16 reminds us that the depths of the oceans contain many unknown mysteries hidden there by our Creator. In addition, scientists never know when a discovery will make a significant contribution to a scientific understanding of the earth.

Beholding the Waters

Scientists and engineers acknowledge that the technical aspects of keeping a human safe deep in the ocean is in most respects more difficult than keeping him safe in space. The most significant problem is keeping the crushing pressure of the ocean at bay. In view of potential hazards to humans, should Christians be involved in manned deep-sea exploration?

19-46 The *Jason II* ROV (left); the *DeepWorker* (right), a deep-water "micro-sub"

Encourage your students to investigate career and ministry opportunities as oceanographers. The ocean has the potential to feed the world and provide unlimited sources of energy once the secrets to its proper utilization are discovered. Oceanography for this purpose is God-honoring and is another example of man's obedience to the Creation Mandate.

An even more recent advance depends on artificial intelligence, which eliminates the need for a power and control connection to a surface tending vessel. These submersibles are called *autonomous underwater vehicles* (AUV). AUVs have their own propulsion systems and are programmed in advance to proceed along a specific course and collect data at specified points on the journey. They may send data back to the researchers via satellite, or they may store it until the vehicle is recovered.

Several chapters would be needed to describe all of the new varieties of *unmanned undersea vehicles* (UUV). Some UUVs drift with the currents, taking measurements of temperature, salinity, current speed and direction, and so on. They can report their position and data by sound pulses, or they may be programmed to rise to the surface to transmit their data by radio and then descend back to a preprogrammed depth to continue their survey. Others glide through the depths, taking samples and surveying using sonar. And yet others may rest on the bottom for long periods of time, photographing the activities of bottom-dwelling organisms and then returning to the surface when programmed or commanded by a remote signal.

19-47 The *Slocum Glider*, an autonomous undersea vehicle designed for oceanographic research

19D   Section Review

1. Who does history record was the first person to enter the sea in a submersible chamber? What kind of vehicle was this chamber?

2. In which vessel did the first round-the-world oceanographic expedition sail? How did the findings of this expedition affect scientific knowledge at the time?

3. What instrument is used to obtain water samples deep in the ocean?

4. What was the advantage of a bathyscaph over the *Bathysphere*?

5. Why were most Man-in-Sea programs discontinued?

6. Why do most people find manned submersibles the most interesting of ocean exploration equipment?

7. (True or False) A new world record for the deepest dive by a submersible depends on the development of newer, stronger materials.

Answers to 19D Section Review Questions

1. According to history, Alexander the Great was the first person to visit the sea bottom in a submersible chamber. It was supposedly a glass barrel, a design similar to later ones called *diving bells*. (§19.20)

2. The first round-the-world oceanographic expedition sailed in the HMS *Challenger*. The findings of the expedition radically changed the current understanding of the oceans and of many other aspects of science. (§19.21)

3. The *Nansen bottle*, or its modern equivalent, is used to obtain deep-water samples. (§19.22)

4. A bathyscaph could move around freely near the bottom and take water and biological samples. The *Bathysphere* could move only up and down on a cable, and it had no means of taking samples. (§19.23–19.24)

5. Sustaining humans in underwater habitats for long-term occupation on the sea bottom was too costly and difficult for the potential benefits. (§19.25)

6. People are interested in the risk, adventure, and technological advances required to place humans in adverse environments. (§19.26)

7. False. The bathyscaph *Trieste* reached the deepest known depth in any ocean in 1960. (§19.24)

Answers to Chapter Review Questions

What Did You Learn?

1. They were surprised to find that the ocean bottoms had more and higher mountains, larger and flatter plains, and deeper valleys than anywhere on land. (§19.3)

2. Typically, a flat, broad *continental shelf* lies adjacent to the shoreline as an extension of the coastal topography. Next is the *continental slope* that descends into deep water at a steeper angle. At the bottom of the slope is the *continental rise,* lying at a smaller angle and consisting of sediments from the shelf. The deepest, relatively level regions of the ocean basins are called the *abyssal plains* or the *abyss.* (§19.4)

3. In order to form dry land from a coral reef, which can only grow under water, either the sea level must have dropped or the bottom must have risen. (§19.6)

4. Dissolved minerals enter the ocean in stream water. The water exits the ocean by evaporation, but most of the minerals remain in the ocean. (§19.8)

5. No, sodium chloride (table salt) accounts for much of the dissolved minerals in seawater, but seawater contains many other dissolved minerals. (§19.8)

6. The most economical system for providing fresh water to the village would be a reverse osmosis plant powered by photovoltaic panels. (§19.9)

7. The other bulge would be about 180° away, on the opposite side of the earth, near 100° E longitude (near Burma, Malaysia, and off the west coast of Australia). (§19.12)

8. The earth's rotation causes it to move under the relatively stationary bulges of the tides. The earth rotates once in 24 hours. During the same time, the moon moves forward in its orbit, and it takes 50 minutes per day for the earth to catch up with its previous position relative to the moon. It takes about half of the 24-hour 50-minute cycle to go from one bulge (high tide) to the next. (§19.12)

9. The moon, earth, and sun must form a right angle for a neap tide to occur. (§19.13)

10. See Figure 19-19 on page 498.

11. If a wave approaches the shore at an angle, the end of the wave closest to shore reaches the shallow bottom first and thus slows down first due to friction. This allows the distant end to catch up to the near-shore end, resulting in a wave that is almost parallel to the shore (the waves refract). (§19.16)

12. The major surface gyres are caused by a combination of the prevailing winds and the Coriolis effect. The winds start the flow of the currents, and in the Northern Hemisphere the Coriolis effect deflects the currents to the right. (§19.18)

13. Winds blowing across warm currents bring warmer, moisture-laden air to otherwise cold areas. Winds blowing across cold currents bring cooler, drier air to otherwise warm areas. (§19.18)

14. Differences in water salinity, temperature, and sediments in a volume of water will cause differences in water density. Gravity will cause the denser water higher in the volume of water to sink and the less-dense water to rise relative to each other. This action forms a density current. (§19.19)

15. History seems to indicate that most learned men believed the ocean bottoms were featureless and probably lifeless. Also accept that the crushing pressure at deeper depths prevented deepwater exploration. (§19.3, 19.20)

16. The AUVs are much more economical because they do not need to provide for human survival and thus can be made much smaller, less complicated, and less expensive. (§19.26–19.27)

In Terms of Oceanography

sea	485
echo sounding	486
continental shelf	486
continental slope	487
submarine canyon	487
continental rise	487
abyssal plain	487
seamount	488
guyot	488
trench	488
island arc	488
coral reef	489
fringing reef	489
barrier reef	489
atoll	489
residence time	492
desalinate	492
reverse osmosis	493
tide	494
spring tide	495
neap tide	495
sea level	497
mean sea level (MSL)	497
crest	498
trough	498
wave height	498
wave base	498
breaker	499
longshore current	500
rip current	500
sea cave	501
sea arch	501
stack	501
spit	502
bay barrier	502
hook	502
barrier island	502
tombolo	502
gyre	503
Ekman spiral	504
salinity	504
thermohaline current	504
density current	505
turbidity current	505
upwelling	506

Chapter Summary

- Oceans cover 71 percent of the earth's surface and account for 97 percent of the earth's water.

- Scientists who study the ocean are called oceanographers. They may work in nearly any physical or biological area of science.

- The ocean basins are interconnected and surround all of the continents, forming a single global ocean. The major basins and smaller connected seas are named according to their size.

- Below the surface of the oceans are many and varied topographical features that exceed those on land in number and size, including submerged mountains, ridges, deep plains, and trenches.

- Seawater contains dissolved minerals from the earth and dissolved gases from the atmosphere. Many of the minerals found in the oceans are economically important. Unfortunately, most of these minerals are too diluted to be extracted economically.

- The most important chemical in seawater is water itself. Many different methods have been developed to extract drinkable water from seawater.

- The gravitational pull of the moon and sun on the earth's oceans cause the tidal bulges in the oceans. Most locations experience two high and two low tides a day as the earth rotates under the tidal bulges.

- Ocean waves are caused mainly by the wind. Waves travel great distances, but the particles in waves travel in orbital patterns that stay in essentially one place.

- Waves can be described by their wavelength and wave height. The energy and motion of a wave extends to half its length into the water beneath it.

- Waves approaching shore can create breakers, longshore currents, and rip currents. Waves can also cause shore erosion. Erosional features include various kinds of sand bars, tombolos, sea caves, arches, and stacks.

- The global surface currents are formed by a combination of the prevailing winds and the Coriolis effect. They have a major effect on the weather and climate of every continent.

- Subsurface currents form because of friction (e.g., the Ekman spiral), the direct action of gravity on pile-ups of water, or differences in density due to temperature and salinity.

- Oceanography, like the other sciences, has its own set of specialized instruments and tools to collect data. Among these are echo sounders, Nansen bottles, Secchi disks, plankton nets, and bottom grab samplers.

- Scientific ocean exploration became a recognized discipline following the voyage of the HMS *Challenger* in the 1800s. Many vessels, especially various kinds of submersibles, have been developed to increase human knowledge of the seas.

True or False

17. False. Since the oceans cover more surface area than the landmasses, it is correct to say that the oceans completely surround the landmasses. (§19.2)

18. True. (§19.3)

19. False. Some continental plate margins are right along a coastline (e.g., the U.S. Pacific Northwest), where the coastal bottom descends into a trench. (§19.4)

20. False. The lagoons within atolls are usually formed above collapsed or submerged volcanic cones. (§19.6)

21. False. The abyssal plains are deep, but the trenches are even deeper. (§19.5)

What Did You Learn?

1. What surprised scientists when they began measuring the depths of the oceans?

2. Moving away from land, name the features typically found as one progresses toward the bottom of the ocean basins.

3. If an island has formed from an old coral reef, what two things may have happened to form dry land?

4. How does the ocean accumulate dissolved minerals?

5. Can seawater be made by simply dissolving table salt in water?

6. What would be the most economical method for providing fresh water for a poor village on the coast of Africa near the equator?

7. If one tidal bulge of water was over 80° W longitude (high tide on the eastern U.S. coast), at approximately what longitude would the other high tide be?

8. Why are high tides twelve hours and twenty-five minutes apart, not twelve hours exactly?

9. How must the moon, earth, and sun be positioned for a neap tide to occur?

10. Draw a profile of a series of several ocean waves and label the crest, trough, wave height, and wavelength.

11. Explain why waves approaching the shoreline at an angle become more nearly parallel to the shore by the time they break.

12. Why do major surface current gyres in the Northern Hemisphere flow clockwise?

13. Explain how warm and cold surface currents can affect continental climates.

14. Explain how gravity can make density currents.

15. What seems to have been the major obstacle to studying the ocean depths as a separate area of science?

16. Which is more economical, sending humans in manned submersibles into the depths or using AUVs?

True or False

17. Landmasses completely surround each ocean.

18. Although echo sounding can tell us a great deal about the bottom of the ocean, we still need to send people down to observe in order to study the bottom completely.

19. Every continent is bounded by a continental shelf with a continental slope containing submarine canyons.

20. The central lagoons of atolls are often the flooded centers of meteorite craters.

21. The abyssal plains are the deepest parts of any ocean.

22. We can assume that due to the dissolving of large quantities of minerals during the worldwide Flood, the only aquatic organisms to survive the yearlong catastrophe at that time would be called saltwater organisms today.

23. Manganese nodules are the major source of manganese and other rare minerals for the United States today.

24. Marine snow occurs only in late winter in the Northern and Southern Hemispheres.

25. Unusual tides include "tidal waves."

26. If wave steepness exceeds $\frac{1}{7}$, the wave will collapse as a breaking wave.

27. Deep-sea currents are usually in the opposite direction from surface currents.

28. Good deep-sea fishing is often found where the continental shelf ends and the continental slope begins because of the upwelling of nutrients.

29. *Trieste*, *Alvin*, and *Challenger* are the three most famous bathyscaphs.

What Do You Think?

1. Does the earth have one ocean, four oceans, or seven seas?

2. What problems might be encountered when using a weighted rope to measure the depth of the ocean?

3. What problems would have to be overcome to build and live in a self-supporting undersea city?

4. What problems would have to be overcome if you wanted to hike across the Atlantic Ocean bottom to Europe?

5. If both a manned submersible and a UUV are equipped with the same instruments and samplers, which will likely produce more scientifically usable information?

My Review Checklist

☐ I have carefully read the entire chapter.

☐ I have reviewed all of the photographs, illustrations, and graphs.

☐ I have reviewed all of my notes in the margins.

☐ I have reviewed and corrected the quizzes on this chapter.

☐ I have studied all of the vocabulary terms.

☐ I have had all of my questions answered.

---

22. True. (§19.7)

23. False. Manganese nodule mining has not been developed significantly because of legal issues and the technical difficulties of mining in the deep sea. (§19.8)

24. False. Marine snow is unrelated to atmospheric snow. Marine snow is the gentle shower of organic and inorganic material from the surface into the depths that forms a major food source for deep-water creatures. (box, p. 491)

25. False. "Tidal wave" was a popular but incorrect name for a tsunami, or earthquake-generated wave. (§19.14–19.15)

26. True. (§19.16)

27. False. Deep currents usually flow in directions completely unrelated to the directions of surface currents above them. (§19.19)

28. True. (§19.19)

29. False. *Trieste* was the famous U.S. Navy bathyscaph. *Alvin* is a deep submergence vehicle (a small submarine). *Challenger* was a sailing warship. (§19.21, 19.24, 19.26)

What Do You Think?

1. There is no correct answer to this question because it depends on what characteristics one considers most important. One person may note that all of the major and minor bodies of salt water are interconnected, so he could rightfully say that there is a single world ocean. Another might notice that there are four major bodies of water that are more or less bounded by land, so he could be justified in saying there are four (or five) oceans. A professional sailor could say there are seven ocean regions having distinct wind patterns that make for the traditional seven seas (North and South Pacific, North and South Atlantic, the Indian Ocean, the Southern Ocean, and the Arctic Ocean).

2. Deep currents could carry the weight away at an angle, increasing the indicated depth (measuring the hypotenuse of a right triangle instead of the vertical leg). For very deep depths, it would be difficult to know when the weight was on the bottom because of the elasticity of the rope. The weight of the rope required for very deep soundings could be enough to break the rope. (For this reason deep soundings were done with wire rope.) It is very time consuming to drop and retrieve many kilometers of rope for deep soundings, and accurately measuring that much rope was difficult.

3. There are many possible answers, but the following are obvious considerations: The structural strength needed to resist water pressure is far greater than that required for an equivalent shelter in a space colony. Large-volume underwater buildings are nearly impossible to design with any economy of materials. Some kind of power source appropriate for underwater habitats must be provided (nuclear; fuel cell). Oxygen must be replenished, and carbon dioxide and other noxious gases must be removed from the enclosed atmosphere. Food and fresh water must be resupplied by deliveries or produced within the habitat. Communications to the outside world and transportation to and from the surface are needed. High humidity and corrosion would be a problem for electronic and mechanical equipment.

4. Answers will vary. This topic could generate a lively discussion. Is the hiker going to be exposed to sea pressure, or is he going to wear an armored suit with normal atmospheric pressure inside? Obvious things that would have to be provided are air, food, and water. Physiological considerations include rapid heat loss, the need for a breathing gas mixture that will not cause *nitrogen narcosis* under high pressure (research opportunity), and the need for rest. Is the hiker going to "camp out" directly on the sea bottom to rest and eat, or will there be a shelter that accompanies him? What about protection from sea creatures? Power for lights and equipment? Route over the sea bottom? Communications? First aid?

5. Answers will vary. Consider that the main difference between the two vehicles is that the human in the manned submersible can make reasoned decisions on the spot in response to an unexpected opportunity to take a sample, snap a photo, record a video, or change the direction of the exploration mission. The UUV is limited by its programming and may not be able to respond in a similar way. For routine work, the UUV could probably stay down longer and cost less.

Overview

In the previous chapter, we considered the world's oceans, which contain the vast majority of the water on Earth. In Chapter 20 we delve into the study of the next-largest reservoir of water, which exists in solid form—glaciers. These unstoppable rivers of ice can carve out and permanently alter landscapes and are themselves landforms. This chapter is essential in remolding students' view of the earth's history by discussing a creationary model for a single ice age that was a direct consequence of the Genesis Flood.

Section 20A discusses the conditions needed for glaciers to form. The different types and locations of glaciers reflect man's attempts to classify glacial ice. Floating glacial ice (icebergs) is briefly mentioned.

Section 20B investigates how glaciers shape the earth's surface by their motion. The different distinct erosional and depositional landforms are described, and some interesting inferences resulting from glacial deposits are discussed.

A creationary perspective of a single ice age is the focus of Section 20C. We note the inadequacies of long, multiple ice ages within the context of a young-earth history. A creationary theory that demonstrates the plausibility of a single ice age resulting naturally as a consequence of the Flood is discussed in some detail.

Schedule Summary

Section 20A: 1–2 periods

Section 20B: 1–2 periods

Section 20C: 1–2 periods

Investigation Summary

20F "Glacial Erosion"

20G "Representative Glaciers"

 Bulletin Board Ideas

1. Develop a photo montage of various glaciers. Many photo suppliers on the Internet as well as the NASA and USGS websites allow free use of photos for educational purposes.

2. Make a model of a glacier similar to Figure 20-3 or Visual 20-1, using cotton balls as the zone of accumulation and hard white plastic for the zone of wastage (cut in crevasses). Staple pieces of sandpaper to

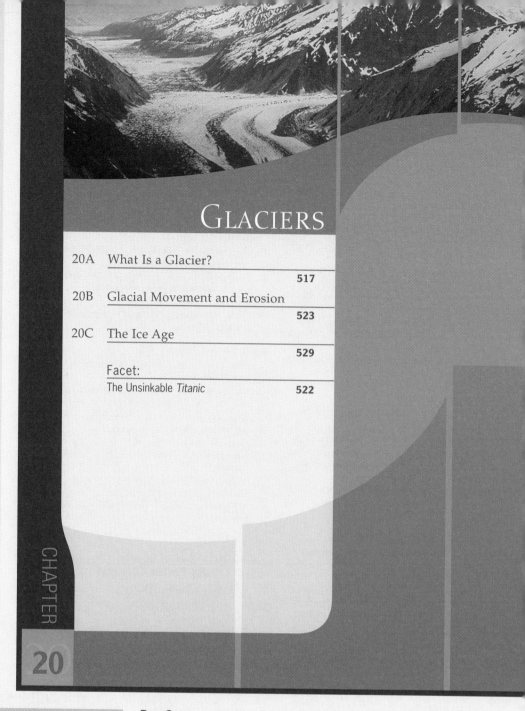

GLACIERS

CHAPTER

20

SUGGESTED TEACHING SCHEDULE

DAY 0

Assignment

Reading: Section 20A, "What is a Glacier?"

DAY 1

Describe the conditions and processes that form glaciers. Categorize the different forms and the locations where glaciers may be found. Discuss the significance and hazards of floating glacial ice in the form of icebergs.

Assignment

Complete: 20A Section Review Questions

Applications 20B, "Types of Glaciers"

Reading: Section 20B, "Glacial Movement and Erosion"

DAY 2

Quiz—Section 20A, "What is a Glacier?"

Examine landforms caused by the erosional action of glaciers. If you have time, begin describing the depositional glacial landforms.

Assignment

Complete: 20B Section Review Questions

Applications 20A, "Glacier Structure"

Applications 20C, "Effects of Glaciers"

Reading: Investigation 20F, "Glacial Erosion"

DAY 3

Do Investigation 20F, "Glacial Erosion." Review the instructions for Investigation 20G, "Representative Glaciers," which students can work on while waiting on part of the previous investigation. They may complete Investigation 20G as homework.

20A WHAT IS A GLACIER?

20.1 Introduction

"Out of whose womb came the ice? and the hoary frost of heaven, who hath gendered it? The waters are hid as with a stone, and the face of the deep is frozen" (Job 38:29–30). With these poetic words, God challenges Job to trust Him even when life falls apart. It sounds strange at first, but the Bible clearly teaches that even ice says something about the Creator. The icy portions of the globe stand as a constant reminder of the unique greatness and goodness of God.

These regions are huge, complex, dangerous, and yet beautiful. No human could have brought them into existence, and no human can control them—either by turning them back into water or by stopping their movements. As we look at these frozen marvels through the lens of Scripture, we learn—as Job did—that it is not our place to call into question the wisdom and goodness of God. He alone knows best how to rule this world, of which we are only a part. *"Behold, I am vile; what shall I answer thee? I will lay mine hand upon my mouth"* (Job 40:4).

Having previously studied the effects of liquid water in motion, we now turn to the effects of solid water—ice—in motion. The environment of permanently frozen water is so unique that the collection of all forms of frozen water on the earth's surface is sometimes called the *cryosphere*. In this chapter, we will be mainly interested in glaciers and the sources of ice that feed glaciers, but the study of the cryosphere can include icecaps, ocean ice shelves, and icebergs. Ice in the form of a glacier can be a powerful agent of change. A **glacier** is a large mass of compacted ice that flows under the influence of gravity.

20.2 Glacier Formation

Glaciers formed in areas where the winter snow failed to melt completely in the summer. These snow-covered areas are called **snowfields**. The lower edge of a snowfield is the **snow line**. Below this line the snow melts completely away in the summer, but above it some snow from the previous winter remains through the summer. Near the equator, snowfields occur only on high mountains. The equatorial snow line is often more than 5.5 km (3.4 mi) above sea level. In the middle latitudes, snowfields occur on lower mountains as well; thus, the snow line is at a lower elevation. Near the poles, snowfields occur at even lower elevations; often the snow line is at sea level.

Over many years the snow in a glacial snowfield built up to a great thickness. The snow falls as fluffy crystals, but as it accumulates, the weight of the newer snow compresses the older snow. As the snow is compressed, it slowly melts, refreezes, and compacts into a form of granular ice called **firn**. Gradually the weight of the accumulated ice squeezes out most of the air spaces between firn crystals, and the mass becomes **glacier ice**. This ice is a solid with

20-1 The extremely hostile surface conditions of the oceanic icecap in the Far North make surface travel extremely difficult. Here a U.S. nuclear submarine has surfaced through the relatively thin summer ice to assist scientists in their study of the Arctic Ocean.

cryosphere: cryo- (Gk. *kryos*—icy, cold) + -sphere

firn (FYURN)

20-2 The photo shows an accumulation of new snow (right side) on a valley glacier in Greenland.

represent the rock over which the glacier moves. Use blue plastic wrap to symbolize the meltwater under the glacier.

Objectives—Section 20A

Upon completing this section, students should be able to

- describe the formation and general structure of a glacier.
- compare and contrast snow, firn, and glacial ice.
- classify specific types of glaciers by location and structure.
- discuss the formation of icebergs from glaciers and the hazards they present. Contrast them with nonglacial floating ice.

In Figure 20-1, a modern Seawolf-class submarine is shown after it has surfaced through a thin layer of frozen seawater in the Arctic. Patches of thin ice form in the much thicker pack ice when wind and currents rip the pack ice covering apart and expose the sea's surface to the frigid arctic air. Arctic explorers call these openings *polynyas* (POL EN YAH), the Russian word for them. Submarines are specially equipped to look for thin ice overhead as they steam beneath the ice. Arctic pack ice is not similar to glacial ice in structure or manner of formation.

 Visual 20-1: Cross Section of a Glacier

This visual is a reproduction of Figure 20-3 on the next page. Use this visual as you present the formation and general structure of a glacier.

Assignment

Complete: Investigation 20G, "Representative Glaciers"

Applications 20D, "Glacial Deposits"

Reading: Section 20C, "The Ice Age"

DAY 4

Finish your discussion of glacial deposits from Day 2 if required.

Quiz—Section 20B, "Glacial Movement and Erosion"

Compare and contrast the uniformitarian and creationary views of ice ages. Present the chronology of the Ice Age according to one plausible creationary model.

Assignment

Complete: 20C Section Review Questions

Selected Chapter Review Questions

DAY 5

Do Applications 20E, "Glacier Review," as a chapter review exercise. Review for a chapter test.

Assignment

Study for a chapter test.

DAY 6

Test—Chapter 20

Assignment

Reading: Section 21A, "Underground Reservoirs"

20-3 A typical glacier showing the accumulation zone above the snow line and the wastage zone below the snow line

Another term used by glaciologists for the wastage zone is the *ablation* zone.

Note that most glaciologists and historical geologists believe that many ice ages have occurred during the course of the earth's history, the last retreating around 10,000 years ago. Most creationary scientists believe there was only a single Ice Age that lasted for perhaps no more than several hundred years immediately after the Flood. See Section 20C for a discussion of the ice age controversy.

 Visual 20-2: Types of Glaciers

This visual is a reproduction of the figures on pages 518–20. Use the visual as you discuss the various forms of glaciers.

 Additional Resources

On September 19, 1991, two German hikers discovered a mummified human corpse in a melting glacier of the Ötzal Alps of Italy. It was determined that these remains are about 5300 years old, which means they are among the oldest known. The "Ice Man," dubbed "Ötzi" by researchers, now resides in a cold-storage vault in the Archaeological Museum of Bolzano in Italy. He was remarkably well preserved, and much has been learned about the food he ate, his weapons, and his clothes. See the story in *Science*, October 11, 1991, 187–88 and *National Geographic*, June 1993, 36–67.

20-4 Valley glacier in the St. Elias Mountains in the southwest Yukon (above); illustration of a valley glacier with a single tributary (right)—there can be many tributaries on both sides

interlocking crystals. It is usually opaque, with a bluish gray color, and it may contain fine particles of rock or soil called **glacial flour** or *rock flour*. Sometimes the glacial ice is milky white because many tiny air bubbles are entrapped in it.

A glacier is born in a snowfield. Eventually, the glacier ice will start moving as a mass under the influence of gravity if its weight and the angle of its slope are great enough. For most glaciers, movement is a combination of the solid ice changing shape, or flowing, and gradually slipping over the ground. As long as it remains above the snow line, it continues to accumulate mass. This area of the glacier is called its **accumulation zone**. When the glacier creeps below the altitude where melting, evaporation, and sublimation equal or exceed the annual ice accumulation, it enters its **wastage zone**. The imaginary line separating the accumulation zone from the wastage zone is called the **equilibrium line** or the snow line. The lower end of the glacier is called its **terminus**. The terminus of a glacier is the location where the ice melts away faster than it can be replaced by ice flow from uphill. For many glaciers near coastlines, the terminus is in the ocean.

If the glacier accumulates more ice than it loses, the terminus *advances* downhill; if it loses more than it accumulates, the terminus of the glacier *retreats* up the slope, even as the mass of ice continues to move downhill. Knowing whether a glacier is advancing or retreating can give *glaciologists* (glacier scientists) information about the local climate and possibly about global climates as well. If the glacier is retreating, the climate may be warming (increased melting) or becoming drier (less snow accumulation). If the glacier is advancing, the climate may be cooling (decreased melting) or becoming more humid (more snow accumulation). Glaciologists have noted that most of the world's glaciers are retreating. Many scientists believe this is caused directly by the slow rise in global temperatures observed since the 1800s although glaciers were retreating even before that time.

20.3 Types of Glaciers

When you think about glaciers, you probably picture a long, narrow river of ice in a high valley. This type of glacier is a **valley glacier**. It can also be called a *mountain glacier* or *alpine glacier*. All present-day glaciers, including valley glaciers, have been in existence continuously or intermittently since the Ice Age. Glaciologists, examining how glaciers grow and retreat, have developed a description for the origin of glaciers. Each valley glacier began in a hollow area high in a mountainous region where snow accumulated. When the glacial ice was deep enough to cause the ice along the bottom to flow, the glacier began to move due to gravity, usually down a pre-existing river or Flood-eroded drainage valley. Valley glaciers may be only a few hundred meters long, or they may extend several hundred kilometers. The valley glacier is the most common type of glacier.

At the base of a mountainous region, several valley glaciers emerging from their valleys may flow together and spread out onto a plain to form a **piedmont glacier**. Piedmont glaciers are usually both wider and deeper than valley glaciers. They may slowly flow toward a lower elevation as well. Malaspina Glacier in Alaska is the world's largest piedmont glacier.

20.4 Ice Sheets

Ice sheets are broad masses of ice that cover large areas. Instead of following a valley, ice sheets spread out in all directions from their snowfield source and cover nearly everything, including all but the highest mountain peaks. Rather than flowing down a mountainous valley, the ice flows by gravity from thicker areas of glacial ice toward thinner areas. All ice sheets are close to the poles because they require a large cold area to form. Two kinds of ice sheets exist, **continental glaciers** and **icecaps**.

A continental glacier, as the name implies, is a vast ice sheet covering most of a continent or large island. Two continental glaciers exist today, one in Greenland and the other in Antarctica. More than four-fifths of Greenland is permanently covered with ice in a large central depression in the island's bedrock. Glaciologists believe that the ice in the interior is more than 4200 m (13,800 ft) thick and covers 1,800,000 km² (708,000 mi²). The people of Greenland live

piedmont (PEED mahnt)

20-5 The Malaspina Glacier in Alaska is a piedmont glacier (top). Illustration of a piedmont glacier (bottom)—five valley glaciers meet to form a large glacial plain.

20-6 Continental glacier in northern Greenland (above); map showing the vast area of Greenland covered by glacial ice (right)

20-7 Aerial view of the Nunatak Mountains of Greenland poking through the continental glacier

Greenland's rock basement is depressed in the center of the island due to the weight of the overlying ice sheet. Therefore, the ice sheet is much thicker in the center than along the coasts. In Figure 20-6 the view is looking inland, showing how the mountains are covered by the thicker ice farther from the coastline.

Additional Resources

Take a moment to delve into some history and summarize the experiences of Ernest Shackleton's second and greatest polar adventure, which is a story of survival in the Antarctic. The story is told in the classic book *Endurance: Shackleton's Incredible Adventure* by Alfred Lansing, and *South: A Memoir of the* Endurance *Voyage* by Ernest Shackleton himself. Look for DVDs and educational videotapes on this topic as well.

on the coastal lowlands around the edge of the island. Glaciologists and environmentalists are concerned that the Greenland glaciers are rapidly receding and at the same time flowing faster than ever.

The continental glacier on Antarctica is the world's largest glacier. Its area is about 14.2 million km² (5.5 million mi²); its maximum thickness is nearly 4800 m (15,700 ft). This mass of ice contains 90% of the world's ice and 77% of the world's fresh water. Only the eastern part of Antarctica is supported by continental crust above sea level; the rest is a group of "islands" joined by ice. Research suggests that the weight of the ice has depressed the bedrock as much as 2400 m (8000 ft) below sea level in some places.

Icecaps are smaller than continental glaciers. Most of them are in northern Canada, but icecaps also exist in Iceland, Ireland, southern Argentina, and Svalbard (a Norwegian island group). The largest ice sheet classified as an icecap is on northern Ellesmere Island in Canada; its area is almost 26,000 km² (10,000 mi²). Ellesmere Island is considered an "arctic desert" since very little precipitation occurs there. This huge icecap is believed by some to be a remnant of the Ice Age.

20-8 Illustration of an ice cap

Ross Ice Shelf

The largest ice shelf in the world is located in Antarctica. Fed by eight large glaciers and many smaller ones, a "shelf" of ice floats on the gentle Ross Sea. The Ross Ice Shelf, which at its maximum extent was the size of France (500,000 km², or 200,000 mi²), terminates as a wall of ice cliffs 45 m (150 ft) high and 800 km (500 mi) long. Most of the ice is below sea level, stretching to depths of over 600 m (2000 ft).

The shelf is hemmed in by the Trans-Antarctic Mountains. This mountain range provides a barrier that prevents the continent's ice sheet from sliding into the ocean. If you look at a map, you will see that the Ross Ice Shelf cuts deep into the continent, providing the closest "land" route to the South Pole. Understandably, the first explorers started their trek to the South Pole here. After crossing the ice shelf, they climbed the valley glaciers to Antarctica's flat interior.

The Ross Ice Shelf is a major center of scientific investigation. Using drills, glaciologists have taken samples through the entire depth of the shelf. They want to understand the origin and movement of this large crystalline mass. Their knowledge will help them understand more about land movement and glacial movement throughout the world. The Ross Ice Shelf has much to tell us about glaciers, the formation of icebergs, and the interaction of water and ice. Glaciologists are especially amazed that the ice shelf has remained so stable for so long. For more than 90 years, glaciers have added ice to one end of the shelf slightly faster than it lost ice at the outer edge from calving. Now this pattern has reversed, and the Ross Shelf is breaking up. It is believed to be the same size it was when the Robert F. Scott expedition first mapped it in 1904.

The seaward edge of the Ross Ice Shelf can be as much as 45 m (150 ft) high.

Box Summary: Ross Ice Shelf

This box highlights the largest ice shelf in the world, the Ross Ice Shelf in Antarctica. The ongoing breakup of this huge mass of ice produced the largest iceberg in history, Iceberg B15a. There are no vocabulary terms in this box.

20.5 Floating Glacial Ice

Glaciers in subarctic and temperate zones often do not end at a coastline because their terminuses lie high up in mountainous valleys. However, in polar regions, coastal glaciers can move outward into the sea and begin to float when the bottom deepens sufficiently. When the ice is no longer supported underneath by the bottom, heavily crevassed glacier ice breaks off into large floating chunks to form **icebergs**. This process of iceberg formation is called **calving**. Any kind of glacier that reaches the sea may calve, but most icebergs come from the huge continental glaciers. Glaciologists estimate that the Greenland glacier loses billions of tons to calving each year, and about 150 of these icebergs last long enough to drift southward far enough to become a hazard for shipping in the North Atlantic. Approximately 20,000 icebergs are calved worldwide each year.

20-9   A glacier calving an iceberg

B15a

Huge icebergs have been calved from the Antarctic glaciers. The world's largest at the time of this writing was a monster iceberg 11,000 km² (3700 mi²) in area, named B15a. It was the largest fragment of an even larger segment of ice that broke off of western Antarctica's Ross Ice Shelf in 2000. Its top was estimated to be nearly 50 m (164 ft) above water and its total thickness was 500 m (1640 ft)!

These facts point out a property of icebergs that may not be obvious in looking at a photograph of one—80 to 90 percent of any iceberg will be below the water's surface. This makes navigation in the vicinity of icebergs especially hazardous, since the bulk of the iceberg is under water and the underwater part is often much broader than the visible portion. The proportion of an iceberg that is submerged depends on the salinity of the ocean and the density of the ice. The higher the salinity of the ocean water, the more the iceberg will float out of the water. Areas of the ocean that have many icebergs have lower salinity than the rest of the ocean because the melting ice dilutes these areas with fresh water.

Icebergs are not the only kind of floating ice pieces. The seawater in the bays around Antarctica and the Arctic Ocean freezes over during the long winters in these polar regions. The sea-ice thickness can grow to several meters in places. Ice breakers are designed to plow through frozen sea ice, and many submarines can surface through a meter or more of ice. In the spring and summer, wind and waves break up these relatively thin floating ice sheets into pieces called **ice floes**. Floes generally have much less mass and are more fragile than icebergs and, of course, do not originate from glaciers.

500 m   modern submarine
               (108 m long)

20-10   Iceberg B15a in the Ross Sea (left) was the largest iceberg ever calved since icebergs have been tracked following the loss of the *Titanic*. The relative size and depth of a large iceberg (above).

20-11   Ice floes and icebergs in the Weddell Sea

 Visual 20-3: A Typical Iceberg

This visual gives a good 3-D representation of an iceberg.

The huge iceberg depicted in Figure 20-10 would be considered a rarity, but it illustrates the potential for such behemoths derived from a source such as the Ross Ice Shelf. Most icebergs are much smaller, being formed from the more common process shown in Figure 20-9.

As of this writing, iceberg B15a is slowly breaking up as a result of Antarctic storms. This breakup is good news for the wildlife—especially the Adele penguins—in McMurdo sound, which has been barricaded from the sea.

Also regarded as unsinkable, the Danish passenger cargo ship *Hans Hedtoft* met with a fate similar to the *Titanic's*. Ultramodern, with a double steel bottom, armored bow and stern, seven watertight compartments, and radar, it was built for use in northern waters. Launched on January 29, 1959, it struck an iceberg and sank on January 30 on the return leg of its maiden voyage.

Much lore has accumulated around the *Titanic* tragedy. Anecdotes of the passengers and rescuers put a human face on the event. Many have commented that the sinking was God's judgment on arrogant humans who believed their technology could thwart the will of God. This latter view may have some truth, but students should realize that there is nothing wrong with building a safer, faster, more comfortable ship in accordance with the Creation Mandate. It is when we do so with the attitude that we have developed technology that is beyond the control of God that we err and open ourselves to correction as He asserts His sovereignty.

The *Titanic* was commanded by one of the White Star Line's most experienced captains. Many wonder why he had ordered the ship to steam so fast on a dark night when icebergs had been reported by other vessels in its vicinity. One theory that has come forward in recent years is that the captain was trying to put out a coal bunker fire that had been burning for many days. These fires were not uncommon in the days of coal-fired steam boilers and were not particularly dangerous, but they generated noxious gases and were hard to put out. The common practice to deal with them was to use up the coal in the affected bunker rapidly until the burning layer was exposed and then to shovel the smoldering coals into the boilers. The ship could have been steaming fast that night in order to use up the coal in the burning bunker before it reached New York.

 ## Additional Resources

Read about and see photos of the exploration of the *Titanic* wreckage in the article "A Long Last Look at *Titanic*" (*National Geographic*, December 1986, 698–727). Then read how the wreck has been deteriorating in the more recent article "Why Is *Titanic* Vanishing?" (*National Geographic*, December 2004, 96–112).

THE UNSINKABLE *TITANIC*

The *Titanic* departing on its first and last voyage

"God himself could not sink this ship," a crewman reportedly said as the RMS *Titanic* sailed from the English harbor en route to New York. It was the pride of the world's luxury liners, headed out on its maiden voyage. The double-plated steel hull could withstand anything nature could send against her, they said. Should a leak somehow develop, the captain could throw a lever and close up any of sixteen watertight compartments below decks.

Rich and famous Englishmen and Americans made special arrangements to ensure a place on that historic pleasure trip of April 1912. The luxury liner boasted crystal chandeliers, Turkish baths, a swimming pool, a live band, and a well-stocked bar. The weather was unusually calm and pleasant for the 2227 people on board as they celebrated late into the night. Late Sunday night on April 14, few people took notice when the engines suddenly reversed and the swiftly moving ship veered sharply left.

A lookout had spotted an iceberg dead ahead in the darkness. The surprised seaman quickly warned the bridge, "Iceberg right ahead!" The deck officer turned the ship left to avoid it. Even so, the ship scraped the edge of the iceberg, spraying ice over the bridge. Soon everyone returned to their games, and the band struck up some lively tunes.

Slowly the captain realized the severity of the damage. Water began to pour into the lower compartments, and the pumps could not keep up. Even with the water-tight doors shut, there were too many spaces flooding from the long gash in the *Titanic's* hull. When the engine rooms had to be abandoned because of the rising water, the captain finally sent out distress signals.

The wreck of the *Titanic* was discovered and explored in 1985–86.

The *Titanic* began to list dangerously and her bow settled into the sea. Yet the passengers could not believe that the ship might actually sink. Lifeboats were available for only half of them anyway because the owners had reasoned that the unsinkable *Titanic* would be the safest place for them to stay in an emergency. The 705 passengers who made it to safety watched in awe as the great ship, with its electric lights still blazing, angled its stern straight up into the air and then slipped bow-first beneath the freezing waters of the North Atlantic. Another hour passed before a rescue ship arrived at the tragic scene.

Between the years 1833 and 1912, fifteen vessels had been sunk and forty more damaged by collisions with icebergs, but the *Titanic* was the worst disaster of all. The worldwide shock and outcry that followed led thirteen nations to fund an International Ice Patrol to scout "Iceberg Alley" along this major

Without radar, collisions with icebergs on dark nights were inevitable.

shipping route between Europe and North America. The U.S. Coast Guard assumed the responsibility and has continued this service ever since, warning ships of danger. Until World War II, Coast Guard vessels were used to patrol the shipping lanes during iceberg season. Today the function is accomplished much less expensively and more efficiently by aircraft and satellites. Sixteen nations share the cost of this service. Ships are still necessary to tow or push icebergs that threaten shipping channels or oil rigs into safer waters.

Facet Summary: The Unsinkable *Titanic*

The focus of this Facet is the tragic circumstances that resulted when the supposedly unsinkable RMS *Titanic* collided with an iceberg in the North Atlantic on April 14, 1912. A direct response to that disaster was the establishment of the North Atlantic International Ice Patrol. Unknown numbers of people and ships have been preserved as a result of this effort. There are no vocabulary terms in this Facet.

20A Section Review

1. What are areas where snow does not melt completely in the summer called? What may form under these conditions?

2. What is the form of granular ice having a composition midway between that of snow and glacier ice called?

3. What is the lowest edge of a snowfield called?

4. What is the part of a glacier that is located below the equilibrium line called?

5. What is the most common type of glacier? What are other names for this type of glacier?

6. What forms when two valley glaciers merge onto a plain?

7. Where is the world's largest glacier? What kind of glacier is it?

8. What does the term *calving* refer to?

9. Why is ship navigation near an iceberg hazardous?

10. (True or False) Most glaciers in the world are retreating.

20B GLACIAL MOVEMENT AND EROSION

20.6 Introduction

In this section we will consider several interesting things that have been observed about glaciers. First, we will consider how glaciers move and change and what happens to them when they move. Second, we will note the various ways glaciers erode the underlying land as they move. And third, we will study the landforms produced as the glacier advances and as it deposits eroded material when it retreats. This information will be useful when we discuss the evidences for a single Ice Age in Section 20C.

20.7 Glacier Motions

Recall from subsection 20.2 that there are two factors that contribute to a glacier's movement downhill—the flow of solid ice and the slippage of the glacier over the ground. These motions are especially noticeable in the wastage zone. Glacial ice within a moving glacier has two layers that move differently. The uppermost 50 m (165 ft) layer, called the **zone of fracture**, consists of hard, brittle ice that cannot adjust to the glacier's motion over uneven ground or changes in the glacier's direction. To relieve the stress caused by its motion, the ice breaks to form deep, narrow **crevasses**. These clefts are treacherous for explorers, especially when covered with fresh snow. The layer of ice deeper than 50 m is under such great pressure that its crystals can flow and change shape as the glacier passes over changing terrain even though the ice remains a solid. This layer is called the **zone of flow** and extends all the way to the bottom of the glacier. The ice in this zone does not flow at the same rate. The ice near the bottom moves more slowly than the ice farther up due to friction with the bedrock.

flow profile

zone of fracture (crevasses, brittle ice)

zone of flow ("plastic ice")

20-12 Side view of a glacier showing the two zones of movement. The zone of flow is more "plastic" due to pressure from the weight of snow. This is where the movement of the glacier is initiated. As the brittle ice in the zone of fracture "floats" along on the "plastic" ice, it cracks, forming crevasses.

crevasse (krih VAS)

20-13 Crevasses

Objectives—Section 20B

Upon completing this section, students should be able to

- identify the interior zones of a glacier based on mode of flow.
- explain why glaciers appear to advance and retreat.
- identify features caused by glacial erosion from figures or descriptions.
- identify landforms that are the result of glacial deposition from figures or descriptions.
- discuss the processes that form specific glacial deposits.

  Review: Plasticity

Solids that can bend and change shape without breaking, such as glacier ice in the zone of flow, are said to be *plastic*. In other words, the solids exhibit *ductility*. Modeling clay is a good example of a plastic solid. Remind your students that rocks in the earth's mantle are said to be plastic because they flow slowly. Ask students to give examples of other solids that could be described as plastic (plastics, hardened tar, wax, soft metals, etc.).

Answers to 20A Section Review Questions

1. Areas where snow remains year round are called *snowfields*. Glaciers or ice sheets can form from snowfields. (§20.2)

2. Granular ice having a composition midway between that of snow and glacier ice is called *firn*. (§20.2)

3. The lowest edge of a snowfield is called the *equilibrium* or *snow line*. (§20.2)

4. The part of the glacier that is located below the equilibrium line is called the *wastage zone*. (§20.2)

5. The most common type of glacier is the *valley glacier*, also called an *alpine* or *mountain glacier*. (§20.3)

6. *Piedmont glaciers* form when two (or more) valley glaciers merge onto a plain. (§20.3)

7. The world's largest glacier is in Antarctica. It is a *continental glacier*. (§20.4)

8. The term *calving* refers to the formation of icebergs when parts of a glacier break off as it enters a body of water. (§20.5)

9. Ship navigation near an iceberg is hazardous because the submerged part of the berg is much larger and often broader than the visible part. A ship might easily run into the ice while many meters away from the above-water portion of the iceberg. (§20.5)

10. True. (§20.2)

20-14 The center of a glacier moves faster than the edges and the bottom, where friction with the valley walls is greatest.

The slippage of the glacier also contributes to its advance downhill. Except for some polar glaciers that are probably frozen to the bedrock beneath them, most glaciers can and do slide somewhat as they move. Glaciologists have suggested that liquid water underneath the glacier helps lift it free from direct contact with the ground and lubricates the surface of movement. Water under a glacier may come from various sources. Ice along the bottom can melt due to the great weight of ice above it, and heat from within the earth can melt the ice. Heat is also released when meltwater refreezes.

Glaciologists originally studied details of valley glacier motion by placing a line of markers across a glacier's surface from one side of its valley to the other. They found that a glacier's speed is greatest in its center and less toward the edges because the markers near the middle traveled farthest with time. The sides and the bottom of the glacier experience the greatest friction, so they move the slowest. This unequal ice motion contributes to the breakup of the ice in the fracture zone.

For many years it was believed that the amount of snowfall in the accumulation zone was the main factor in determining how fast a glacier moves. With the development of satellite monitoring and the collection of much more data, the speed of glacier movement was found to be a complex combination of many factors, including rate and quantity of snowfall, the relative lengths of winter and summer, the average temperatures during these seasons, the existence of pools of meltwater on the glacier's surface, and the amount of glacial flour and debris coloring the surface of the ice.

Most glaciers move only a few centimeters or meters each day, but occasionally a glacier moves rapidly in what is known as **surge**. Glaciologists do not fully understand surge, but one theory suggests it is related to the collapse of ice shelves; another theory tries to correlate glacial surges with equatorial ocean warming events (called El Niño), which occur every decade or so. The fastest glacier movement ever recorded was an average of 112 m (370 ft) per day for the Kutiah Glacier in northern India in 1953. The fastest glacier surge in recent years is occurring in the Columbia Glacier that empties into Prince William Sound in Alaska. It averages an advance of 35 m (115 ft) per day.

20-15 Close-up of glacial striations on a highly polished rock in Yoho National Park, Canada (left). A rock surface in the Sierra Nevada Range polished by a glacier (right).

20.8 Glacial Erosion

You have probably heard the question "What happens when an irresistible force meets an immovable object?" The force of an enormous moving mass of ice is one of the nearest things to "irresistible force" that is encountered in the study of geology. Glaciers level

---

Most glaciers that surge do so repetitively at somewhat regular intervals. One theory concerning why glaciers surge suggests that the rate of accumulation is too slow for fast glacial flow and too fast for slow flow, so it alternates between the two. Another theory says that heavy snowfall causes internal increases in drainage and basal sliding. Other possible causes are seismic activity and a sudden influx of glacial material from a hanging valley or other glacial tributary. Surging glaciers are important because they frequently create ice dams across rivers, backing up huge lakes. The ice dams can fail unpredictably and cause catastrophic flooding downstream.

 Visual 20-4: Landforms Eroded by Glaciers

Use this visual as you discuss the various glacial erosional landforms in this section.

almost everything in their path. For example, a valley that once held a glacier is much deeper and wider than the original stream valley. Glaciated valleys have a U-shaped profile, while mountain stream valleys have a V-shaped profile.

As they move along, glaciers pick up rocks and other debris. A glacier can even break up bedrock by a process called **plucking**. As the glacier travels, some of its ice may melt and enter the cracks and pores in the bedrock. Then the water freezes again, enlarging the cracks and loosening large chunks of rock. The frozen water adheres to the glacier and tears out these huge chunks of bedrock by this process.

The rocks and other debris on the underside of a glacier act as sandpaper, scouring the bedrock as the ice drags embedded stones and boulders over it. Rocks over which a glacier has moved often have parallel scratch marks called **striations**. Deeper grooves in the rock sometimes extend hundreds of meters along the glacier's path. In some places where the glacier is carrying quartz sand, the underlying rock is smoothed to a fine finish called **glacial polish**.

Small valleys often enter a glaciated valley from high on its sides. These **hanging valleys** were formed by tributaries of the glacier that occupied the main valley. The more extensive erosion of the main valley left the tributary valleys high above the floor. The tributary valley may be empty or it may contain a small glacier. Below the snow line a stream in a hanging valley enters the main valley by waterfalls and steep plunges. If a glacier enters the main valley from a hanging valley, it does so by an **icefall**, which has the appearance similar to that of a frozen waterfall.

Some mountains show evidence of extensive glacial erosion. The freezing and thawing of the upper ends of valley glaciers break off rocks from valley walls and pluck loosened rocks from valley floors. This erosive process forms basins called **cirques**. After the glacier retreats, a cirque often holds a lake or pond called a **tarn**. If three or more cirques encircle a mountain peak, a slender spire called a **horn** may be all that remains of the peak. The Matterhorn in Switzerland is a famous horn. If a slender ridge remains, this is called an **arête**.

Sometimes glaciers erode their valley floors below sea level. When they retreat, the sea enters the glaciated valley, now called a

20-16 A typical glaciated valley in the Tongass National Forest in Alaska (left)—note the characteristic U shape. Glaciated valleys (above) have been eroded into a U-shaped profile by the plucking and scouring action of ice in the glacier.

striation (stry AY shun): stria- (L. *stria*—a furrow or groove on a column) + -tion

20-17 Bridalveil Falls (above left) emerges from a hanging valley into the heavily glaciated Yosemite Valley in California. Lake Grinnell in Glacier National Park, Montana, is a tarn (above). The world's most famous example of a horn is the Matterhorn (bottom).

cirque (SURK): (L. *circus*—a circle)
tarn: (Norw. *tjörn*—small glacial lake)
arête (uh RATE): (Fr. *areste*—sharp fish bone, spine)

Striations oriented at different directions on the same rock surface have been interpreted by geologists as evidence for more than one glacial episode. However, such a condition could arise from flowing bodies of ice meandering back and forth across a broad valley or from multiple advances and retreats within a single glacial episode.

Before leaving the discussion of glacial erosion, students should be asked to consider that the Flood seems to have deposited layers of sediment hundreds or even thousands of meters thick. In many places these strata are visible in high, sharply eroded features such as horns and arêtes. What does this fact indicate about the thickness and power of the continental glaciers? Do any such glaciers exist in the middle latitudes today? If not, what does this say about the doctrine of uniformity?

Stones of Witness

God's judgment is often the precondition for God's blessing. Many of the geographical features that have resulted from the movement of glaciers are breathtakingly beautiful and are also helpful for sustaining life. Shortly before God judged His people with the Babylonian captivity, Habakkuk prayed that God would "*in wrath remember mercy*" (Hab. 3:2). God answers such prayers because He delights in weaving mercy into His judgment. This principle can be seen over and over again with the children of Israel in their wilderness wanderings and again in the book of Judges.

Erratics are a subset of a larger category of rocks deposited by glaciers—*drop stones*. These are individual rocks that are dropped by glacier ice as it melts and retreats. In most cases, rocks that are deposited become part of the ground moraine or become incorporated into larger depositional features, such as kames, drumlins, and eskers. Drop stones are a distinctive feature of floating glacial ice. As the glacier floats on the water and loses contact with the bottom, stones carried in the ice drop from the bottom of the glacier as it moves farther into the sea and melts. When an iceberg forms, there is the potential for a boulder to be carried far from where it was plucked and then dropped in the middle of an ocean somewhere as the berg melts.

Visual 20-5: Landforms Deposited by Glaciers

Use this visual to show how the various glacial depositional features form. The upper diagram is a cutaway of a typical glacier showing a subglacial stream cutting its way through the ice. Stones and rubble suspended in the ice from plucking and erosion upstream can also be seen. Masses of pulverized rock are being shoved along the floor of the valley under the glacier. In the lower diagram, the glacier has melted, showing the various moraines, the remnant of the stream bed that is now an esker, the pile of rubble called a kame, and the drumlins left behind.

fiord (or fjord) (FYORD)

Stones of Witness

According to the thinking of many creationary scientists, glacial activity was the follow-on to the Flood, which was God's judgment on mankind and the earth. When one considers that the Matterhorn in Switzerland and the Finger Lakes of New York are indirect results of the Flood, what does one learn about the nature of divine judgment?

In glacial geology, sorting refers to how uniform the sizes of rocks, pebbles, and sand grains are in a given sedimentary deposit. Unsorted drift means all sizes of particles are mixed together in unstratified (unlayered) deposits. Well-sorted drift occurs in stratified layers of nearly equal-size particles.

erratic (ih RAT ik): (L. *erratic*—to wander)

20-19   Erratic boulders left by a glacier in Yellowstone National Park, Wyoming

fiord. Some fiords extend inland for more than 100 km. Fiords are prominent features of the coastal geography of Norway, Iceland, Alaska, and New Zealand's South Island. Similar erosion farther inland produces elongated lakes such as the Finger Lakes of New York.

20.9   Glacial Deposits

Glaciers deposit their debris in two ways as they melt—the debris simply drops as the ice melts under it, or streams of meltwater deposit the debris. Both kinds of glacial deposits are called **glacial drift**. When a glacier just melts, dropping its load of rocks, pebbles, and sand, the debris forms piles of drift called **glacial till**. The different-size fragments of till are evenly mixed together, or *unsorted*.

20-18   A fiord is a glaciated valley that reaches the sea. (Glacier Bay National Park)

Large boulders can be transported for many kilometers within the ice. When the glacier melts, the boulders may end up sitting conspicuously on top of the till. Boulders that are not like the bedrock under them are called **erratics** because they obviously came from somewhere else. A group of erratic boulders from the same distant bedrock source is called a **boulder train**. These trains help scientists trace a glacier's path. Sometimes finding the source of erratics has practical value. For example, some erratics in Finland contained copper ore. By tracing the path of the glacier, prospectors found the source of the copper and established a successful copper mine there.

As mentioned in Chapter 16, glaciers often deposit ridges of till called *moraines*. A *terminal moraine* is a pile of till that the glacier pushed in front of it until it stopped advancing. Thus, terminal moraines mark the glacier's farthest advance. A glacier erodes sideways as well as downward as it advances. When the glacier retreats, the debris carried along its sides is deposited as **lateral moraines**. When two valley glaciers merge, the debris from their inside walls joins to form a ribbon of rubble carried along in the center of the gla-

20-20   The terminal moraine, outwash, and kettles formed at the terminus of a glacier in central Iceland

20-21 Several valley glaciers merge in the Bernard Glacier in Alaska. The photo shows the lateral and medial banding of eroded debris that will become moraines if the glacier retreats.

cier flow. When the glacier retreats, this material is deposited as a **medial moraine**. Finally, the blanket of till that is laid down in a layer over the bottom of the glacier valley is called the **ground moraine**. This moraine forms when the entire glacier melts and drops eroded material all along its route. Ground moraines tend to smooth out the terrain, producing a gently rolling surface. The low, rounded hills and valleys in the northeastern United States were formed by ground moraines.

Drumlins are long streamlined hills composed of glacial till rising from ground moraines. They were formed when rubble was shoved along the valley floor in piles by the underside of the glacier. They became visible when the glacier retreated. From the air, drumlins appear roughly parallel to one another and aligned in the direction that the glacier moved, with the thicker part of the hill pointing "upstream." In North American moraines, these glacial hills are found from North Dakota to New England, as well as in Canada. Drumlins and all other forms of glacial deposition can be found in northern Europe, Asia, and the southern continents as well.

Deposits that are formed by running water are sorted in layers according to particle size. As you learned in Chapter 18, the sizes of rocks and pebbles carried by flowing water are related to the speed of water flow. Faster, more turbulent water can carry larger rocks and boulders. Slower, quieter flow can carry only sand and silt. Meltwater streams flowing from a broad glacial terminus carry sand and gravel far from the glacier to produce an **outwash plain**. Larger rocks are laid down in sediments closer to the glacier and smaller rocks, sand, and silt are laid down farther away as the streams lose speed.

Sometimes outwash plains and ground moraines are pitted with holes called **kettles**. These "holes" form when chunks of ice separate from the glacier, are buried, and then melt, leaving a depression. A kettle may fill with water and become a *kettle lake*. *Eskers* are long, winding ridges of stratified sediments apparently deposited by meltwater streams flowing under a glacier. *Kames* are steep-sided hills much like eskers but shorter. Kames occur when stratified sediment is laid down in a depression in the ice on the surface of the glacier. When the ice melts, the sediment is dropped onto the ground moraine in an irregular stratified pile.

20-22 A drumlin in the MacKaren Valley in Alaska

drumlin: (Gaelic *druim*—back or ridge)

20-23 An esker (top) and a kame (bottom) in Wisconsin

esker (ES kur): (Ir. *eiscir*—ridgelike glacial deposits)
kame (KAME): (various, esp. Sc. *comb, camb, kaim*—steep-sided hill)

Review: Depositional Mountains

This section covers glacially deposited mountains, which were discussed previously in §16.5. Review that subsection for photos and diagrams of the different kinds of glacial deposits.

A kame often occurs as a steep-sided alluvial fan at the terminus of a glacier.

varve: (Swed. *varv*—layer)

Lakes or other quiet bodies of water that receive streams of glacial meltwater accumulate thin layers of sediment called **varves**. Each varve is a layer with coarser particles at the bottom and finer particles at the top. A varve may be anywhere from a few millimeters to a few centimeters thick. Most uniformitarian scientists believe that glacial streams deposited exactly one varve each year. The rapidly flowing water in the spring carried the coarser particles, while the slower flows later in the year could carry only the finer particles. This characteristic, like tree rings, was believed to be useful for dating glacial deposits. Scientists have now discovered that more than one varve may form each year. Storms, floods, and other events can add varves to outwash deposits. Thus, varve counting is considered by some scientists to be unreliable as a dating method.

20-24 Varves in the sediments of a lake that formed at the terminus of a glacier

20B Section Review

1. Why do glaciers contain crevasses in the zone of fracture?
2. What causes shallow parallel scratch marks in bedrock? What are these marks called?
3. What term is used to describe very rapid glacier movement? Name at least two factors that can increase the speed of glacier movement.
4. What characteristics distinguish a glaciated valley from a stream valley?
5. Name the rounded basins carved into the sides of mountains by valley glaciers.
6. What happens when a coastal glacier carves out a valley below sea level?
7. How does glacial till form?
8. Which glacial deposits are unstratified? Which are stratified?
9. What is a flat deposit of sand and gravel extending for many miles from the terminus of a continental glacier called?
10. Why can glacial varves not be used as a reliable annual date marker?
11. (True or False) A group of drumlins can indicate the direction of motion of the glacier that formed them.

Answers to 20B Section Review Questions

1. The upper layer of moving glacier ice is too brittle to flow as the glacier bends and turns, so the ice fractures and forms deep crevasses. (§20.7)

2. Scratch marks in bedrock are caused by rocks and debris being dragged along by a glacier. These marks are called *striations*. (§20.8)

3. Very rapid glacier movement is called a *surge*. Many factors may cause a surge, such as increased snow accumulation, long winters and short summers, higher average temperatures during those seasons, meltwater pools on the surface of glaciers, and large amounts of glacial debris on the surface of glaciers. (§20.7)

4. Glaciated valleys are deeper and wider than stream valleys, and they may have hanging valleys entering them. Glaciated valleys have a U-shaped cross section; mountain stream valleys are more V-shaped. (§20.8)

5. Rounded basins carved into the sides of mountains by valley glaciers are called *cirques*. (§20.8)

6. As the coastal glacier retreats, the sea fills in the glaciated valley to form a *fiord*. (§20.8)

7. Glacial till is formed when eroded bedrock is carried along by glacial ice and then deposited when the ice melts. (§20.9)

8. *Drumlins* and the various kinds of *moraines* are unstratified glacial deposits. Stratified deposits include *eskers*, *kames*, and *varves*. (§20.9)

9. A flat deposit of sand and gravel extending in front of a continental glacier is called an *outwash plain*. (§20.9)

10. It is possible for more than one glacial varve to be deposited per year. (§20.9)

11. True. (§20.9)

20C THE ICE AGE

20.10 Uniformitarian Ice Ages

Much geological evidence shows that glaciers were once far more widespread than they are today. Continental glaciers apparently covered northern Europe, Asia, Canada, and the northern United States as well as southern portions of Australia, Africa, and South America.

Uniformitarian geologists believe that the earth's history has been marked by long periods of cooling and warming spanning millions of years. These temperature changes are believed to be linked to slow, repeated changes in the earth's orbit or to changes within the sun. In this model, the entire earth cooled slowly along with the ocean. During the cool periods, huge continental glaciers took tens of thousands or hundreds of thousands of years to form and push south from the Arctic and north from the Antarctic regions of the globe. These glaciers are believed to have left their mark on the continents with many of the erosional and depositional features we described in the last section. In many areas, multiple glacial advances in a given location have left overlapping marks, such as crisscrossed striations on bedrock, moraines and eskers "bulldozed" by later glacial advances, and layers of weathered till that lie under less weathered till.

Interpreting the glacial history of a locality by inspecting the remnants of glacial erosion and deposition is very difficult. Most uniformitarian geologists agree that at least four and as many as twenty or more **ice ages** have occurred in the past.

20.11 The Creationary Ice Age

Many creationary scientists believe that a relatively brief period of glacial action (700 to 1300 years) followed Noah's Flood. These scientists think an ice age had to occur, considering the catastrophic events of the Flood. We will present a possible sequence of events that could have led to a single glacial period in the earth's history. This description is based on atmospheric modeling done by Larry Vardiman, an atmospheric physicist with the Institute for Creation Research, and on ice-age research done by Michael Oard, a retired National Weather Service meteorologist.

An ice age is not an easy thing to start because of the unique conditions that must exist. First, there must be a source of large amounts of atmospheric moisture to produce precipitation. This requires warm oceans all over the world that can evaporate vast quantities of water. Second, there must be wind patterns that will carry the moisture to locations where it can accumulate as snow. Finally, the continental areas where the snow accumulates must be cold enough to retain the snow that will eventually become glacial ice.

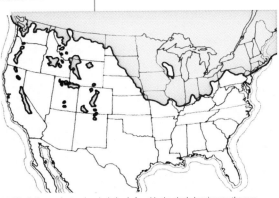

20-25 Evidence of extensive glaciation is found in the shaded regions on the map.

Stones of Witness

Comment on the validity of the following statement: "A Bible-believing Christian cannot accept the occurrence of an ice age in historical times. Unlike the Flood, which is clearly discussed in the Bible, there is no mention of such a significant event as the Ice Age in Scripture."

Michael Oard works as a field researcher for Answers in Genesis (AiG), a prominent evangelical organization that promotes proper science based on biblical presuppositions.

20-26 The earth would have been almost completely covered by clouds during the Ice Age.

Objectives—Section 20C

Upon completing this section, students should be able to

- compare and contrast the standard evolutionary model of multiple ice ages over tens of thousands of years and a creationary model that suggests only a single ice age that occurred as a direct consequence of the Flood.

- within the context of the creationary model, describe in chronological order how the Ice Age developed and ended and how the world is still experiencing its effects today.

Stones of Witness

Students should be quick to point out the evidence of past glaciation in regions of the world that no longer have glaciers. This evidence indicates that more extensive glaciation occurred in the past than is occurring today. Once they have presented this evidence, they will probably be unable to carry their argument any farther unless a well-read student mentions the references to ice and cold found in Job 37 and 38.

Regarding the silence of Scripture pertaining to an ice age, you can point out that in the case of the Flood we are working with clear biblical data and a world full of evidence of a global inundation. We are confident when working with the evidence because the evidence and Scripture fit together perfectly. In the case of the Ice Age, we have little or no biblical narrative to support such an event, but the inference of an ice age fits perfectly into the biblical account of history. A Christian scientist will have a lifetime of joy seeing the truth contained in the Bible lining up with what he observes scientifically. This is not limited to science. Every human who lives in this world has to account for the world around him in relation to the claims of Scripture. He will never be disappointed when he examines the world in the light of Scripture.

See Mike Oard's salvation testimony and background in the Teacher's Edition margin notes on page 190.

Review: Albedo

Review with your students the concept of albedo mentioned in §5.3. Factors contributing to Earth's albedo during this period of time would have been very extensive cloud coverage of the earth and increasing snow and ice accumulations in the upper latitudes.

Some students may recall that according to the model of global pressure zones we presented in Chapter 11, the polar regions consist of high-pressure subsiding air. Hurricanes need a low-pressure center with rising air. How could this low-pressure scenario have occurred during the Ice Age? Note in Figure 20-27 and Visual 20-6 that the Arctic Ocean was warm and unfrozen, while the continents were cool or cold. The polar air circulation tended to rise at the poles and subside over the continents. The atmosphere would have set up an immense rotating circulation with an intense Coriolis effect near the poles, causing strong circulating winds that could have pulled much humid air from above the oceans and moved it over the continents.

Recall from Chapter 5 that the measure of the amount of sunlight a planet reflects is called its *albedo*. During the Ice Age, the earth's albedo probably was much higher than it is today.

20.12 Warming the Oceans

As we discussed in Unit Four, global tectonic action probably involved significant volcanism during the Flood and for hundreds of years afterward. Much of the volcanism was under water, as evidenced by the thousands of extinct submarine volcanoes littering the ocean floor. Submarine volcanism along with the rupturing of the "fountains of the great deep" (Gen. 7:11) may have raised average ocean temperatures to as much as 30 °C (86 °F). Such warm temperatures in the past have been supported by analysis of the fossils of microscopic organisms that lived on the ocean bottom.

The volcanic activity would have ejected great quantities of volcanic dust and steam high into the atmosphere. At the same time, much water evaporated from the warm oceans and could have formed thick cloud cover over much of the earth, especially in the middle and high latitudes. The cloudy and dusty atmosphere would have reflected a high percentage of sunlight—the continents would have begun to cool down.

Precipitation would have been frequent following the Flood. In the equatorial and mid-latitude regions of the earth, rains would have been the main form of precipitation. In high latitudes, snow accumulation would have been heavy.

20.13 Polar Wind Circulation

As the high-latitude continental landmasses began to cool rapidly from lack of solar heating, significant differences in temperature would have developed between the northern ocean waters and the land. Large hurricane-like storm systems in the high latitudes could have developed, according to computer models of the earth's atmosphere following the Flood. The humid air over the oceans would have been swept onto the continents, accelerating the accumulation of snow in the high latitudes and on high mountain ranges in North America, Europe, Asia, South Africa, Australia, South America, and Antarctica.

20-27 According to one creationary model of the Ice Age, the warm Arctic Ocean remained unfrozen for hundreds of years while the continental glaciers advanced on land. This view shows the earth without cloud cover during this period.

As the snow cover increased, even more solar energy would have been reflected back into space, cooling the continents even further. The high-latitude atmospheric circulation would have become even more intense, producing violent snowstorms as the warm, moist air was dragged into the polar latitudes. For hundreds of years following the Flood, there is evidence that volcanic activity was sporadic. But each burst of volcanism would have released fresh ash into the atmosphere that could have caused further cooling of the land-masses.

During the first several hundred years following the Flood, Oard believes, the Arctic Ocean never froze and that the coastal lowlands of the continents were unglaciated. Oceans were warm enough to keep the coastal climates temperate. Semitropical plants and animals were able to live at the edges of the glaciers along the coasts, even up to the Arctic Circle. In the highlands and places where snow was accumulating, it may have piled up at the rate of 150–300 m (500–1000 ft) per year. Little snow melted from year to year, which contributed to the rapid accumulation of glacier ice.

20.14 The Ice Sheets Advance

In the first 250 to 500 years after the Flood, as much as 15,000 m (50,000 ft) of snow could have accumulated in the far northern and southern latitudes. This could have compacted to form about 1500 m (5000 ft) of ice although no one knows for sure how thick the ice actually got. When the weight of the ice was sufficient, the glaciers would have begun moving outward from the snowfields in the higher latitudes and elevations. After a time, a general movement toward the equator would have predominated.

After about 500 years following the Flood, Oard believes, the average ocean temperatures had cooled to around 10 °C (50 °F). A cooler ocean would have resulted in decreased evaporation and therefore reduced cloud formation and precipitation. Snow accumulation probably slowed enough that glaciers were at their maximum point of advance during this period.

At this time, the balance between snow accumulation and glacier melting was probably very delicate. Small variations in cloud cover and volcanic dust in the atmosphere would make the difference between glacial advances and retreats. Since the global climate probably oscillated like a pendulum between periods of warming and cooling for as long as 1300 years after the Flood, the terminus of many glaciers would have retreated and advanced in similar spurts. The geologic evidence for multiple glacial advances and retreats could easily be explained by these climatic changes. Throughout this period, the continents and oceans would have continued to cool.

20.15 End of the Ice Age

Toward the end of the Ice Age, the interior of the continents in the northern latitudes would have been frigid most of the year, and the Arctic Ocean would have finally begun to freeze over. Ice shelves formed in Antarctica and along the coasts of the continents in the high northern latitudes. The oceans' average temperature was close to what it is today, around 4 °C (39 °F), so evaporation was low and precipitation was limited. Perhaps surprisingly, the vast continental glaciers in the North probably had been retreating for several

20-28 Around the time of the maximum extent of the Ice Age, several glacial retreats and advances probably occurred as the balance of ice accumulation and global warming changed from time to time. Here, a glacier is retreating.

Visual 20-6: Northern Hemisphere Glaciation During the Ice Age

This visual is a reproduction of Figure 20-27. Some features to note include the open Arctic Ocean and the narrow green belts around most of the northern continental shores and islands, indicating temperate climates that persisted well into the Ice Age because of the warm ocean waters. It is in these belts along the margins of the continental glacier that a diverse collection of large mammals lived right up until the latter stages of the Ice Age, when it has been suggested the Arctic Ocean suddenly froze over and plunged the northern regions into a deep freeze that killed off many species.

20-29 A thick loess deposit along the Yukon River

hundred years because snow accumulation had not been able to keep up with glacial melting in the longer, warmer summers. Because of a lack of moisture, deserts had formed where the glaciers had retreated. The global winds were carrying great quantities of dust and depositing it as thick blankets of **loess** (wind-borne silt) along the fronts of the glaciers. The loess probably also settled out on the glacier surfaces, increasing the amount of solar heat absorbed. Melting would have became much more rapid.

The continents in the middle latitudes would have been warming up during this period, encouraging the northward migration of plants and animals. Eventually, after as much as 1300 years following the Flood, glacial ice had retreated to approximately its current limits. Great inland lakes of melted glacial water remained on most continents. Evidence exists that many of these lakes eventually broke through the moraines that contained them. On their way to the sea, the rushing waters gouged out extensive erosional landforms that remain today. One such huge lake in the north may have initiated a final freeze-up of the Arctic Ocean that sealed the fate of many mammals, including herds of mammoths. (See the box on page 533.)

Remnants of the Ice Age may have continued throughout much of the Old Testament time. It is interesting to note that God asked Job about the source of frost, ice, and frozen solid waters (Job 37:9–10; 38:22–23, 29–30). It is possible that Job lived in the final years of the Ice Age or knew of it, so that these references to ice and snow would be familiar to him.

20C Section Review

1. What areas were apparently covered by continental glaciers during the Ice Age that are not covered today?

2. What is one evolutionary theory for the cause of multiple ice ages?

3. According to one creationary model, what triggered the start of the Ice Age?

4. What evidence is there that glaciers were once widespread?

5. How does the young-earth creationary interpretation of the glacial evidence differ from old-earth views?

6. List the conditions that some creationary scientists believe were necessary to cause an ice age.

7. What is *albedo*, and what three factors could have affected the earth's albedo during the Ice Age?

8. What changes probably brought the Ice Age to an end?

9. (True or False) Thousands of mammoths and other large mammals are believed to have died and were preserved in frozen sediments near the end of the Ice Age.

 Visual 20-7: Demise of Large Mammals at the End of the Ice Age

This visual is a reproduction of Figure 20-29 and the illustration on the bottom page 533. Contrary to what many people believe, woolly mammoths, saber tooth tigers, and giant sloths probably were not snap-frozen in a freak ice-age climatic event. It seems that many of them were killed by suffocation and burial in massive silt storms toward the end of the Ice Age. See the box on page 533.

You may choose to spend a class period talking about the polar regions although specific information about these regions is not covered in the text. Check your local library for resources in preparing for a class presentation on this subject. Some suggested topics are the differences between the North and South poles, wildlife at the North and South poles, and how the polar regions affect worldwide weather and ocean currents.

Answers to 20C Section Review Questions

1. Northern Europe, Canada, and the northern United States, as well as the southern portions of Australia, Africa, and South America, were covered by continental glaciers during the Ice Age but are not today. (§20.10)

2. Some evolutionists believe that long, slow, repeated changes to the earth's orbit or changes in the sun have caused multiple ice ages throughout the earth's history. (§20.10)

3. It is possible that the Ice Age was triggered by the Flood. Students may also mention that the combination of the warm oceans and the cloudy skies following the Flood were the specific causes of the Ice Age. (§20.11)

4. Widespread distribution of glacial till and other glacial features show that glaciers were once much more extensive. (§20.10)

5. The young-earth creationary scientist interprets the glacial evidence as having been produced by one Ice Age that was triggered by a worldwide, catastrophic Flood. The old-earth interpretations hold to multiple ice ages over millions of years. (§20.10–20.11)

6. According to some creationary scientists, an ice age would require very warm oceans, wind patterns that could carry moist air over the continents, and cool continents that could accumulate snow. (§20.11)

7. Albedo is the fraction of sunlight that is reflected by a planet's atmosphere and surface. The earth's albedo could have been higher during the Ice Age as a result of the addition of volcanic dust into the atmosphere, increased cloud cover from ocean evaporation, and an increased amount of land covered by continental snowfields and glaciers. (Chap. 5, §20.12)

8. According to the creationary model discussed in the text, the Ice Age probably came to an end when the oceans cooled to present-day temperatures and the skies cleared of volcanic debris as global volcanism tapered off. (§20.15)

9. True. (box, §20.15)

A Mammoth Mystery

For more than 300 years people have been finding the frozen, well-preserved carcasses of mammoths, rhinoceroses, tigers, horses, antelopes, and other animals in the frozen mud formed from fine, wind-blown sediment surrounding the Arctic Ocean. Evolutionists say this proves there was a gradual change in the climate that produced one of the many ice ages. An area that was semitropical became too cold for these animals to survive. Creationists agree that the area was semitropical, but they strongly disagree with the idea of a gradual change in the climate. The evidence points to a rapid change that sealed the fate of these animals that were designed for living in more moderate temperatures.

Most of the animal remains discovered today are skeletons, with only a few having any flesh remaining. Even fewer of these carcasses are complete enough so that their final meal could be determined. However, some are so well preserved that delicate sedges and grasses were found in their mouths and stomachs, indicating they died in the act of eating or shortly thereafter. Some investigators believe they were frozen before the vegetable matter could become digested or decayed. An autopsy on a few of the well-preserved animals revealed that they died of suffocation. No cause of death other than freezing was found for several others. One young mammoth had particles of silt, clay, and small gravel in both his digestive and respiratory passages, suggesting a strong wind was blowing as he died.

The frozen mud in which most of these animals are found is called "*muck*" by pedologists (soil scientists). Muck consists of wind-deposited silt, or loess, and it contains decomposed animal and vegetable matter as well as much ice. It provides additional clues concerning the cause and circumstances of the animals' deaths. It is found on land areas surrounding the greatest extent of the continental glaciers in the Northern Hemisphere. In many places it is hundreds of meters deep. In addition to the animal carcasses already mentioned, it contains thousands of broken trees of species that today grow only in subtropical climates. Some of these trees still have leaves and fruit attached, indicating that they had not been transported far from where they were growing before they were buried.

Michael Oard, a creationary meteorologist, notes that many of the carcasses are found in muck layers on top of sediments deposited by the Flood and glacial deposits. This location indicates that they probably died near the end of the Ice Age. Oard suggests that these animals were buried in loess carried

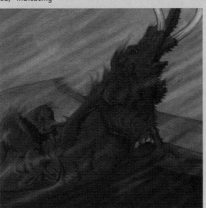

by strong winds, which suffocated some animals and buried their food and water supplies. Shortly thereafter, he believes, a large frigid lake of glacial meltwater burst its moraine walls and emptied into the cold but still liquid Arctic Ocean. The fresh water floated on top of the denser salt water and froze solid, isolating the Arctic air from the slightly warmer seawater. The resulting drop in air temperature plunged the whole Arctic region into a deep freeze that allowed the glaciers to advance to the coastlines for many decades and froze the ground solid. The buried animals were locked in the permafrost, which is just now beginning to thaw out, revealing yet another catastrophe that overwhelmed certain land creatures after the Flood.

The details of the demise of the mammoths and other large extinct mammals may never be known, but using the Bible to establish the key events in the earth's history can lead us to reasonable conclusions about the events surrounding the Flood.

Lakes of glacial meltwater with a core of ice dammed up by moraines can be found today. Mt. Everest's Khumbu Icefalls are melting, producing a lake. Imja Lake near Everest could flood the Khumbu Valley of Nepal if it burst through its moraine wall. (See "Big Thaw," *National Geographic Adventure*, May 2005, 37.)

Box Summary: A Mammoth Mystery

This box provides a possible explanation for the formation of large numbers of well-preserved fossils during the Ice Age. Fossils of mammoths, rhinoceroses, tigers, and other large mammals lie in the muck in the regions surrounding the perimeters of the continental ice sheets. There are no vocabulary terms in this box.

In Terms of Glaciology

Chapter Summary

- Permanently frozen water creates a unique environment that can have drastic effects on the earth. Glaciers are particularly powerful sources of erosion and deposition. A glacier is a large mass of ice that flows under the influence of gravity.

- Glaciers form in snowfields above the snow line, where winter snow survives the summer and becomes compacted into dense ice crystals called glacier ice.

- Ice accumulations may be classified by their location and sizes. Common glaciers include valley glaciers (also called mountain glaciers or alpine glaciers), piedmont glaciers, and continental glaciers. Ice sheets and icecaps cover all but the highest mountains over large areas.

- Glaciers flowing out from a coastline can produce ice shelves and icebergs. Ice floes come from broken-up sheets of frozen sea ice rather than from glaciers.

- Glacier ice consists of two zones of movement. The upper zone of fracture consists of hard glacier ice which is full of crevasses. The plastic zone of flow is the lower layer of a glacier that changes shape with the glacier's movement.

- Glaciers change landscapes by plucking and erosion to create U-shaped valleys, hanging valleys, cirques, tarns, horns, arêtes, and moraine deposits.

- Features of glaciated bedrock include striations and glacial polish. Glacial ground moraines and outwash plains include features such as drumlins, kettles and kettle lakes, and kames.

- Those who hold to an old-earth interpretation of the glacial evidence believe that four or more glacial periods have occurred through the earth's history. Young-earth Creationists believe that the glacial evidence supports a single short Ice Age that began soon after the Genesis Flood ended.

- Creationary atmospheric scientists believe that the very warm oceans and cool continents following the Flood triggered the Ice Age. The greatest extent of the ice sheets occurred about 500 years after the Flood. The Ice Age ended when the oceans cooled and the skies cleared of volcanic dust and clouds.

Answers to Chapter Review Questions

What Did You Learn?

1. Answers may vary. Students may say that year-round temperatures are cold enough near the poles that accumulation takes place faster than melting. They may also say that the snow line is at a much lower elevation in polar regions compared to elsewhere. (§20.2)

2. The weight of the snow compacts the older snow to make firn. Further compaction forms the solid, brittle glacier ice. (§20.2)

3. If accumulation exceeds wastage (colder average temperatures, more precipitation, longer winters and shorter summers), a glacier will advance; if wastage exceeds accumulation (warmer average temperatures, longer summers and shorter winters, less precipitation), a glacier will retreat. (§20.2)

4. A retreating glacier still moves downhill. However, its wastage zone is losing more ice from melting than is flowing down from higher up, so its terminus is retreating or moving up-slope. (§20.2)

5. *Valley* or *alpine glaciers* are narrow and are found in mountain valleys. *Piedmont glaciers* are formed when two or more valley glaciers merge near the base of the mountain and flow out onto a plain. *Ice sheets* are broad masses of glacier ice lying on top of most geographical features. *Icecaps* are small ice sheets. *Continental glaciers* are large ice sheets. (§20.3)

6. Only *valley* (also *mountain* or *alpine*) glaciers would be found near the equator because only glaciers in high mountains can exist at equatorial latitudes. (§20.3)

7. The International Ice Patrol monitors the shipping lanes of the North Atlantic during iceberg seasons and warns ships about icebergs to prevent another disaster like that of the *Titanic*. (Facet, p. 522)

8. Gravity is the force that causes glaciers to move. They move downhill, or in the case of ice sheets, thicker portions push outward toward thinner portions. (§20.2–20.3)

9. Glacial drift originates from material eroded or plucked by the action of ice movement from valley walls and floors. (§20.9)

10. Prospectors can sometimes trace the train of ore-bearing boulders back along the glacier's path to the source. (§20.9)

What Did You Learn?

1. Why are glaciers more numerous near the poles?

2. Why is the *weight* of snow needed to make glacier ice?

3. What factors determine whether a glacier will advance or retreat?

4. In what direction is a glacier's ice moving when it retreats? Explain.

5. List five kinds of glaciers and glacial accumulations. How do they differ?

6. What kind of glacier would you expect to find near the equator? Why?

7. What is the function of the International Ice Patrol?

8. What causes glaciers to move?

9. What is the origin of the material in glacial drift?

10. How could a boulder train lead to the discovery of an ore deposit?

11. List four types of moraines. How are they similar?

12. How do creationary scientists explain the widespread evidence of glaciation?

True or False

13. It is expected that with global warming the increase of precipitation will cause most of the world's glaciers to advance.

14. When two or more mountain glaciers flow together, the result is a valley glacier.

15. The world's largest icecap is located in Antarctica.

16. If a military submarine could go no deeper than 400 m, it would be relatively safe traveling submerged through a field of large icebergs.

17. Boulders transported by glaciers are called erratics because they are not like the underlying bedrock in the location where the glacier dropped them.

18. Streamlined, unstratified glacial deposits that often occur in clusters are called drumlins.

19. Scientists have shown that varves deposited annually in lakes are useful for determining the age of sediments.

20. Noah and his sons probably had to learn to farm during short, cool summers.

What Do You Think?

1. What obstacles would need to be overcome to use icebergs as a source of fresh water in drought-stricken areas?

2. Do you think ice cubes cut from glacier ice could be a marketable fad item?

3. What do you think would happen to the continental glacier if a volcano erupted in the middle of Antarctica?

4. If an ice age requires high rates of evaporation to produce lots of atmospheric water that will result in large quantities of snow, and at the same time a cooler than normal climate over much of the world in order to allow snow to accumulate as glacier ice, discuss how an old-earth model cannot account for these two mutually exclusive conditions.

My Review Checklist

☐ I have carefully read the entire chapter.

☐ I have reviewed all of the photographs, illustrations, and graphs.

☐ I have reviewed all of my notes in the margins.

☐ I have reviewed and corrected the quizzes on this chapter.

☐ I have studied all of the vocabulary terms.

☐ I have had all of my questions answered.

11. The four types of moraines are *terminal* moraines, *lateral* moraines, *medial* moraines, and *ground* moraines. All moraines are deposits of unstratified (unsorted) glacial till. (§20.9)

12. Many creationary scientists believe that a single, intense ice age of relatively short duration occurred following and as a consequence of the Genesis Flood. According to this model, the warm oceans resulting from the tectonic activity during the Flood readily evaporated, resulting in high humidity that caused heavy precipitation. The decreased sunlight due to concentrations of volcanic dust and heavy cloud cover cooled the continents, causing the accumulation of huge amounts of ice in higher latitudes. The ice became continental glaciers that produced the evidence of glaciation seen today. (§20.11–20.15)

True or False

13. False. The global warming trend is causing most glaciers to retreat through accelerated wastage, even with the higher amounts of precipitation. (§20.2)

14. False. The resulting glacier is called a *piedmont glacier*. (§20.3)

15. False. It is located in Canada. (§20.4)

16. False. Very large icebergs can extend almost half a kilometer into the depths, which is far deeper than most military submarines can go. Since submarines do not normally steam at their maximum operating depths, collisions with icebergs can be a real hazard in polar seas. (§20.5)

17. True. (§20.9)

18. True. (§20.9)

19. False. While many uniformitarian scientists generally still believe this to be the case, research has shown that varves can be deposited at intervals more or less frequently than annually, so varves cannot be used reliably for dating sediments. (§20.9)

20. True. (§20.15)

What Do You Think?

1. Answers will vary. The icebergs would have to be towed or pushed by tugboats to get them to their destination before they completely melted. Somehow they must be sealed off from the salt water they are floating in. Since 80–90% of an iceberg is under water, one probably cannot be towed into the shallow waters near shore, so the fresh water would have to be melted and pumped into tanker ships and transported to shore. The former glacier ice would contain sand and gravel that would have to be separated out. Could the water be sold for enough to recover the transportation and energy costs of getting it to the area where it is needed?

2. Answers may vary. Obviously, the cost of obtaining them, transporting them to the market, and keeping them frozen until they were sold would make blocks of glacier ice quite expensive. Maybe some clever person could find a way to create sufficient demand for them, but it is hard to imagine how. Unfortunately, glacier ice is full of dust, meteoric particles, and glacial flour, so it is not really suitable for consumption without filtering and purification, which would add to its cost.

3. When compared to the size of the entire continent, the lava from a single volcano would melt only a tiny part of the continental glacier. That water would be quickly frozen again as it reached more distant parts of the ice sheet. But there could be some long-term effects as the volcanic ash settled. How much of the ice sheet would be covered? Would the darker-colored ash increase the absorption of energy from sunlight to the extent that widespread melting would occur? How long would this melting phase last before fresh snow covered the layer of ash? These unknown factors make it hard to predict the eruption's effects with any degree of certainty. There are several active volcanoes, including Mt. Erebus near the U.S. McMurdo base in Antarctica.

4. An old-earth model cannot explain how colder global temperatures can produce excessive evaporation to support the much greater precipitation required for snowfield accumulations. Colder temperatures result in less evaporation, not more. A gradually cooling interglacial period of millions of years cannot result in the evaporation of large amounts of water. Cold, dry deserts would be the result of such a model, not continental ice sheets.

Overview

In Chapter 21, the final chapter dealing with the hydrosphere, we look at the presence, movement, and storage of liquid fresh water on the earth. We address a number of practical topics, such as defining the water table and the problem of hard water. Groundwater is yet another factor that reshapes the earth as well as being essential to life.

Section 21A discusses the hydrologic cycle as an introduction to the storage and movement of groundwater. The problems associated with aquifer depletion and the need for water conservation are also addressed.

Section 21B lays the foundation for Section 21C by discussing the dissolving power of water. Minerals can become dissolved in water, resulting in hard water.

Section 21C describes solution caves and investigates their origins and features. It illustrates various kinds of cave formations and gives evidence for their rapid formation. It also presents the causes and features of karst topography.

Schedule Summary

21A: 1–2 periods
21B: 1 period
21C: 2–3 periods

Investigation Summary

21E "Permeability"
21F "Mineral Water"
21G "Stalactites and Stalagmites"
21H "Solution of Limestone"

 Bulletin Board Ideas

1. Display photographs of caves and cave structures. This would be a good reinforcement tool.

2. Display photographs of spelunkers doing various activities. Use the photos to illustrate the safety rules of cave exploring.

 Field Trip Ideas

1. Take a day trip to a cave open to tourists if there is one located nearby. Have students note uniformitarian statements and assumptions mentioned by guides and signs during their visit.

CHAPTER

21

THE GROUNDWATER SYSTEM

SUGGESTED TEACHING SCHEDULE

DAY 0

Assignment

Reading: Section 21A, "Underground Reservoir"

You may want to do Investigations 21G, "Stalactites and Stalagmites," and 21H, "Solution of Limestone," as teacher demonstrations rather than taking class time to have the students set them up. If so, set them up before you begin the chapter and take time to introduce them to the students on Day 1 or 2. Have students make observations later in the chapter when these topics are covered.

DAY 1

Introduce the hydrologic cycle, also known as the water cycle. Discuss the importance of groundwater storage and the nature of the water table. Describe the properties of ground and rock that stores and moves groundwater (aquifers), emphasizing the understanding of porosity and permeability.

Illustrate how water usage can affect the water table in an aquifer and the need for aquifer recharge.

Assignment

Complete: Section 21A Section Review Questions
            Applications 21A, "The Hydrologic Cycle"

Reading: Investigation 21E, "Permeability"

DAY 2

Do Investigation 21E, "Permeability," and Applications 21B, " Groundwater."

Assignment

Reading: Section 21B, "Groundwater's Dissolving Power"
            Investigation 21F, "Mineral Water"

21A UNDERGROUND RESERVOIR

21.1 Introduction

The earth is the only planet in our solar system with liquid water on its surface. You learned in Chapter 19 that over 97% of the water is in the oceans, which cover almost three-fourths of the planet. Ocean water is too salty for humans to drink. Over three-fourths of the earth's fresh water is frozen in the polar ice caps and glaciers, but this ice is difficult to use as a source of fresh water. The second largest reserve of fresh water is **groundwater**, which accounts for about 22% of the earth's fresh water. Lakes and streams contain only about 0.33% of the earth's fresh water.

21.2 The Water Cycle

Where does groundwater come from? To answer that question, you must think about the **hydrologic cycle**. Water continually moves from the continents to the oceans, evaporates into the atmosphere, and is carried back to the continents as clouds by the prevailing winds. The cycle is complete when the clouds release precipitation back onto the continents. Each day, 10–20 *trillion* liters of moisture in one form or another fall on the United States alone.

When rain falls, where does the rainwater go? Some of it runs off the surface of the ground into streams, which eventually carry it into the oceans. Some water forms puddles on the ground, where it evaporates back into the air, and some water soaks into the ground. Plants absorb water from the ground, and some of this water escapes back into the air by *transpiration*. The remainder of the water continues to *percolate* downward through pores, cracks, and other spaces between rock particles until it reaches a depth at which water fills all the available spaces. The water at this level is groundwater. This water is not on a dead-end path to be permanently locked away underground. It is still an active part of the hydrologic cycle and will eventually return to the surface.

21.3 The Water Table

The upper surface of the groundwater reservoir is called the **water table**. Its shape is irregular. Beneath level ground, the water table's depth varies with the type of rock and the ability of surface water to reach it. Beneath ground that is not level, the water table follows the general shape of the surface. Though it is high under hills and low under valleys, its contour changes less than does the earth's surface.

The Earth's Water

oceans
97.2%

groundwater
0.62%

ice caps
and glaciers
2.15%

other
0.03%

21-1 Only a small portion of the earth's water is groundwater, but this water is vital to the survival of life.

The term "hydrologic" refers to any aspect of water in its natural setting.

percolate (PER ke LAYT): (L. *percolare*—to sift, strain, or filter)

21-2 The water cycle is a vast purification process for the earth's freshwater supply (left). The water table generally follows the contour of the surface (right).

swamp ground surface stream lake

water table

 Beholding the Waters
Clean drinking water is necessary to sustain human life. God made the earth with an abundance of water, but it is surprising that only a very small percentage of that amount is drinkable. Why would a good God put His creatures in such a situation?

DAY 3

Quiz—Section 21A, "Underground Reservoir"

Define the term *solvent* and explain how water is a very effective solvent. Discuss the differences between hard and soft water. Mention the kind(s) of groundwater supplying your area. Do Investigation 21F, "Mineral Water."

Assignment

Complete: 21B Section Review Questions
Applications 21C, "Hard and Soft Water"

Reading: Section 21C-1 (§21.8–21.11), caves and cave formations (speleothems)

(schedule continued on p. 538)

---

2. If you live in an area with karst topography, take your students to a destination where you can point out several karst features.

3. Visit a water treatment plant.

Objectives—Section 21A

Upon completing this section, students should be able to

- identify groundwater's place and function within the hydrologic cycle.
- describe the water table and how its shape varies with rate of usage.
- distinguish between porosity and permeability of aquifer rocks.
- discuss how permeability affects the water table.
- explain what causes an artesian well.
- describe the movement of groundwater.

Visual 21-1: Pie Chart of the Earth's Fresh Water

This visual is a reproduction of Figure 21-1. The "other" freshwater sources include lakes and streams.

The process of transpiration in plants is the release of excess water vapor through stomata in leaves and pores in their twigs and branches.

Visual 21-2: Hydrologic (Water) Cycle

This visual is a reproduction of Figure 21-2 (left). Ecclesiastes 1:7 refers to the hydrologic cycle. This visual shows the ocean as the ultimate destination of groundwater, but the destination might be any large body of water. In addition, depending on the orientation of the local strata, large bodies of water might actually be a source of water in an aquifer or for the groundwater supply.

Beholding the Waters

Answers will vary. Try to direct the students to mention the following three considerations. First, the relative scarcity of good drinking water may be God's way of giving us an opportunity to glorify Him through the fulfillment of the Creation Mandate. By giving us the challenge of meeting our physical needs, God encourages us to work out creative ways to maximize the usefulness of His world. As we exercise our God-given creativity and strength, we declare the glory of the God who made us in His image. Second, this challenge gives us an opportunity to show love for others. As we labor to make sure that the earth's freshwater supply is adequate for the earth's population, we enjoy the privilege of caring for others in much the same way that God has been caring for us. Third, much of the problem of water scarcity is probably due to the Fall. God has made good water relatively hard to find as a judgment on us for our sin. But even in this judgment, God has gracious purposes. By making it difficult for us to meet our most basic physical needs, He encourages us to seek a relationship with Him and depend on Him. This scarcity also gives Him an opportunity to show His people His unique love for them—as He does with Isaac in Genesis 26:1–33.

21-3 Typical hillside spring (top). This spring emerges from a hillside in Kadakh, India (bottom).

aeration (ehr AY shun): (Gk. *aer*—air) + -ation

capillary: capillar- (L. *capillar*—hair-like) + -y

21-5 The zone of aeration holds some air in its spaces. In the zone of saturation, all spaces are filled with water. The water table is the upper boundary of the zone of saturation. Soil that contains water absorbed upward from the water table by capillary action is called the capillary fringe.

permeable (PUR mee uh bul)

Visual 21-3: Characteristics of the Water Table

This visual is a reproduction of Figures 21-3 and 21-4. Refer to these images as you discuss the various features of water tables.

Demonstration: Water Table

Arrange soil or sand in a 10-gallon fish tank with glass sides to make a landscape with hills and low-lying areas. Carefully pour water into the tank without disturbing the features. Determine the height of the water table in your landscape. Note that there is a band of wet sand that is above the liquid level. This is the capillary fringe. Observe whether a pond was created in the low-lying areas because of the level of the water table.

In some places the water table is only a few meters below the surface, and in other places it is at a depth of hundreds of meters. At certain locations, called springs, the water table intersects the ground's surface. A **spring** is a place, usually on a hillside, where water comes from the ground, often continuously. The height of the water table also varies seasonally. Generally it is higher in the springtime, when rain and melting snow are plentiful and *recharge* the groundwater supplies.

The water table is not merely a theoretical concept that helps us to understand groundwater; it is an actual location of water that must be known before a well is drilled. A well fills only if its pipe reaches below the level of the water table. If the well is to produce water for the entire year, it must reach below the level of the dry-season water table.

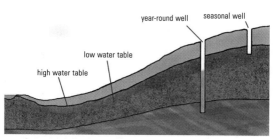

21-4 Seasonal variation of water table

To aid in the study of groundwater, scientists have divided the ground into several zones. The **zone of aeration** is the rock and soil above the water table, in which some of the available spaces between rock particles are filled with air instead of water. The **zone of saturation** is the ground below the water table, in which every available space is filled with water. Immediately above the zone of saturation is a small region in which water has worked its way upward by *capillary* action, much as the raw edge of a paper towel soaks up a small puddle of water. The area in the ground where capillary action takes place is called the **capillary fringe**.

21.4 Storage of Groundwater

A rock that has many open spaces within it is **porous**. An example of a porous rock is pumice, which contains many holes throughout its interior. To hold groundwater, a rock first must be porous, but that alone is not enough. Pumice contains holes that are not connected to one another or to the surface of the rock. Thus, water cannot easily flow into the interior spaces.

Another factor affecting a rock's ability to hold groundwater is its *permeability*, or how easily it allows water to pass through. A **permeable** material transmits water easily; it contains many open spaces that are connected so that water can flow through them. The

---

DAY 4

Quiz—Section 21B, "Groundwater's Dissolving Power"

Describe the main models for the formation of solution caves. Show that the Flood is a sufficient and reasonable primary cause for the existence of solution caves. Describe the major kinds of speleothems, emphasizing that the different formations are caused by differing types of water flows. Note the historical and scientific evidence that proves speleothems can form quickly and probably did so in the past.

Assignment

Complete: 21C-1 Section Review Questions

Reading: Section 21C-2 (§21.12–21.13), karst topography

DAY 5

Describe the characteristic features of karst topography. Explain that this kind of topography is derived from the erosion of the underlying chemical sedimentary rocks. Uniformitarian and creationary scientists differ in their descriptions of the processes and the amounts of time required for this

topography to have developed. Do Applications 21D, "Karst Topography." Make final observations of Investigations 21G, "Stalactites and Stalagmites," and 21H, "Solution of Limestone," and answer the Summing Up questions for each.

Assignment

Complete: 21C-2 Section Review Questions

Selected Chapter Review Questions

DAY 6

Quiz—Section 21C, "Groundwater Erosion"

Review for a chapter test.

Assignment

Study for a chapter test.

DAY 7

Test—Chapter 21

openings are also large enough that they do not impede the movement of water through them. A material that does not permit water to flow through it is considered **impermeable**, no matter how porous it may be. Materials with high permeability include sand, gravel, and

21-6 Sandstone (left) is porous and permeable to water, while shale (right) is porous but has low permeability.

sandstone. These materials have particles with many relatively large, connected spaces between them. Some types of limestone are also permeable to water because they contain many small joints. On the other hand, undisturbed clay, shale, and most igneous and metamorphic rocks are nearly impermeable. Some of these rocks can have relatively high porosity, but the spaces between particles and joints are so small that water becomes trapped and cannot move through them.

Because impermeable rock strata do not allow water to pass through them easily, they may disrupt the natural flow of groundwater. In some places, a thin stratum of impermeable rock is located above the water table. Since surface water cannot seep downward through the rock to the main reservoir of groundwater, it collects above the rock. The surface of this collected water is called a **perched water table**. Many hillside springs result from perched water tables that intersect the surface.

In many locations, a permeable layer of sandstone was deposited between layers of shale, and then the whole sedimentary unit was tipped at an angle. If erosion has cut across these layers, exposing them on a hillside, the sandstone can become a conduit for surface water to enter the ground as it flows downhill through the sandstone. If a well located farther down the hill extends through the impermeable rock into the water-filled stratum, the water may have enough pressure to spurt up through the well. This kind of unassisted water flow is an **artesian well**, named after the French province of Artois (formerly called Artesium), where Roman soldiers first observed such wells. Artesian wells were an important source of water throughout much of the United States in the early days of its history. However, depletion of water in the permeable stratum has made pumping necessary in many of the wells.

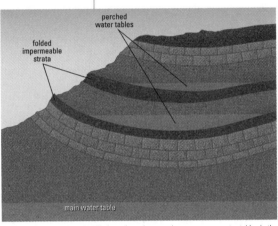

perched water tables

folded impermeable strata

main water table

21-7 This cross section of a hill shows how there can be two or more water tables in the same area.

artesian (ar TEE zhun)

elevation of water source

21-8 An artesian well is one in which the water rises above the water table under its own pressure.

An aquifer does not always consist of rigid rock. In many instances, aquifers are strata of gravel or sand. When fully charged, these aquifers have relatively large spaces between their particles because of the hydraulic pressure exerted by the water. When excessive groundwater is removed from the aquifer, the sediments and ground compact to eliminate the empty spaces that formerly held water. The resulting lowering of the ground surface above is called *subsidence*.

FACETS OF HYDROLOGY

DEPLETED AQUIFERS

Shlump! It swallowed a tree. *Rhomp! Shlussh!* Now it just swallowed two cars! No, it is not the monster that devoured Miami. It is a sinkhole opening at the surface. Sinkholes are underground cavities, dissolved in the rock by groundwater, which open at the surface. The accelerated occurrence of sinkholes is just one sign of a lowering water table in Florida.

The level of the water table across the United States varies, depending on how much it rains or snows and how much water is removed by humans. In times of drought or great demand for water, the depth of the water table can be lowered too much, with disastrous consequences.

One such consequence is the collapse of underground caverns, resulting in sinkholes. Such collapses are more common when the water table is low because the water that normally supports the rock ceilings no longer does so. Without the extra support, weakened cavern ceilings cave in.

Increased occurrence of sinkholes is not the only problem caused by lowering water tables, and Florida is not the only state where lowering water tables are a problem. In coastal regions, if the groundwater is pumped out, salt water will *infiltrate* from the ocean and make the well water undrinkable. In desert areas such as Arizona, huge cracks appear in the ground where the groundwater is depleted. As the water table is lowered, the ground sinks, but it does not sink uniformly. This sinking is called *subsidence*. Some of the cracks are hundreds of feet long and may extend hundreds of feet down to the water table.

These problems cannot be completely avoided since we cannot control droughts. However, we can control our use of groundwater and reduce the demand on the water table. In the United States, farm irrigation uses three to four times as much groundwater as public water systems use in all the cities together. One method of irrigation that has reduced water use by up to 50 percent is "drip irrigation." With drip irrigation, pipes supply water directly to the plant roots and thus eliminate much waste from water going where it is not really

Sinkholes like this one in Florida create serious problems for property owners and human activities.

needed. However, the cost of installing such an irrigation system is often prohibitively expensive. Another approach to conserving water is legislation. Laws regulating water use for irrigation or for residential use are already in effect in many cities and states.

21.5 Movement of Groundwater

Groundwater tends to move downhill under the influence of gravity, but it moves more slowly than surface water does. Its flow rate varies from 100 m per day to as little as 0.5 m in ten years. Usually subsurface water moves in the same direction as surface water, although the direction of groundwater flow is controlled mostly by the orientation of the rock strata underground. Groundwater moving

21-9 Groundwater eventually ends up in lakes or oceans.

Facet Summary: Depleted Aquifers

This Facet discusses some of the consequences of depleted aquifers—sinkholes, infiltration of salt water, and subsidence. There are no vocabulary terms in this Facet.

downhill may come out of the ground as a spring, enter a surface stream or lake, or join an underground stream. Some regions contain several underground streams at different levels. Eventually these streams feed into lakes, surface streams, or the ocean.

Groundwater moves sideways as well as downward. Therefore, pumping water from one place can affect the water table immediately around the well and also farther away. A well that is over-pumped can cause a **cone of depression**, a cone-shaped lowering of the water table that is deepest at the well. If the water table falls too much, nearby wells that were previously dependable may become dry. A cone of depression also may change the direction of groundwater flow nearby. The groundwater in that area will tend to flow toward the lowest part of the depression, even if it used to flow in the opposite direction. This can be a problem if the well is near the sea or a source of contamination. The contaminated water that previously flowed away from the well site may now flow toward it and pollute it.

One of the factors that determines the likelihood of a cone of depression forming at a well pipe is the permeability of the ground or rock at the well. For homes with wells, one of the tests that must often be passed before a homeowner can sell his house is a satisfactory well "perc" (percolation) test. This test determines how fast the well can supply water by pumping it down until it runs dry and then measuring the time it takes to recover, or, if it cannot be pumped dry, ensuring that it can supply water at a certain rate for a specified period of time. Low perc rates or heavy consumption result in large and deep cones of depression. High perc rates and low consumption result in small and shallow cones.

21-10 The well on the right has deprived the homeowner on the left of well water.

The groundwater is recharged when rainwater seeps through to the water table or when water from a stream or lake seeps into the ground. A **recharge zone** is an area that resupplies groundwater. Such zones are often important for the water supply in cities many miles away. Recharge zones and aquifers also contribute to water purity by providing a place for beneficial bacteria to break down wastes and toxins. In some places where natural recharge cannot keep pace with the demand, state and municipal governments use artificial means to recharge the groundwater. Treated wastewater that meets drinking water standards is pumped back into depleted aquifers. In the U.S., there are between 1700 and 2000 aquifer recharge wells in 11 states.

 Visual 21-6: Natural Recharge of Groundwater

This visual is a reproduction of Figure 21-11. Note that creeks, small streams, and standing ponds usually are supplied by the local groundwater sources and often represent the intersection of the water table with the land surface. On the other hand, large flowing streams and lakes often recharge local groundwater supplies.

21-11 Recharge of groundwater

Objectives—Section 21B

Upon completing this section, students should be able to

- differentiate between hard and soft water.
- list two problems associated with hard water.
- describe methods for softening hard water.

The water molecule makes a particularly good solvent because of its structure and the nature of its chemical bonds. The molecule is "bent" (see the diagram below). In addition, the covalent bonds between the oxygen and hydrogens are highly polar, due to the strongly electronegative oxygen. The result is a molecule that has a strongly polar character, which is effective in dissolving both ionic substances, such as salts, and polar covalent substances.

21A Section Review

1. What percentage of the earth's water is fresh water?
2. What percentage of the earth's fresh water is groundwater? What percentage is this of the earth's entire water resources?
3. What is the continual movement of water between land, sea, air, and back to land called? What would happen if this movement of water did not take place?
4. What is an intersection of the water table with the earth's surface from which water flows more or less continuously called?
5. What property of a material indicates how easily water can flow through it? What factors contribute to this property?
6. List three natural materials noted for their high permeability.
7. When two water tables are separated by a horizontal impermeable stratum of rock, what name is given to the upper water table?
8. What name is given to a well in which the water discharges from the well pipe under its own pressure? What must be true about the level of the water table supplying the well compared to the top of such a well?
9. What water sources normally recharge groundwater? How can humans replenish depleted aquifers?
10. What particular problem may occur in coastal regions if wells pump water out faster than the ground can recharge the water?
11. (True or False) Porous rock is permeable rock.

21B GROUNDWATER'S DISSOLVING POWER

21.6 Water—The Universal Solvent

You have probably dissolved sugar or salt in water. Water is known as the "universal solvent" because of its ability to dissolve so many different kinds of substances. A **solvent** is a substance that dissolves something else. When a substance dissolves in a solvent, its particles are separated by the action of the solvent, and they become thoroughly mixed with the solvent's particles. There are two properties of water that make it such a good solvent. One is the shape of the H_2O molecule; the other is that groundwater tends to be acidic, which allows it to dissolve various rocks and minerals, especially limestone.

21.7 Dissolved Minerals

Although it may look like pure water, groundwater always contains various dissolved minerals. In fact, truly pure water is rare anywhere on the earth. Even rainwater contains dissolved gases, smoke, and dust particles. Water that remains in the ground dissolves minerals as it passes through soil and rock. Dissolved minerals are usually harmless. In fact, many resort areas, called mineral spas, advertise that their mineral waters are especially healthful.

Water with high levels of dissolved minerals is called *hard water*. Hard water contains a high concentration of dissolved calcium or magnesium compounds and ions of other metals, such as

Answers to 21A Section Review Questions

1. Slightly less than 3% (2.8%) of the earth's water is fresh. (§21.1)

2. Groundwater is 22% of the earth's fresh water. This is about 0.62% of the total water resources. (§21.1)

3. The continual movement of water between land, sea, air, and back to land is called the *hydrologic* (or *water*) *cycle*. Without the water cycle, eventually almost all of the world's fresh water would end up in the oceans and living things on land would die. (The only sources of fresh water would be volcanoes and hydrothermal water from within the earth.) (§21.2)

4. An intersection of the water table with the earth's surface from which water flows is called a *spring*. (§21.3)

5. The property of a material that determines how easily water flows through it is its *permeability*. A permeable material must have interconnected openings that are large enough not to impede the flow of water through it. (§21.4)

6. *Sand*, *gravel*, and *sandstone* all have high permeability. Other answers are possible. (§21.4)

7. The upper water table is called a *perched water table*. (§21.4)

8. A well in which the water discharges under its own pressure is an *artesian well*. The water table supplying an artesian well must be higher than the wellhead. (§21.4)

9. Groundwater is recharged by rain, stream, and lake water that seeps into the ground. Depleted aquifers can be artificially replenished by pumping fresh water or treated wastewater into recharge wells. (§21.5)

10. If groundwater in coastal regions is pumped out too rapidly, the cone of depression may allow salt water from the ocean to flow down into the wells and make the wells unusable. (§21.5)

11. False (not always true). Some rock is very porous, but the pores are either so small that water cannot move through the rock by capillary action or the pores are not interconnected. (§21.4)

iron. Lathering soap in such water is difficult because a chemical reaction binds up the soap's molecules, blocking their dissolving action. A sticky scum forms instead of lather. This scum is what causes bathtub rings. It can also collect on clothing that is washed with soap or detergent. High concentrations of iron can stain fabric and sinks or toilets a yellow-brown color.

If the calcium and magnesium compounds are bicarbonates, boiling can reduce the hardness of the water. Heat changes the dissolved bicarbonates to insoluble carbonates that precipitate and settle to the bottom of the container. In places that have this kind of water, carbonate deposits may form in teakettles and in hot-water pipes. If carbonate deposition continues long enough, the buildup can clog pipes and damage valves.

Soft water, on the other hand, is naturally low in calcium and magnesium compounds. Any process that removes these undesirable minerals from hard water is called water softening. As we just mentioned, heating water containing certain compounds can unintentionally soften water, often with undesirable effects. Hard water that contains compounds such as chlorides and sulfates, rather than bicarbonates, does not soften with heat. However, borax or washing soda can be mixed with this kind of hard water to remove the minerals.

Water demineralizers or ion-exchange columns are plumbing devices (water filters) that can soften water without adding anything to it. These fixtures consist of cylinders containing millions of tiny resin beads on which are bonded ions that attract metal and compound ions in water. Such ion exchangers have long been available for home use and are capable of improving the taste of drinking water and removing minerals that stain clothing and porcelain plumbing fixtures.

21-12 Carbonate deposits from hard water can clog plumbing pipes. Water flow through such pipes would be severely restricted.

21-13 Demineralizers are used to soften or remove mineral impurities from water in many industrial facilities (above) as well as in homes.

21B Section Review

1. What characteristics make groundwater such a good solvent?
2. What dissolved elements does hard water usually contain? What kinds of compounds are often present in hard water?
3. List three ways of softening hard water.
4. (True or False) Distilled water is pure water.

Answers to 21B Section Review Questions

1. Groundwater is a good solvent because of the shape of the water molecule and because it forms acidic solutions when exposed to air or soil. (§21.6)

2. Hard water usually contains the dissolved elements *calcium* and *magnesium*. Hard water often contains *bicarbonates*, *chlorides*, and *sulfates*. (§21.7)

3. Water can be softened by *boiling* (if bicarbonates are present), by *demineralizing*, or by *adding chemicals* such as borax or washing soda. (§21.7)

4. False. Chemically pure water would contain only H_2O molecules and nothing else. However, the normal distillation process mixes air molecules in with the water as the water condenses. Water also picks up minute quantities of atoms or molecules from the piping and containers in which it is distilled or demineralized. Finally, the distillation process can carry over some of the impurities of the original water. Highly purified water can be produced by distillation, reverse osmosis, and demineralization, but the water is not completely pure. (§21.7, 19.19)

- discuss the uniformitarian and creationary models for the origin of solution caves.

- name and describe several common speleothems.

- explain speleothem formation as a result of the precipitation of dissolved minerals.

- distinguish between a spelunker and a speleologist.

- state where karst topography may form and the processes that produce this distinctive landscape.

- describe some distinguishing features of karst topography.

21-14 After the Flood, people used their creative talents to depict important events in their lives by painting beautiful illustrations on the walls of caves.

21-15 Some rock caves have average temperatures below freezing. Groundwater freezes into beautiful crystalline shapes such as those shown here.

A cavern is a large cave.

21C GROUNDWATER EROSION

21.8 Caves and Their Origins

Throughout recorded history, humans have had a close association with the accessible natural underground chambers called **caves**. Archeological research has shown that caves were used as tombs, shelter from bad weather, protection from wild beasts and enemies, prisons, and perhaps long-term dwellings. The Bible documents all of these uses for caves. The existence of cave paintings indicates that they served as protected canvasses for human creative talents as well.

But what natural processes formed caves? First, we need to distinguish between different kinds of caves. Some caves formed when great slabs of rock were torn apart by a combination of weathering and gravity, especially in desert areas, leaving spaces between the tilted slabs large enough for humans to enter. Other caves were formed by the erosive action of winds and surface waters, such as rivers and the ocean, against the faces of cliffs. Empty lava tubes can become caves if they open at the surface of a lava field. Glacier caves, or ice caves, form when flowing meltwater enlarges cracks and joints in glacier ice.

The largest and most spectacular caves are underground and seem to have been formed by the erosion of great underground streams flowing through soluble rocks such as limestone, dolomite, halite (rock salt), and rock gypsum. Because of their beauty and size, it is these *solution caves* that we will discuss in this section. See Table 21-1 for a list of some famous caves of the world.

Geologists do not agree about how solution caves formed. It is well known that rainwater absorbs atmospheric carbon dioxide as it falls to earth, forming weak solutions of carbonic acid. Once in the ground, it can dissolve compounds from organic substances that increase its acidity. As the water percolates downward into the joints of limestone bedrock, the water can quickly begin dissolving the rock, especially if the temperature is well above freezing.

Evolutionary geologists believe that the majority of solution caves were formed through tens of thousands of years by groundwater. They believe streams of water flowed at or below the water table under the influence of gravity toward a base level, just as surface rivers do. They note that the caves often follow the general direction of joint patterns in the rock, which they believe controlled the direction of flow through the rock. In the evolutionary model, the weakly acidic groundwater flow dissolved narrow channels along the joints, which then widened to become great underwater river streams. Later, as tectonic forces uplifted the land, the groundwater level dropped, leaving the empty passages and *caverns* that we call caves today.

21-16 Groundwater deposits calcium carbonate in interesting formations after the caverns are eroded.

Research has uncovered some difficulties with this model of cave formation. First, the acidity of the surface water disappears in the first 4–10 meters of travel downward into the rock, so its power to dissolve rocks beyond that depth is negligible. Acidified surface waters trickling downward into the rocks could not have eroded the extremely large cave systems hundreds of meters underground. Second, *speleologists* (scientists who study caves) agree that for cave formation to occur, an underground stream with an outlet from the rock had to exist beforehand. Groundwater percolating under the influence of gravity has insufficient flow (or time) to accomplish the erosion observed in solution caves today.

Most creationary geologists link solution-cave formation to the Flood. We have discussed in earlier chapters that the great beds of

speleologist (spee lee AHL eh jist): speleo-
(Gk. *spelaion*—cave) + -logist

21-1		NOTABLE CAVES OF THE WORLD	
Name	**Location**	**Interesting facts**
Altamira	Spain	ceiling paintings discovered in 1879 by a five-year-old girl; called "the Sistine Chapel of Paleolithic art"
Blue Grotto	Italy	sea cave that seems to be lit from underwater, making it beautifully blue
Carlsbad Caverns	New Mexico	largest cave chamber in the U.S., the Big Room, could hold an aircraft carrier; Indian wall paintings
Craters of the Moon	Idaho	caves called lava tubes formed during volcanic activity
Dead Sea Caves	Israel	desert caves near the Dead Sea where ancient scrolls were found; manuscripts included portions of all Old Testament books except Esther, as well as many other documents
Eisreisenwelt Cave	Austria	world's largest ice cave
Grotto de Lascaux	France	cave paintings discovered in 1940; famous *Hall of Bulls*
Lava Beds National Monument	California	world's largest collection of volcanic caves
Luray Caverns	Virginia	many spectacular formations; a stalacpipe organ creates musical notes by striking hollow stalactites
Mammoth Cave	Kentucky	most extensive known cave in the world, 579 km (360 mi) of passages and rooms
Ox Bel Ha	Mexico	most extensive known underwater cave, 122 km (76 mi)
Perpetual Ice Cave	New Mexico	altitude and insulating effects of lava cave walls maintain blue-green ice formations year round
Pinnacles National Monument	California	unusual talus caves formed when lava rocks fell from the canyon pinnacles and wedged in the narrow canyon, leaving spaces between and beneath each other
Sarawak Chamber	Borneo	world's largest known cave chamber—600 m×400 m×100 m
Voronya	Abkhazia, Georgia	deepest known cave in the world at 1710 m
Waitomo Cave	New Zealand	glowworms cling to the ceiling, giving the appearance of stars in a night sky
Wind Cave National Park	South Dakota	winds flow in and out of the cave as the air pressure changes; cave walls are covered by unique boxwork speleothems and look like stone honeycomb

Additional Resources

The following two scientific papers elaborate on the cave formation model discussed in this section:

Emil Silvestru, PhD, "A Hydrothermal Model of Rapid Post-Flood Karsting" (Paper presented at the Fifth International Conference on Creationism, Pittsburgh, PA, 2003).

Emil Silvestru, PhD, "The Significance of Caves in the Post-Flood History of Mankind" (Paper presented at the Fifth International Conference on Creationism, Pittsburgh, PA, 2003).

Both of these papers may be obtained by ordering the 2003 ICC CD-ROM from Creation Science Fellowship, Inc., Pittsburgh, PA.

This table is provided for interest only. It is not necessary for students to memorize this information.

Visual 21-7: A Creationary Model of Solution Cave Formation

This visual is a reproduction of Figure 21-17. The source of the hot, acidic hydrothermal solutions is postulated to be floodwaters trapped in deeper sediments and heated by the intense tectonic activity associated with the Flood. Thick layers of carbonate rocks could have precipitated from carbon-dioxide-saturated waters.

21-17 Some creationary scientists believe that most of the solution caves that exist today were formed by acidic hydrothermal water from deep in the earth during or shortly after the Flood.

Stones of Witness

God is a merciful God who often uses even His judgment to produce things of marvelous—and even delicate—beauty. As beings called to declare God's glory through the work of dominion (Gen. 1:28; Rom. 11:36), we should seek to maximize the usefulness of God's world in aesthetically pleasing ways. If we bear the image of the One who makes even His acts of judgment marvelous in their beauty, then certainly we should endeavor to lead not just lives that are useful but also lives that create beauty.

Stones of Witness

Some of the most spectacular caves in our planet may have been formed through God's judgment in the Flood. What does this possibility suggest about God? What does it suggest about the way we should keep the Creation Mandate?

speleothem (SPEE lee oh *THEM*): speleo- (cave) + -them (Gk. *thema*—deposit)

chemical sedimentary rocks could easily have been precipitated in the floodwaters and then buried during the middle and later stages of the Flood.

Late in the retreat of the floodwaters, surface water was abundant on the continents. The atmosphere was probably fairly warm due to volcanic activity, and carbon dioxide concentration in the atmosphere was likely high for the same reason. Rapid solution-cave formation would have been possible as the acidic water sought every possible path toward a base level (ultimately the sea), seeping through the cracks and joints in the limestone strata.

In another model, some scientists believe that the caves could have formed by the corrosive action of hot, acidic water rising from deeper in the earth *against* the force of gravity. This hydrothermal water was heated by the geothermal gradient or by mineral-making chemical reactions that released heat. The acidity could have developed from dissolving carbon-dioxide gases released deep within the earth by magma or from decomposing organic matter trapped in the sediments. Some hydrothermal waters could have been acidified by the action of bacteria, especially near oil deposits. These waters would have tended to flow together along subterranean joint systems in the rock strata. The high acidity and hot temperatures could have easily dissolved large mazes of caverns and conduits in a short period.

It is likely that the actual origin of solution caves is some combination of erosion by upward-flowing hydrothermal waters followed by downward-flowing surface waters. Rather than taking millions of years, these conditions could have produced large caves in just months or a few years. Today, the dissolving action of the cave streams originating with surface waters continues to enlarge solution caves, but at a greatly reduced rate.

21.9   Cave Formations

Groundwater carrying dissolved limestone works its way through joints in limestone bedrock until it enters an air-filled cave by drips or trickles. When the water drops evaporate, the dissolved carbon dioxide leaves the water and reduces the acidity of the water left behind. Water with lower acidity cannot hold the dissolved limestone in solution, so the calcium carbonate precipitates and is deposited as the mineral calcite within the cave. The rock formed by these deposits of calcite is called **dripstone** or **flowstone**. Cave dripstone and flowstone can make many wonderful and unusual shapes, called **speleothems**.

Most geologists agree that dripstone and flowstone deposits form above the water table. Also, a cave must have a supply of moving air to promote evaporation so that the deposits will form. When these conditions occur, groundwater containing dissolved limestone may form stalactites, stalagmites, and similar structures. As water drips or flows from the ceiling onto the floor of a cave, a chemical reaction may occur at either or both of these places. The calcium bicarbonate that was dissolved in the water precipitates. This compound is chemically the same as the main constituent of limestone (calcite) that was originally dissolved by the groundwater. This deposited material is sometimes called *secondary limestone.*

Speleologists classify speleothems according to their general shape and location. Stalactites, stalagmites, and columns are dripstone deposited from seepage out of the cave ceiling. **Stalactites** are icicle-like projections that hang downward from the ceiling. Speleologists believe that stalactites start as *soda straws,* fine tubular structures in which calcite precipitation leaves the centers hollow, and eventually fill in to form standard stalactites. **Stalagmites** are similar to stalactites but project upward from the floor of the cave. They tend to be more rounded and often include a splash cup at their tip. In some places, a stalactite meets a stalagmite and forms a **column,** which can thicken to several meters in circumference.

Flowstone creates speleothems from thin films of water flowing from the ceiling over the sides and floors of the caves. Thin sheets of flowstone hanging from the ceiling or inclined walls are called **curtains;** arched, disk-shaped flowstones are called **shields.** Other forms of flowstone include **bacon** (striped ribbons of flowstone) and **shelves** (flat deposits of calcite that grew out from rock supports at the surface of standing water sometime in the past). Dripstone and flowstone produce many other unusual shapes that have special names assigned by speleologists.

Most speleothems consist of mainly calcium carbonate. Pure calcium carbonate is white, but impurities give it different colors. For example, iron oxide produces the reddish brown color that many cave formations have. Yellows may come from dissolved organic matter from the land surface above the cave. Green colors could come from copper compounds. The bizarre shapes and varied colors of the formations produce a picturesque underground spectacle.

21.10 Rapid Speleothems

Although evolutionary geologists have said that the formation of stalactites and stalagmites is evidence that the earth is very old, creationary geologists have demonstrated that these speleothems can form rapidly. In caves that have dried up, the growth rate of these structures is slow. However, stalactites and stalagmites grow rapidly in moist, active caves. For example, in Sequoyah Caverns, Alabama, stalactites were measured over a ten-year period to grow an inch a year. The carcasses of bats are sometimes found encased in stalagmite calcite at Carlsbad Caverns. If the stalagmite's rate of formation had not been fast, the bats would have decayed before becoming fossilized. In one dramatic example, a curtain of stalactites formed from the ceiling of the foundation underneath the Lincoln Memorial in Washington, DC. A photograph taken in 1968 showed the stalactites had grown 1.5 meters in the 45 years since it was built in 1923.

stalactite (stuh LAK TYT): (Gk. *stalaktos*—a dripping)

stalagmite (stuh LAG MYT): (Gk. *stalagma*—a dropping)

One way to remember the difference between these similar sounding names is the following:
Stalactites and ceiling both have the letter *c;*
Stalagmites and ground both have the letter *g.*

21-18 Stalactites, stalagmites, curtains, shields, and columns are visible in these photographs of Lehman Cave in the Great Basin National Park in Nevada (left) and Mercer Caverns, California (right).

21-19 The otherworldly appearance of solution-cave formations can be clearly seen in these photographs of Carlsbad Caverns, New Mexico (top), and Luray Caverns, Virginia (bottom).

Visual 21-8: Common Speleothems

Point out the dripstone formations (stalactite, stalagmite, and column) and the flowstone formations (shield and curtain).

Visual 21-9: Unusual Speleothems

In addition to the speleothems mentioned in the text and shown in this visual, speleologists recognize the following formations:

aragonite	moonmilk
balloons	mud stalagmites
bathtubs	pearls
bell canopies	pool fingers
blisters	pool spar
bottlebrushes	popcorn
boxwork	raft cones
conulites	rafts
coralloids	rims
deflected stalagmites	rimstone
fibrous forms	showerheads
folia	spar
gypsum flowers	splattermites
halite flowers	stegamites
helictites	trays
mammillaries	

Web Resource

For photos of these and other speleothems, visit the BJU Press Online Resources/*SPACE AND EARTH SCIENCE* webpage. Under Chapter 21, click on the *Speleothems* link.

FACETS OF HYDROLOGY

SPELUNKING

The hope of discovering vast underground caverns and rock formations of breathtaking beauty lures many spelunkers to caves. Others simply enjoy the challenge of pushing into a world of darkness and silence unlike any other place on earth. The spelunker feels alone and hidden from the world above, which can provide an opportunity for personal reflection without outside distractions. Spelunkers are virtually mountaineers in reverse. They carry much of the same equipment, they require many of the same skills, and they face a few of the same dangers. However, other aspects of spelunking are unique. One of the most obvious differences is that spelunkers must be prepared to get dirty. They may crawl around on their hands and knees in sticky mud as well as slime from bacterial deposits. The basic equipment of a spelunker is as follows:

Lights—Take at least three sources of light with spare bulbs and batteries. You should be able to do the entire trip with any one of these lights.

Helmet—Wear a helmet equipped with a chin strap and mounted with the primary light source.

Footwear—Wear substantial boots that will protect your feet over rough cave floors and help keep your feet warm. Consider wearing waterproof footgear if you anticipate wet conditions.

Clothing—Dress in insulating layers such as synthetic fleece. An outer layer such as a one-piece coverall can provide extra warmth and protection. Note that the clothes you wear on a cave trip may become soiled and torn, making them unsuitable for further normal use.

Gloves—Wear gloves to protect your hands and keep them warm. Even cheap leather work gloves will make your trip more comfortable than no gloves.

First-Aid Kit—Each person should carry a personal kit. On short trips, leave a larger kit near the cave entrance; on longer trips, carry the kit with you.

Food—Carry enough high-energy food to sustain you throughout the trip. Bring some extra food in case

the trip is longer than expected. Fragile foods (bananas, sandwiches) may get crushed during a rough caving trip, but solid foods (bagels, energy bars) usually remain intact.

Other Equipment—Carry your gear in a durable pack such as an inexpensive military surplus pack. Protect drinks and other sensitive items in hard-shell containers. Carry a large trash bag in your pack; it can be used for emergency warmth or for carrying dirty cave clothes home. Some spelunkers carry a compass and a cave map (if one is available) to help them navigate in complex caves.

If you want to be a successful spelunker, you must follow some common-sense procedures. First, you should become accustomed to cave terrains by visiting caves that offer guided tours and lighted paths. In addition to getting some experience in underground terrain, you can confirm whether you really want to become a spelunker! Next, you can join a local club of experienced spelunkers, located through either a local museum or the National Speleological Society. If there isn't a club in your area, maybe you can start one.

Follow the basic rules of spelunking:

1. Inform someone on the surface where you are going and your expected time of return. Write it down so they won't forget or think you said something else. It may save your life.

2. Go in a group so that someone can help you if you have any difficulties. Never go alone.

3. Turn back immediately if you suddenly become fatigued. It may be an indication that there is an oxygen deficiency in the cave's air, or it may be your body's way of warning you that you have overexerted yourself.

4. Don't panic if you get lost; stay where you are in a safe place and wait patiently until help arrives.

Facet Summary: Spelunking

This Facet outlines the basic equipment needed to explore caves and provides safety procedures and general guidelines for this interesting activity. There are no vocabulary terms in this Facet.

As you become experienced in simple caves, you can enter more difficult caves that require rappelling down deep holes, crossing "bottomless pits" with ladders, wading through underground streams, or inching on your belly through narrow cracks. You might even have to take up snorkeling or scuba diving to get through underwater passageways. Some people buy special gear and devote their lives to speleology—the study of caves. They are called speleologists.

No matter how enthusiastic you become, as a spelunker you must show proper respect for others.

- Ask permission before you go spelunking on private land.

- Make sure you leave the cave exactly as it was before you entered, or better, so that future spelunkers can enjoy it too.

- Take out everything, including all the materials and equipment that you bring in. Don't leave empty cans or food wrappers.

- Leave all rock formations and cave-dwelling creatures undisturbed. Do not even touch speleothems (cave rock formations) when it can be avoided. The oil from your skin destroys their beauty.

- Do not make markings (such as your initials) on the walls.

- Do not take souvenirs. Take a camera and record your unique and rewarding experiences.

The National Speleological Society provides all of these guidelines and much more information about this fascinating sport in a pamphlet that is available on their website.

Scientists at Bob Jones University, using simulated cave conditions, have studied the growth of stalactites in the laboratory. In one experiment, they installed a 50 cm (20 in.) stalactite having a mass of about 1.8 kg (4 lb) in an apparatus that supplied a solution of calcium carbonate and water that flowed over it. The stalactite added 35 g (1.2 oz) of calcite in eighty days. This rate of deposition corresponds

21-20 Experimental apparatus used for stalactite research at Bob Jones University (left). Carbon dioxide was supplied by a gas cylinder. Stalactites begin as "soda straws" (middle) and keep growing (right).

to an increase of 0.45 kg (1 lb) every three years. At this rate, the entire original stalactite could have formed in only twelve years. At the same time, 17.5 g (0.6 oz) of stalagmite accumulated beneath the stalactite.

21.11 Spelunking

Caves and their concealed formations are tempting tourist attractions. A person who explores caves for recreation is a **spelunker**.

spelunker (spee LUNG kur): spelunk- (L. *spelunca*—cave or grotto) + -er

In the middle photo in Figure 21-20, the apparatus was turned on its side so that the soda straws could be examined.

The term *caver* is more popular outside the United States.

Because *spelunking* is a hazardous pastime, only people who thoroughly know what they are doing and have all the necessary equipment should engage in it. Exploration of some caves requires elaborate ropes, scuba-diving gear, bottled oxygen, and other special equipment. Spelunkers may be faced with a flooding cave stream, suffocation, a rock fall, a loss of sense of direction, or a dangerously steep slope. Beginners should enter only those caves that are open to the public.

21C-1 Section Review

1. What factors following the Flood could have contributed to the formation of extensive cave systems underground?
2. What is the scientific name for limestone caves in general?
3. What is the name of the type of rock that makes up cave formations? What is the scientific name for these formations?
4. What are the icicle-like projections that hang from a cave ceiling called?
5. Name the structure that is formed when a stalactite and a stalagmite join together.
6. Discuss the relative level of the water table during the formation of caves and of speleothems.
7. Do geologists today generally agree that speleothems require tens of thousands or millions of years to form? Explain.
8. What is a scientist who studies caves called? What is a recreational cave explorer called?
9. What precautions should a spelunker take that would help if he were to become lost or injured?
10. (True or False) Caves can form in limestone, sandstone, ice, and lava.

21-21 Karst topography includes some or all of these features.

21.12 Karst Topography

In many regions of the world where thick strata of nonclastic, chemical sedimentary rocks underlie the earth's surface, the chemical erosion of these rocks can produce a distinctive landscape called **karst topography**. The name comes from the Karst Plateau in Slovenia, where this type of landscape is strikingly evident. Karst topography is the heavily eroded and hilly terrain that is associated with features such as solution caves, sinkholes, and natural bridges. Florida, Indiana, Kentucky, Tennessee, and Virginia have areas with notable karst topography. China has regions of heavily eroded but picturesque terrain resulting from karst processes.

21.13 Karst Features

Some of the most distinctive features of karst topography are **sinkholes**. A sinkhole develops when a section of a solution-cave ceiling becomes so thin that it can no longer support its own weight and collapses. On the land surface above the collapse, a bowl-shaped

Answers to 21C-1 Section Review Questions

1. Factors that could have contributed to the formation of caves include the existence of thick limestone strata, high atmospheric carbon dioxide concentrations, warm temperatures, and a lot of water flowing off the land to the sea. (§21.8)

2. The scientific name for limestone caves is *solution caves*. (§21.8)

3. The rock that makes up cave formations is called *dripstone* or *flowstone*. (You may accept *calcium carbonate* as an answer, but that is the mineral, not the rock type.) The cave formations are called *speleothems*. (§21.9)

4. The icicle-like projections that hang from a cave ceiling are called *stalactites*. (§21.9)

5. When a stalactite and a stalagmite join together, they form a *column*. (§21.9)

6. Geologists believe that caves were eroded just below the water table by flowing groundwater. Most speleothems were formed above the water table. (§21.9)

7. No. Geologists realize that there are many examples of calcite deposition in recent man-made caves and structures, clearly indicating that large speleothems can form in just hundreds, or at most a few thousands, of years. (§21.10)

8. A scientist who studies caves is a *speleologist*. Recreational cave explorers are called *spelunkers* (or *cavers*). (§21.8)

9. The spelunker should tell people where he is going and when he will return. In no case

should a spelunker explore caves alone. When a spelunker realizes he is lost, he should avoid panic and stay in one place while waiting for help to arrive. (Facet, p. 548.)

10. True. (§21.8)

depression appears. These may be small or quite large. Periodically the news media will report that a homeowner, often in Florida, woke up one morning and found a large sinkhole in his yard. He may not even have known that he had a cave under his property. Unfortunately, because the hole is often above a larger cave, it may keep growing, and there is no way for the homeowner to fill it in. Sinkholes have destroyed vehicles and buildings. In many places, sinkholes fill with water to form *sinkhole ponds*. Interestingly, the Arecibo radio telescope antenna in Puerto Rico was built into a huge sinkhole (see p. 60 for a picture of this telescope).

Karst topography generally includes a network of interconnected caverns, sinkholes, and cave openings. The irregular topography associated with karst formations results from the collapse of multiple levels of solution caves. In extreme instances, the countryside is littered with tall towerlike hills that are isolated eroded remnants of the original limestone strata. Such terrain is called *tower karst topography*.

When most of a tunnel-like cave's ceiling collapses, except for a short section, a **natural bridge** forms. One famous natural bridge in the Eastern U.S. is found in the Natural Bridge State Park in the Southern Shenandoah Valley of Virginia. This bridge is 66 m (215 ft) tall and spans a 27 m (90 ft) gap.

Karst topography often contains **disappearing streams**. Seepage from a surface stream can erode a joint in the underlying rock. If the downward trickle opens into a cave ceiling, the water flow can erode a wider passage. Eventually, the stream follows the hole down into the cave and disappears from the surface at that spot. The bed that the stream abandoned is a **streamless valley**. In the reverse case, cave streams can erode a hole in the side of a cave that opens in a hillside, forming an **appearing stream**.

21-22   A sinkhole (left) and a sinkhole pond (right) are surface features of karst regions.

21-23   Tower karst topography near the Lijiang River in China

21-24   Natural Bridge near Lexington, Virginia

21C-2 Section Review

1. Bedrock consisting of soluble rock can often produce distinctive landscapes as the result of the dissolving action of water. What is the general name for this kind of landscape?

2. What is a bowl-shaped depression due to a collapsed cave ceiling called?

3. What name is given to a stone span that remains after the cave ceiling on both sides of it has collapsed?

4. What may happen to the terrain containing karst formations with the collapse of multiple levels of solution caves and passages?

5. (True or False) In karst topography, it is possible for an appearing stream to become a disappearing stream a short distance later.

Geologists have noted that natural bridges and tunnels typically occur at the bottom of syncline folds in the limestone/dolomite bedrock, where a solution cave formed more or less perpendicular to the axis of the fold. The bottom (or trough) of the syncline generally contains rock with fewer joints, which makes the rock more durable. The weaker rock on both sides of the syncline trough contained more joints and fissures, so the cave ceiling collapsed while the bridge remained standing.

 Visual 21-10: Karst Topography

Use this visual to review the features of karst topography.

Answers to 21C-2 Section Review Questions

1. The general name for landscapes produced by the dissolving action of water on soluble bedrock is called *karst topography*. (§21.12)

2. A depression on the ground surface caused by a collapsed cave ceiling is called a *sinkhole*. (§21.13)

3. A stone span that remains after the adjoining cave ceilings have collapsed is called a *natural bridge*. (§21.13)

4. Karst terrain may become irregular and even contain steep-sided, towerlike hills. (§21.13)

5. True. This is especially true where there are multiple levels of solution caves in a given area. (§21.13)

In Terms of Hydrology

Chapter Summary

- Groundwater constitutes 22% of the earth's fresh water inventory. Nearly 99% of the earth's liquid fresh water is groundwater.

- The hydrologic cycle is the process by which water falls as precipitation, flows by streams and groundwater into the oceans, evaporates, and falls again as precipitation.

- Groundwater in the hydrologic cycle percolates downward through permeable soil and rock until it fills up all available spaces between particles. The upper surface of this zone of saturation is called the water table.

- Groundwater flows mainly under the influence of gravity, just as surface water does. The permeabilities of different rock strata, the way they are folded, and the way they intersect the land surface all influence the formation of springs, perched water tables, and artesian wells.

- Drawing water from a well faster than the water is replenished causes a cone of depression.

- Water can be returned to the ground through the recharge zone or by seeping through the zone of aeration into the water table.

- Water that contains dissolved calcium, magnesium, iron, or mineral compounds is considered "hard." Water lacking these minerals is considered "soft." Hard water can clog pipes with mineral deposits and discolor laundry and plumbing fixtures. There are several methods for softening water.

- Caves may form in a variety of ways, but the largest and most spectacular caves seem to have been formed by the dissolving of soluble sedimentary rocks by flowing groundwater.

- Evolutionists believe that during tens of thousands of years, acidified surface water flowing downward through joints in soluble rocks under the influence of gravity eroded large passageways.

- Creationary scientists believe that several other processes may have been involved in cave formation. Cave formation could have occurred over several months during the Flood or at the most a few years immediately following the Flood.

- Speleothems are the various forms of dripstone and flowstone deposited by groundwater entering caves. Creationary scientists have shown that they can form rapidly.

- Karst topography includes not only surface terrain that contains sinkholes, natural bridges, streamless valleys, and disappearing streams, but also the underlying mazes of solution caves and the soluble rock in which all of these features occur.

Answers to Chapter Review Questions
What Did You Learn?

1. Groundwater is the second largest but most easily accessible source of fresh water. (§21.1)

2. If a well is to provide water the entire year, it must be deeper than the dry-season water table. By drilling during the dry season, you know where the dry-season water table is. (§21.3)

3. Artesian wells do not need pumps to bring the water to the surface. (§21.4)

4. Hard water reacts chemically with soaps and detergents. It makes them less active and leaves deposits. Laundry and linen services prefer soft water since less soap or detergent is needed to clean the laundry. (§21.7)

5. You would expect a well in an area with karst topography to produce hard water. Karst topography is usually an indication that limestone or some other soluble mineral is present and has been dissolved by the groundwater. Water that contains calcium and other dissolved minerals is called *hard*. (§21.7, 21.12)

6. The longest (or most extensive) cave system in the world is Mammoth Cave in Kentucky. (§21.8, Table 21-1)

7. Answers will vary. The text discusses that groundwater originating from the surface loses its acidity within 10 m of the surface, making it incapable of dissolving rock many hundreds of meters into the earth. Also, there must be a preexisting outlet for the streams to flow through so that they can erode the caves. Students may also mention that the

What Did You Learn?

1. Why is groundwater an important resource even though it accounts for only 22 percent of the earth's fresh water?

2. Why should you drill water wells during a dry season instead of a wet season?

3. What is the benefit of having an artesian well?

4. Why do laundry and linen services prefer to use soft water rather than hard water?

5. Would you expect a well in an area with karst topography to produce hard or soft water? Why?

6. Name the cave containing the longest surveyed passages in the world.

7. What are two problems with the evolutionary model for solution-cave formation?

8. Of what substance do speleothems mainly consist?

9. Why are stalagmites often found directly under stalactites?

10. What are some dangers commonly faced by spelunkers?

11. Name two features that are associated with karst topography.

True or False

12. The majority of world's liquid fresh water is in lakes, streams, and rivers.

13. Fresh water that does not flow to the sea or is not immediately evaporated back into the atmosphere is lost to the hydrologic cycle.

14. The water table must intersect the land surface in order for a spring to exist.

15. Even so-called impermeable rock can be highly porous.

16. A recharge zone is an area that replenishes groundwater.

17. One of the reasons water is such a good solvent is that pure water is naturally acidic.

18. According to a creationary model of cave formation, only the deepest caves in limestone strata could have survived the Flood.

19. *Speleothem* refers to any type of cave formation consisting of calcite or another mineral deposited by dripping or flowing water.

20. Geologists have proven using carbon-14 dating methods that stalactites required thousands of years to form.

21. The name *karst topography* comes from a plateau in Slovenia that has many caves, sinkholes, natural bridges, and streamless valleys.

What Do You Think?

1. How would life on earth be different if no rocks were permeable?

2. Why would caves have made good shelter for the growing human population shortly after the Flood?

3. When researching an area of karst topography, how could you tell for sure that a disappearing stream in one place is the same one that reappears in another?

4. If you have access to the Internet, find and read recent articles giving evidence that speleothems can form rapidly.

My Review Checklist

☐ I have carefully read the entire chapter.

☐ I have reviewed all of the photographs, illustrations, and graphs.

☐ I have reviewed all of my notes in the margins.

☐ I have reviewed and corrected the quizzes on this chapter.

☐ I have studied all of the vocabulary terms.

☐ I have had all of my questions answered.

---

earth's history is not long enough for cave formation to have taken place according to the conventional theory. (§21.8)

8. Speleothems consist mainly of calcium carbonate (calcite). (§21.9)

9. Stalagmites on the floor are formed from the precipitation of calcite in the water dripping from stalactites on the ceiling. (§21.9)

10. Spelunkers could face sudden flooding of streams, lack of good air, a rockfall, becoming trapped or lost, running out of supplies (especially lamp carbide, water, or flashlight batteries), and falling. (Facet, p. 548)

11. Answers will vary. The text discusses solution caves, sinkholes, sinkhole ponds, disappearing or appearing streams, streamless valleys, natural bridges (or tunnels), and tower karst. (§21.13)

True or False

12. False. Less than half of 1 percent of the earth's liquid fresh water resides in streams and lakes. The vast majority exists in the groundwater reserves and aquifers. (§21.1)

13. False. Groundwater eventually reaches a lake or the ocean or is evaporated, so it is then subject to the hydrologic cycle. (§21.2)

14. True. (§21.3)

15. True. (§21.4)

16. True. (§21.5)

17. False. Pure water is neutral. Groundwater becomes acidic with the absorption of carbon dioxide and organic acids. (§21.6, 21.8)

18. False. Creationary geologists believe that most if not all the great limestone rock strata were laid down during the Flood, so caves in these layers could not have existed before the Flood. Many of these scientists believe the caves formed in the soft rock during and after the recessionary stage of the Flood. (§21.8)

19. True. (§21.9)

20. False. While uniformitarian scientists would agree with the statement, numerous examples exist within historical times that show calcite deposition can proceed very rapidly. Additionally, although not discussed in the text, scientists have discovered many problems with the assumptions used to support radiocarbon dating of speleothems. (§21.10)

21. True. (§21.12)

What Do You Think?

1. The lack of permeable rocks would limit the amount of water that could be stored in the groundwater system. Water would percolate down through the soil horizons to the impermeable bedrock and then flow under the influence of gravity until some obstruction stopped it or it flowed into the sea. Deep aquifers would not exist, so arid regions would have no access to groundwater reserves from distant recharge zones. Groundwater in aquifers is purified by bacterial action. The absence of aquifers or permeable rocks could mean less drinkable water.

2. Caves were ready-made places to live. They were relatively easy to defend against marauding animals (or other humans). Deeper inside, their temperature was fairly constant all year long. There was often a supply of fresh water flowing in the cave somewhere. Many caves were large enough that whole communities could live in them. They were permanent places that could be used as bases of operation for hunting parties or as temporary shelter for nomadic people as they moved from place to place in a circuit during the year.

3. A marker, such as dye or food coloring, could be released in the disappearing stream and observed where it reappears. (Remind students that they should not introduce such substances into streams without proper permissions from landowners and government officials.)

4. Answers will vary.

MEASUREMENT CONVERSION FACTORS

To convert from the given unit to the corresponding required unit, multiply by the conversion factor. To convert to the opposite unit, divide by the conversion factor. A separate table is provided for temperature conversions.

Measurement Conversion Factors

Dimension	Given unit	Unit symbol	Conversion factor	Required unit	Unit symbol
Length	meter	m	1.09	yard	yd
	meter	m	3.28	foot	ft
	centimeter	cm	0.0328	foot	ft
	centimeter	cm	0.394	inch	in.
	millimeter	mm	0.0394	inch	in.
	kilometer	km	0.621	mile	mi
	light-year	ly	9.46×10^{12} (9.46 trillion)	kilometer	km
	light-year	ly	5.88×10^{12} (5.88 trillion)	mile	mi
Area	square meter	m²	1.20	square yard	yd²
	square meter	m²	10.8	square foot	ft²
	square centimeter	cm²	0.00108	square foot	ft²
	square centimeter	cm²	0.155	square inch	in.²
	square millimeter	mm²	0.00155	square inch	in.²
	square kilometer	km²	0.386	square mile	mi²
Mass	gram	g	0.0353	ounce (mass)	oz
	gram	g	0.00221	pound (mass)	lb
	kilogram	kg	2.21	pound (mass)	lb
	ton (metric)	t	1.10	ton (short)	tn or T
Weight (Force)	newton	N	4.45	pound (force)	lb
	newton	N	0.278	ounce (force)	oz
Pressure	newtons/square meter	N/m²	0.000145	pounds/square inch	lb/in.² or psi
	newtons/square meter	N/m²	0.00000987	atmosphere	atm
	pascal	Pa	0.000145	pounds/square inch	lb/in.² or psi
	pascal	Pa	0.00000987	atmosphere	atm
	millibar	mb	0.0145	pounds/square inch	lb/in.² or psi
	millibar	mb	0.000987	atmosphere	atm
	torr	torr	0.0193	pounds/square inch	lb/in.² or psi
	torr	torr	0.00132	atmosphere	atm

Measurement Conversion Factors

Dimension	Given unit	Unit symbol	Conversion factor	Required unit	Unit symbol
Pressure (cont.)	millimeter of Mercury	mm (Hg)	0.0193	pounds/square inch	lb/in.^{2} or psi
	millimeter of Mercury	mm (Hg)	0.00132	atmosphere	atm
	atmosphere	atm	14.7	pounds/square inch	lb/in.^{2} or psi
Volume	cubic meter	m^3	35.5	cubic feet	ft^3
	liter	L	0.00353	cubic foot	ft^3
	liter	L	0.264	gallon	gal
	liter	L	1.06	quart	qt
	milliliter	mL	0.0338	ounce (fluid)	oz
	cubic centimeter	cm^3	0.0338	ounce (fluid)	oz

Temperature Conversion Equations

Dimension	Given unit	Unit symbol	Conversion factor	Required unit	Unit symbol
Temperature	degrees Celsius	°C	$t_F = (1.8 \times t_C) + 32$	degrees Fahrenheit	°F
	degrees Fahrenheit	°F	$t_C = (t_F - 32) \div 1.8$	degrees Celsius	°C
	kelvins	K	$t_C = T - 273.15$	degrees Celsius	°C
	degrees Celsius	°C	$T = t_C + 273.15$	kelvins	K

Appendix B2

SCIENTIFIC ROOTS, PREFIXES, AND SUFFIXES

Scientists must use words with meanings that are agreed on by all scientists. For this reason, most scientific terms are constructed from words that have their origins in the ancient languages of Greek and Latin. In order to help you better understand the patterns of meaning in earth science terminology, this table of common scientific roots, prefixes, and suffixes has been provided.

Scientific Roots, Prefixes, and Suffixes

Word part	Meaning	Examples
ap-, ab-, apo-	away, distant	aphelion, apogee
astr-, aster-	star	astronomy, asteroid
bar-, -bar, baro-	pressure, weight	barometer, isobar
bathy-, batho-	depth	bathyscaph, batholith
chrom-, chromo-	color	chromosphere, chromatic
chron-	time	dendrochronology, geochronology, geosynchronous
circum-	around, circle	circumpolar, circum-Pacific
cosm-, cosmo-	universe	cosmonaut, cosmology, cosmos
-cline	lean, angle	syncline, anticline
cryo-	cold	cryosphere

Word part	Meaning	Examples
epi-	on, outside	epicycle, epicenter
ex-, exo-	outside	exosphere, extrusive, exfoliation
geo-	earth	geocentric, geostrophic, geology
-graph	write, written record	barograph, seismograph
helio-, -helion	sun	heliocentric, heliopause, perihelion
hydro-	water	hydrothermal, hydrosphere
iso-	equal	isobar, isotope
litho-, -lith	rock	lithosphere, laccolith, batholith
-ology, -logy	study of	meteorology, mineralogy
magn-	large, powerful	magnitude
mar-	sea, ocean	mare, marine
meta-, meso-	changed, between, among	metamorphic, Mesozoic
-meter	to measure	spectrometer, anemometer
meteor-	having to do with the sky	meteorology, meteor
micro-	small, tiny	microgravity
-morph, -morphic	shape, form	metamorphism
nebula	cloud, fog, mist	nebula
occ-, occl-	hidden, cut off	occlude, occult
oro-	lift up	orographic, orogeny
-pause	stop, end	tropopause, stratopause
paleo-	old, ancient	paleontology, Paleozoic
ped-, pedo-	soil, ground	pedologist
peri-	around, close to	perigee, perihelion
petro-	rock	petrology, petroleum
photo-	light	photosphere, photons, photovoltaic
seism-, seismo-	earthquake, shake	seismologist, seismic
sol-	sun	solar, solstice
spectr-, spectro-	examine, look at	spectrum, spectrograph
spe-, speleo-	cave	spelunker, speleothem
-sphere	ball, globe	atmosphere, bathysphere
strat-, strati-, strato-	layer	stratus, stratum, stratovolcano, stratosphere
syn-	together, similar	syncline, geosynchronous
terra-, terre-	earth, ground	terrestrial, terrain
thermo-, -thermal	heat, temperature	thermosphere, hydrothermal
top-, topo-	place, position	topographic
trop-, tropo-	respond to, change, turn	tropopause, tropic

ASTRONOMICAL DATA

PHYSICAL AND ORBITAL PROPERTIES OF THE SUN, PLANETS, AND MOON

Property	Sun	Mercury	Venus	Earth
Mean distance from the sun (ua)	NA	0.39	0.72	1.00
Diameter (km) (mi)	1,391,980 864,976	4878 3024	12,104 7504	12,756 7909
Volume, compared to Earth's	1,308,000	0.06	0.85	1.00
Mass, compared to Earth's	332,946	0.055	0.815	1.000
Density (g/cm³)	1.409	5.427	5.204	5.520
Average surface temperature (°C) (Range)	5500	167 (−183 to + 430)	464	15 (−50 to + 50)
Orbital period	NA	87.97 d	225 d	1 y
Average orbital speed (km/s)	NA	47.88	35.0	29.8
Rotational period	25–36 d	58.65 d (1407.6 h)	243 d (5832 h) retrograde	24 h
Number of satellites	Unknown 9 planets	0	0	1 moon
Atmospheric content	91.2% hydrogen 8.7% helium 0.08% oxygen trace of many others	98% helium 2% hydrogen trace of carbon dioxide	96.5% carbon dioxide 3.5% nitrogen trace of sulfuric acid	78% nitrogen 21% oxygen 1% other
Gravity, compared to Earth's	27.96	0.37	0.88	1.00
Inclination of equator to orbit (°)	7 (to ecliptic)	0.1	177	23.5
Albedo	NA	0.011	0.65	0.367

Sun's mass: 1.99×10^{30} kg
Earth's mass: 5.97×10^{24} kg
Moon's mass: 7.35×10^{22} kg

1 astronomical unit (ua):   149,600,000 km
1 light year (ly): 9.46×10^{12} km

The numbers for planetary diameters stated in this table were taken from sources that used a conversion factor several places more precise than that given in Appendices A1/B1. Thus, if you used the conversion factor of 0.621 to convert kilometers to miles, you would get a slightly different result.

Moon	Mars	Jupiter	Saturn	Uranus	Neptune	Pluto
NA	1.52	5.20	9.54	19.19	30.06	39.53
3476 2160	6786 4207	142,984 88,650	120,536 74,732	51,118 31,693	49,532 30,764	2294 1410
0.02	0.15	1408	846	64.4	58.5	0.006
0.0123	0.107	318	95.1	14.5	17.1	0.0021
3.34	3.933	1.326	0.687	1.318	1.638	2.050
20	−63 (−140 to + 120)	−144	−176	−215	−215	−223
27.32 d	1.88 y	11.9 y	29.5 y	84.07 y	164.8 y	248.5 y
1.034	25.98	13.1	9.66	6.82	5.48	4.75
27.32 d (655.7 h)	24.62 h	9.92 h	10.5 h	17.24 h retrograde	16.11 h	153.3 h retrograde
0	2 moons	4 moons 59+ minor 1 ring	9 moons 22+ minor 1000+ rings	5 moons 22 minor 11 rings	3 moons 10 minor 4 rings	1 moon
trace gases	95.3% carbon dioxide 2.7% nitrogen 2% other	89% hydrogen 11% helium traces of methane, ammonia	89% hydrogen 11% helium trace of methane	89% hydrogen 11% helium, methane, and ammonia	89% hydrogen 11% helium trace of methane	nitrogen and methane
0.165	0.38	2.64	1.15	1.15	1.12	0.04
6.68	25.2	3.12	26.7	97.9	29.6	122
0.12	0.15	0.52	0.47	0.51	0.41	0.30

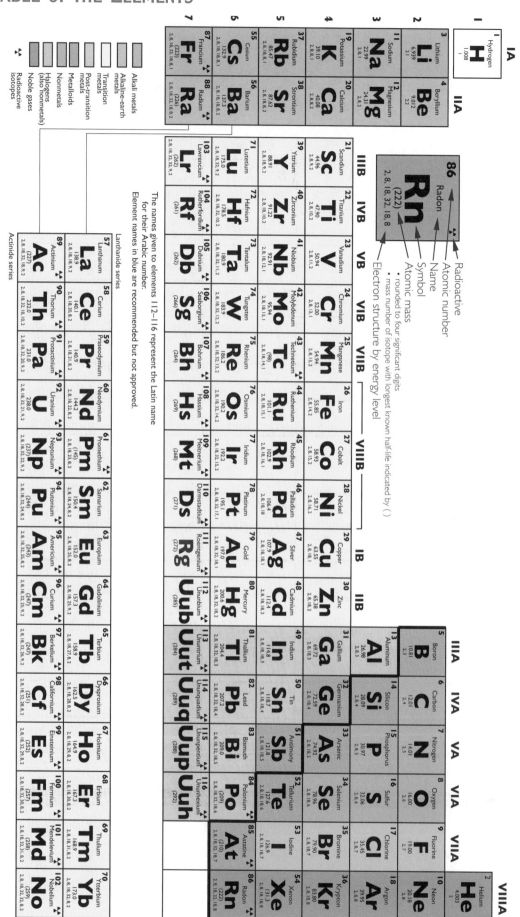

MINERAL IDENTIFICATION KEY

Basic luster	Color range	Hardness range	General cleavage	Distinctive properties	Hardness	Probable mineral	Confirming properties	Sample
Nonmetallic	Light-colored	Softer than fingernail	Poor	Greasy feel; marks cloth	1	Talc	Often white, greenish, or yellowish; white streak	
			Single direction; good cleavage	Splits into thick sheets	2	Gypsum	Glassy or pearly luster; white streak	
		Harder than fingernail; softer than glass		Splits into thin sheets	2½ on cleavage; 4 across	Muscovite	Mica; glassy luster; usually green, gray, or brown; harder than fingernail across cleavage; white streak	
			Good cubic cleavage	Crystals usually cubic	2½	Halite	Tastes salty; crystals usually white cubes but may be gray, yellow, or red; white streak	
			Good noncubic cleavage (rhombic, prismatic, etc.)	Fizzes in dilute HCl acid	3	Calcite	Variable crystal shapes but often rectangular or rhombohedral prisms; may be colorless, white, or many other colors depending on composition; glassy luster; may fluoresce under UV; white or grayish streak	
				Only powdered mineral fizzes in HCl acid	3½ – 4	Dolomite	Crystals are usually rhombohedral but mineral may have no distinct crystal form (massive); transparent and colorless, white, gray, greenish, yellowish, brown color; glassy to pearly luster; white streak	
				Does not react with HCl acid	4	Fluorite	Octahedral cleavage; often as cubic crystals; colorless and transparent but may also be yellowish, green to greenish blue, and other colors; glassy luster; white streak	
		Harder than glass	Perfect cleavage in one direction and good cleavage in others	Often shows striations on tabular* surfaces	6–6½	Plagioclase	Subgroup of the feldspars; usually cleaves in tabular slabs; color white or gray, sometimes reddish or brown; glassy luster, sometimes pearly on cleavage surfaces; white streak	
				No striations on cleavage surfaces	6	Orthoclase	Also known as K-feldspar; lack of striations on tabular surfaces is key; color usually white or pink; glassy luster, sometimes pearly on cleavage surfaces; white streak	
			None	Conchoidal fracture, hard and glassy	7	Quartz	As crystals, usually in six-sided prisms with multifaceted pyramid ends; often massive; usually colorless or white but may be any color; glassy luster in crystals but luster may be greasy in massive varieties; white streak	

*tabular = flat, table-like surfaces or pieces

Basic luster	Color range	Hardness range	General cleavage	Distinctive properties	Hardness	Probable mineral	Confirming properties	Sample
Nonmetallic	Dark-colored	Harder than glass	Good cleavage	Cleavage in two directions but not at right angles, silky, fibrous luster	6	Amphibole (group)	Most minerals in this group occur as fibrous masses like asbestos; color can be white, brown, green, or black; fine, glassy crystals; white streak	
				Cleavage in two directions at approximately right angles	5–6½	Pyroxene (group)	Crystals rare for most minerals in group; usually massive; color white, green, brown, brownish green, or greenish black; glassy luster; white-to-gray streak	
			Poor or no cleavage	Crystals often dodecahedral (12-faces); color dark brown or maroon	7–7½	Garnet	Dodecahedral crystals embedded in rock are common; no cleavage; glassy to resinous luster; streak white or pale color of mineral	
				Mineral massive; glassy green color	6½	Olivine	Color usually olive green but may be white or brown-to-black; usually found in igneous rocks; glassy luster; white or gray streak	
		Softer than glass	Perfect in one direction	Cleaves into paper-like sheets that are semi-transparent, dark colored	2½–3 (on cleavage)	Biotite	Color dark green, brown, or black; perfect leaf-like cleavage and dark color distinctive; glassy, pearly, or sometimes almost metallic luster; white-to-gray streak	
Metallic	Various		None; uneven fracture	Massive black or steel-gray mineral with reddish streak	5–6	Hematite	Mineral form of rust; appearance may be highly variable; usually dark steel-gray that polishes to shiny black; earthy varieties can be orange-red; red or red-brown streak	
		Harder than glass	None; uneven fracture	Black, massive mineral that is magnetic	5½–6½	Magnetite	Crystals octahedral but often massive; black color; slightly soluble in HCl; magnetic; black streak	
		Harder than glass	Poor; conchoidal fracture	Brassy or gold metallic appearance	6–6½	Pyrite	"Fool's gold"; brass-yellow color; tarnished surfaces often iridescent; crystals often cubic or octahedral; nonmagnetic or very slightly magnetic; greenish black or brownish black streak	
		Harder than fingernail	Perfect cubic cleavage	Lead gray, metallic color; very dense	2½	Galena	Crystals cubic or a combination of cubic and octahedral; often massive; density 7.6	
		Softer than fingernail	Good cleavage in one direction	Black, soft, crumbly mineral; easily marks paper; greasy feel	1–2	Graphite	Crystals as plate-like masses on rock but usually massive; metallic-to-dull luster; black color; black streak	

DIGITAL ELEVATION MAP OF THE CONTINENTAL UNITED STATES

Shaded relief map of the United States. (Data provided by the United States Geological Survey)

LANDFORM REGIONS OF THE CONTINENTAL UNITED STATES

Shaded areas indicate the major landforms in the United States. (Digital Elevation map provided by the United States Geological Survey)

USGS TOPOGRAPHIC MAP SYMBOLS

BATHYMETRIC FEATURES

Area exposed at mean low tide; sounding datum line***	
Channel***	
Sunken rock***	

BOUNDARIES

National	
State or territorial	
County or equivalent	
Civil township or equivalent	
Incorporated city or equivalent	
Federally administered park, reservation, or monument (external)	
Federally administered park, reservation, or monument (internal)	
State forest, park, reservation, or monument and large county park	
Forest Service administrative area*	
Forest Service ranger district*	
National Forest System land status, Forest Service lands*	
National Forest System land status, non-Forest Service lands*	
Small park (county or city)	

BUILDINGS AND RELATED FEATURES

Building	
School; house of worship	
Athletic field	
Built-up area	
Forest headquarters*	
Ranger district office*	
Guard station or work center*	
Racetrack or raceway	
Airport, paved landing strip, runway, taxiway, or apron	
Unpaved landing strip	
Well (other than water), windmill or wind generator	
Tanks	
Covered reservoir	
Gaging station	
Located or landmark object (feature as labeled)	
Boat ramp or boat access*	

COASTAL FEATURES

Foreshore flat	
Coral or rock reef	
Rock, bare or awash; dangerous to navigation	
Group of rocks, bare or awash	
Exposed wreck	
Depth curve; sounding	
Breakwater, pier, jetty, or wharf	
Seawall	
Oil or gas well; platform	

CONTOURS

Topographic

Index	
Approximate or indefinite	
Intermediate	
Approximate or indefinite	
Supplementary	
Depression	
Cut	
Fill	
Continental divide	

Bathymetric

Index***	
Intermediate***	
Index primary***	
Primary***	
Supplementary***	

CONTROL DATA AND MONUMENTS

Principal point**	⊕ 3-20
U.S. mineral or location monument	▲ USMM 438
River mileage marker	Mile 69

Boundary monument

Third-order or better elevation, with tablet	BM ▫ 9134 BM ⊕ 277
Third-order or better elevation, recoverable mark, no tablet	▫ 5628
With number and elevation	67 ▫ 4567

CONTROL DATA AND MONUMENTS – *continued*

Vertical control

Third-order or better elevation, with tablet	BM $\times$ 5280
Third-order or better elevation, recoverable mark, no tablet	$\times$ 528
Bench mark coincident with found section corner	BM ⊹ 5280
Spot elevation	$\times$ 7523

GLACIERS AND PERMANENT SNOWFIELDS

Contours and limits	
Formlines	
Glacial advance	
Glacial retreat	

LAND SURVEYS

Public land survey system

Range or Township line	
Location approximate	
Location doubtful	
Protracted	
Protracted (AK 1:63,360-scale)	
Range or Township labels	R1E T2N R3W T4S
Section line	
Location approximate	
Location doubtful	
Protracted	
Protracted (AK 1:63,360-scale)	
Section numbers	1 - 36 1 - 36
Found section corner	
Found closing corner	
Witness corner	WC
Meander corner	MC
Weak corner*	

Other land surveys

Range or Township line	
Section line	
Land grant, mining claim, donation land claim, or tract	
Land grant, homestead, mineral, or other special survey monument	□
Fence or field lines	

MARINE SHORELINES

Shoreline	
Apparent (edge of vegetation)***	
Indefinite or unsurveyed	

MINES AND CAVES

Quarry or open pit mine	⚒
Gravel, sand, clay, or borrow pit	✕
Mine tunnel or cave entrance	⊰
Mine shaft	◪
Prospect	X
Tailings	(Tailings)
Mine dump	
Former disposal site or mine	

PROJECTION AND GRIDS

Neatline	39°15′ / 90°37′30″
Graticule tick	55′
Graticule intersection	⊹
Datum shift tick	

State plane coordinate systems

Primary zone tick	640 000 FEET
Secondary zone tick	247 500 METERS
Tertiary zone tick	260 000 FEET
Quaternary zone tick	98 500 METERS
Quintary zone tick	320 000 FEET

Universal transverse metcator grid

UTM grid (full grid)	273
UTM grid ticks*	269

RAILROADS AND RELATED FEATURES

Standard guage railroad, single track	
Standard guage railroad, multiple track	
Narrow guage railroad, single track	
Narrow guage railroad, multiple track	
Railroad siding	
Railroad in highway / Railroad in road / Railroad in light duty road*	
Railroad underpass; overpass	
Railroad bridge; drawbridge	
Railroad tunnel	
Railroad yard	
Railroad turntable; roundhouse	

RIVERS, LAKES, AND CANALS

Perennial stream	
Perennial river	
Intermittent stream	
Intermittent river	
Disappearing stream	
Falls, small	
Falls, large	
Rapids, small	
Rapids, large	
Masonry dam	
Dam with lock	
Dam carrying road	

RIVERS, LAKES, AND CANALS – *continued*

Perennial lake/pond	
Intermittent lake/pond	
Dry lake/pond	*Dry Lake*
Narrow wash	
Wide wash	*Wash*
Canal, flume, or aqueduct with lock	
Elevated aqueduct, flume, or conduit	
Aqueduct tunnel	
Water well, geyser, fumarole, or mud pot	o o
Spring or seep	

ROADS AND RELATED FEATURES

Please note: Roads on Provisional-edition maps are not classified as primary, secondary, or light duty. These roads are all classified as improved roads and are symbolized the same as light duty roads.

Primary highway	
Secondary highway	
Light duty road	
Light duty road, paved*	
Light duty road, gravel*	
Light duty road, dirt*	
Light duty road, unspecified*	
Unimproved road	
Unimproved road*	
4WD road	
4WD road*	
Trail	
Highway or road with median strip	
Highway or road under construction	*Under Const*
Highway or road underpass; overpass	
Highway or road bridge; drawbridge	
Highway or road tunnel	
Road block, berm, or barrier*	
Gate on road*	
Trailhead*	

SUBMERGED AREAS AND BOGS

Marsh or swamp	
Submerged marsh or swamp	
Wooded marsh or swamp	
Submerged wooded marsh or swamp	
Land subject to inundation	*Max Pool 431*

SURFACE FEATURES

Levee	*Levee*
Sand or mud	*Sand*
Disturbed surface	
Gravel beach or glacial moraine	*Gravel*
Tailings pond	*Tailings Pond*

TRANSMISSION LINES AND PIPELINES

Power transmission line; pole; tower	
Telephone line	*Telephone*
Aboveground pipeline	
Underground pipeline	*Pipeline*

VEGETATION

Woodland	
Shrubland	
Orchard	
Vineyard	
Mangrove	*Mangrove*

* USGS-USDA Forest Service Single-Edition Quadrangle maps only.
In August 1993, the U.S. Geological Survey and the U.S. Department of Agriculture's Forest Service signed an Interagency Agreement to begin a single-edition joint mapping program. This agreement established the coordination for producing and maintaining single-edition primary series topographic maps for quadrangles containing National Forest System lands. The joint mapping program eliminates duplication of effort by the agencies and results in a more frequent revision cycle for quadrangles containing National Forests. Maps are revised on the basis of jointly developed standards and contain normal features mapped by the USGS, as well as additional features required for efficient management of National Forest System lands. Single-edition maps look slightly different but meet the content, accuracy, and quality criteria of other USGS products.

** Provisional-Edition maps only.
Provisional-edition maps were established to expedite completion of the remaining large-scale topographic quadrangles of the conterminous United States. They contain essentially the same level of information as the standard series maps. This series can be easily recognized by the title "Provisional Edition" in the lower right-hand corner.

*** Topographic Bathymetric maps only.

Modified Mercalli Earthquake Intensity Scale

Mercalli magnitude	Effects observed
I	Not felt except by a very few under especially favorable conditions.
II	Felt only by a few persons at rest, especially on upper floors of buildings. Delicately suspended objects may swing.
III	Felt quite noticeably by persons indoors, especially on the upper floors of buildings. Many people do not recognize it as an earthquake. Standing vehicles may rock slightly. Vibration similar to the passing of a truck. Duration estimated.
IV	Felt indoors by many, outdoors by few during the day. At night, some awakened. Dishes, windows, doors disturbed; walls make cracking sound. Sensation like heavy truck striking building. Standing vehicles rocked noticeably.
V	Felt by nearly everyone; many awakened. Some dishes and windows broken. Unstable objects overturned. Pendulum clocks may stop.
VI	Felt by all; many frightened. Windows, dishes, glassware broken, books fall off shelves, some heavy furniture moved or overturned; a few instances of fallen plaster. Damage slight.
VII	Difficult to stand. Furniture broken. Damage negligible in buildings of good design and construction; slight to moderate in well-built ordinary structures; considerable damage in poorly built or badly designed structures; some chimneys broken. Noticed by persons driving vehicles.
VIII	Damage slight in specially designed structures; considerable in ordinary substantial buildings, with partial collapse. Damage great in poorly built structures. Fall of chimneys, factory stacks, columns, monuments, walls. Heavy furniture overturned.
IX	General panic. Damage considerable in specially designed structures, well-designed frame structures thrown out of plumb. Damage great even in substantial buildings, with partial collapse. Buildings shifted off foundations.
X	Some well-built wooden structures destroyed; most masonry and frame structures destroyed as well as foundations. Track rails bent.
XI	Few, if any (masonry) structures remain standing. Bridges destroyed. Track rails bent greatly.
XII	Damage total. Lines of sight and level distorted. Objects thrown into the air.

This description of the Mercalli scale is from the U.S. Geological Survey pamphlet *The Severity of an Earthquake* (1986).

Glossary

A

absolute humidity The amount of water a certain volume of air holds.

abyssal plain The flat, deep sea floor of an ocean basin.

accelerated mass spectrometer (AMS) An instrument that combines a mass spectrometer and an accelerator and can be used to measure the very small amounts of elements and their different isotopes in a sample.

accretion The growth or enlargement of a crystal by the attachment of additional particles from a solution or melt.

accretion theory The uniformitarian theory that all celestial objects, but especially those of the solar system, were formed by the gravitational accumulation of space dust.

accumulation zone That zone of a glacier above the snow line where fallen snow does not completely melt from year to year and therefore accumulates to form glacier ice.

acid precipitation Precipitation (rain, snow, or hail) that is more acidic than is believed to be normal because it contains air pollutants such as sulfur and nitrogen compounds.

acid test A method for identifying certain minerals by noting the presence or absence of effervescence of a gas when a mineral is exposed to dilute acids.

active volcano A volcano that has erupted within historical times or shows signs that it could erupt at any time.

actual height The height of a mountain peak above its base. The base may be at, above, or below sea level.

***ad hominem* argument** A logical fallacy in which the speaker is attacked rather than the speaker's argument. Latin for "to the man."

adiabatic cooling Cooling of an air mass (without a change in the air mass's overall thermal energy) by a reduction in atmospheric pressure and/or an increase in volume.

air mass A large body of air covering hundreds or thousands of square kilometers that has a relatively uniform temperature, pressure, and humidity.

albedo The fraction or percentage of the light shining on a planet or other nonluminous celestial object that it reflects.

alluvial fan A fan-shaped deposit of sediments formed at the point where a stream emerges from a narrow valley onto a plain or other relatively flat surface.

Alpine-Himalayan belt A belt of active and extinct volcanoes that extends eastward from Central Europe through Turkey to the Himalayan Mountains.

anemometer An instrument for measuring wind speed using cupped scoops mounted on a rotating shaft.

aneroid barometer An instrument for measuring atmospheric pressure using the expansion and contraction of a sealed metal bellows to move a pointer.

annular eclipse An eclipse of the sun in which a narrow ring (annulus) of the sun's disk shows around the moon because the moon is too far from the earth to cover the sun's disk completely.

anomalous sample A sample tested by the radiocarbon dating method that gives a sample age different from an age that has been determined by other means.

anticline A folded rock formation that is similar in appearance to the crest of a wave. That is, the rock strata bend downward on both sides from a higher line along the center of the formation.

anticyclone An area of relatively higher atmospheric pressure. It typically contains a clockwise-rotating wind system in the Northern Hemisphere.

aphelion The point in the orbit of a planet or other object orbiting the sun where it is farthest from the sun.

apogee The point in the orbit of the moon or a man-made satellite where it is farthest from Earth.

appearing stream A stream that seems to flow directly out of a hillside. One of the characteristic features of karst topography.

applications satellite A satellite that is used for a specific purpose other than pure scientific data collection. Applications include weather prediction, communications, navigational references, and surveying.

arête A thin, knife-like ridge of rock that remains after glaciation has removed most of a mountain from both sides of the ridge.

artesian well A well sunk into a rock formation where groundwater pressure is adequate to provide a constant flow of water without pumping.

ash Volcanic debris consisting of tiny, angular, glassy fragments of solidified magma (up to 2 mm in diameter).

asteroid Any of the rocky minor planets that orbit the sun, mainly between the orbits of Mars and Jupiter. They are far smaller than even the smallest of the nine main planets. (See *meteoroid* and *minor planet*.)

asthenosphere That portion of the upper mantle extending from the rigid lithosphere down to about 200 km (125 mi) or deeper beneath the continents, which is believed to be plastic enough that the rock can flow.

astronomical unit (ua) A unit of astronomical distance equal to the average distance between Earth and the sun (150 million km or 93 million mi). Useful for measuring distances in and near the solar system.

atmosphere   The envelope of the gaseous mixture surrounding Earth.

atmospheric pressure   The force per unit area exerted by the atmosphere at a given location.

atoll   A ring of low coral islands and reefs surrounding a central lagoon that is in most cases built on a submerged volcano.

aurora australis   The same phenomenon as aurora borealis, except it occurs in the Southern Hemisphere. (See *aurora borealis*.)

aurora borealis   The streamers or bands of light that appear in the sky of the Northern Hemisphere when high-energy charged particles from the magnetosphere collide with atmospheric molecules.

autumnal equinox   The day that the sun's overhead noon position crosses the equator (about September 22) as it moves southward. At the equinox, the day and night are of equal length in all parts of the earth.

axis   An imaginary line passing through the center of an object about which the object spins or rotates.

B

bacon (speleothem)   A striped ribbon of flowstone in a cave that looks like strips of salted bacon.

Baily's beads   Bright pinpoints of light that appear briefly during a total solar eclipse as sunlight shines through valleys around the moon's edge.

barograph   A recording barometer.

barometer   An instrument that measures atmospheric pressure.

barrier island   An island formed when waves deposit sand across the mouth of a bay or along a coastline but has no connection with the mainland.

barrier reef   A coral reef located away from the shore that creates a lagoon between the reef and the shore.

base level   The lowest level to which a stream can flow.

basin   A geologic formation similar to a syncline, where the regional rock strata are depressed in a bowl-like fashion.

bay barrier   A spit that extends across the mouth of a bay, closing it to the sea.

Beaufort wind scale   An internationally approved scale for reporting wind speeds based on the way the wind affects the water and common objects such as trees, flags, smoke, and so forth.

big bang theory   The most popular evolutionary theory for the origin of the universe. Supposedly, around 15 billion years ago, all the matter seen in the universe today was condensed and compacted into a tiny point that exploded and evolved into the immense expanse of galaxies, stars, and planets that now exists.

bimetallic thermometer   A temperature-measuring device consisting of two strips of metal having different rates of thermal expansion that are bonded together into a coil, such that changes in temperature cause the coil to curl or uncurl. The coil is attached to an indicating pointer to display temperature.

black hole   A small object or region in space with gravity so intense that it is believed that matter, energy, and even light cannot escape from within its boundaries.

blowout   An excavated desert basin caused by the wind carrying away loose material such as sand and silt.

boil   The rapid vaporization of a liquid whose temperature is at its boiling point. (See *evaporation*.)

bolide   An unusually bright meteor that typically explodes.

bomb   A streamlined mass of lava ejected from a volcano that solidifies in midair. Volcanic bombs are larger than ash or cinder particles.

boulder train   A group of glacial erratic boulders from the same distant bedrock source strewn across a ground moraine.

Bourdon tube thermometer   A temperature-measuring instrument consisting of a coiled tube of metal filled with a fluid, sealed at one end and connected to a hollow sensing tube and bulb at the other. The sealed end of the coiled tube is attached to a pointer that indicates temperature on a dial. Changes in temperature in the remote sensing bulb cause corresponding changes in pressure in the fluid, causing the tube to coil or uncoil, moving the pointer.

breaker   A water wave in which the top falls over on the forward side of the wave. A wave becomes unstable and produces a breaking wave when its height is more than $\frac{1}{7}$ or 0.143 of its length.

breccia   A coarsely clastic rock consisting of relatively large angular fragments bonded in a matrix of finer particles. May be formed by sedimentary or volcanic processes, or from meteorite impacts.

C

caldera   A large crater, often water filled, formed by an explosion or collapse of the original volcanic cone.

calibration curve (radiocarbon)   A graph that is used to correct the age of a sample of organic material obtained by radiocarbon decay to a calendar date. This is necessary because carbon-14 concentration in the earth's atmosphere has varied throughout its history. (*See carbon-14*.)

calving   The process of iceberg formation by the breakup of a glacier.

capillary fringe   The zone within the soil horizons immediately above the zone of saturation where water has worked its way upward a short distance from the water table by capillary action.

capsule A small space vehicle with extremely limited living and working areas, designed to carry humans or animals into orbit around the earth or the moon.

capture theory (lunar) The naturalistic theory that the moon was once a planet in its own orbit around the sun but that the earth somehow deflected it into an orbit around the earth.

carat A unit of weight (actually mass) for gem stones equal to 0.2 grams.

carbon-14 A radioactive form of carbon used in the radiocarbon dating method for determining the age of organic matter.

carbonate A class of minerals that contain the carbonate ion, which consists of a carbon atom and three oxygen atoms bonded together. Most carbonates release bubbles of carbon dioxide gas when exposed to dilute hydrochloric acid.

Cassegrainian reflector A compact form of reflector telescope in which the sky is viewed from behind the main mirror. Named after its inventor, about whom little is known.

Cassini's Division The large central gap in Saturn's ring system when viewed from Earth. The *Cassini-Huygens* mission to Saturn demonstrated that the Cassini Division actually contains thousands of thin rings.

catastrophic plate tectonics A creationary theory of the origin of the continents that suggests the earth's crust was created with a single super-continent. This continent broke into tectonic plates during the initial stage of the Genesis Flood. Rapid subduction of the oceanic plates drew the fragments of the continents apart to approximately their present-day positions in less than a year.

cave An underground tunnel or chamber of natural origin that is accessible from the earth's surface.

celestial equator The projection of the earth's equator onto the celestial sphere; position of 0° declination.

Celsius scale A temperature scale having fiducial (fixed reference) points at the freezing point (0 °C) and the boiling point (100 °C) of pure water at one atmosphere of pressure.

Cepheid variable A type of star that changes in brightness regularly, apparently because it expands and contracts on a regular basis.

chemical weathering The breakdown of rock by the action of natural acids (and oxygen as well as other chemicals) dissolved in water. It is a result of chemical changes in the minerals composing the rock.

chondrule Small silicate spheres often found in meteorites.

chromosphere The layer of gases that forms the innermost layer of the sun's atmosphere.

cinder A solidified piece of lava similar to volcanic ash but larger, ranging from 2–64 mm (0.1–2.5 in) in diameter.

cinder cone A generally small, steep-sided volcano that explosively ejects mostly ash, cinders, and bombs.

circular reasoning The logical fallacy of assuming a conclusion to be true in the course of arguing for that conclusion.

Circum-Pacific belt The belt of active and extinct volcanoes and volcanic islands around the northern, eastern, and western perimeter of the Pacific Ocean. It is also known as the "Ring of Fire."

cirque A steep-sided, hollow excavation in a mountainside made by glacial erosion.

clastic Sedimentary rock consisting of rock fragments (clasts) compacted and cemented together. Clasts come from the erosion of other rocks.

cleavage A property of certain minerals that allows them to split easily along certain preferred planes.

cloud A mass of fine water droplets or ice crystals suspended in the air.

coalescence Smaller pieces joining together to form a single larger mass. Raindrops grow in size through coalescence.

cold air mass An air mass that is colder than the surface over which it moves.

cold front The advancing surface of a cold air mass as it moves under a warmer air mass.

column A cave formation (speleothem) that forms when a stalactite merges with a stalagmite.

coma The spherical region of glowing gas and dust that surrounds the nucleus of a comet.

comet A relatively small, icy satellite of the sun, usually with a very eccentric orbit. When near the sun in its orbit, it produces one or more tails of dust and gas that glow or reflect sunlight.

composite telescope A telescope that uses both a primary mirror and a large objective corrective lens as the main light-gathering elements of the telescope.

composite volcano A volcano built up of alternating layers of lava and cinders, caused by alternating episodes of quiescent and explosive eruptions.

compound (chemical) A substance formed from two or more elements combined in a fixed ratio characteristic for that compound.

compound lens Two or more lenses made of different kinds of glass mounted together to correct for chromatic aberration.

condensation The change of a gaseous vapor into the liquid state as the result of a decreasing temperature. Condensation occurs in cloud and dew formation.

condensation nucleus A microscopic particle of material such as salt or smoke around which a water droplet can begin to form.

conduction The direct transfer of thermal energy through a substance or from one object in physical contact with another.

cone of depression An inverted cone-shaped lowering of the water table centered on a well in an area where the rate of water removal exceeds the rate of water percolation.

conglomerate A clastic sedimentary rock composed of rounded pieces of rock, pebbles, and sand cemented together. "Nature's concrete."

Congreve rocket An early solid-fuel rocket designed by Sir William Congreve of England. It was inaccurate due to reliance on the stick guidance system.

conservation The principle that the sum total of all matter and energy in the universe is constant. Matter and energy are not now being created nor destroyed but are only converted from one form to another.

constellation In ancient times, a named pattern of stars that represented famous characters, animals, or familiar objects. In modern times, it is an area of the sky marked off by segments of celestial latitude and longitude.

continental drift theory A naturalistic theory that accounts for the shape and arrangement of the present-day continents by the slow movement of plates of crust floating on a semi-liquid layer of rock through many millions of years.

continental glacier A vast, thick ice sheet that covers a large portion of a continent or a large island.

continental rise The sea bottom at the foot of the continental slope, consisting of sediments washed down the slope from the continental shelf above. The slope angle of the continental rise is less steep than that of the continental slope.

continental shelf The submerged edge of a continent extending from the coastline to some distance offshore. It is characterized by having gentle slopes and similar geologic formations and topography to the adjacent land.

continental slope The relatively steep drop-off from the continental shelf into the deep ocean basin.

contour line In general, any line on a map that shows elevation above (or below) some reference height, such as sea level. All the points on a contour line have the same elevation.

contrail A visible trail of condensed water vapor or ice crystals forming in the wake of an aircraft.

convection The indirect transfer of thermal energy from one place to another by the movement of currents of cooler, more dense matter into regions of warmer, less dense matter. Convection occurs in liquids and gases because their particles are mobile.

convective zone In the model of the sun's interior it is the outermost region, composed of extremely hot plasmas, where heat transfer from the radiative zone to the surface occurs by convection.

convergence The collision of two or more air masses or winds at a single location. This results in air being lifting vertically, which causes cooling and precipitation.

coordinates In general, a set of two numbers (e.g., an x value and a y value) that specifies the location of a point on a graph. For an astronomical body, its celestial coordinates are declination (DEC), given in degrees north or south of the celestial equator, and right ascension (RA), given in hours, minutes, and seconds east of the prime hour circle.

Copernican theory A heliocentric theory or sun-centered model of the solar system, published by Nicolaus Copernicus in 1543, in which the earth rotates on its axis, and the earth and other planets revolve around the sun in perfect circles.

copper A common metal often found as a native mineral and used in many applications because it conducts both electricity and heat very well.

coral reef A massive marine geologic feature made up of calcium carbonate secreted by colonies of coral polyps in relatively shallow tropical waters and near continents and islands.

core In general, the central region of the interior of a celestial object. In the sun and other stars, it is the location of the thermonuclear reactions that generate the star's energy. In the earth, it is the extremely dense metallic center surrounded by the rocklike mantle.

Coriolis effect The tendency of objects initially moving in a straight path over the earth's surface to be deflected due to the earth's rotation. This effect causes the deflection of wind and water currents to the right in the Northern Hemisphere and to the left in the Southern Hemisphere.

corona The extremely hot, low-density, and extensive outer portion of the sun's atmosphere that becomes the solar wind.

coronagraph An instrument used to observe the corona of the sun by creating an artificial eclipse.

crater In general, a round depression in a planet's surface set apart by a raised rim of rocky debris. It may be classified as meteoric—caused by a meteorite—or as volcanic.

creational goodness The principle that the universe, as God originally created it, perfectly fulfilled His intentions for its existence.

Creation Mandate The command contained in Genesis 1:28 in which God delegates to Adam and Eve, and hence to all mankind, the authority and responsibility for subduing and managing the earth for God's glory and man's benefit.

creep Slow movement of soil down a slope due to gravity.

crest The peak or apex of a wave.

crevasse A deep fissure in a glacier.

crust The relatively solid outermost layer of the earth.

curtain A thin sheet of dripstone that hangs from the ceiling of a cave.

cusp (lunar) A pointed end of a crescent moon.

cyclone In general, a weather system centered on a low-pressure area surrounded by a wind circulation pattern spiraling counterclockwise in the Northern Hemisphere and clockwise in the Southern Hemisphere. A hurricane in the Southwestern Pacific and Indian Ocean regions. Also, an informal name for a tornado.

D

datum (pl. *data*) A scientific observation recorded as a detailed description or a measurement. Scientists draw conclusions based on analysis of their data.

debris slide A landslide involving mostly loose soil and rocks lying on top of bedrock.

decay A nuclear change in which the nucleus of an atom spontaneously emits a subatomic particle or an energetic electromagnetic ray.

declination (DEC) Celestial latitude. Angular distance north or south of the celestial equator measured in degrees.

deductive reasoning A logical process in which a specific statement is determined to be true from the consideration of more general statements that are known or believed to be true.

deep time A concept underlying nearly all naturalistic historical science that refers to the unobservable distant past in terms of millions or billions of years ago.

deferent In the Ptolemaic geocentric model of the solar system, a crystal sphere surrounding the earth for each of the visible planets, the moon, and the sun, all of which revolved around the earth.

degeneration The principle that all things tend to die, become more disordered, fall apart, and run down.

delta A usually fan-shaped deposit of sediment where a stream enters a relatively quiet lake or the ocean.

dendrochronology The determination of a radiocarbon calibration curve by using a series of overlapping tree ring records from a population of ancient, dead tree trunks. Counting the tree rings supposedly provides an accurate calendar date, and measuring the actual carbon-14 in the tree tissue samples provides the data for the radiocarbon calibration.

density The amount of matter (mass) contained in a single volumetric unit of a substance.

density current A current created by the tendency of denser, more saline water to sink and displace less dense, less saline water, which rises.

depositional mountain A hill or a mountain formed from sedimentary materials that were deposited by volcanic, glacial, or wind action.

desalinate The removal of salt and minerals from seawater to produce fresh, drinkable water.

desert pavement A thin crust that forms in deserts when sand and silt have been blown away and only pebbles and cobbles remain.

dew Water that condenses on a cool surface when air in contact with the surface cools to below its dew point.

dew point The temperature at which air, by cooling, becomes saturated with water vapor and the vapor begins to condense around condensation nuclei.

diamond (mineral) A native mineral composed of pure inorganic carbon. Diamond is the hardest known mineral and has perfect cleavage. Diamonds have a greasy luster before they are cut, but the cut and polished gems have a brilliant adamantine luster.

diamond pipe Cylindrical bodies of volcanic breccia in the necks of extinct volcanoes where diamonds are sometimes found.

diamond ring effect During a total solar eclipse, the effect produced by a single Baily's bead flash occurring along the thin remaining solar crescent at the limb of the moon. It occurs immediately before or after totality in a solar eclipse. See *Baily's beads*.

diffraction grating A plate of transparent material having thousands of microscopic parallel lines ruled or molded onto its surface. The spacing of the lines is small enough that the lines interfere with transmitted light waves to produce a colored spectrum.

digital thermometer A thermometer that measures temperature electronically and displays the temperature in a digital format.

dike An igneous rock intrusion that cuts more or less perpendicularly across the original sedimentary rock strata.

disappearing stream A stream that seems to vanish into a hole in the ground. It occurs when chemical erosion opens a hole through the ceiling of a cave that underlies the stream bed, allowing the water to flow into the cave rather than down the hill. One of the characteristic features of karst typography.

discontinuity In general, a sharp change in a measured quantity as one crosses a boundary between two materials. In seismology, it is the boundary between two layers of the earth below the crust, where earthquake waves abruptly change speed.

divide The crest of a ridge of highlands separating one stream's drainage basin from another's.

doctrine of uniformity Also called *uniformitarianism*. The belief system that holds "the present is the key to the past" and that geological change is caused by gradual naturalistic processes rather than sudden supernatural catastrophes. Creationary scientists reject uniformitarianism because it contradicts Scripture on every important point regarding the history of the earth.

doldrums A permanent low-pressure belt of usually windless air near the equator caused by the vertical rising of warm air.

dome A geologic formation similar to an anticline, where the regional rock strata are arched, as in an inverted bowl.

dormant volcano A volcano that has not erupted in historical times but could erupt based on seismic indications of tectonic activity beneath the volcano.

double refraction The optical effect caused by certain minerals that can split a transmitted beam of light into two beams and thereby produce a double image.

drainage basin The area that is drained by a river and its tributaries.

dredging A method of underwater mining where mineral placer deposits are scooped off river or lake beds by floating machinery and mechanically processed to remove valuable minerals.

dripstone Cave deposits that are formed from the precipitation of minerals contained in groundwater that drips on the same spot repeatedly. Stalactites and stalagmites are examples of dripstones.

drizzle Small, slowly falling droplets of rain.

E

earthquake A series of inaudible shock waves traveling through the earth.

earthshine Sunlight reflected from the dark side of the moon that was originally reflected from the earth.

earth-trailing orbit A special space probe orbit that follows the earth around the sun at about the same distance from the sun as the earth.

eccentric In circular motion, an off-center rotation. In orbital motion, the fact that the central body is at the focus of an elliptical orbit rather than at the center of the ellipse.

echo sounding A form of sonar used to measure water depth beneath the vessel. Echo sounders measure the time it takes for sound waves to travel to the ocean floor and back and assumes a constant speed of sound through the water to obtain the distance.

eclipsing binary Two stars revolving around each other such that they periodically pass in front of each other relative to the observer.

ecliptic The apparent path of the sun among the stars. Also, it is the plane of the earth's orbit.

eisegesis The error of reading meaning or intent into a text (especially Scripture) that is not present or was not intended by the author. It is the opposite of exegesis, which is a careful interpretation of Scripture based on what the text says.

elastic rebound Rapid movement of rocks along a fault surface, like a rubber band snapping, as excessive stress is released during an earthquake.

electromagnetic waves A form of energy that can be transmitted through a vacuum. Its spectrum contains radio waves, infrared waves, visible light waves, ultraviolet waves, x-rays, and gamma rays.

element A substance composed of one kind of atom, that is, atoms having the same number of protons in their nuclei.

elevation The altitude of a mountain's summit above sea level.

ellipse A special geometric figure that can best be described as a flattened circle. Given two points in a plane, an ellipse consists of all the other points in the plane such that the sum of their distances from the two given points is a constant.

entropy The measure of the disorderliness of a system. Less orderliness in a system implies it has more entropy. More orderliness implies less entropy. An ice cube has far less entropy than a cloud of water vapor formed from the same water molecules.

epicenter The point on the surface of the earth directly above the focus of an earthquake.

epicycle In the Ptolemaic geocentric model of the solar system, a small crystal sphere centered on the surface of the deferent of certain planets to account for that planet's retrograde motion at certain points in its orbit.

equilibrium line An imaginary line on a glacier that separates the accumulation zone from the wastage zone. It is essentially the same line as the snow line.

equinox Either of two days during a year when the sun's noon position is directly above the equator, making day and night approximately equal in all places on the earth. Astronomically, the two locations in the sky where the ecliptic and the celestial equator intersect.

erode To wear away by abrasion and solution.

erosional mountain A mountain that has been carved out by extensive erosion, usually from a plateau. It is sometimes called a *residual mountain*.

erratic A boulder in glacial till or a ground moraine that is not like the bedrock under it.

escape velocity The initial speed an object must have in order to free itself from the gravitational pull of a planet or other celestial body.

evaporation The process of vaporization when a liquid's temperature is below its boiling point. See *boil* and *vaporization*.

evaporite A mineral type formed after the water in which the minerals were dissolved has completely evaporated.

exfoliation A process by which thin slabs or flakes of rock are removed from larger rocks by mechanical and/or chemical weathering.

exosphere The outermost zone of the earth's atmosphere that extends into space itself.

extinct volcano   A volcano that has no historical record of eruption, gives evidence for long periods of inactivity based on erosion and sedimentation patterns, and has no significant seismic activity in the earth beneath it.

extrusive rock   Igneous rock formed by the emission and cooling of magma on the surface of the earth.

eye   The circular center of low pressure in a hurricane that is characterized by few clouds, relative calm, and vertical air movement.

F

facula   A large, bright, veined patch or spot in the sun's photosphere, usually near one or more sunspots.

Fahrenheit scale   A temperature scale having fiducial (fixed reference) points at the freezing point (32 °F) and the boiling point (212 °F) of pure water at one atmosphere of pressure.

faith   Belief in the authority and reliability of something because it or its ultimate source is believed to be trustworthy.

fallacy   An error in reasoning.

fault   A fracture in a rock formation such that adjacent surfaces are displaced relative to each other along the plane of fracture.

fault-block mountain   A mountain bounded by at least one normal fault.

fiducial point   Any of one or more fixed reference points that anchor a measurement scale to some easily determined physical quantity. In the case of temperature scales, a common set of fiducial points is the freezing and boiling points of pure water at one atmosphere of pressure. Other fiducial points exist for temperature scales.

fiord   A glacially deepened inlet or arm of the sea characterized by steep-sided walls.

fireball   A large, brilliant meteor. Also called a *bolide*.

firn   Granular ice within a glacier formed by the compacting and refreezing of snow.

first law of thermodynamics   The conservation principle that matter and energy are not now being created or destroyed but only converted from one form to another.

first quarter (lunar)   The phase of the moon when the western half of the moon is lighted and the eastern half is dark.

fission theory (lunar)   A naturalistic theory of the origin of the moon suggesting that somehow the moon split away from the earth when the earth was still molten.

flame test   A means of identifying the presence of certain elements in a mineral by observing the mineral's color when heated in a flame.

flood plain   A plain bordering a stream and composed of sediment deposited by the stream during floods.

flowstone   A cave formation containing deposits left by a thin film of water flowing over the wall or floor of a cave rather than dripping from the ceiling.

fluorescent   Having the property of emitting visible light when exposed to ultraviolet light.

focus   (pl. *foci*) In general, a point of geometric significance in the description of a system of points or physical phenomena. One of two points used to define an ellipse. In optics, it is the point at which light rays come together after being bent by a lens or reflected by a curved mirror. In seismology, it is the point generally some distance below the earth's surface at which earthquake waves are generated.

fog   A stratus cloud in contact with the ground.

fold mountain   A mountain that seems to have been formed by the folding of rock layers in adjacent anticlines and synclines.

foliated rock   Metamorphic rock that has a banded or layered appearance, such as gneiss.

force   A push or a pull exerted on an object. A force may be transmitted by contact between two objects (e.g., an impact) or exerted over a distance between objects (e.g., gravity).

forked lightning   Lightning consisting of branches connected to the main stroke. (See *lightning*.)

fossil   Any trace or remains of a living organism that has been preserved by natural means.

fossil fuel   A general term for coal, petroleum (oil), and natural gas. Derived from the idea that the organic materials in these fuels originated from the chemically altered remains of plants and animals living in ancient times (i.e., just prior to the Flood).

fossil graveyard   Usually a jumbled assortment of fossils embedded in a hardened matrix of sediment, giving every evidence for the catastrophic death of the organisms along with a rapid burial.

Foucault pendulum   A pendulum first used by Jean Foucault in 1851 to demonstrate that the earth rotates on its axis. Any similar pendulum consisting of a large pendulum mass suspended by a long wire.

fracture   The characteristic manner in which a mineral breaks when it does not exhibit cleavage.

Frasch process   A method of mining sulfur in which extremely hot water is pumped into the deposit, melting the sulfur so it can be forced to the surface by compressed air. No longer used in the U.S.

freeze   The change from the liquid state to the solid state by lowering a liquid's temperature.

freezing nucleus   A microscopic particle of clay, dust, or smoke around which an ice crystal may form in a cloud.

freezing rain   Supercooled water that falls as rain and then freezes on the surface it contacts.

fringing reef A coral reef along a coastline that is in contact with the shore. Generally, it has only a very narrow lagoon or none at all.

front The boundary surface between two dissimilar air masses.

frontal wedging Vertical movement of a warm air mass due to a wedge of cold air moving in under it.

frost The ice crystals that sublimate on a cold surface when the film of air in contact with the surface is cooled to a dew point below freezing.

frost heaving The pushing of rocks upward in soil by repeated freezing and thawing of water in the soil.

frost wedging The weathering process that occurs when water standing in cracks and pores of rock expands as it freezes, widening the cracks and eventually breaking up the rock into smaller pieces.

full moon The lunar phase in which the moon's entire near side is lighted.

fumarole A vent where steam and other hot gases heated by geothermal energy continuously escape into the atmosphere.

G

galaxy A collection of millions of stars that are arranged in a variety of patterns around a gravitational center.

Galilean moon Any of Jupiter's four largest moons that were named after their discoverer, Galileo Galilei.

gas giant One of the large, gaseous planets: Jupiter, Saturn, Uranus, or Neptune. Also called a *Jovian planet*.

geocentric theory The discredited theory of the arrangement of the solar system that places the earth at the center with the sun and the planets orbiting the earth.

geologic column A uniformitarian sequence of rock units and layers, each dated by the fossils it contains (or does not contain), which supposedly extends through time from the earliest periods in Earth's history to present-day deposits.

geologic time scale The relative ages of the various geologic periods and their absolute time duration according to evolutionary theory. Boundaries are determined by the appearance and disappearance of index fossil assemblages.

geology The study of the structures, materials, and processes of the solid part of the earth.

geostrophic wind A high-altitude wind that is controlled by the relative influence of the pressure gradient force and the Coriolis effect.

geosynchronous orbit An equatorial orbit that has a period of one 24-hour day; sometimes called a *geostationary orbit*.

geosyncline theory A naturalistic theory that unsuccessfully attempts to describe the origin of fold mountains and other tectonic features as the products of an uplifted regional syncline, called a *geosyncline*, that was filled in with sedimentary strata.

geothermal energy Thermal energy produced within the crust of the earth from magma intrusions. The term also refers to the practical use to which such energy can be put, such as the tapping of heated groundwater for generating electrical power and heat.

geothermal gradient The rate of increase in the earth's temperature with increased depth. It varies with location but is typically between 15 °C and 50 °C per kilometer of depth (97–200 °F/mi).

geyser A vent for geothermally heated water and steam that erupts at predictable intervals.

glacial drift Any kind of deposit left by a glacier; can include unsorted debris dropped in place as a glacier melts (drumlins, moraines) as well as sorted, stratified debris deposited by streams of meltwater (eskers, kames).

glacial polish An especially smooth area on bedrock created by glacial action.

glacial till The unsorted debris dropped in place as a glacier melts away.

glacier A mass of ice produced when snow is compacted and refrozen that moves under the influence of gravity.

glacier ice A form of ice consisting of interlocking crystals; produced by the recrystallization of snow under great pressure.

Global Positioning System (GPS) A system of 24 satellites that provide latitude, longitude, and altitude positions to very accurate standards. A GPS receiver receives and analyzes signals from two or more different satellites to determine the position.

glowing avalanche A rapidly flowing volcanic emission of red-hot solid particles suspended in steam or other hot gases.

gnomon An upright object set in place for the purpose of casting a shadow in sunlight. By observing its shadow, early astronomers could determine the time of day, the time of year, and the position and motion of certain heavenly bodies. Gnomons are an essential part of sundials.

gold A precious, dense, yellow metal that often occurs as a native mineral in the form of veins or placer deposits. It has a specific gravity of about 19 and can be easily pounded into thin sheets or drawn into thin wires (i.e., it is malleable and ductile).

gradient The change of some measurable property with distance. The change of atmospheric pressure with distance is the pressure gradient. The change of temperature with depth into the earth is the geothermal gradient. The change of a stream's elevation for a given distance it flows horizontally is simply its gradient.

granule One of innumerable bumps in the sun's photosphere thought to result from convection currents bringing up hot plasma from beneath the sun's surface. Also, a rounded rock fragment that is larger than a grain of sand but smaller than a pebble.

Great Red Spot A reddish colored, oval-shaped area within the atmosphere of Jupiter that is probably a centuries-long storm system.

greenhouse effect The warming of the lower atmosphere by infrared radiation that is radiated by the earth's surface after it absorbs visible radiation from the sun.

greenhouse gas Any of the gases present in the atmosphere that enhance the absorption of infrared radiation by the atmosphere. Water vapor, carbon dioxide, and several other naturally occurring gases are the predominant greenhouse gases.

ground moraine Unsorted glacial debris deposited over the earth's surface that was once underneath a glacier.

groundwater Any water from natural sources found underground.

guyot A submarine mountain (seamount) that has a flat top.

gyre A large, closed-loop surface current in an ocean basin formed under the influence of prevailing winds and the Coriolis effect. Gyres flow clockwise in the Northern Hemisphere and counterclockwise in the Southern Hemisphere.

H

hail Precipitation in the form of spheres or irregular lumps of ice. It is always produced by strongly convective clouds such as cumulonimbus.

Hale rocket A nineteenth-century military rocket that carried an explosive warhead in the nose, had three curved fins in the exhaust stream to impart a stabilizing spin, and had a greater range than the artillery of its day.

halo orbit A saddle-shaped orbit around the point in space where the gravities of two massive objects, such as a planet and the sun, exactly balance each other.

hanging valley A small glacial valley that enters a glaciated valley from high on one side. It was formed by a smaller tributary glacier that did not erode as deeply as the larger main glacier.

hardness test A comparison of the ability of one substance to scratch or be scratched by another, resulting in a numerical rating from 1 to 10 on the Mohs hardness scale.

harvest moon The full moon nearest the autumnal equinox (about September 22 in the Northern Hemisphere).

hasty generalization A logical fallacy resulting from drawing conclusions from too few examples or from examples that are not representative of all the possibilities.

head (comet) The nucleus and coma of a comet.

headwaters The highest point, or the point of origin of a stream.

heliocentric theory Any theory of the arrangement of the solar system that places the sun at the center with the earth and the other planets in orbit around it.

heliopause The outermost boundary of the material influence of the solar system, where the pressure of the outgoing solar wind balances the pressure of incoming particles from interstellar space.

heterosphere One of the zones of the atmosphere defined by composition. It is the collection of gas layers above the homosphere consisting of separate layers of oxygen, helium, and hydrogen.

historical geology That branch of geology that deals with the origin and history of the earth's structures, materials, and processes.

homosphere One of the zones of the atmosphere when it is subdivided by composition; the layer of the atmosphere nearest the earth's surface consisting of a homogenous mixture of gases.

hook A sand formation extending from a headland, deposited by waves and currents, which contains a sharp bend.

horizon In general, any line or layer that lies flat with respect to gravity. A layer or zone of the soil that is relatively uniform in composition.

horn A jagged mountain peak left when glacial erosion forms three or more cirques around it. The Matterhorn in the Swiss Alps is one example.

horse latitudes Bands of nearly permanent high pressure at approximately 30° north or south latitude caused by descending cold air. They were so named because sailing ships that drifted for weeks in these areas were forced to eliminate their cargoes of livestock when water ran short.

hot spring A place where heated water rises to the surface and collects in a pool.

Hubble Space Telescope (HST) An astronomical reflecting telescope placed in Earth orbit by the space shuttle in 1990. The HST has provided amazing images of the universe that have changed the course of astronomy.

humus Decayed organic matter in soil. It is the constituent that makes soil "rich" in nutrients.

hunter's moon The next full moon after the harvest moon.

hurricane In the Atlantic and Eastern Pacific oceans, a strong, large-area cyclonic storm with wind speeds exceeding 117 km/h (73 mi/h). Also called a *typhoon* or *cyclone* in other parts of the world.

hydrologic cycle The natural water cycle in which water evaporates into the atmosphere from oceans, lakes, and rivers, clouds develop from the vapor, and the water falls to the ground as precipitation and then returns to the rivers, lakes, or oceans.

hygrometer An instrument for measuring atmospheric humidity.

hypothesis A testable and tentative (not fully worked out) description for an observed phenomenon.

I

ICBM Acronym for intercontinental ballistic missile, a type of long range, rocket-powered weapon capable of crossing the distances between continents. The rocket engine(s) boost the warhead high into or above the atmosphere and then the warhead travels the rest of the distance to the target without any form of propulsion.

ice age A time in the earth's history during which much of the higher latitudes in both the Northern and Southern Hemispheres were covered by glaciers. Most creationary scientists believe there was a single ice age following the Flood.

iceberg A large fragment of floating ice that broke off of the edge of a glacier into the ocean. Most of an iceberg's bulk lies underwater.

ice cap A thick, widespread, and permanent cover of glacial ice and snow on a flat landmass, such as an arctic island, or covering a mountain range, through which mountaintops may protrude.

icefall Glacial ice flowing down a steep incline or cliff from a hanging valley into a deeper valley or the ocean as would a waterfall.

ice floe A flat expanse of floating ice formed when frozen seawater breaks up.

ices Frozen liquids and gases such as methane, ammonia, and water found in the heads of comets and in the atmospheres of the outer planets.

ice sheet A thick layer of glacial ice covering an extensive area.

igneous rock Any of several kinds of rock that appear to have been molten in the past.

impact theory (lunar) A naturalistic theory for the origin of the moon that suggests the matter in the moon was once a part of the earth, but a collision with another celestial object ejected the matter from the earth, and some of the matter coalesced and went into orbit around the earth as the moon.

impermeable Describes rock through which liquids and gases cannot penetrate because of the absence of connected pores, voids, or cracks of sufficient size.

index fossil A fossil that evolutionary geologists believe identifies the age of certain rock strata.

inductive reasoning A logical process by which a general conclusion is drawn from the implications of a set of specific examples.

inertia The tendency of all objects in the universe to remain at rest if initially at rest or, if moving, to continue moving at the same speed and in the same direction unless acted upon by an outside force.

inferior planet One of the planets whose orbit is closer to the sun than the earth's orbit (i.e., Mercury or Venus).

intensity In general, the amount of energy that is produced by a phenomenon; in seismology, the measure of the destructiveness of an earthquake as indicated by the Modified Mercalli Intensity (MMI) scale.

International Space Station (ISS) The ISS is a continuously manned orbital scientific and technological research outpost sponsored by 16 nations. It is located 450 kilometers above the earth. When completed, it will be 88 meters long, 109 meters across, and have a mass of more than 450 metric tons. It will have almost 5200 square meters of solar panels to provide electrical power for six state-of-the-art laboratories.

intrusive rock Igneous rock formed by magma solidifying beneath the earth's surface.

ion An atom or molecule having a positive or negative charge.

ionize To add electrons to or remove electrons from a particle to create an ion. (See *ion*.)

ionosphere That portion of Earth's upper atmosphere where solar ultraviolet radiation breaks down the gas molecules into individual atoms and ions. It reflects shortwave radio signals. The bottom of the zone starts about 70 to 80 km (40 to 50 mi) above the earth and extends to the edge of the atmosphere (500 km or more).

iron (meteorite) A type of meteorite that consists of 85–90 percent iron.

island arc A long, curved chain of volcanic islands that lines the oceanic margin of a tectonic plate.

isobar A line drawn on a weather map connecting stations with the same barometric pressure.

isotherm A line drawn on a weather map connecting stations with the same temperature.

J

jet stream A high-speed meandering wind current, usually flowing from west to east at altitudes of 15 to 25 km (10 to 15 mi). Its speed often exceeds 400 km/h (250 mi/h).

joint A crack in a rock formation along which there are no indications of slippage.

Jovian Resembling the planet Jupiter or pertaining to Jupiter or the Jupiter-like planets.

K

karst topography Topography in soluble nonclastic sedimentary rocks such as limestone that is characterized by solution caves, natural bridges, streamless valleys, and sinkholes.

Kuiper Belt A hypothetical belt of relatively small rocky objects containing a large percentage of ices that orbit the sun in a region starting beyond Uranus and extending outward for perhaps 20 ua. Several hundred objects smaller than the planet Pluto have been identified in this region, supporting its existence.

Kuiper Belt object (KBO) Any object located in the Kuiper Belt. The planet Pluto is thought to be the largest one of these. (See *Kuiper Belt*.)

L

lahar A mudslide that occurs when the venting of hot gases from a snow-capped volcano causes rapid melting of snow.

land breeze A breeze that blows from shore to sea, usually at night.

landslide The rapid movement of a mass of soil and rock downward on a steep slope.

lapse rate The rate at which temperature changes with altitude in the atmosphere. The average tropospheric lapse rate is –6.4 °C/km (–3.5 °F/1000 ft).

last quarter (lunar) Same as *third quarter*. It is that phase of the moon in which the eastern half is lighted and the western half is dark.

lateral moraine A ridge of glacial till deposited at the sides of a retreating glacier.

lava Molten rock that is discharged onto the earth's surface by a volcano.

lava plateau A thick igneous rock formation produced when lava flowed out of long cracks in the earth's surface, flooding all the surrounding land features for hundreds of square kilometers.

law A scientific theory that has become well established because it has been repeatedly confirmed by experimentation, has made many accurate predictions, or is readily accepted by the majority of scientists.

law of universal gravitation The principle that states any two objects attract each other with a force proportional to the product of their masses and inversely proportional to the square of the distance between them.

leap year In general, a calendar year in which one or more extra days is added to the calendar to keep it in phase with the seasons. The number of days depends on the calendar system being used.

Leonids A meteor shower that occurs about the middle of November every year when the earth runs into meteoric debris from comet 55P/Tempel-Tuttle. To an observer on the ground, the meteors appear to radiate from the direction of the constellation Leo.

levee An elevated ridge on each side of a stream. It may be man made, or it may be sand and soil deposited naturally during episodes of stream flooding.

lightning An electrical discharge that occurs either between clouds or between a cloud and the ground.

lightning rod A metal rod attached to the highest point of a building that prevents damage to the building from a lightning strike by conducting the electrical discharge through cables to the ground.

light-year A unit of distance (not time) to objects beyond our solar system, such as stars and galaxies; the distance light travels in one year, approximately 9.6 trillion km (6 trillion mi).

limb The edge of the disk of a planet, the sun, or the moon.

liquid scintillation counting (LSC) A method of determining the rate of radioactive decay in a sample by mixing it with a liquefied chemical that glows momentarily each time a carbon-14 atom decays. A special optical instrument counts and records the number of flashes per unit of time.

lithosphere The rigid, rocky outer layer of the earth consisting of the crust and the outer mantle that act together as a unit. It averages 77 km (48 mi) thick under the oceans to nearly 300 km (186 mi) thick under the continents.

loam An especially fertile soil that contains about equal parts of sand and silt, about half as much clay, and a generous amount of humus.

local metamorphism A relatively small-scale process that occurs when intrusive or extrusive magma heats and compresses the surrounding rock materials, altering their crystal structure and chemical composition.

lodestone A magnetic mineral called *magnetite* that was once used as the magnetic element in navigation compasses.

loess A thick deposit of fine windblown dust and silt.

longshore current A current that flows parallel to the shore and is caused by waves that approach the shore at an angle.

low-Earth orbit An orbital path relatively close to the earth (e.g., 350–500 km above the earth).

luminescence A visible glow given off by some minerals when they absorb high-energy but invisible ultraviolet light.

lunar calendar A calendar with months that correspond to the length of the moon's cycle.

lunar eclipse The darkening of the full moon when it passes into the earth's shadow.

lunisolar calendar A calendar that takes into account both the solar year and the lunar month, making the necessary adjustments to keep the calendar in agreement with the seasons.

luster   An identifying property of some minerals. It refers to the quality and intensity of light reflected from the mineral's surface.

L wave   The last waves to reach a seismic station after an earthquake. They are earthquake waves that travel along the earth's surface and thus are the most destructive waves.

M

mackerel sky   Cirro- and altocumulus clouds that form in patterns that resemble the striped markings on the sides of a mackerel.

magma   Molten rock beneath the surface of the earth.

magnetism   In general, a force related to the alignment of the magnetic poles of atoms in certain materials where the strength of each atom's magnetic field is combined, with the result that these materials attract or repel similar materials. An identifying property of certain minerals whereby they are able to attract iron.

magnetosphere   The magnetic field that encircles the earth and traps high-energy ions from the sun's solar wind. It protects living things from damage by the sun's particle radiation.

magnitude   The measure of the brightness of a star; a measure of the amount of energy released by an earthquake.

mantle   The portion of the earth's interior between the crust and the core.

mare   (pl. *maria*) A dark, flat lowland region on the moon's surface.

mares' tails   Cirrus clouds that are arranged in wispy streaks or bands across the sky.

mass   A measure of the amount of matter an object contains; not dependent on the force of gravity.

mass wasting   The downhill movement of large masses of soil and rocks under the influence of gravity.

materialism   The philosophical belief that only physical, material, or measurable things are real. It denies the existence of supernatural beings or their activities. An underlying principle in evolutionary thought.

matrix   The rock material in which a gem, mineral, fossil, or rock fragment is enclosed or embedded.

maximum thermometer   A temperature-measuring instrument that indicates the maximum temperature since the last time the instrument was reset.

mean sea level (MSL)   The average local sea level between high and low tide determined over the course of years. (See *sea level*.)

meander   A sharp looping bend in the channel of a low-gradient stream.

mechanical weathering   The breakdown of rocks into smaller pieces by the action of physical forces such as freezing water, growing plant roots, or wind-driven sand.

medial moraine   The moraine that formed from debris carried in the center of a glacier when the debris from the inner edges of two merging valley glaciers flowed together.

melt   The change of state from solid to liquid by the application of heat. Also, the molten rock mixture from which certain minerals form as the mixture cools.

mercurial barometer   An instrument for measuring atmospheric pressure from the height of a column of mercury in a long glass tube.

mesopause   The upper boundary of the atmospheric mesosphere.

mesosphere   One of the layers of the atmosphere defined by temperature profile. The zone of the earth's atmosphere between about 50 to 80 km (31 to 50 mi) above sea level, characterized by decreasing temperature with increasing altitude.

metamorphic rock   A rock that has been altered in its basic characteristics by heat, pressure, and/or hydrothermal chemical action since it was created or formed.

meteor   A mass of stone and/or metal that falls through the earth's atmosphere and is heated by air friction until it glows brightly. It is informally called a "shooting star."

meteorite   A remnant of a meteor large enough that it survives the fall through the atmosphere and hits the ground.

meteoroid   A mass of stone or metal that orbits the sun but is too small to be called a planet or asteroid (i.e., any such object that is too small to be observed from the surface of the earth). It can become a meteor if it enters the earth's atmosphere.

meteorology   The science of the earth's atmosphere, especially the weather.

microgravity   The absence or greatly reduced sensation of gravitational force, as when in orbit around the earth. Significant gravity exists at the altitude of the orbit, but the spacecraft is continuously falling as it orbits so that there is no sensation of gravity.

Milky Way   The galaxy that contains our solar system; visible as a broad band of stars across the night sky.

millibar   A unit of atmospheric pressure equal to one thousandth of a bar. One millibar is a pressure of 100 newtons per square meter.

mineral   A naturally occurring, homogenous, crystalline, inorganic solid.

minimum thermometer   A temperature-measuring instrument that indicates the lowest temperature experienced since the last time the instrument was reset.

minor planet   A rocky object in orbit around the sun, smaller than a planet but large enough to be observed from the surface of the earth; also known as an asteroid. (See *asteroid* and *meteoroid*.)

mixture Two or more substances mixed together but not chemically combined.

model A working representation of what a scientist thinks is occurring in a phenomenon he is studying.

Mohorovičić discontinuity ("Moho") The boundary between the earth's crust and mantle. It varies from about 7 km (4.5 mi) under oceans to about 50 km (31 mi) under continental mountain chains.

Mohs scale A scale from 1 to 10 for classifying minerals according to their relative hardness.

monocline The simplest fold in stratified rock in which the angle of inclination sharply increases for a short distance. A step-like fold in rocks.

monsoon A regional wind system that reverses periodically, alternately bringing wet and dry seasons.

mountain breeze A breeze that flows down the mountain into the valley at night that is caused by cooling air at higher elevations.

mountain range A series of mountains that seem to have a similar history and are more or less connected by elevated ground between them.

mountain system A group of mountain ranges.

mouth The point at which a stream empties into a larger body of water. Also, the elevation of the local base line for that stream.

mud pot Muddy bubbles of steam produced by a hot spring within a volcanic ash or cinder field.

N

native mineral A mineral that contains only one kind of atom and is therefore a pure element.

natural bridge A section of stone that arches over a narrow walled valley formed by erosion in karst topography. It is believed to be the remnant of a cave roof where the rest of the roof on both sides of the bridge has collapsed.

neap tide A lower-than-usual tide that occurs when the sun, the earth, and the moon form a right angle and cause the sun's gravity to work against the moon's gravity. Neap tides occur twice each month, at the first and third quarters of the moon.

nebula (pl. *nebulae*) A cloud of gas and dust in outer space; may be a bright, dark, or emission nebula.

neck cutoff A shortcut across a meander that a low-gradient stream sometimes takes, turning the meander into an oxbow lake.

neutrino An electrically neutral, subatomic, nearly massless particle emitted by the fusion reaction within the sun that travels at nearly the speed of light. Neutrinos do not readily interact with matter and are very hard to detect.

neutron star A small, extremely dense, dark starlike object made of neutrons. Because of its high density, only high-energy rays can escape its gravity.

new moon That phase of the moon when it is positioned in its orbit between the sun and the earth and is not visible because of the sun's glare.

Newtonian reflector A telescope in which light from an object is collected by a concave mirror mounted at the bottom of a rigid tube, reflected to a small diagonal mirror near the top of the tube, and then reflected out through the side of the tube to the eyepiece.

Newton's third law of motion For every force exerted on an object, the object exerts an equal but opposite force on the source of the original force. Forces always occur in pairs.

nitrogen A colorless, odorless, tasteless gas that forms approximately 78 percent of the earth's atmosphere (by volume).

nonclastic A property of sedimentary rocks indicating the absence of any smaller eroded rock particles embedded within the matrix. Such rock is believed to have formed when dissolved minerals in seawater or groundwater precipitated.

nonfoliated rock Metamorphic rock that is not banded or layered.

normal fault A fault in which the body of rock under the fault rises in relation to the rock above the fault.

nova A star that explodes and increases in brightness up to ten magnitudes but is not destroyed in the process. It may explode again later.

nucleation To provide a nucleus for moisture freezing, condensation, or sublimation.

nucleus The solid central part of a comet's head, consisting of rocks, ices, and organic matter. Also, the solid particle around which moisture condenses to form most clouds. The tiny central region of an atom that contains the majority of the atom's mass where protons and neutrons reside.

O

objective lens The lens nearest the object in a compound optical instrument. In astronomy, the large, light-gathering lens of a refractor telescope.

occluded front A front formed when a cool air mass and a rapidly moving cold air mass trap a warm air mass between them. The warm air mass is lifted, losing all contact with the ground.

occult (astronomy) The eclipsing of a heavenly body such as a star or planet by the moon or another planet.

ocular The eyepiece of an optical instrument such as a telescope.

ore Rock containing one or more minerals that are the source of elements or compounds important to industry or agriculture.

organic In mineralogy, describes materials that are obtained from living or once-living organisms.

orogeny The general term referring to any mountain-building process that is responsible for the internal structure of mountains.

orographic Associated with the presence of mountains. In meteorology, the lifting of an air mass and resulting precipitation as it flows over a mountain.

outer planet Any planet beyond the orbit of Mars (and by extension, beyond the main asteroid belt, which is considered by some to be the dividing line between the inner and outer planets).

outwash plain The broad plain in front of the terminus of a glacier consisting of deposits of glacial sediment and intertwined ribbonlike streamlets formed by glacial meltwater.

overthrust A reverse fault with an angle of less than 45°, where the rocks on the upper side of the fault are believed to have been pushed over the rocks on the lower side of the fault.

oxbow lake A U-shaped lake formed by the cutting off of a meander in a low-gradient stream.

oxide A nonsilicate mineral composed of oxygen and some other element, usually a metal.

oxygen A colorless, tasteless, odorless gas that forms approximately 21 percent of the earth's atmosphere and is the essential element for respiration. It is the most abundant element in the earth's crust.

ozone layer A layer of concentrated ozone (O_3) located 20–50 km (12–31 mi) above the earth's surface that shields the earth from the harmful forms of ultraviolet light.

P

P wave The first waves that reach a seismic station after an earthquake. Such earthquake waves are capable of passing through the earth's core.

paleontology The study of fossil animals and plants.

Pangaea The single large continent proposed by Alfred Wegener in his continental displacement theory from which all the present-day continents originated. The original supercontinent that may have existed before a disruption of the earth's crust produced today's arrangement of continents.

panning A method for separating placer gold from the sand and gravel in which it is found. Uses a shallow pan and a rocking motion to wash away the lighter materials.

Panthalassa Ocean The name given to the hypothetical global ocean surrounding the supercontinent Pangaea by Alfred Wegener in his original continental displacement theory.

parallax An apparent shift in position of an observed object caused by a change in the point of observation. It is used to measure the distances to nearby stars and is irrefutable proof of the earth's revolution around the sun.

partial eclipse An eclipse in which the face of the sun is never fully covered, as observed at a particular location.

penumbra The lighter outer portion of a shadow cast by a planet or moon, where an observer in the shadow would see a partial solar eclipse. Also, the outer lower temperature region of a sunspot.

perched water table A second water table resting on top of an impermeable layer above the general water table for an area.

perigee The point nearest the earth in the orbit of the moon or of an earth-orbiting satellite.

perihelion The point nearest the sun in the orbit of a planet or other sun-orbiting object.

period In general, the length of time it takes a repeating event to occur. Examples include the time required for a complete Cepheid variable cycle or for a satellite to make one complete orbit.

periodic comet A comet that returns or is expected to return to the inner solar system because it has an elliptical orbit.

permeable Describes rock where the size and number of the interconnected pores is sufficient for liquids and gases to penetrate or pass through.

Perseids A meteor shower that occurs about the middle of August every year when the earth runs into meteoric debris from comet 109P/Swift-Tuttle. To an observer on the ground, the meteors appear to radiate from the direction of the constellation Perseus.

petrology The study of rocks, including their composition, identification, and classification.

phase The appearance of the moon according to the amount of the lighted side that is visible from Earth. Also, another name for a state of matter.

phosphorescent Having the property of emitting visible light after a high-energy light source no longer illuminates the surface.

photon A packet of electromagnetic energy believed to be a discrete particle having zero mass, no electric charge, and an indefinitely long lifetime.

photosphere The visible surface of the sun.

photovoltaic (PV) cell A device that changes radiant energy (especially light) into an electric voltage.

piedmont glacier A broad glacier formed by the merging of two or more valley glaciers near the foot of a mountain.

pilot balloon A lighter-than-air balloon set loose and tracked to determine wind speeds and directions at various altitudes.

placer deposit A deposit consisting of fine flecks of gold or other dense native minerals eroded out of the parent rocks. It may be found in streambeds or on beaches.

planet   In general, any large body orbiting any star. One of the nine largest bodies orbiting the sun.

plasma   A state of matter that forms at extremely high temperatures and is not solid, liquid, or gas. All the particles in a plasma are partially or completely ionized, especially in stellar plasmas.

plate tectonics theory   The theory that the crust of the earth consists of a relatively few semi-rigid plates floating on a plastic or semi-fluid mantle. It is the fundamental naturalistic theory that accounts for mountain ranges, earthquakes, volcanoes, sea-floor spreading, continental drift, and most geologic processes that have supposedly taken place over billions of years.

platinum   A precious, white-silver, metallic, native mineral with a specific gravity of 21.5—denser than gold. Platinum can act as a catalyst in many chemical reactions and is considered more valuable than an equal mass of gold.

plucking   A process of glacial erosion in which fragments of bedrock are pulled away by the ice as it moves over the bedrock.

pluton   Any large intrusive igneous rock mass originally formed deep in the earth, such as a batholith or a stock.

polar easterlies   Winds blowing consistently from northeast to southwest from the northern polar region, bringing cold, dry air to the northern parts of North America, Asia, and Europe.

polar high   An area of high atmospheric pressure at either pole caused by subsiding cold air.

polarization   The process in which light waves are filtered so that they vibrate in only one direction when they exit the filter. Some minerals can polarize light that passes through them.

polar orbit   An orbital path that takes an earth satellite over the poles during each orbit.

polystrate fossil   A fossil such as a tree trunk that extends through at least two rock strata.

porosity   The ratio of the volume of empty space between the particles in a rock to its total volume. A rock that has high porosity has either a few large pores, many tiny pores, or both.

porous   Having many small open spaces.

***post hoc* fallacy**   The logical error of assuming that because a more recent event occurred after a previous event, the latter was caused by former. Abbreviated from the Latin phrase *post hoc ergo propter hoc*, meaning, "after this, therefore, because of this."

potassium-argon method   A radioactive dating method still in use by naturalistic geologists that is based on the amount of argon-40 in a sample compared to its content of potassium-40, from which it is assumed to have decayed. The method has been thoroughly and scientifically discredited by creationary geologists.

precipitate   The solid that crystallizes out of a super-saturated solution and settles to the bottom of the solution.

precipitation   In meteorology, moisture falling from the atmosphere as rain, hail, snow, or sleet. In chemistry, the formation of a chemical precipitate, as in the deposition of speleothems in a cave.

pressure   The total amount of force exerted over a standard area, such as a square meter or square foot. Units of pressure are given in units of force per square area, such as newtons per square meter (pascals) or pounds per square inch.

pressure gradient force   The horizontal force exerted on a mass of air that has a higher pressure on one side than on the other.

presupposition   An idea that is held to be true or is taken for granted when making decisions or arguing to a conclusion. It is the main reason for a bias.

"pretended neutrality" fallacy   The logical error of claiming to have no presuppositions. (See *presupposition*.)

prevailing westerlies   Winds blowing consistently from southwest to northeast between 30° and 60° north and south latitudes.

prime hour circle   The reference line for celestial longitude, extending from the north to the south celestial poles through the point of the vernal equinox. (See *vernal equinox*.) Position of zero hours of right ascension.

probe   An instrumented, unmanned, expendable vehicle used to explore space.

Project Apollo   The manned U.S. space program established to land on and briefly explore the moon.

Project Gemini   An early U.S. manned space program using two-man crews to prepare for Project Apollo flights.

Project Mercury   The first manned U.S. space program established to place a man in a low-Earth orbit.

prominence   An immense disturbance in the corona of the sun that may appear as a loop, a feathery structure, or an irregular mass rising from and falling back into the sun.

proper motion   The portion of a star's motion that is perpendicular to an observer's line of sight. The star's apparent motion across the face of the heavens, not due to parallax.

psychrometer   An instrument used to determine relative humidity, consisting of wet- and dry-bulb thermometers.

Ptolemaic theory   An early, widely held geocentric theory, that the earth was the fixed center of the universe and that all celestial objects revolved around it.

pyroclastic material   Volcanic emissions of solidified lava in pieces of any size, including ash, cinders, bombs, and sometimes large blocks of rock.

Q

quadrant A navigational instrument used to measure a star's angular position above the horizon. A quadrant's frame, or sector, forms a 90° angle and contains an angular scale and a sighting mirror attached to a movable arm.

quasar An unusually bright celestial object that produces strong radio emissions. Most seem to be distant and are moving rapidly away from the earth. They have unusual properties compared to other celestial objects.

R

radar The method of determining the distance, speed, or shape of an object by bouncing radio waves back from its surface.

radial motion The portion of a star's motion that is either directly toward or away from the observer.

radiant In astronomy, the point in the sky from which shower meteors seem to radiate. Describes energy transmitted by electromagnetic waves.

radiation The heat or light emitted by a glowing object. Also, the particles and rays emitted by a radioactive material.

radiative zone The middle zone of the model of the sun's interior where thermal energy moves outward from the core by radiation.

radioactive Describes a substance that emits nuclear radiation.

radioactivity The rate at which nuclear particles and rays are emitted by a radioactive substance.

radiosonde An instrument package carried aloft by a balloon to transmit atmospheric data back to a weather station.

radio telescope A radio receiver with a large, dish-shaped antenna system. It receives, focuses, amplifies, and analyzes radio waves from outer space. In some telescopes, radio signals can be transmitted as well, just as in standard radar systems. See *radar*.

rain gauge A cylindrical or tipping device used to measure the amount of rain that falls in a given period.

rawinsonde A pilot balloon carrying a radio transmitter so it can be tracked when visibility is low.

ray Any of the bright streaks on the moon's surface radiating from some of the moon's craters. Also, a high-energy electromagnetic wave emitted by an atom or its nucleus (e.g., x-rays or gamma rays).

recharge zone An area where rainwater or stream water seeps through to the water table to resupply groundwater in an aquifer.

red shift The difference in the observed wavelengths of light from a celestial body compared to the wavelengths emitted at the source.

reflector telescope Any one of several telescope designs that uses a concave mirror as the primary light-gathering optical component.

refraction In general, the bending of a wave when it changes speed because the material through which it is moving changes in some way. It occurs in optics when light passes from air into glass and in water waves when the bottom becomes shallower than the wave base.

refractor telescope A telescope that uses only lenses to concentrate the light from an object and focus it into an image.

regional metamorphism Metamorphism that occurred over large areas because of the heat and pressure from immense forces—forces that folded great tracts of rock, lifted mountains, and pushed plates of the earth's crust together.

relative humidity A ratio of the amount of water the air is actually holding to the amount it could hold at that same temperature, expressed as a percentage.

relief A term used to define the extremes of height or elevation in an area. It is the difference between the highest and lowest points in a region.

residence time The average time between a particle's entrance into the ocean and its removal by some means.

residual mountain Another name for an erosional mountain, such as a mesa, butte, monadnock, horn, and so forth.

resolution (optical) The ability of a lens or mirror to visually separate two objects that are separated by a small angle.

retrograde motion The apparent backward movement of the superior planets caused by the difference in orbital speed between Earth and the planet being observed.

return stroke A lightning discharge from the ground up to a cloud along the ionized path taken by the original strike from the cloud to the ground.

reverse fault A fault in which the fault face is greater than 45° to the horizontal and the body of rock above the fault rises in relation to the rock below the fault. (See *thrust fault*.)

reverse osmosis A method of desalinization in which seawater is pumped at high pressure against a special membrane that allows water molecules to pass through but prevents the salt and other particles from crossing over.

revolve To circle around a point that does not lie within the object, as a planet around the sun.

Richter scale An open-ended scale of earthquake magnitude. A magnitude of 3 can be barely felt. A magnitude of 9 or more is completely devastating.

rift A crack in the earth's crust along which outward spreading takes place. The mid-ocean ridges contain rifts.

right ascension (RA) Celestial longitude; measured in hours, minutes, and seconds east of the prime hour circle.

rills Long, narrow, snaking valleys especially evident on the moon's surface.

rime ice Frozen fog that adheres to structures and often produces bizarre shapes.

rip current Rapid currents flowing outward to sea from indentations along a shore on which large waves are breaking. These currents are also called *undertow*.

rock A relatively hard natural substance formed from one or more minerals or organic materials.

rock cycle A naturalistic concept that supposedly describes how the earth's rocks are recycled between the crust and the upper mantle. One complete cycle would require millions of years based on the current rate of geologic processes.

rocket An aerial vehicle or device propelled by the rapid emission of hot gases that are produced from combustion not requiring atmospheric oxygen.

rock glacier A glacier consisting mostly of rock fragments held together with ice. It moves slowly under the influence of gravity, just like a standard glacier.

rock slide A sudden, massive, catastrophic slippage of bedrock fragments, caused by weakness or loss of friction between layers of bedrock.

rotate To spin on an axis that passes through the center of an object.

runaway subduction The hypothetical cause of catastrophic plate tectonics in which hot mantle rocks under great pressure liquefy, causing the overlying oceanic crust to slide "downhill" into the mantle under adjacent plates (subduction) at speeds of many kilometers per hour. (See *catastrophic plate tectonics* and *plate tectonics*.)

S

salinity Describes the relative amount of salts dissolved in water. Highly saline water, as found in salt lakes or the Dead Sea, contains a relatively large amount of dissolved salts. Fresh water from snowfield runoff has very low salinity. Seawater salinity varies midway between these extremes.

salt dome An immense mass of nearly pure salt (halite) that was pushed upward through overlying layers of sedimentary rock into vertical, domelike structures.

sand dune A mound or wavelike ridge of loose sand heaped up by the wind.

satellite An object that orbits another, usually larger, object.

Schmidt-Cassegrainian A composite telescope that uses a spherical concave main mirror and a spherical convex secondary mirror arranged according to the Cassegrainian design but also includes an aspherical correction plate that both eliminates the spherical aberration in the mirror system and supports the secondary mirror.

science The total collection of knowledge from man's methodical observations of the universe as well as the activities by which that knowledge is obtained. Ultimately, the concept of science is not easily definable.

scientific methodology A set of standards and procedures a scientist uses when studying a scientific problem.

scientific satellite A satellite that is designed mainly to acquire scientific information, such as an earth resources satellite or an orbiting telescope.

scientism The belief that scientific inquiry is the only path to truth.

sea A large body of salt water partially or nearly completely enclosed by land.

sea arch A coastal erosional formation resembling a natural bridge that was caused by wave erosion of a sea cave through a narrow headland.

sea breeze A breeze that blows onshore from the ocean, usually during the daytime.

sea cave A cave formed by erosion of a cliff face by waves.

sea-floor spreading The observation that the oceanic tectonic plates are spreading away from the mid-ocean ridges and seem to be carrying the continents with them.

sea level The level of the sea at a particular time. Sea level thus changes with the rising and falling tides. The term is often used interchangeably with mean sea level (MSL).

seamount Any submerged mountain-like structure on the sea bottom; most are extinct volcanoes.

second law of thermodynamics Includes the concept that all natural processes proceed toward a state of greater disorder (greater entropy) and of less usable energy.

secular Any idea or human activity that is not supposed to be related to a religion or religious teaching. Also, a viewpoint of religious skepticism that opposes a Christian worldview in science and education.

sediment Earthy matter suspended in or deposited by water, wind, or ice.

sedimentary rock Rock consisting of particles of sediment that have been bonded together by natural cements; solids that have precipitated from water solutions.

seismograph An instrument for detecting, measuring, and recording earthquake activity.

shelf A cave formation of flat deposits of calcite that precipitated on the surface of standing water.

shield A flat, rounded deposit of calcium carbonate attached to a cave ceiling, wall, or floor.

shield volcano A broad, flat, dome-shaped volcano built up by successive eruptions of lava.

shower meteors Meteors that originate as meteoroids orbiting along the path of a former or active comet. The shower occurs when the earth intersects the comet's orbit.

silicate A class of minerals that contains mainly silicon and oxygen along with minor amounts of other elements. Quartz and feldspars, both silicates, are the most common minerals in the crust.

sill A sheet of intrusive igneous rock that has been forced between existing rock strata.

silver A precious, metallic, native mineral with a specific gravity of 10.5. It is not as valuable as gold but has many applications from electronic circuits to photography.

sinkhole A depression in the ground that occurs when the roof of a solution cave collapses at a single point.

sleet Small frozen or partially frozen raindrops that form when rain falls through a layer of cold air.

sling psychrometer A psychrometer designed to be whirled in the air to promote evaporation around the wet-bulb thermometer. (See *psychrometer*.)

sluicing A method of mechanically processing ores in order to extract dense metals by flowing crusted rock mixed with water down a long, ridged trough. The sand, dirt, and gravel are washed free from the denser metals that remain in the bottom of the sluice.

snow Frozen precipitation formed by the sublimation of water vapor onto freezing nuclei.

snowfield A large expanse of snow-covered terrain above the snow line.

snow line In a glacier, the imaginary line that separates the lower, warmer areas, where the winter snow melts in the summertime, from higher, colder areas where some or all of the snow remains from one winter to the next.

soil Ideally, a mixture of sand, silt, and clay containing some humus; proportions vary depending on the source and fertility of the soil.

solar calendar A calendar that is based on the solar year and ignores the lunar cycle.

solar eclipse An eclipse that occurs when the moon passes between the earth and the sun, blocking some or all of the sun's light to the earth at a given location.

solar energy In general, refers to the energy received by the earth from the sun. It can also refer to all forms of energy obtainable from the sun, such as solar-generated electricity, solar heating, solar hot water, and so on.

solar flare An extremely violent eruption on the surface of the sun resulting in intense emissions of ultraviolet radiation, x-rays, and solar matter. Exceptionally large solar flares are called *coronal mass ejections* (*CME*), which can create "geomagnetic storms" on Earth that affect satellites, the electrical power grid, and communications systems.

solar wind High-speed particles from the sun's corona, mostly protons and electrons, traveling outward in all directions into interstellar space.

solution In general, a type of uniform mixture where one substance (the solute) is completely dissolved in another (the solvent). In hydrology, it describes a type of erosion in which groundwater dissolves minerals and removes them from rocks and soil. It also refers to a type of cave believed to have been formed by the action of acidic hydrothermal solutions. Today these caves continue to be enlarged and modified by mildly acidic groundwater originating from the ground surface.

solvent A substance that breaks down other substances into their constituent molecules or ions and forms a uniform mixture. Water is often called the "universal solvent."

sounding In general, taking a measurement from a remote location. In meteorology, it is collecting environmental data in the upper atmosphere using an instrumented rocket launched for the purpose. In oceanography or marine navigation, it means measuring the depth of the water beneath a vessel.

sounding rocket A rocket and its instrumented probe used to obtain environmental and meteoric data in the upper atmosphere.

source (stream) In hydrology, the highest point or origin of a stream.

source region In meteorology, a region with relatively uniform temperature and humidity over which air masses form.

space shuttle A reusable manned space vehicle designed to carry heavy satellites, space probes, and equipment to Earth orbit. It also transports people and cargo for the construction and resupply of the International Space Station.

space station A habitable structure in Earth orbit from which astronomical observations and scientific research may be conducted.

specific gravity A ratio of the mass of a mineral to that of an equal volume of water.

spectroscope An instrument used to identify the elements in an incandescent (heated until glowing) substance by separating and measuring the component wavelengths.

spectrum A distribution of electromagnetic energies arranged in order of wavelengths.

speleothem Any cave formation deposited by dripping or flowing water.

spelunker In the U.S., a person who explores and maps caves as a hobby. Also known as a *caver*.

spicule A pointed jet of gasses from the top of the sun's chromosphere extending into the corona.

spit A narrow sand formation deposited by waves and currents that extends out from a headland, often across the mouth of a bay or inlet.

sporadic meteor A meteor that comes from a random, unpredictable direction and may occur any time of the year.

spring A location, usually on a hillside, where the water table intersects the ground and water flows onto the ground surface more-or-less continuously.

spring tide An unusually high tide that occurs when the sun, earth, and moon are lined up, either at new moon or at full moon.

squall line A line of violent thunderstorms that sometimes accompanies an advancing cold front.

stack A mass of rock that wave erosion has isolated from the shore, often formed by the collapse of a sea arch.

stage In rocketry, a unit containing rocket engines, fuel, and/or instruments that is attached to other similar units to form a multi-stage rocket. The multiple stages are fired sequentially, each stage falling off as its fuel is exhausted in order to reduce the mass of the remaining rocket.

stalactite An icicle-shaped mineral formation hanging from the ceiling of a cave, deposited by dripping water.

stalagmite A narrow, conical mineral formation growing upward from the floor of a cave, usually deposited by water dripping from a stalactite.

star cluster A group of stars that appear to be relatively close to each other and have the same radial and proper motions.

stationary front A zone of contact between two dissimilar air masses where neither is advancing. It usually results in no change in the weather for several days.

station model A symbolic method of showing the weather conditions at a weather station on a map. It consists of a location circle with the weather conditions of the station represented by symbols in assigned positions around the circle.

stepped leader Prior to a lightning stroke, a zigzag column of highly ionized air that establishes the channel for subsequent lightning discharges and return strokes.

stone (stony meteorite) The most common type of meteorite, composed mostly of silicate minerals with 10–15 percent other materials, such as the metals iron and nickel.

stony-iron (meteorite) A meteorite composed approximately of half silicates and half iron.

storm surge A large increase in sea level along the shore in front of and below a hurricane as high winds pile water up against the land, often causing catastrophic flooding and erosion. It is the difference between the measured sea level and the tide caused by just the sun and moon at the time of measurement.

storm swell The larger-than-normal surface waves that proceed outward from a slow-moving hurricane.

stratopause The upper boundary of the stratosphere, between the stratosphere and the mesosphere, about 50 km (31 mi) above the earth's surface.

stratosphere A region of the earth's atmosphere defined by temperature profile located between the troposphere and the mesosphere and between 12 and 50 km (7.4–31 mi) above the earth's surface. The temperature increases with altitude through this region.

stratovolcano A volcano whose cone is made up of alternating layers of solidified lava and pyroclastic materials from different eruptions; a composite volcano.

stratum (pl. *strata*) In general, a flat, horizontal, well-defined layer. Typically a layer of sedimentary rock, usually horizontal but often tilted to various angles or folded by movements within the earth's crust.

streak A mineral identification test made by rubbing a specimen across an unglazed porcelain tile and observing the color of the powdered mineral that remains.

streak plate A piece of unglazed porcelain on which a mineral is rubbed in performing a streak test.

stream A flowing body of water that moves downhill either continuously or seasonally on the surface or underground. It can be a rivulet, brook, stream, creek, or river.

streamless valley A karst valley that contains an abandoned stream bed because the stream has been diverted underground through a sinkhole.

strewn field The elongated area on the ground where scattered meteorite fragments from an exploded fireball (meteor) are found.

striation Parallel scratch marks in bedrock over which a glacier has moved.

strike-slip fault A fault along which the movement is horizontal.

subduction A process that is believed to occur as the relatively thin and denser oceanic lithosphere slides under a more massive but less dense continental crust and is bent downward hundreds of kilometers into the mantle.

sublimation A change of state directly from the solid to the gaseous state or from the gaseous to the solid state without passing through the liquid state.

submarine canyon A canyon that occurs on the ocean floor, often on the continental slope.

subpolar low The prevailing low-pressure belt at approximately 60° north or south latitude. In the Northern Hemisphere the prevailing westerlies rise above the polar easterlies, lifting air in this zone.

sulfide A compound composed of one or more elements and sulfur.

sulfur A nonmetallic, native mineral consisting of the pure element sulfur, which is identified by its yellow color and conchoidal fracture.

summer solstice The day (about June 21) when the sun's overhead noon position is the farthest north. (See *Tropic of Cancer*.)

sunspot A relatively small, cooler, darker area on the sun's surface believed to be associated with local irregularities in the sun's magnetic field.

sun-synchronous orbit One of the polar orbits designed to place the satellite over a certain place on the earth's surface at the same time every day.

supercooled water Water droplets having temperatures below freezing that remain in the liquid state. If supercooled water contacts a surface at or near freezing, ice buildup rapidly occurs, as in ice storms.

supergiant A term used to classify the largest and most luminous stars. Typically they are fifteen to twenty times as massive as our sun, but they are several hundred times as large and are much more luminous.

superior planet A planet whose orbit is farther from the sun than the earth's orbit.

supernova A star that suddenly increases its apparent brightness by about twenty magnitudes because of an explosion that essentially destroys it.

surface gravity The gravitational force measured at the actual or designated surface of a celestial object (the sun and the Jovian planets have no definite surfaces).

surge A sudden increase in the speed of glacial movement.

S wave The second type of earthquake wave to reach a seismic station after the P waves from the earthquake. This type of wave cannot pass through the core of the earth.

syncline Sedimentary strata folded downward in the shape of a trough.

synoptic weather map A map that presents a synopsis (general view) of the weather data for a given time frame (e.g., the Surface Weather map, the 500 Millibar Height Contours map, the Highest and Lowest Temperatures map, and the Precipitation Areas and Amounts map).

T

tail A long tenuous streamer extending from the head of a comet when the comet is near the sun. The tail is oriented in the direction away from the sun because of the pressure of the solar wind. (See *solar wind*.)

talus A sloping pile of weathered rock at the base of a cliff composed of rock pieces that have fallen from the cliff.

tarn A small pond or lake in a glaciated mountain valley that has no outlet.

tectonic plate One of some fifteen semi-rigid pieces of the earth's lithosphere that make up the outer shell of the earth. Most show some movement relative to adjacent plates.

temperature A measure of the average energy of motion (kinetic energy) of the atoms or molecules of a substance, stated in degrees. It is also the measure of the hotness or coldness of an object.

tephra An accumulation of loose volcanic ash.

terminator The line dividing the lighted portion of a nonluminous celestial body from the dark portion.

terminus The lowest end, or the front, of a glacier.

terrestrial planet A primarily solid planet (i.e., Mercury, Venus, Earth, Mars, and according to some astronomers, Pluto) that has a relatively thin atmosphere and is about the same size as Earth or smaller.

texture A term that describes the size of the crystals in a mineral. Large crystal sizes give a rock a coarse texture, while very small crystals give a rock a fine texture.

theodolite A telescopic instrument used to track pilot balloons to permit calculation of the direction and speed of winds aloft.

theory A tool used by scientists to study scientific problems. In many cases, it is a hypothesis that has been tested and is a workable description of a phenomenon.

thermograph A thermometer that records the temperature while measuring it.

thermohaline current A deep ocean current caused by differences in temperature or salinity between large masses of ocean water.

thermometer An instrument for measuring temperature.

thermometer shelter A structure that shades an outdoor thermometer to exclude sources of radiant heat (sun, ground, etc.), which would result in false readings.

thermopause The upper boundary of the thermosphere, approximately 200–500 km above sea level depending on solar activity.

thermoscope A temperature-measuring device invented by Galileo that relied on temperature-related changes in a volume of air contained within a glass bulb.

thermosphere The highest and largest of the four atmospheric layers defined by temperature profile, ranging from about 80 km (50 mi) to 500 km (310 mi) above sea level. It is characterized by the highest daily temperatures in the atmosphere.

third quarter (lunar) Same as *last quarter*. It is that phase of the moon in which the eastern half is lighted and the western half is dark.

thrust fault A reverse fault that dips less than 45°. (See *reverse fault*.)

thunderhead A towering cumulonimbus cloud that builds rapidly to high altitudes (approaching 7600 m or 25,000 ft) and usually brings heavy rain, lightning, thunder, and sometimes hail.

thunderstorm A rainstorm that includes lightning and thunder.

tide A periodic fluctuation in sea level that is caused by the gravitational forces of the moon and the sun as well as by the inertia of the waters on the rotating earth.

tombolo A wave-deposited sandbar that connects islands with each other or with the mainland.

tornado A violent, narrow, rotating, funnel-shaped local windstorm containing the highest wind speeds measured, extending down from a cumulonimbus cloud.

total depravity The doctrine that from our birth every aspect of our being (mind, will, and emotions) has been turned away from God. This condition was inherited from fallen Adam, and the work of Christ is the only thing able to correct it.

total eclipse An event where the direct (solar) or reflected (lunar) light from the sun as viewed by an observer at a given location is completely cut off by another astronomical body.

trade winds Consistent winds extending from the subtropical highs toward the equator, turned by the Coriolis effect into easterlies. They were formerly used by sailing ships to go from Europe to North and South America.

train (meteoric) The glowing trail behind a fireball.

transit The passage of an inferior planet across the sun's disk.

trench A deep canyon in the sea floor. Trenches seem to be associated with subduction at the margins of oceanic plates.

tributary A stream that flows into and feeds a larger stream.

Tropic of Cancer The line of latitude located at $23\frac{1}{2}°$ N. It is defined by the sun's northernmost overhead noon position at the summer solstice.

Tropic of Capricorn The line of latitude located at $23\frac{1}{2}°$ S. It is defined by the sun's southernmost overhead position at the winter solstice.

tropopause The upper boundary of the troposphere that separates the troposphere from the stratosphere.

troposphere The lowest of the four layers of the earth's atmosphere defined by the temperature profile. It is the location of all weather that affects the earth's surface.

trough The lowest part of a waveform.

tsunami A long-wavelength sea wave produced by volcanic or seismic action near or under the ocean; can cause great and sudden devastation when it comes ashore in a populated area.

turbidity current A fast subsurface density current caused by the weight of large amounts of suspended sediment. Such flows are believed to result in erosion of the continental slope.

type I tail The straight, bluish cometary tail composed of ionized gasses.

type II tail The curved, variously colored cometary tail composed of dust.

typhoon What hurricanes are called in the Western Pacific and Indian Ocean regions.

U

umbra The darker, inner part of a shadow cast by a planet where an observer within the shadow would experience a total solar eclipse. Also, the dark inner part of a sunspot.

uniformitarianism See *doctrine of uniformity*.

upwelling The rising to the surface of cold, nutrient-rich water from the depths of the ocean; often occurs when prevailing winds blow surface waters away, allowing deeper waters to rise and take their place.

uranium-lead method A method of radioactive dating based on the amount of lead isotopes in the sample compared to its content of uranium isotopes, from which the lead is assumed to have decayed.

V

valley breeze A breeze that blows up the mountainside from the valley when air high on the mountain heats and rises. Usually occurs late in the day.

valley glacier A glacier found in a narrow valley surrounded by mountains.

vaporization The change from a liquid to the vapor state. When the liquid is below the boiling point temperature, it is called *evaporation*. When at the boiling point, it is called *boiling*.

varve A thin layer of sediment that forms on the bottom of lakes fed by glacial meltwater. Varves were originally believed to be deposited annually but it is now known that they can be deposited more frequently than annually.

vent An opening in the crust of the earth from which lava and gases can be emitted.

vernal equinox   The day that the sun's overhead noon position crosses the equator (about March 21). At the equinox, day and night are of equal length in all parts of the earth.

volcanic cone   A conical landform built up by successive eruptions of a volcano.

volcanic neck   A vertical columnlike formation of igneous rock formed by erosion of the surrounding volcanic cone that leaves only the solidified lava originally contained within the volcano's vent passage.

volcano   A mountainlike landform built up by the emission of various forms of molten rock through a vent in the earth's surface.

W

waning crescent (lunar)   The decreasing phase of the moon during the last week of the lunar cycle.

waning gibbous (lunar)   The decreasing phase of the moon, following a full moon, when the illuminated disk gradually diminishes to the third quarter.

warm air mass   An air mass that is warmer than the surface over which it moves.

warm front   The advancing surface of a warm air mass as it pushes against and over a cooler air mass.

wastage zone   The zone of a glacier in lower, warmer elevations that is decreasing in size due to melting, calving, evaporation, or sublimation. It is also called the *ablation zone*.

waterspout   A tornado that occurs at sea.

water table   The level below which the ground is saturated with groundwater.

wave base   The water depth to which a wave disturbance reaches, equal to half the wavelength below the still-water level.

wave height   The vertical distance between a wave's crest and its trough.

wavelength   The horizontal distance from one wave crest to the next wave crest.

waxing crescent (lunar)   The increasing phase of the moon, during the week following a new moon, when its illuminated portion appears as a thin, gradually thickening crescent.

waxing gibbous (lunar)   The increasing phase of the moon, during the second week following the first quarter, when the illuminated portion is gradually enlarging toward a full moon.

weather   The condition of the atmosphere at a given time.

weather satellite   An earth-orbiting instrumented satellite used to observe and report various weather-related data, such as surface temperature, cloud patterns, and moisture content.

weight   The force of gravity exerted on an object.

white dwarf   A very dense, very bright star of about the same mass as the sun but only about a hundredth of its diameter. White dwarfs in binary systems may produce novas. Some may be remnants of supernovas.

Widmanstätten lines   Crosshatched lines that appear on the polished surface of a sectioned iron meteorite that has been acid etched.

wind-chill factor   The temperature of still air that would have the same effect on exposed human skin as a certain combination of air temperature and wind speed.

wind vane   A device for indicating wind direction.

winter solstice   The day (about December 21) when the sun's overhead noon position is southernmost. (See *Tropic of Capricorn*.)

worldview   The philosophical perspective from which a person interprets all evidence in life. One's worldview is arrived at by faith. Also, a person's set of beliefs and presuppositions about what is true in life.

X, Y, Z

zone of aeration   The zone within the ground above the water table in which the spaces between soil particles are filled with air.

zone of flow   The lower depth-zone of a glacier that flows over the underlying bedrock because the tremendous pressure of more than 50 m of ice above it makes it a plasticlike (semi-rigid) solid.

zone of fracture   The vertical depth zone of a glacier consisting of brittle ice that extends from the surface to a depth of about 50 m. The ice adjusts to the stresses of unequal motion and irregular terrain by fracturing and forming crevasses.

INDEX

Italicized page numbers denote margin definitions of terms or biographical notes. Boldface page numbers denote illustrations, margin notes, or information boxes.

PHOTOGRAPH CREDITS

These agencies and individuals have furnished materials to meet the photographic needs of this textbook. We wish to express our gratitude to them for their important contribution:

Advanced Water Systems
Alexander Turnbull Museum
Theo Allofs
Walt Anderson
Anglo-Australian Observatory
Answers in Genesis (AIG)
Associated Press/Wide World (AP)
Argyle Diamonds
Arizona Geological Survey
Art Resource
Sanford Berry
Martin Bond
Robert Brook
Bureau International des Poids et Measures
Dr. Richard Busch
Carolina Biological
Cartesia Software
Rod Catanach
City of Dunedin, FL
Clemson University
Brandon Cole
George R. Collins
Albert Copley
Gerald and Buffi Corsi
Dr. Stewart Custer
Beth Davidow
DeBeers
Denver Museum of Natural History
Department of Defense
Department of the Treasury
Rich Dererling
Jacques Descloitres
Earth Science World
Eastman Kodak, Co.
Wally Eberhart
Bernard Edmaier
École Supérieure d'Informatique et d'Applications de Lorraine (ESIAL)
Fabre Minerals
Douglas Faulkner
Larry Fellows
Dave Fleetham
Florida Geological Survey

Megan Foreman
Jason Fornari
Alessandro Forte
Fuji Film
Carolyn Galati
Getty Images
Mark Gibson
Pascal Goetgheluck
Francois Gohier
Great Images in NASA (GRIN)
National Research Center for Environment and Health (GSF)
Adam Hart-Davis
Hemera Technologies
Dr. Henson
HIP
Kurt Hollocher
Institute for Creation Research
Integrated Ocean Drilling Program
Israel Museum
Richard R. Jacobs
Jet Propulsion Laboratory (JPL)
Brian D. Johnson
Dane S. Johnson
Adam Jones
Bill Kamin
John Kauffmann
Kennecott Utah Copper Corporation
Breck Kent
Dr. Richard Kessel
James King-Holmes
Japanese Agency for Marine-Earth Science and Technology (JAMSTEC)
Jim Knowlton
Krafft
Laboratory of Tree Ring Research
Andrew Lambert Photography
Library of Congress
Ken Lucas
Lunar & Planetary Institute
Q.T. Luong
David Malin Images
James McCullagh

Steve McCutchen
Joe and Mary Ann McDonald
Dr. Ken McDonald
John McLean
Marli Miller
Moderate Resolution Imaging Spectroradiometer (MODIS) Land Rapid Response Team
Bruce Molnia
National Aeronautics and Space Administration (NASA)
National Archives
National Institute of Standards and Technology
National Library of Medicine
National Oceanic and Atmospheric Administration (NOAA)
National Park Service
National Speleological Society
Navy Historical Society
Nutyco, LTD
Ocean Drilling Program
Ocean Imaging Corporation
Oklahoma University
Jim Peaco
Susan Perry
PhotoDisc
Photo Researchers, Inc.
Pikes Peak Attractions Association
pk4
Mike Porter
Replacements, Ltd.
Dick Roberts
Alexis Rosenfeld
Al Salter Photography, Inc.
Samuel Roberts Noble Foundation
Kjell Sandved
Jerry Schad
Mark Schneider
Peter Schoones
Science Photo Library
Science VU
Scott's Company
V.L. Sharpton
Dr. Gene Shih
Oddur Sigurdsson

Rob and Ann Simpson
Smith and Loveless, Inc.
Smithsonian Institution
Troy Snow
John Sohlden
Doug Sokell
South Dakota State Historical Society
Inga Spence
Larry Stepanowicz
Peter Lane Taylor
Simon Taylor
Ten 31 Productions
Terragalleria
Terra Photography
Richard Thom
J. Trent
D. E. Trimble
Jon Turk
Undersea Research Center
Union College
United States Department of Agriculture (USDA)
United States Geological Survey (USGS)
United States Navy Arctic Submarine Lab
Université du Québec à Montréal
University of Arizona
University of North Carolina
Unusual Films
US Navy Arctic Submarine Lab
US Navy
UW Photos
Visuals Unlimited
Ward's Natural Science Establishment, Inc.
Charles Ro Washington
Webb Research
Wildlife Supply Company
Charles D. Winters
Woods Hole Oceanographic Institution
David Wrobel
Stephan Wüthrich
Daniel Zirinsky

Cover

PhotoDisc/Getty Images: grass, clouds

Front Matter Book B

PhotoDisc/Getty Images iii, (Ch. 16); © Oklahoma University;www.earthscienceworld.org v (Ch. 13); © Albert Copley/Visuals Unlimited v (Ch. 14); Breck Kent v (Ch. 15); USGS vi (Ch. 17); © Gerald and Buffi Corsi/Visuals Unlimited vi (Ch. 18); Dr. Ken McDonald/Science Photo Library vi (Ch. 19); National Park Service Photograph by John Kauffmann vi (Ch. 20); Stephan Wüthrich, Zurich, Switzerland vi (Ch. 21)

Unit 4 Opener

PhotoDisc/Getty Images x-335 (top), 335 (Ch. 17); Institute for Creation Research x (bottom); NOAA 335 (bottom middle); Ken Lucas/Visuals Unlimited 335 (bottom right); © Oklahoma University/www.earthscienceworld.org 335 (Ch. 13); © Albert Copley/Visuals Unlimited 335 (Ch. 14); Breck Kent 335 (Ch. 15); © Gerald and Buffi Corsi/Visuals Unlimited 335 (Ch. 18)

Chapter 13

© Oklahoma University; www.earthscienceworld.org 336, 358; NASA-JPL 337 (bottom); © 2004 Hemera Technologies, Inc. All Rights Reserved 337 (top); Jerry Schad/Photo Researchers, Inc. 339; NASA-HQ-GRIN 338; © Inga Spence/Visuals Unlimited 340 (right); USGS 340 (top left, bottom left); © James King-Holmes/Photo Researchers, Inc. 340 (middle left); Integrated Ocean Drilling Program 342; Ocean Drilling Program 343 (top, bottom); Breck Kent 346 (top); Scott's Company 346 (bottom); Anglo-Australian Observatory/David Malin Images 347; © Troy Snow/Visuals Unlimited 348 (bottom right); Larry Fellows, Arizona Geological Survey/www.earthscienceworld.org 350 (top); Denver Museum of Natural History 350 (middle); Susan Perry 351 (all); PhotoDisc/Getty Images 353 (top); National Library of Medicine 353 (bottom); Israel Museum, Jerusalem 354; John McLean/Photo Researchers, Inc. 355; samples courtesy of the Laboratory of Tree Ring Research, University of Arizona/ Unusual Films 355 (bottom);

Pikes Peak Attractions Association 356; PhotoDisc/Getty Images 357

Chapter 14

© Albert Copley/Visuals Unlimited 360, 382; Breck Kent 361 (top, middle), 370 (top), 377 (bottom left); © Wally Eberhart/Visuals Unlimited 361 (bottom); Unusual Films, courtesy Dr. Stewart Custer 363 (top left, top middle, top right, middle left, bottom middle, bottom right), 365 (right), 366 (bottom), 368 (bottom), 369 (top left, top right) 381 (right); © Ken Lucas/Visuals Unlimited 363 (middle), 366 (top left), 376 (top), 380; © Mark Schneider/Visuals Unlimited 363 (middle right); Ward's Natural Science Establishment, Inc. 363 (bottom left), 364 (top, bottom), 377 (bottom right); © Marli Miller, Visuals Unlimited 365 (top right), 366 (middle), 368 (middle); Unusual Films 365 (left), 367 (all), 370 (bottom)371 (both bottom left, middle), 375 (top left, top right, middle left); © A.J. Copley/Visuals Unlimited 366 (top right), 366 (bottom right); © Andrew Lambert Photography/ Photo Researchers, Inc. 368 (top); © Larry Stepanowicz/Visuals Unlimited 368 (right); © Carolina Biological/Visuals Unlimited 369 (middle); Department of the Treasury, US Mint 371 (top, both bottom left, bottom right); Clemson University, EM Facility 372 (top left); NASA 372 (top right); Library of Congress 372 (bottom); South Dakota State Historical Society 373; Fuji Film 374 (top left); Eastman Kodak, Co. 374 (top right); Replacements, Ltd. 374 (bottom); National Institute of Standards and Technology 375 (bottom); Bureau International des Poids et Measures 375 (middle); DeBeers 376 (middle); Argyle Diamonds 376 (bottom left); © Gerald and Buffi Corsi/Visuals Unlimited 377 (top); Courtesy Kennecott Utah Copper Corporation 378; Al Salter Photography, Inc. 381 (left)

Chapter 15

Breck Kent 384, 408 (bottom), 410; © Larry Fellows, Arizona Geological Survey/www.earthscienceworld.org 385; Institute of Creation Research 386 (top), 399 (bottom right, bottom left), 400; © Marli Miller/Visuals Unlimited 386

(middle, bottom), 401 (bottom); © Albert Copley/Visuals Unlimited 388 (right), 389 (top right), 403 (bottom), 405 (top), 405 (middle right); © Troy Snow/Visuals Unlimited 388 (left); © Wally Eberhart/Visuals Unlimited 389 (top left), 403 (top right), 405 (bottom right); © Inga Spence/Visuals Unlimited 389 (bottom left), 405 (bottom right); © John Sohlden/Visuals Unlimited 389 (bottom right); Courtesy of Dr. Henson/Unusual Films 390 (top left), 401 (top); © Larry Stepanowicz/Visuals Unlimited 390 (top right); © Ken Lucas/Visuals Unlimited 391 (middle), 393 (others), 394 (right, bottom), 399, 403 (middle); Peter Schoones/Photo Researchers, Inc. 391 (both bottom left); Brian D. Johnson 393 (middle left), 404 (bottom); Francois Gohier/Photo Researchers, Inc. 394 (left); Image by V.L. Sharpton, Courtesy: Lunar & Planetary Institute 395; Pascal Goetgheluck / Photo Researchers, Inc. 396 (top left); National Anthropological Archives, Smithsonian Institution 396 (top right); Simon Taylor 399 (top); © Doug Sokell/Visuals Unlimited 403 (top left); © Mark Gibson/Visuals Unlimited 404 (top); Unusual Films 407 (left); © Mark Schneider/Visuals Unlimited 407 (bottom); PhotoDisc/Getty Images 408 (top), 409 (left); Adam Hart-Davis/SPL/Photo Researchers, Inc. 409 (right)

Chapter 16

PhotoDisc/Getty Images 412, 414 (top), 415 (bottom), 436; USGS 414 (bottom); Alexander Turnbull Museum 415 (top left); AP/Wide World Photos 415 (top right); NOAA 417, 424; Corbis 418 (top, bottom), 429; Ward's Natural Science Establishment, Inc. 419 (top); Richard P. Jacobs 419 (top); George R. Collins 420 (right, bottom left); D. E. Trimble, USGS 420 (top left), 421 (top), 429, 430; © Dick Roberts, Visuals Unlimited 421 (bottom); Breck Kent 422, 423; Bruce Molnia, Terra Photography/www.earthscienceworld.org 425; © Dr. Marli Miller/Visuals Unlimited 426 (top); NASA 426 (bottom); Courtesy of Alessandro Forte, Université du Québec à Montréal 431; Ten 31 Productions 432

Chapter 17

USGS 438, 439, 441 (top), 462; © Inga Spence/Visuals Unlimited 440 (both), 461 (bottom); National Archives 441 (middle); AP/Wide World Photo 442; © Science VU/Visuals Unlimited 446, 447; © Krafft/Photo Researchers, Inc. 450 (bottom); NOAA 450 (top), 451 (top right, middle right, bottom right), 452 (left, middle); Breck Kent 451 (top left); © Albert Copley/Visuals Unlimited 452 (right); Jim Knowlton 454 (left); © Marli Miller/Visuals Unlimited 454 (bottom left, bottom right), 456 (top); © Charles Ro Washington/Visuals Unlimited; NASA 456 (bottom); Jacques Descloitres, MODIS Land Rapid Response Team at NASA/GSFC 456 (bottom); NASA/Photo Researchers, Inc. 457; NASA/GSFC 458; Brian D. Johnson 460 (top); Ward's Natural Science Establishment, Inc. 460 (bottom); Martin Bond/Science Photo Library 461 (top)

Chapter 18

© Gerald and Buffi Corsi/Visuals Unlimited 464, 465, 467 (top left), 480; © Joe and Mary Ann McDonald/Visuals Unlimited 466 (right) © Steve McCutchen/Visuals Unlimited 466 (left); USGS 466 (middle), 471 (bottom); © Marli Miller/Visuals Unlimited 467 (top middle, bottom left), 471 (top), 472 (both); PhotoDisc/Getty Images 467 (top right), 476 (top); Breck Kent 467 (bottom right), 470; © Dick Roberts/Visuals Unlimited 469 (top), 474 (top), 475 (bottom); © Inga Spence/Visuals Unlimited 469 (bottom); © Science VU/Visuals Unlimited 478 (bottom left); © Walt Anderson/Visuals Unlimited 478 (bottom right); USDA 478 (top), 477 (top); © Bill Kamin/Visuals Unlimited 478 (middle); National Park Service, photo by Jim Peaco 474 (bottom); George R. Collins 475 (top); Institute of Creation Research 476 (bottom); Brian D. Johnson, based on NASA image 477 (bottom); USGS 479 (top right)

Unit 5 Opener

Alexis Rosenfeld/Photo Researchers, Inc 482-483 (top); Answers in Genesis (AIG) 482 (bottom); Dr. Ken McDonald/Science Photo Library 483 (Ch. 19); National Park Service Photograph by John Kauffmann (Ch. 20); Stephan Wüthrich, Zurich, Switzerland (Ch. 21); © Dave Fleetham/Visuals Unlimited 482-483 (bottom); Bernard Edmaier/Photo Researchers, Inc 483 (bottom middle); JAMSTEC 483 (bottom left)

Chapter 19

Dr. Ken McDonald/Science Photo Library 484, 514; Created by Ocean Imaging Corporation 487; USGS 488; © Kjell Sandved/Visuals Unlimited 489 (top left); © Brandon Cole/Visuals Unlimited 489 (top right); © Dave Fleetham/Visuals Unlimited 489 (middle); Douglas Faulkner/Photo Researchers, Inc 489 (bottom); Dr. Richard Kessel & Dr. Gene Shih/Visuals Unlimited 491 (middle); courtesy of J. Trent 491 (bottom); Robert Brook/Photo Researchers, Inc. 492 (top); © Science VU/Visuals Unlimited 492 (bottom); City of Dunedin, FL 493; © Carolyn Galati/Visuals Unlimited 495 (both); George R. Collins 496 (top), 501 (top right); Breck Kent 496 (both bottom), 501 (both bottom left); GSF 497; © Dick Roberts/Visuals Unlimited 499; © Marli Miller/Visuals Unlimited 500 (top), 502 (top left); © Sanford Berry/Visuals Unlimited 500 (bottom); © James McCullagh/Visuals Unlimited 501 (top left); NASA/Photo Researchers, Inc. 502 (bottom left); HIP/Art Resource, NY 507 (top); UW Photos 507 (middle); NOAA 507 (bottom), 508 (both); Mike Porter/Samuel Roberts Noble Foundation 509 (top); © David Wrobel/Visuals Unlimited 509 (middle); Wildlife Supply Company 509 (bottom); AP Photo 510 (top); Navy Historical Society 510 (bottom); US Navy 511 (top); Department of Defense 511 (bottom); Image provided by the NOAA Undersea Research Center at the University of North Carolina at Wilmington, all rights reserved 512 (top); Webb Research 513 (bottom); © Rod Catanach, Woods Hole Oceanographic Institution 512 (bottom left); © Jason Fornari, Woods Hole Oceanographic Institution 513 (top right); JAMSTEC 512 (bottom right); Coral Reef Research Project, Palau/Courtesy Nutyco. LTD. 513 (top right)

Chapter 20

National Park Service Photograph by John Kauffmann 516, 527 (top left), 534; US Navy Arctic Submarine Lab 517 (top); © Marli Miller/Visuals Unlimited 517 (bottom), 518, 519 (bottom), 523, 524 (left); © ESIAL/NASA/Visuals Unlimited 519 (top); © pk4, GR0002 519 (middle); NOAA 520; Bernard Edmaier/Photo Researchers, Inc. 521 (top); NASA/GSFC 521 (middle); © Theo Allofs/Visuals Unlimited 521 (bottom); National Archives 522 (top); © Woods Hole Oceanographic Institution 522 (bottom); © Gerald and Buffi Corsi/Visuals Unlimited 524 (right); © Bill Kamin/Visuals Unlimited 525 (top); © Adam Jones/Visuals Unlimited 525 (middle left); Breck Kent 525 (middle right); Daniel Zirinsky/Photo Researchers, Inc. 525 (bottom); © Beth Davidow/Visuals Unlimited 526 (top); Brian D. Johnson 526 (middle); © Oddur Sigurdsson/Visuals Unlimited 526 (bottom); © Steve McCutcheon/Visuals Unlimited 527 (top right), 531, 532; Photo by Richard R. Jacobs 527 (middle, bottom); © Albert Copley/Visuals Unlimited 533

Chapter 21

Stephan Wüthrich, Zurich, Switzerland 536, 552; © Jon Turk/Visuals Unlimited 538; Kurt Hollocher, Union College Geology Department 539 (both); Rich Dererling, Florida Geological Survey 540 (top); © Q.T. Luong, www.terragalleria.com 540 (bottom); Advanced Water Systems 543 (top); Smith and Loveless, Inc. 543 (bottom); Art Resource, NY/Art Resource, NY 544 (top); Bernhard Edmaier/SPL/Photo Researchers, Inc. 544 (middle); © Richard Thom/Visuals Unlimited 544 (bottom); © Gerald and Buffi Corsi/Visuals Unlimited 547 (top right, top left); © Rob and Ann Simpson/Visuals Unlimited 547 (bottom); National Park Service 548; Courtesy of the National Speleological Society 549 (top); Unusual Films 549 (all bottom); Florida Geological Survey 551 (top left); © Peter Lane Taylor/Visuals Unlimited 551 (top right); © Dick Roberts/Visuals Unlimited 551 (middle); PhotoDisc/Getty Images 551 (bottom)

Back Matter Book B

Unusual Films 561: talc, gypsum, plagioclase; © Albert J. Copley/Visuals Unlimited 561: muscovite, halite; © Dane S. Johnson/Visuals Unlimited 561: calcite; © Mark A. Schneider/Visuals Unlimited 561: dolomite, fluorite; Fabre Minerals/www.fabreminerals.com: orthoclase 561, hematite 562; Breck Kent 561: quartz; Charles D. Winters/Photo Researchers, Inc 562: asbestos; © Carolina Biological/Visuals Unlimited 562: augite, biotite; www.irocks.com specimen/ Megan Foreman photo 562: garnet; © Marli Miller/Visuals Unlimited: olivine; © Larry Stepanowicz/Visuals Unlimited 562: magnetite; © Ken Lucas/Visuals Unlimited 562: pyrite, galena; © Dr. Richard Busch 562: graphite; USGS: SA563, art based upon USGS map 564, 565, 566, 567

STUDENT ACTIVITES MANUAL
Chapter 13
© Oklahoma University; www .earthscienceworld.org SA183

Chapter 14
© Albert Copley/Visuals Unlimited SA191

Chapter 15
Breck Kent SA203

Chapter 16
PhotoDisc/Getty Images SA217; USGS SA227, SA229

Chapter 17
USGS SA223, SA246; Cartesia Software SA237; based on USGS map SA244

Chapter 18
© Gerald and Buffi Corsi/Visuals Unlimited SA247

Chapter 19
Dr. Ken McDonald/Science Photo Library SA257

Chapter 20
Dr. Ken McDonald/Science Photo Library SA271; USGS SA278, SA280; SA282 (both)

Chapter 21
Stephan Wüthrich, Zurich, Switzerland SA283; USGS

SPACE & EARTH SCIENCE

STUDENT ACTIVITIES

B

Third Edition

13 INTRODUCTION TO GEOLOGY

Applications

13A What is Geology?

Directions: Answer the following questions in complete sentences.

1. What is the literal meaning of the word *geology*? The word *geology* means the study of (-logy) the earth (geo-).

2. What is the definition of the word *geology*? Geology is the scientific study of the earth's rocks and other solid materials, its structures, and the processes that affect those structures.

3. What is a geologist? A geologist is a scientist who specializes in the study of the geology of the earth or other planets.

4. List five things that geologists might study. Answers will vary. Responses may be from the areas of seismology, volcanology, sedimentology, mineralogy, geophysics, oceanography, resource exploration and mining, and environmental geology. (See §13.1.)

5. How do geologists learn about the earth's interior? Geologists study the earth's interior by analyzing earthquake waves and by drilling.

Tell students to identify the parts of the drawing carefully. Mistakes here will affect the rest of their answers in this exercise.

Applications
13B The Earth's Interior

Directions: The figure shows a section of the earth's interior. Refer to the diagram as you complete the following questions.

1. Identify the parts labeled with numbers 1–8 on the drawing.

   1. _____crust_____   5. _____mantle_____

   2. ____Mohorovičić discontinuity (Moho)____   6. _____core_____

   3. _____lithosphere_____   7. _____outer core_____

   4. _____asthenosphere_____   8. _____inner core_____

2. Describe the characteristics of regions 1, 4, and 8.

   Region 1 _solid rock_

   Region 4 _much hotter than crust; thought to be nearer its melting point than the rest of mantle;_ _earthquake waves move slower through this zone_

   Region 8 _extremely hot and dense; probably not liquid_

3. Describe item 2, and tell how it was discovered. _It is the boundary between the crust and the upper mantle,_ _where earthquake waves change speed abruptly. A Croatian seismologist discovered it while conducting_ _research on the behavior of earthquake waves._

4. What does *discontinuity* mean? _A discontinuity is any place where something changes suddenly. In the case_ _of the Moho, it is where earthquake waves change speed._

5. What percentage of the earth's volume are items 1, 5, and 6 respectively?

   Region 1 _less than 1%_   Region 5 _84%_   Region 6 _15–16%_
   (by inference)

6. Give the specified dimensions for each of the regions in the figure.

   Region 1 Thickness: _7–50 km_

   Region 3 Depth: _from the surface to a depth of 70–250 km below the Moho_

   Region 4 Thickness: _200 km or more_

   Region 5 Thickness: _2600 km_

   Region 6 Radius: _3470 km_

   Region 7 Thickness: _2250 km_

   Region 8 Radius: _1220 km_

Applications

13C The Structure of the Earth

Directions: Using the following words, label this diagram of the cross section of the earth. Then use the same words to answer the questions that follow.

crust   Moho   lithosphere   mantle   asthenosphere   core

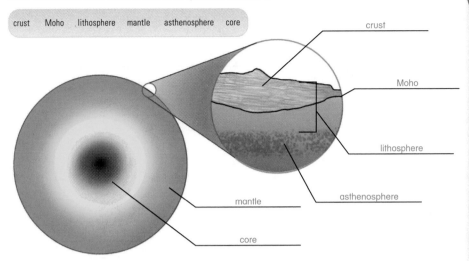

core	1.	The pressure and temperature of this part of the earth are extremely high.
Moho	2.	This part of the earth is named after the Croatian scientist who discovered it.
mantle	3.	This occupies about 84% of the earth's volume.
crust	4.	This part of the earth is solid, relatively low-density rock.
mantle	5.	At some levels of this region, rock is thought to flow in slow convective patterns.
lithosphere	6.	Two different zones of rock act together as a unit to form the plates of the earth's shell.
Moho	7.	This marks the depth where earthquake waves suddenly change speed as they travel through the earth.
core	8.	Most geologists believe this region consists of mostly iron, with some nickel, oxygen and several other light elements.
core	9.	This is believed to have a liquid outer part.
mantle	10.	All earthquake waves travel faster through this region than through the crust.
crust	11.	This region is an average of six times thicker under the continents than it is under the oceans.
Moho	12.	This is a seismic discontinuity in the earth.
core	13.	This region contains about 16% of the earth's volume.
asthenosphere	14.	Earthquake waves do not increase with depth as fast in this zone as they do in the rest of the mantle, perhaps because rocks are closer to melting at this depth.
crust	15.	Its thickness ranges from 7 km (4.5 mi) to 50 km (31 mi).
core	16.	This occupies the earth's remaining volume below the mantle.

Applications

13D The Earth's History According to Creationists

Directions: Complete the sentences below with information consistent with a Creationist view of the earth's history.

1. A person will not have a true appreciation for the world in which he lives until he is willing to face
   <u>the fact of a supernatural Creation—complete, miraculous, and rapidly accomplished. Answers will vary.</u>

2. A Christian who studies the earth's history must remember these major events: <u>Creation, the Curse (as a result of the Fall), and the Flood.</u>

3. God told us how <u>long</u> Creation took and how <u>complete</u> it was. The <u>Sabbath</u> was a commemoration of the completed Creation.

4. God cursed the earth because man <u>sinned</u>.

5. Though we do not know everything that happened as a result of the Curse, we know that there were many profound <u>changes</u> in the earth and living things.

6. God judged the earth at the time of the worldwide <u>Flood</u> of Noah's time by making permanent changes to it. Some examples of those changes include the following:
   <u>global volcanic eruptions, erosion on a continental scale, sediment deposits all over the world, formation of fossils, climate changes, and separation of the continents. Answers will vary.</u>

7. People who deny the major events in Number 2 are said in 2 Peter 3:5–6 to be willingly <u>ignorant</u>.

8. The Bible says that God created a fully functional world. Here are several examples of this fact:
   <u>Adam and Eve were created capable of taking care of themselves and could understand language and instructions; plants had seeds and trees had fruit; birds could fly; whales appeared large; and living things could reproduce. Answers will vary.</u>

9. Imagine how a small part of the original creation looked. What would the land-forms have looked like? Try to picture in your mind all of the different kinds of organisms that might have inhabited this part of the earth. Write your description here:
   <u>Answers will vary.</u>

10. God shows His <u>mighty power</u> with wonders such as His physical creation.

Question 9 would make for a good classroom discussion. It is likely that the land was fairly level or, at most, hilly, but there is no reason to think that God couldn't have created high elevations. High elevations probably were not craggy in the same way modern mountains are, since modern mountains are likely the products of global tectonic forces unleashed during and after the Flood, long after the Creation week. Artesian springs may have been common, since it is likely that much of the water that now exists above ground was created below ground. Animal groups could have included flying and ground dinosaurs, large mammals, huge insects, and many other unusual animals and plants that are now extinct. Most of these plant, mammal, and bird species might look vaguely familiar but would have been distinctly different from modern species of the same kind. Some or possibly all snakes (serpents) would have had legs!

Applications

13E Uniformitarianism

Directions: Complete the sentences below with information about uniformitarianism from pages 349–51.

1. Evolutionists try to learn about the earth's past by using the doctrine of ____uniformity____, or uniformitarianism.

2. This doctrine says that the ____present____ is the key to the past.

3. People who accept uniformitarianism think that the processes occurring on the earth today are the same processes that have
   ____shaped the earth throughout its history.____

4. To a certain extent, it is true that some aspects of nature do not change. For example, ____scientific laws do not change.____

5. Evolutionary scientists are in error when they believe that these scientific laws existed ____before the earth was formed.____

6. Some evolutionists may believe in God; but if so, they believe that God is not bound by ____scientific laws.____
   ____

7. If uniformitarianism is correct, features unlike those forming today should not have formed in the past. Some examples of the earth's features seen today that are not observed to be forming today include the following:
   ____nonvolcanic mountains, fossil graveyards, and some kinds of rock.____

8. Evolutionists believe that the ocean's water came from ____condensed volcanic steam.____

9. The Bible warns against errors such as uniformitarianism in the following passage: ____2 Peter 3:3–4.____

10. God has intervened ____supernaturally____ in the affairs of the world in the past and may do so again, contrary to what those who accept uniformitarianism may believe.

In answering Question 7, evolutionists would argue that these processes are so slow that little change can be observed over the human life span or even centuries. Explain to your students that observing the aftermath of the 1980 Mount Saint Helens eruption and other similar events, many creationary scientists now believe that these features likely developed in a matter of weeks or months.

Applications

13F Dating the Earth

Directions: In the spaces provided, write *True* if a statement is true and *False* if a statement is false.

True　　1. Evolutionists and Creationists do not agree on the age of the earth.

False　　2. Present-day observations can be used as a basis for determining the age of the earth.

True　　3. Trying to find the earth's age from present processes is like trying to figure out how long a candle has been burning.

False　　4. We can tell how old the earth is by looking at how fast various substances are accumulating and knowing how much of each substance is now present.

False　　5. Evolutionists and Creationists agree on the earth's origin.

True　　6. Many evolutionists believe that the earth began as a molten mass of rock that condensed out of a disk of dust.

True　　7. Historical records can be used to help establish dates.

True　　8. James Ussher calculated an age for the earth by referring to the genealogies given in Scripture.

False　　9. An age of the earth obtained using biblical genealogical records is completely certain because the records are found in Scripture.

True　　10. A process that is known to occur at a constant rate, such as radioactive decay, may be used to determine the age of an object if all other assumptions that a researcher makes are scientifically reasonable.

Question 9: As mentioned on page 353, the age of the earth is deduced from many pieces of information in the Bible and historical records and is based on various manuscripts that do not always agree with each other. Since this process involves human reasoning and the available information may be incomplete, it is possible that the date may be somewhat in error (but by no more than a few hundred to a thousand years).

Applications

13G Three Methods of Dating the Earth

Directions: Read the following statements carefully and decide which of the types of dating method are being described. Then indicate your answers by writing the proper letters in the blanks provided. Some statements have more than one answer.

a　　1. A worthwhile tool if used with the proper precautions

b, c　　2. Does not involve carbon in any form

c　　3. Gave ages ranging from 160 million years to 3 billion years for volcanic rocks known to be only 170 years old

a　　4. Unreliable for ages beyond about 5000 years

a, b, c　　5. Based on the assumption that the ratio of one substance to another indicates the age

a　　6. Used only on materials containing carbon

a　　7. Uses a calibration curve to determine ages

b, c　　8. Makes an unscientific assumption about the contents of the original rock

a　　9. May use a liquid scintillation counter

a, b, c　　10. Based on the fact that radioactive elements are unstable and break down into other elements or isotopes

a. Radiocarbon dating
b. Uranium-lead method
c. Potassium-argon method

Investigation
13H The Radiocarbon Method

If you obtain a number of carbon-containing samples of known age and measure their radioactivity per unit weight, you can construct a graph of radioactivity versus age. This is called a *calibration curve*. Once you have such a graph, you can then find the age of an unknown sample by a simple two-step procedure. First, measure its radioactivity per unit weight with a counter. Second, read its age from the graph.

This method of dating, called the radiocarbon method, does have some problems. One difficulty is that the calibration curve cuts off at about 5000 years. Therefore, the oldest samples that this method can legitimately handle will be about 5000 years old. Another difficulty is that the amount of carbon-14 in the atmosphere has not stayed the same down through the centuries. In spite of these difficulties, radiocarbon dates (if restricted to the last 5000 years) are reasonably accurate. For this reason the method appears to have definite merit and will undoubtedly continue to be used by scientists.

Procedures and observations

1. Construct a calibration curve.

   a. Plot the following information on the graph given below. (*Note*: The vertical axis represents the radioactivity [disintegration per gram per minute—abbreviated d/g/m] of the sample as

Goals
Construct a calibration curve, using data from objects of known age. Use the calibration curve to date several objects of unknown age.

Materials
ruler

measured with a radiation detector. The horizontal axis represents the age of the sample as measured by an independent dating method [something other than radiocarbon], such as a human historical record.)

   b. Draw the best smooth curve you can through the points. It should intersect most of the points without sharp breaks or bends. Sketch the curve lightly at first; then darken it as you become more sure of its location.

Make sure your students do not simply "connect the dots." This may be a good opportunity to talk about "best-fit" when analyzing graphs. You can even discuss how a scientist may use a calculator or computer to plot data and then get an equation from the data.

DATA FOR CALIBRATION CURVE

Material	Known age (y)	Radioactivity (d/g/m)
1. Tree ring	880	13.7
2. Tree ring	1370	13.3
3. Tree ring	1375	12.8
4. Manuscript	2050	12.0
5. Mummy (Ptolemy)	2150	11.6
6. Mummy (Tayinat)	2625	11.2
7. Redwood tree	2930	11.0
8. Mummy (Sesostris)	3870	9.8
9. Mummy (Sneferu)	4575	8.4
10. Mummy (Zoser)	4750	8.3
11. Mummy (Hemaka)	5000	7.2

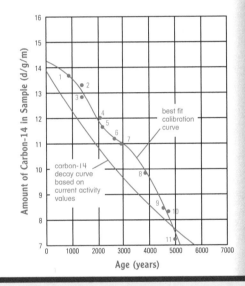

2. Use the calibration curve to date the following four samples. Answers will vary.

Material	Radioactivity (d/g/m)	Age (y)
1. Bone	12.4	1750
2. Wood	8.8	4400
3. Charcoal	10.7	3300
4. Linen	11.5	2300

a. Locate the amount of carbon-14 in the sample on the vertical axis.

b. Draw a line from this point to the calibration curve. Then draw a line from the curve down to the horizontal axis. Read the age from the horizontal axis and record it in the chart.

Summing Up

1. Suppose that another method indicated the age of the piece of bone in Step 2 to be 500 years.

Does this agree with the age you gave the piece of bone? _____no_____

If the ages do not agree, what term would you use to refer to this sample? _____anomalous sample_____

2. Suppose someone gave you a sample whose radioactivity measured 7.0 d/g/m.

Could you use the calibration curve you made to estimate its age? _____no_____

Why or why not? You can only guess about any dating beyond the last points of the calibration curve.

3. To what specific kinds of materials is the radiocarbon method applicable? The radiocarbon method is applicable to carbon-containing materials such as wood, charcoal, shells, and bone (if the sample has not been completely mineralized as a fossil).

4. Does the radiocarbon method in any way help to establish that the earth is millions or billions of years old? _____no_____ Explain. The radiocarbon method deals at most with thousands of years, not millions or billions of years. Carbon-14 is theoretically undetectable after only about 50,000 years.

5. Compared to a fossil, does a living organism have a large or a small amount of radioactivity? a large amount

14 MINERALS AND ORES

Applications
14A Types of Matter

PART 1: ORGANIC AND INORGANIC

Directions: According to your text, minerals by definition do not contain carbon (or any other elements or compounds of organic origin). Classify the following substances under the heading "Organic Materials" or "Inorganic Materials."

coal	igneous rocks	shells	silver
fingernails	iron	copper	wood
gold	oil	hair	platinum

Organic Materials	Inorganic Materials
coal	gold
fingernails	igneous rocks
oil	iron
shells	copper
hair	silver
wood	platinum

PART 2: DEFINITIONS AND DESCRIPTIONS

matter	1. Anything that has mass and occupies space
pure substances	2. Substances that are made up of either one element or one compound
mixtures	3. Materials that are made up of two or more pure substances not chemically combined; the materials do not have a fixed ratio of elements and can be separated into their substances by physical means
elements	4. Pure substances made up of only one kind of atom
compounds	5. Pure substances made up of two or more kinds of atoms chemically combined; they have a fixed ratio of elements
organic	6. Substances that are mostly carbon compounds (or other materials) that are products of living things
inorganic	7. Substances that do not contain substantial amounts of carbon or do not come from living things
	8. List two more organic substances other than those listed above.
	Answers will vary. Some possible answers are blood, sugar, pearls, and broccoli.

Applications

14B Mineral Tests

Directions: Read the following descriptions carefully and decide which type of mineral identification property or test is being described. Write the correct letters in the blanks provided.

__e__ 1. Has five ratings: perfect, good, fair, poor, and none

__d__ 2. Is specific for each mineral because it is based on the arrangement of atoms in the mineral

__a__ 3. Sometimes changes when exposed to air

__b__ 4. Is always the same in spite of impurities

__f__ 5. Is measured using the Mohs scale, which ranges from 1 to 10

__e__ 6. Deals with the number of directions or planes in which a mineral will break

__c__ 7. Describes the way light reflects from a mineral's surface

__f__ 8. Testing can involve the use of these common objects: fingernail, penny, glass plate, knife blade, and steel file

__h__ 9. Uses a platinum wire dipped into a powder of the mineral

__i__ 10. Is performed to see if the mineral will give off gas (effervescence)

__k__ 11. Is identified and measured using a radiation detector

__m__ 12. A measure of the amount that light is bent or rotated as it passes through a mineral

__b__ 13. The characteristic color that is produced when a mineral is rubbed across the surface of unglazed porcelain

__c__ 14. Descriptions include vitreous, pearly, adamantine, earthy, greasy, dull, and resinous

__e__ 15. The tendency to break into flat sheets or along certain planes

__f__ 16. The ability to withstand scratching and abrasion

__j__ 17. A property of lodestone

__m__ 18. Produces a double image as light passes through certain minerals

__l__ 19. Involves the absorption of invisible ultraviolet light and the production of a glow or afterglow

__g__ 20. Is estimated by lifting

__b__ 21. Is more reliable than outward color

__d__ 22. Involves enlargement by accretion

__g__ 23. Is the ratio of the weight of a mineral to the weight of an equal volume of water

__l__ 24. Involves fluorescence or phosphorescence

a. Color
b. Streak
c. Luster
d. Crystal shape
e. Cleavage
f. Hardness
g. Specific gravity
h. Flame test
i. Acid test
j. Magnetism
k. Radioactivity
l. Luminescence
m. Refraction or Polarization

Applications

14C Elements and Compounds

Directions: In Part 1 write the names of the minerals under the heading "Elements" or "Compounds." In Part 2 read each statement carefully and then decide which mineral is being described. Write the correct mineral names in the blanks provided. Two of the statements have two correct answers. Two of the minerals are not used.

| bauxite | copper | galena | platinum | silver |
| calcite | diamond | gold | quartz | sulfur |

PART 1

Elements	Compounds
copper	bauxite
diamond	calcite
gold	galena
platinum	quartz
silver	
sulfur	

PART 2

1. Mined with dredges _gold_
2. Sticks to grease during separation from ore _diamond_
3. Burns with a blue flame _sulfur_
4. Used by the Native Americans _copper_
5. Almost always mixed with silver _gold_
6. First discovered in Colombia, South America _platinum_
7. Obtained mainly as a byproduct of the fossil fuel industries _sulfur_
8. Composed of a metal and sulfur _galena_
9. Usually pale yellow or colorless _diamond_
10. Has perfect cleavage _diamond_
11. Has a metallic luster (five items) _copper, gold, platinum, silver, galena_
12. Found in Louisiana and Texas _sulfur_
13. Weighed in units called carats _diamond_
14. Mined extensively from placer deposits _gold_
15. Sometimes retrieved by panning _gold_
16. Is yellow with conchoidal fracture _sulfur_

(continued on next page)

bauxite	copper	galena	platinum	silver
calcite	diamond	gold	quartz	sulfur

17. Has a greasy luster when uncut __diamond__

18. Found near active or extinct volcanoes and in sedimentary beds deep underground __sulfur__

19. Has the chemical name silicon dioxide __quartz__

20. Mined from the Argyle pipe in Australia __diamond__

21. The second most abundant mineral in the earth's crust __quartz__

22. Found in fine strands, thin sheets, and irregular masses __silver, copper__

23. Mined today in Russia and South Africa __platinum__

24. Found on the Keweenaw Peninsula, Michigan __silver, copper__

25. Produces a silver-white streak __silver__

Investigation
14D Accretion of Crystals

Minerals form various crystal structures in nature. In this investigation you will be able to observe crystal formation that is similar to mineral crystal formation. You will grow crystals from solutions of sugar, alum, and Epsom salts. Though sugar is not a mineral, it does form crystals.

Procedure

1. Add 100 mL of water to the saucepan and bring it to a boil. Remove the saucepan from the hot plate.

2. Slowly stir the sugar into the hot water. Continue to add sugar until no more will dissolve.

3. Add enough food coloring to color the solution. (optional)

4. Pour the solution into a *clean* glass beaker. Do not include any of the undissolved sugar.

5. Tie one end of a string around the rod or pencil. Lay the rod across the beaker, with the other end of the string dangling down into the sugar solution. Adjust the string until the end is at least a centimeter above the bottom of the beaker.

6. Put the beaker in a place where it will be undisturbed for several days. Avoid direct sunlight or heating system ducts.

Goal
Grow crystals and compare the crystal shapes of various substances.

Materials
saucepan
water
hot plate or stove
sugar (sucrose), 200 g
alum (aluminum ammonium sulfate), 100 g
Epsom salts (magnesium sulfate heptahydrate), 100 g
food coloring (optional)
glass beakers, 250 mL (3)
rods, glass or metal, or pencils (3)
cotton strings, 15 cm (3)
hand magnifying lens

7. Repeat Steps 1–6 with the alum and with the Epsom salts.

8. After several days remove each string and allow the crystals to dry. Observe the crystals with a magnifying lens. Draw the shape of each type of crystal in the space below.

Epsom salts occurs naturally as the mineral *epsomite.*

You may want to do only one substance or try others not listed. Epsom salts is particularly interesting because it makes long, needlelike crystals.

Shapes of crystals are typical. Actual shapes will vary.

Sugar	Alum	Epsom Salts

Summing Up

1. As each solution cools, it is said to be *supersaturated*. What do you think this means? There is more material dissolved than can ordinarily be contained in a solution.

2. Why do you think the solution is supersaturated when cool but not supersaturated when hot? Liquids usually can contain more substances in solution when hotter than when cooler.

3. What formed on the string? crystals of the dissolved material

4. Are the crystals that you observed separate crystals? No, they are many crystals joined together.

5. When you stir sugar into a drink such as tea, it disappears. What happens to it? It loses its crystalline structure when it dissolves into the liquid. Its molecules separate and mix with the water molecules to become part of the solution (a mixture).

6. How could you recrystallize the sugar stirred into a cup of tea? Boil the tea to evaporate the water until only the sugar is left (along with some tea solids).

14E Accretion of Crystals—Going a Step Further

Procedure

1. Put 200 mL of water into the saucepan and bring it to a boil. Remove the saucepan from the hot plate.

2. Stir in as much solute as can be dissolved.

3. Pour the solution equally into two Styrofoam cups. Do not include any of the undissolved solute.

4. Tie one end of a string around a rod or pencil. Lay the rod across one of the cups, with the other end of the string dangling down into the solution.

5. Place the other cup of solution inside the remaining empty cup to insulate the solution. Punch a small hole near the center of the small Styrofoam plate. Tie one end of a string around a pencil or rod, and push the other end of the string through the hole in the plate. Cover the doubled cups with the small Styrofoam plate, allowing the string to dangle into the solution.

6. Place the doubled cups where they will not be disturbed.

7. Set the single cup in a refrigerator.

8. Observe from time to time over several hours. Allow the solutions to stand undisturbed overnight.

9. Observe the crystals with a magnifying glass.

Summing Up

1. In which cup were the larger crystals formed? Answers will vary. Usually, the unrefrigerated cup will have larger crystals.

2. What caused some crystals to be larger? In this demonstration, the larger crystals resulted from a slower cooling rate, which allowed time for the molecules to arrange themselves in a more orderly fashion.

3. What does this experiment tell you about the size of crystals found in various minerals? Only that all other factors being held constant, cooling rate may affect crystal size.

4. How could you grow even larger crystals? Answers will vary. Possibilities include increasing the initial concentration of the solute, adding solute to the solution to keep the solute concentration high, decreasing the number of nucleation sites, and decreasing the rate of cooling.

Goal
Determine the effect of temperature on crystal formation.

Materials
water, 200 mL

saucepan

hot plate or stove

twice as much of the solute in Investigation 14D that you think made the best crystals

Styrofoam cups (3)

cotton strings, 15 cm (2)

rods, glass or metal, or pencils (2)

small Styrofoam plate

refrigerator

This investigation could easily be modified to demonstrate a scientific methodology.

If you have access to a calorimeter, you could substitute it for the doubled cups in Step 5.

Additional factors to investigate
These ideas can be expanded into a scientific experiment complete with a problem statement, literature research, hypotheses, experiment design, data collection, analysis, and formal conclusions.

1. Instead of the cotton thread, suspend a fine platinum wire with the end wrapped around a tiny crystal of the solute. Follow Steps 1–3 of this investigation for the room-temperature cup only. This will create a single nucleation site.

2. Alternatively, set up five cup-and-platinum-wire sets. Use epoxy to fix solute crystals to the five wires—the first wire has one, the second, two, and so on. Space the crystals so all of them will be submerged in the solution. Do not coat the entire crystal with epoxy, or this activity will not work! Suspend the wires in room-temperature supersaturated solutions and leave them undisturbed until the accretion stops. Compare crystal sizes.

3. To change the rate of crystallization without altering the rate of temperature change, do the following:

   a. Cut a plywood board square about 25 cm on each side or larger. Place the board on a flat block of foam rubber.

   b. Screw or clamp a small DC motor to the board.

   c. Attach an unbalanced weight to the motor shaft. This can easily be done with Lego parts.

   d. Connect the motor to a fresh battery supply that will run for at least half a day.

   e. Set up two cups as in Step 1 above with a single crystal of solute. Place one cup on the board and turn on the motor. Place the other cup in a similar environment but away from the vibrations of the motor-board apparatus.

   f. The rapid vibrations should delay the formation of crystals or affect their size.

14F Properties of Minerals

Minerals are naturally occurring, inorganic, crystalline solids that form the building blocks of rocks. Though well over three thousand minerals are known, only a few make up the bulk of the rocks in the earth's crust. This investigation will deal with a representative sampling of those common rock-forming minerals.

Procedure

Five different identifying properties will be covered in Part 1 of this study: color, streak, luster, hardness, and specific gravity. Several other properties will be briefly noted in Part 2.

PART 1

1. *Color.* "Color" refers to the appearance of the mineral in ordinary light. Record the color of the following minerals.

   bauxite (ore) ___reddish brown___

   magnetite ___black___

   chalcopyrite ___brass yellow___

   microcline ___white, pink, tan___

   galena ___gray to silver___

   milky quartz ___white___

   gypsum ___white, gray___

   pyrite ___deep yellow___

   hematite ___reddish brown___

   rose quartz ___pink___

2. *Streak.* "Streak" is the color of the powdered mineral. If the hardness of the specimen is less than 7, you can perform the streak test by rubbing the specimen against unglazed porcelain and observing the color of the mark it produces. Perform the streak test on each of the following (all of which are relatively soft minerals) and record the color in each case.

   magnetite ___black___

   chalcopyrite ___black___

   galena ___gray black___

   gypsum ___white___

   hematite ___reddish brown___

   calcite ___white___

Goal

Study some of the more readily observed properties used to identify minerals.

Materials

rock and mineral collection
ceramic tile or streak plate
copper penny (pre-1983)
steel knife
glass plate
beaker, 250 mL–1 L
thread
ring stand
spring balance or mass balance
hand magnifying lens
magnet

3. *Luster.* "Luster" is a rating of how a mineral reflects light. If a mineral has a shiny silver or gold appearance like a metal, it is said to have a metallic luster. If it is shiny like glass, it is said to have a vitreous luster. If it is not shiny (if it is like chalk, for example), it is said to have a dull luster. Record the luster of each of the following minerals.

   bauxite ___dull___

   chalcopyrite ___metallic___

   calcite ___vitreous___

   galena ___metallic___

4. *Hardness.* In this test common objects are used to test the hardness of mineral specimens: a fingernail (hardness of 2.5), a copper penny (hardness of 3.5), a steel knife blade (hardness of 5.0–5.5), and a glass plate (hardness of 5.5). Hardness is estimated as follows:

Mohs Hardness Number

1 can easily be scratched with the fingernail

2 can barely be scratched with the fingernail

3 cannot be scratched with the fingernail but can be scratched with a penny

4 cannot be scratched with a penny but can be scratched easily with a steel knife blade

5 can barely be scratched with a steel knife blade

6 cannot be scratched with a steel knife blade but is hard enough to scratch glass

7+ can easily scratch a steel knife blade and glass

Investigations 14F and 15D make use of the fifty-specimen rock and mineral collection available from BJU Press and other distributors. This collection, from Scott Resources, consists of rock-forming minerals, ores, gemstones, sedimentary rocks, metamorphic rocks, and igneous rocks. It is supplied in a compartmented box, with each specimen numbered; the numbers are keyed to the rock and mineral names on a list inside the box.

The supplier may substitute specimens without notice, so verify that this investigation works with your particular kit and substitute other minerals as necessary. Be sure to determine the correct responses for each substitution beforehand. You also may need to make adjustments if you are using a different collection, although the rocks and minerals used in this investigation will be found in most collections.

This investigation is designed in such a way that the specimens are not damaged by the tests.

You should begin collecting the pre-1983 pennies weeks or months before this investigation is scheduled so that you will have enough solid copper pennies to work with. Once you have a sufficient number of pennies, store them from year to year so they will be available for this activity. Copper plumbing hardware may be used instead of copper pennies.

When testing whether a mineral will scratch the glass plate, do not hold the glass plate in your hands; keep it firmly flat on the table or desktop. Also, if you think you have scratched the glass, wet your index finger and see whether you can rub off the scratch mark. If it comes off, it was merely some of the mineral that rubbed off onto the glass. A true scratch mark will remain.

(*Note*: It is not necessary to scratch back and forth several times to determine hardness. A single stroke is sufficient.)

Determine as nearly as you can the hardness of each of the following:

calcite	3	gypsum	2
corundum	7 or higher (9)	magnetite	5.5–6.5
fluorite	4	muscovite	2–2.5
galena	2.5+	quartz	7 or less

5. *Specific Gravity.* To measure specific gravity, a thread is tied to the specimen and it is hung from a spring balance or triple beam balance. The specimen is weighed first when it is in the air and again when it is completely submerged (but not resting on the bottom) in a beaker of water. The mineral weighs less when submerged because of the buoyant force of the water. The difference in weight is equal to the weight of the displaced water. The weight of the mineral in air divided by the difference in weight when weighed under water gives the specific gravity of the mineral.

 weight in air

 weight when submerged

As an alternative to Step 5, you can also find the mass of an equal volume of water by lowering the mineral on a string into a graduated cylinder containing a known volume of water. The increase in volume (mL) equals the mass (g) of the displaced water, since 1 mL of water has a mass of 1 g at 4 °C. (*Note*: Do not drop mineral specimens into a glass graduated cylinder. The cylinder may shatter.)

6. Determine the specific gravity of the following minerals. Before weighing them, estimate their density by "hefting" one in the palm of each hand. You can readily determine that there is a difference in their specific gravities. Record your measurements and calculations below.

	Calcite		Magnetite

Weight in air _____Answers will vary._____   Weight in air _____Answers will vary._____

Weight submerged _Answers will vary._   Weight submerged _Answers will vary._

Difference _____Answers will vary._____   Difference _____Answers will vary._____

$$\text{s.g.} = \frac{\text{weight (mass) in air}}{\text{weight (mass) difference}}$$

Specific gravity _____~2.6–2.7_____   Specific gravity _____~5.2_____

PART 2

1. Study the angles of your calcite crystal sample. Use a hand lens to examine the surface closely. Note that there are many little parallelograms. Calcite has a characteristic rhombohedral crystal shape. The acute plane angles that you see between the face surfaces are about 75°; the obtuse angles, 105°.

2. Some minerals have a characteristic feel. Note the greasy feel of your talc sample.

3. Note that both muscovite and biotite (mica) consist of innumerable thin sheets. This gives them one-direction cleavage (also called basal cleavage). Do not flake sheets off your mica samples unless told to do so.

4. Observe whether your magnetite sample can be picked up with a magnet. Are any other minerals in the collection magnetic?

Summing Up

1. Why is the identification of unknown minerals possible and, in some cases, very easy? _Each mineral_ _has certain known properties that are the same from specimen to specimen._

2. Are all the minerals in your collection naturally occurring, or are some of them manmade? _All the samples_ _are naturally occurring. Minerals are defined as being naturally occurring._

3. All of the streak tests you performed were for relatively soft materials. How would you perform a streak test for a mineral whose hardness is 8.5? _Grind the mineral with a carborundum file and observe the color of the powder against a white background,_ _or scratch it with other minerals of known hardness._

4. What is the relationship of minerals to rocks? _Minerals are the building blocks of rocks._

5. Some of the minerals in the collection are called ores; others are not. What is the difference between them? _Ores are sources of commercially valuable metals._

Explain to your students that estimating the density by "hefting" involves rapidly raising and lowering their hand with the specimen in their palm *without bouncing the specimen* in their hand. The specimens may shatter if they are dropped on the floor.

A sensitive magnetic compass may be used to test for magnetism.

name: _____ SA203

date: _____ hour: _____

Applications

15A Classification of Rocks

Directions: Arrange the following items in an outline in the space provided. (*Hint*: There are two subpoints under each main point.) Then write a definition for each main point and each subpoint. Finally, circle the names of the three rocks that are the most common fossil-bearing rocks.

Alert students to the fact that they may need to look ahead in the chapter in order to correctly complete the outline. You can view this exercise as outlining the contents of the chapter.

anthracite (hard coal)	foliated metamorphic rocks	lignite (brown coal)	pumice
basalt	gabbro	limestone	quartzite
bituminous coal (soft coal)	gneiss	marble	sandstone
clastic (fragmental)	granite	metamorphic rocks	schist
sedimentary rocks	granite gneiss	nonclastic (chemical)	scoria
conglomerate	halite	sedimentary rocks	sedimentary rocks
diorite gneiss	hornblende gneiss	nonfoliated metamorphic	siltstone and shale
extrusive igneous rocks	igneous rocks	rocks	slate
felsite	intrusive igneous rocks	obsidian	

I.   <u>Sedimentary rocks</u> —rocks made of particles that have been bonded together by natural cements or of solids that have settled from water solutions
    A. Clastic sedimentary rocks—rocks made of particles that have been bonded together by natural cements
        1. Conglomerate
        2. (Sandstone)
        3. (Siltstone and shale)
    B. Nonclastic sedimentary rocks—rocks made of solids that have precipitated or evaporated from water solutions
        1. (Limestone)
        2. Halite

II.   <u>Igneous rocks</u> —rocks that have cooled from a molten mixture
    A. Intrusive igneous rocks—rocks that solidify beneath the earth's surface
        1. Granite
        2. Gabbro
    B. Extrusive igneous rocks—rocks that solidify above the earth's surface
        1. Pumice
        2. Scoria
        3. Basalt
        4. Felsite
        5. Obsidian

III.   <u>Metamorphic rocks</u> (classified according to the presence of layers)—sedimentary or igneous rocks that were altered by agents such as heat and pressure
    A. Foliated metamorphic rocks—rocks that exhibit layers
        1. Slate
        2. Schist
        3. Gneiss
           a. Granite gneiss
           b. Ciorite gneiss
           c. Hornblende gneiss
    B. Nonfoliated metamorphic rocks—rocks that do not exhibit layers
        1. Marble
        2. Quartzite
        3. Anthracite (hard coal)
        4. Bituminous coal (soft coal)
        5. Lignite (brown coal)

Applications

15B Fossils

Directions: Use the material on fossils, pages 391–400, to answer the following questions.

1. What is a fossil? A fossil is any trace or remains of a living creature that has been preserved by natural means.

2. What do fossils reveal? They tell us about the past by showing us what living things on the earth were like in the past.

3. What do fossils *not* support? They do not support the theory that gradual changes from one kind to another occurred (biological evolution).

4. Why are "missing link" fossils a powerful evidence for Creation and not for evolution? Very few fossils could be called transitional forms. The fact that these links do not exist supports Creation.

5. How do dinosaur fossils give evidence for a worldwide flood? Dinosaur fossils have been found piled in stacks like logjams in places all over the world. The catastrophe that caused such pileups must have been tremendous.

6. What are the three categories that all of the fossils that supposedly prove man's animal ancestry fall into?
These categories are human fossils, misidentified animal fossils, and hoaxes.

7. How is a trilobite fossil and the age of the rock in which it is found an example of how evolutionists use circular reasoning?
Trilobites were originally dated by the rocks in which they were found according to the assumed age of the rocks. Then other rocks that contain the same kind of trilobite were given the same dates.

8. What is a polystrate fossil? A polystrate fossil extends through several layers of sedimentary rock (strata).

9. How do polystrate fossils provide evidence for rapid burial in the Flood? The fossils extend through many sedimentary layers that evolutionary geologists say should have taken thousands or millions of years to collect. No organism could have remained intact during that length of time. The layer must have formed rapidly, which means the uniformitarian interpretation of the layers is not true.

10. How do evolutionists believe coal formed? They believe that swampy areas containing dead plant matter were covered with sediment whose weight and resulting heat slowly changed the organic material to coal.

11. Through experimentation, how quickly have scientists found that coal can form if the temperature and pressure are correct?
Experiments show that coal can form in less than a day.

12. What are some evidences that coal formed quickly instead of over many years? Radiocarbon dates show that coal is only thousands of years old. Rocks, boulders, and upright tree trunks have been found in coal, which indicates swift-moving currents, not quiet, stagnant swamps. Quickly buried plants can accumulate rapidly without decaying away.

Applications

15C Characteristics of Rocks

Directions: Select the proper terms from the list to complete the statements below. Write
your answers on the blanks provided. You may use each term only once, but more than
one term may be used to complete a statement.

basalt	foliated	laccolith	regional metamorphism
breccia	fossil-bearing	magma	remains
clastic	fossils	matrix	rock
coal	fuel	metamorphic	rock cycle
conglomerate	gas	natural	salt
dikes	gneiss	nonclastic	schist
domes	igneous	plant	sedimentary
extrusive	index	polystrate	sill
felsic	intrusive	porphyry	strata

1. The coarsest grade of clastic sedimentary rock is called _____conglomerate_____.

2. Any traces of a living organism preserved by natural means are called _____fossils_____.

3. _____Breccia_____ is a conglomerate rock containing sharp and angular fragments.

4. A coarsely foliated rock with a banded appearance is called _____gneiss_____.

5. The solid form of fossil fuel is _____coal_____.

6. Changes to rocks over wide areas is called _____regional metamorphism_____.

7. _____Extrusive_____ igneous rocks form above the earth's surface.

8. Rocks that cool from a molten mixture are called _____igneous_____.

9. _____Strata_____ are layers of sedimentary rock.

10. Molten rock beneath the earth's surface is called _____magma_____.

11. Both Creationists and evolutionists believe coal formed from _____plant remains_____.

12. A common metamorphic rock that splits easily is called _____schist_____.

13. Evolutionists attempt to use fossils called _____index_____ fossils to determine the
age of rock strata.

14. A _____laccolith_____ is a small dome-like plutonic intrusion that often forms rounded
hills on the earth's surface.

15. Rock containing two very different sizes of crystals is called _____porphyry_____.

16. _____Intrusive_____ igneous rocks formed beneath the earth's crust.

17. Igneous rocks that contain much silica are classified as _____felsic_____ rocks.

18. Fossil _____fuel_____ comes in solid, liquid, and gaseous forms.

19. _____Polystrate_____ fossils extend through several layers of sedimentary rock that
supposedly represent long periods of time.

20. Limestone, sandstone, and shale are the most common examples of _____fossil-bearing_____
rocks.

21. _____Dikes_____ are formed by magma that fills cracks that cut across existing rock
layers.

22. The gaseous form of fossil fuel is _____natural gas_____.

(continued on next page)

basalt	foliated	laccolith	regional metamorphism
breccia	fossil-bearing	magma	remains
clastic	fossils	matrix	rock
coal	fuel	metamorphic	rock cycle
conglomerate	gas	natural	salt
dikes	gneiss	nonclastic	schist
domes	igneous	plant	sedimentary
extrusive	index	polystrate	sill
felsic	intrusive	porphyry	strata

23. A _____matrix_____ is a material in which something is embedded.

24. _____Clastic_____ sedimentary rock forms from pieces eroded from other rock.

25. Rocks that are made of particles bonded together by natural cements are called _____sedimentary_____ rocks.

26. Halite occasionally exists in nature as vertical cylindrical masses called _____salt domes_____.

27. A former sedimentary or igneous rock altered by heat or pressure is called a _____metamorphic_____ rock.

28. _____Basalt_____ is a dark, greenish gray, extrusive igneous rock.

29. _____Nonclastic_____ sedimentary rocks form from minerals dissolved in water.

30. _____Foliated_____ rocks have bands or layers.

31. A _____sill_____ is a sheet of igneous rock that forced its way between layers of existing rock.

32. A _____rock_____ consists of one or more minerals.

33. The progression from magma, to igneous rock, through erosion to a sedimentary rock, and back to magma, is one possible path of what geologists call the _____rock cycle_____.

Investigation

15D Properties of Rocks

Rocks are the materials of which the earth's crust is made. Now that you have studied some of the important rock-building minerals, you should understand the make-up of rocks more fully than you did before. In this exercise you will be examining about two dozen rock specimens made up of an approximately equal number from each of the three major categories—igneous, sedimentary, and metamorphic.

Procedure

Igneous Rocks

Study the specimens of igneous rocks in your collection.

1. List the igneous rocks that are lightest colored. These rocks have a high silica content.

   pumice, andesite, rhyolite, (perhaps granite)

2. List the ones that are dark colored (black or dark gray). These rocks have a low silica content.

   obsidian, scoria, basalt

3. Which two specimens are coarse grained? These are intrusive igneous rocks that cooled under conditions that permitted the formation of large visible crystals.

   andesite, granite

4. Which of these two has a porphyritic texture (some large grains in a matrix of smaller crystals)? This rock may have cooled in two different stages.

   andesite

5. Granite is made up of three minerals that can be identified by their colors. Name the following three minerals.

   pink or tan feldspar

   black mica (biotite mica)

   white quartz

6. Which specimens have a porous structure? These are volcanic rocks that have bubble holes due to trapped gases.

   pumice, scoria (perhaps basalt)

7. Test your pumice specimen to see if it floats on water. There is a good chance that its overall density will be less than that of water. Does it float?

   Answers will vary.

Goal

Examine the properties of representative samples from the three major classes of rocks.

Materials

rock and mineral collection (50 specimens)

hand magnifying lens or stereo microscope

beaker, 250 mL–1 L

eyedropper

hydrochloric acid, dilute (2 M)

8. Which rock exhibits the best example of conchoidal fracture? This rock was formed from magma or lava that had no dissolved gases and cooled relatively quickly at low pressures.

   obsidian

Sedimentary Rocks

Study the specimens of sedimentary rocks in your collection.

1. Which of the samples shows the best evidence of layering (stratification)? sandstone or shale

   (Answers will vary, depending on the specimen.)

2. Dip each of the seven specimens into a beaker of water, and note which one exhibits an earthy smell.

   shale

3. Dry your specimens with a paper towel. Place them in a row on a clean paper towel. Place a single drop of dilute hydrochloric acid on each one with an eyedropper. Which ones effervesce (fizz)?

   calcareous tufa, limestone

   Rinse the acid from each specimen under a faucet after you have finished testing it.

4. Examine your conglomerate rock specimen.

   What color is the matrix? Answers will vary.

   Note the wide range in the sizes of the fragments. Are the fragments interlocking or separate?

   separate

Investigations 14F and 15D make use of the fifty-specimen rock and mineral collection available from BJU Press and other distributors. This collection, from Scott Resources, consists of rock-forming minerals, ores, gemstones, sedimentary rocks, metamorphic rocks, and igneous rocks. It is supplied in a compartment box, with each specimen numbered; the numbers are keyed to the rock and mineral names on a list inside the box.

The supplier may substitute specimens without notice, so verify that this investigation works with your particular kit and substitute other minerals as necessary. Be sure to determine the correct responses for each substitution beforehand. You also may need to make adjustments if you are using a different collection, although the rocks and minerals used in this investigation will be found in most collections.

This investigation is designed in such a way that the specimens are not damaged by the tests.

Dilute hydrochloric acid should not present a significant safety hazard when used as directed in this investigation. As always when using chemicals, you should have a Material Safety Data Sheet (MSDS) for the chemical on file and have reviewed it prior to using the chemical. Caution students about the corrosive nature of the acid and be prepared to quickly neutralize and wipe up spills. It is good practice to have the students wear safety goggles when performing the acid tests.

Caution students against using a forceful stream of water to rinse the samples, since doing so could splash the acid onto clothes or skin or into the eyes.

Sandstone, shale, and oil shale are porous, but this may not be obvious. Of these three, only sandstone is clearly permeable.

5. Which of the sedimentary rocks is porous? _sandstone, shale, oil shale, calcareous tufa_

6. Which type of rock is regarded as a potentially useful source of fossil fuel? _oil shale_

Metamorphic Rocks

Study the specimens of metamorphic rocks in your collection.

1. From what rock was gneiss probably formed? _granite (or slate)_
   slate? _shale_   quartzite? _sandstone_
   marble? _limestone_   anthracite? _bituminous coal_

2. Which of your specimens exhibit foliation? _slate, gneiss, talc schist, garnet schist_

3. Dip each of the eight specimens into a beaker of water, and note which one exhibits an earthy smell.
   slate

4. Dry your specimens with a paper towel. Add a drop of dilute hydrochloric acid to each one with a medicine dropper. Which one effervesces?
   marble

   Rinse the acid from each specimen under a faucet after you have finished testing it.

Summing Up

1. Name one property that could be useful in identifying both rocks and minerals.
   Answers will vary. Both can be identified using color, specific gravity, crystal structure, texture, fracture, and so forth.

   Properties that are not valid for both include streak, hardness, gross cleavage, and luster.

2. Which of the three major classes of rocks exhibits true stratification?
   Sedimentary rocks show true stratification.

   Foliation is not stratification, although it can be easily mistaken for it.

3. What evidence did you find that slate is related to shale? _Both give off an earthy smell when wet._

4. What evidence did you find that marble is chemically similar to limestone?
   Both effervesce with dilute hydrochloric acid.

5. Which of your metamorphic rocks did you observe to be nonfoliated?
   Nonfoliated metamorphic rocks are quartzite, marble, anthracite.

If the students have done both the "minerals" and "rocks" investigations, they have probably noticed that many of the properties used for identification are the same for both. Thus the strategies used to identify unknown specimens are similar. In both cases an experienced observer can tell the identity of an unknown specimen at a glance if it is a common material. For rarer specimens, it may be necessary to perform a whole group of tests. For the more challenging problems, mineralogists and petrologists use flow charts that methodically eliminate possibilities after each test has been performed. When all the tests have been completed, usually only one possible identity for the rock or mineral remains.

Investigation

15E Fallacies of the Geologic Time Scale

Since you know that the concept of evolution is erroneous, you should reject all schemes of thought that are built upon it. The *geologic time scale* is one such scheme. It is a speculative framework of the earth's history. If evolution had happened, it would have had to have happened slowly and continuously. However, geologists have noticed that new fossil organisms seem to appear in the geologic column fully formed in stages. Each of these stages is given a name and assigned a period of time on the geologic time scale. The largest units of these time periods are called *eras*, the next smaller, *periods*, and the next, *epochs*. Evolutionists claim that these time units can be related to the appearance and extinction of fossil organisms in the earth's rock layers.

An evolutionary geologist believes that representative plants and animals living in each age were buried in sediment by rivers or streams, local floods, dust storms, mudslides, or wave action. In time this sediment turned to rock. The process is said to have been repeated many times, producing layer upon layer of rock, with each new layer representing a time period more recent than the one beneath it (the principle of *superposition*). The evolutionary geologist believes he can tell how old a fossil is by its vertical location with respect to other fossils. But his dating method is full of circular reasoning. He dates rocks by the fossils found in them and dates fossils by the same rocks. In addition, the method is flawed by the basic assumption of evolution. Living things were rapidly created; they did not slowly evolve. Further, there is good reason to believe that most of the fossils were laid down in a year-long period of great catastrophic activity during the Genesis Flood, not over hundreds of millions of years of more gentle activity, as is generally claimed.

Procedure

1. In each column of the table on page SA210, draw a vertical line through the portion of the geologic time scale affected by each numbered item described below. (*Note*: Look at the first column, and then plot the other seven items in the same manner.)

2. Place arrowheads at the ends of the line and make short horizontal lines at the arrowheads to mark the limits of the periods.

3. On each vertical line, place a label describing the evidence. For example, the label for Column 1 is "Iron Pot in Coal."

Column 1. An iron pot was found embedded in coal. The coal was determined to be middle Pennsylvanian, so one end of the line is placed in the middle of the Pennsyl-

Goal
Graph evidence that contradicts the geologic time scale, using three different lines of evidence—fossils, artifacts, and alleged geologic overthrusts.

Materials
none

vanian period. The iron pot must actually have been made in very recent times; so the other end of the line is located on the dashed line near the top of the table.

Column 2. Gymnosperm pollen is found in the Grand Canyon in the lowest strata (Precambrian). Yet evolutionists claim that such plants did not evolve until the Permian. Draw your line from the top of the Precambrian to the middle of the Permian. Label the line "Pollen in Grand Canyon."

Column 3. Fossil wood was found embedded in Precambrian rock in northern Quebec, Canada. Two radiocarbon tests on samples of the wood gave results of about four thousand years. Assuming that the radiocarbon results are correct, draw your line from the top of the Precambrian to the dashed line at the top of the table. Label it "Fossil Wood in Precambrian."

Column 4. A baked clay figurine 4 cm long was brought up from a depth of 92 m by a team of workers drilling for water at Nampa, Idaho. The level at which it was found was determined to be early Pliocene. Draw your line from the lowest part of the Pliocene to the dashed line at the top of the table. Label it "Nampa Image."

Column 5. Cambrian and Mississippian layers are found to alternate back and forth (two complete cycles) in one part of the north rim of the Grand Canyon. Since time cannot alternate back and forth, the portion of the geologic time table encompassed by the Cambrian and Mississippian periods is invalidated by this discovery. Draw your line from the middle of the Cambrian to the middle of the Mississippian and label it "Alternating Layers."

Column 6. Chief Mountain in Glacier National Park in Montana consists of Precambrian rock overlying Cretaceous rock. Since the fossils are out of their alleged developmental order, evolutionists have attempted to salvage their theory by claiming that an overthrust rearranged rock that was originally in its correct order. Yet

We include the iron pot example of an out-of-place human artifact (which was reported in 1912, from a lump of coal from the Wilburton, OK mines) only as an example of the numerous objects that supposedly have been discovered in ancient rock strata and coal beds. Unfortunately, none of the objects has been scientifically documented and therefore scientists reject their validity, since such findings do not fit their view of history.

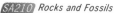

none of the evidences of overthrusting are present. The only logical conclusion is that the rocks were deposited in the order in which they are now found, meaning that the alleged time span between the Precambrian and Cretaceous (about 500 million years) never existed. Draw your line from the top of the Precambrian to the top of the Cretaceous and label it "Chief Mountain."

Columns 7 & 8. Your teacher may provide other examples.

The part above the dotted line represents several thousand years of recorded human history, and the part at the bottom of the table represents, if anything, the time span between the Creation and the Flood. In actuality, the latter probably represents either basement rock left over from the Creation, or igneous or fossil-free sedimentary rock laid down on top of basement rock swept clean by the action of the Flood.

Consider giving the information below for use in Column 7. This information was mentioned in Section 15B:

Protein and blood vessels were found in partially fossilized dinosaur bones. If these bones were at least 65 million years old, as evolutionists claim, according to biologists all the protein and cellular materials should have broken down by now. Evolutionists themselves express surprise that tissues could endure beyond 100,000 to 1 million years. Have students draw the line from the dotted line to the top of the Cretaceous. Label it "Dinosaur Tissues."

Eon	Era	Period	Epoch
Precambrian (Hadean, Archean, Proterozoic)			
Phanerozoic	Paleozoic	Cambrian, Ordovician, Silurian, Devonian, Mississippian, Pennsylvanian, Permian	
	Mesozoic	Triassic, Jurassic, Cretaceous	
	Cenozoic	Tertiary	Paleocene, Eocene, Oligocene, Miocene, Pliocene
		Quaternary	Pleistocene, Recent (Holocene)

Contradictions (columns 1–8):
- Iron Pot in Coal
- Pollen in Grand Canyon
- Fossil Wood in Precambrian
- Nampa Image
- Alternating layers
- Chief Mountain

Millions of years before the present:
4600, 3800, 2500, 555, 520, 438, 408, 365, 320, 286, 245, 208, 144, 66.4, 56.8, 35.6, 23.7, 5.3, 1.6, 0.01

Observations

1. The vertical line drawn through a geologic time unit has the effect of canceling it. Look at the overall effect of the six contradictions. How much of the fossil-bearing geologic time scale survived?

   <u>very little</u>

2. List the surviving parts of the table. <u>the part above the dotted line and a portion at the bottom of</u>

   <u>the table that contains no fossils</u>

Summing Up

1. On what basis do evolutionists label rocks as "Cretaceous," "Cambrian," and so on? <u>Names are given</u>

   <u>according to the fossils contained in the rocks.</u>

2. Explain how circular reasoning enters into the dating of rocks and fossils. <u>Rocks are dated according to</u>

   <u>the fossils they contain, and fossils are then dated according to the rocks in which they are found.</u>

3. What three different kinds of evidence were examined in this exercise? <u>Fossils, human artifacts (which are</u>

   <u>not scientifically documented), and alleged geologic overthrusts were examined.</u>

4. Assuming that a human artifact has been discovered embedded in sedimentary rock, and scientists agree that the artifact appears to be genuine, how could this fact be explained biblically?

   <u>The artifact could have been made by a pre-Flood civilization. During the Flood, the artifacts could have</u>

   <u>been covered with sediment that later turned to rock. (See Job 22:15–17.)</u>

15F Investigation "Trilobite-ology"

A common and easily recognized kind of fossil is a trilobite. Trilobite bodies consisted of three lobes arranged side by side along their length, hence the name, *tri-lobite*. Trilobites are placed in the animal phylum Arthropoda, as are insects, spiders, shrimp, and crabs, because they had exoskeletons and jointed appendages. In fact, some trilobites looked very similar to young horseshoe crabs of today. However, there are no known living trilobites today; they are considered to be extinct. All that is known about trilobites has come from studying their fossils and making "educated guesses" by comparing them with living arthropods.

Procedure and observations

PART 1: THE TRILOBITE BODY

1. Study Diagram A. Notice the raised middle lobe that runs from the head through the tail. Two sections are on either side of the middle lobe and are separated from the middle lobe by the longitudinal (long-wise) *axial furrows*. Trilobites get their name from these three longitudinal lobes.

2. The body can also be divided into three lengthwise sections: *head* (or *cephalon*), *thorax*, and *tail* (or *pygidium*). Often only one of the sections will have been preserved in a fossil. This is because, like most marine arthropods, trilobites molted their exoskeleton as they grew. So many trilobite fossils are just portions of the shed exoskeleton.

3. Notice the eyes and variously-shaped sections of the cephalon. The size, shape, and position of these parts are useful in identification of different trilobite species.

4. How many smaller segments (*pleura*) are there in the thorax?

   _____9_____

   Under each of these segments were gills attached to two pairs of legs for swimming or crawling. The number of segments in the thorax is also used to help identify different species of trilobites.

5. Observe that the pygidium is also made up of several sections. However, in the pygidium, the segments apparently grew together in the form of an inflexible plate.

6. Now study Diagram B. You should notice that although it is a trilobite, the size, shape, position, and number of the various parts are different from

Goal

Study a trilobite fossil and identify its various structural parts. Identify the subgroup to which particular trilobites belong.

Materials

hand lens or stereo microscope

trilobite fossil(s)

the one in Diagram A. Label Diagram B using the same terms that were used with Diagram A. Have your teacher check your work before you proceed further with this investigation.

7. Observe Diagrams C, D, E, and F. Note the scale with each one; some trilobites were up to 70 cm long, whereas others were less than 1 cm. While each differs in *morphology* (structure), they are all trilobites. The fossil record indicates that there were over ten thousand species of trilobites.

Diagram A

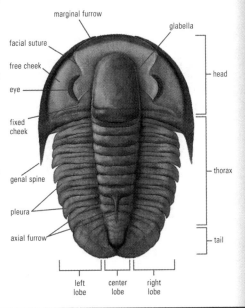

marginal furrow

glabella

facial suture

free cheek

eye

fixed cheek

genal spine

pleura

axial furrow

head

thorax

tail

left lobe · center lobe · right lobe

The purpose of this investigation is to demonstrate that fossils are more than just curiosities. Meaningful information can be obtained from them. This investigation overlaps the field of biology, but this type of overlap is appropriate. Make the point that no area of science is completely separate from all other areas.

Individual trilobites or sets may be purchased through major science material suppliers such as Carolina Biological Supply, Sargent-Welch, Fisher Scientific, Frey Scientific, and others. Classroom kits of smaller, more common trilobite fossils such as *Elrathia kingii* are fairly inexpensive, costing a few dollars per fossil. Hand lenses are required to examine these fossils. Large, good-quality specimens, especially of rarer species, can run into the hundreds of dollars each. You will want to consider obtaining good-quality reproductions for this investigation rather than the real thing.

Diagram B

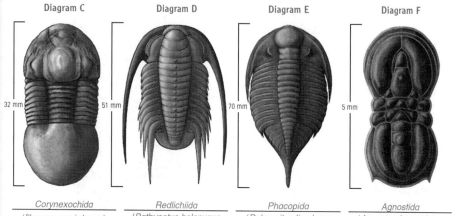

- glabella
- marginal furrow
- facial suture
- free cheek
- eye
- fixed cheek
- genal spine
- pleura
- axial furrow
- head
- thorax
- tail
- left lobe
- center lobe
- right lobe

Diagram C

32 mm

Corynexochida

(*Illaenus sarsi* shown)

Diagram D

51 mm

Redlichiida

(*Bathynotus holopygus* shown)

Diagram E

70 mm

Phacopida

(*Dalmanites limulurus* shown)

Diagram F

5 mm

Agnostida

(*Agnostus interstrictus* shown)

PART 2: THE TRILOBITE FOSSIL

1. Obtain a trilobite fossil and a hand lens from your teacher. As mentioned in Part 1, your fossil may not be complete.

2. Which sections are present in your fossil? _Answers will vary._____

3. Examine the fossil closely, using the hand lens. Pay close attention to the cephalon region if present.

4. Are the eyes simple or compound? (Look at an insect eye for comparison; insects have compound eyes.)
   _compound_____

5. Does it have a *genal spine*? _Answers will vary. (Most commonly available trilobite fossils do.)_

6. Do you think your fossil is of a molted exoskeleton or of the whole organism? Why? _Answers will vary._
   _If the fossil lies flat and is complete, then it probably was a whole organism._____

7. If there is much rock with your fossil, you may find fossils of other trilobites or other organisms. Are there other fossils present? If so, what do you think they are? Why?
   Answers will vary. Possibilities include brachiopods, crinoid stems, hydrozoans and corals.

8. Many living arthropods experience changes in the shape of their bodies each time they molt. Assuming that this also occurred with trilobite molting, how does this affect conclusions you made about your fossil?
   _The fossil may not be of an adult trilobite._____

9. In the space below, draw your trilobite as if it were flat and include as much detail as possible. Be careful not to draw details that you cannot see. Label the parts.

If the fossil is curled up or is missing one or more major sections (in an otherwise intact sample of rock), it is probably just a shed exoskeleton.

Encourage large, detailed (yet accurate) drawings.

Part 3: Identification of Trilobites

There are three to nine orders in the subphylum called Trilobita, depending on the characteristics used for classification. Five of the orders included in most classifications are listed below. Read the description of each subgroup and decide to which subgroup the trilobites in Diagrams C–F belong. Place the correct subgroup name in the blank below the respective diagram. (*Note:* One subgroup is not represented.)

Agnostida: small (total body length is 13 mm or less); 2–3 thoracic segments; blind (no eyes); no facial sutures

Redlichiida: large semicircular cephalon with genal spines; numerous thoracic segments (up to 44); crescent-shaped eyes; small pygidium

Corynexochida: large semicircular cephalon usually with spines; 5–11 thoracic segments; pygidium nearly the same size as the cephalon or only slightly smaller; eyes generally elongated

Phacopida: facial sutures extend from the front of the cephalon, to the eyes, to the rear of the shield; 8–19 thoracic segments; large- to medium-size pygidium

Ptychopariida: more than three thoracic segments; eyes present or absent; blunt pleural spines (Any that do not fit the other descriptions fall into this order.)

Summing Up

1. To what animal phylum do trilobites belong? __Arthropoda__

2. To what does the name *trilobite* refer? __Trilobites have three longitudinal body lobes.__

3. Name the three body sections of trilobites. __The three main sections are the head or cephalon, the thorax, and the tail or pygidium.__

4. In what type of rock (sedimentary, igneous, metamorphic) are trilobite fossils found? __Trilobites are found only in sedimentary rocks.__

5. Of what kind of material was your trilobite fossil composed? __Answers will vary. Some fossils are just casts, so the material will be the same as the rock. In others, dark-colored fossilized organic matter still remains.__

6. When using your hand lens and making a drawing, what did you observe about your trilobite that you did not observe without the hand lens?
__Answers will vary.__

7. What kind of information do you think you could obtain from a live trilobite that you could never get from fossils?
__A live trilobite could show eating habits, reflexes and behavior, life span, color, and so forth.__

These taxonomic descriptions are generalizations; there are always exceptions.

16 MOUNTAINS AND HIGH HILLS

Applications
16A Elevation, Actual Height, and Relief

Directions: Write your responses in the spaces provided.

1. Mount Shasta, in northern California, has an elevation of 4317 m. If the elevation of the surrounding country is 2149 m, what is the actual height of Mount Shasta?

   2168 m

2. Communism Peak, in Tajikistan, has an elevation of 7495 m. If its summit is 5697 m above the surrounding country, what is the elevation of the surrounding country?

   1798 m

3. Does Mount Shasta or Communism Peak look higher compared to the surrounding country?

   Communism Peak

4. If the elevation of the surrounding country is 1341 m and the actual height of Mt. Ushba, in the country of Georgia, is 3353 m, what is the elevation of Ushba?

   4694 m

5. Mount Logan, in the Yukon Territory of Canada, has an elevation of 5959 m. If the elevation of the surrounding country is 772 m, what is the actual height of Mount Logan?

   5187 m

6. The lowest point in the Himalayan range is 305 m above sea level. The highest point, Mount Everest, is 8848 m above sea level. What is the relief of this region?

   8543 m

7. One point in California's Death Valley is 86 m below sea level. Less than 160 km away is Mt. Whitney, 4418 m above sea level. What is the relief of this region?

   4504 m

Consult the figure below for Questions 8 and 9.

8. What is the elevation of the highest point?

   275 ft

9. From which direction could a person climb to the highest point more easily?

   from the west

Applications

16B Types of Mountains

Directions: Match the following types of mountains associated with the words and phrases below. Indicate your answers by writing the proper letters in the blanks provided.

___a___ 1. Terminal moraine

___b___ 2. Probably formed by waters of the Flood flowing off the continent

___d___ 3. Sierra Nevada in California

___b___ 4. Mount Monadnock, New Hampshire

___c___ 5. Anticline, syncline, and monocline

___a___ 6. Eskers

___b___ 7. Narrow, flat-topped hills with steep, nearly vertical sides

___a___ 8. Drumlins

___a___ 9. Igneous materials piled up or pushed out of a vent

___b___ 10. Buttes and mesas

___c___ 11. Domes and basins

___d___ 12. Joints and faults

___c, d___ 13. Could be caused by plate tectonics

___d___ 14. Great Basin and Range Province of Nevada

___a___ 15. Sand dunes

a. Depositional
b. Erosional
c. Fold
d. Fault-block

Applications
16C Describing Mountains

Directions: In the word puzzle below, write the words that are described by the following statements. Each term is related to types of mountains.

1. Terminal _____ are ridges of rock debris that glaciers push into a pile at their front edge.

2. One of the simplest geologic folds is the _____.

3. A crack along which there has been slippage is a/an _____.

4. A syncline that is roughly as long as it is wide is called a/an _____.

5. _____ are narrow, flat-topped hills formed by erosion.

6. A/An _____ is also called a tableland.

7. _____ are elongated, streamlined hills deposited by glaciers.

8. A/An _____ is a crack in a rock where there has been no slippage.

9. _____ are broad, flat-topped hills remaining from the dissection process of erosion.

```
1.  M O R A I N E S
2.  M O N O C L I N E
3.  F A U L T
4.  B A S I N
5.  B U T T E S
6.  P L A T E A U
7.  D R U M L I N S
8.  J O I N T
9.  M E S A S
```

Applications

16D Formation of Mountains (Orogeny)

Directions: Write your response in the spaces provided.

1. Uniformitarian geologists use the overthrust theory to explain why "old" rocks are found on top of "young" rocks. Describe this theory and list any arguments that can be used to refute it.

   The overthrust theory maintains that the strata were originally laid down in proper order but that later the "old rocks" pushed up over (overthrusted) the "young rocks." Such a force would have shattered the rock long before it traveled the required distance. Also, not only do scientists find "old rock" on top of "young rock," but they also find alternating layers. Overthrust would not produce interleaved layers.

2. How do geologists believe mountain ranges formed? Describe the uniformitarian explanation and then give one creationary theory.

   The prevailing theory today is that stresses set up in the crust from colliding plates have produced folding and faulting and in the process have raised (and continue to raise) the great mountain ranges of the world. Subducting plates melt and form zones for volcanic and earthquake activity that further produce individual mountains and ranges of mountains. The uniformitarian process supposedly took millions of years and was driven only by thermal plumes in the mantle. One creationary theory suggests that plate tectonics occurred rapidly and catastrophically during the year of the Genesis Flood, driven by the runaway subduction of tectonic plates and the formation of new oceanic crust to move the continental masses.

Investigation

16E Making a Model and Relief Map of a Mountain

A map that indicates altitude and landforms by color, shading, or some other device is called a relief map. For more precise elevation information, maps are printed with contour lines. An elevation contour line connects all points on the earth's surface that are at the same elevation above a reference height—usually considered mean sea level. Contour lines on the map are labeled with their elevations. Where lines are close together, only every fifth or tenth line may be labeled. This investigation will help you to see and understand the contour lines on a relief map. The diagram below will give you an idea of how a contour relief map should look.

Goal
Make and interpret a contour relief map.

Materials
modeling clay, waterproof (plasticene or equivalent)
dishpan, deep
ruler, plastic metric (must be at least as long as the dishpan is deep)
beaker, 250 mL to 1 L (or water pitcher)
water
pencil, clay tool, or old ballpoint pen

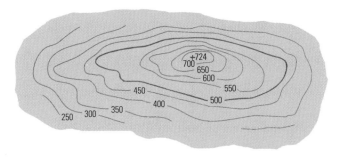

Procedure

1. Fashion a mountain approximately 10–15 cm high out of modeling clay. The model should be no higher than the height of the dishpan. Make one side of the mountain noticeably steeper than the other. Try to give it interesting features. If you'd like, you can even give it two peaks instead of one.

2. Place the mountain model in the dishpan.

3. Tape the ruler to the inside of the dishpan, oriented vertically with 0 cm end on the floor of the dishpan.

4. Using the beaker, pour water into the dishpan to a height of approximately 1 cm.

5. Using the point of a pencil, clay tool, or ballpoint pen, mark a line all the way around the mountain at the water line.

6. Add another centimeter of water and draw another contour line at the water line.

7. Repeat the contour line drawing steps until the entire mountain is underwater.

8. Carefully pour the water out of the container and observe the mountain from directly above.

9. Draw a contour map of the model as accurately as you can in the space on the following page. Include the elevation centimeters to show the level of each line.

Students can bring in their own materials for this investigation. Sometimes parents will donate the supplies, which can be saved and used again.

Use the following procedure to produce a more accurate contour relief map. The only additional materials required are a hacksaw frame (the frame that holds the blade in a hacksaw) and some thin wire. Have the students mark two perpendicular lines across the top of the mountain—from base to peak to base—so that they form an X. In the box on this page, draw two perpendicular lines on the paper so that they intersect approximately where the peak appears on the model (looking down from above). Remove the blade from a hacksaw and replace it with a thin wire wrapped taut around the retaining plugs for the blade. Rotate the blade-tensioning knob to tighten the wire even more. Carefully saw along each contour line and lift the top section free. Place the layer on the paper so that the lines intersect the marks on the layer. Trace around the lower edge of the layer. Repeat for each layer until the bottom layer is done. A fairly accurate contour relief map will result.

Summing Up

1. Where are the lines on your relief map more closely spaced? __The lines are closer where the mountain__ __is steeper.__

2. What does the spacing of the close lines tell you about the features of the mountain? __The closer the contour__ __lines, the steeper the slope of the mountain.__

3. How would the summit of the mountain be represented on your map? __The summit is represented with a__ __dot or a small closed circle.__

4. How would a contour relief map of a mountain be valuable to scientists? __Answers will vary. Engineers__ __can use such maps to determine the easiest route to the top of a mountain for building a road or routing__ __electrical service wires. They can also identify level spots on which to build structures. Mapmakers can__ __determine the location of the ridge and shape of the mountain. Surveyors can determine the location of__ __the peak for use as a benchmark.__

Investigation

16F Making a Profile Map of a Mountain

A relief map shows you the elevation levels of a mountain as observed from above the mountain. This investigation will help you to construct a profile of the mountain from a contour relief map, showing its vertical appearance as if you were observing it from the side.

Procedure

PART 1

1. Note the contour relief map of a mountain provided below. Observe the line drawn horizontally through the peak of the mountain. This line will be called the *profile reference line* for this investigation. Also observe that the elevation of each contour line is recorded on the map.

2. Place the index card so that its short side is exactly on and parallel to the 400 m line in the drawing area, and its long side intersects the profile line on the contour map. Slide the card one way or the other until it lies on the intersection of the profile reference line and the first closed contour line at the right side of the map. Lightly draw a vertical line from that elevation point down to the corresponding numbered line on the elevation scale beneath the drawing. Mark a dot at this intersection point on the applicable elevation scale line.

3. Move the index card in to the next contour line (50 m higher in elevation) where it intersects the

Goal

Construct a profile of a mountain, using a relief map.

Materials

pencil
index card, 3 × 5 in.

profile reference line. Lightly draw another vertical line down to the corresponding line on the elevation scale and mark a dot.

4. Continue to move the index card across the relief map, ensuring that the vertical edge of the index card remains perpendicular to the profile reference line. Carefully draw light vertical lines down to the corresponding heights on the elevation scale for each contour and mark dots on the appropriate elevation lines. Include all the points where a contour line intersects the profile reference line. Also include the point that represents the summit of the mountain, which falls between two contour elevations. Estimate the distance based on the summit's height between the last closed contour line and the next contour elevation.

5. Carefully connect the marks with a smooth line from left to right.

 Visual 16-13A: Investigation 16F— Topographic Map and Relief Scale

This visual is a reproduction of the map and plotting grid on page SA223. Use this visual to explain the techniques necessary to successfully complete the activity.

 Visual 16-13B: Investigation 16F— Topographic Profile (overlay)

This is the completed profile that may be placed on top of Visual 16-13A. Just align the registrations marks at the corners of the relief scale.

PART 2

1. In the space below, make up a relief map of an imaginary mountain. You could also include a depression at the base of the mountain; then raise the elevation back to ground level. Include numbers for the height of elevation on each contour line. (The numbers should be within the range of the elevation scale below.)

2. Carefully draw a straight profile reference line from left to right through the main peak of your mountain.

3. Follow the procedure listed in Part 1 to draw a profile of the mountain you have created.

Student maps and profiles will vary.

Elevation (in meters)

750
700
650
600
550
500
450
400
350
300
250

Summing Up

1. If the contour lines on a relief map are far apart, how should the mountain profile look at that point?
   It should have a low incline.

2. What does a profile help you see about contour lines on a relief map that are close together? The closer the contour lines, the steeper the mountainside.

3. A certain mountain is formed by the intersection of two ridges that come together at an angle of about 120°. How would you determine the profile of the mountain along these two ridges?
   Starting at the peak, draw one profile reference line along one ridge, then draw another along the other ridge. Using an elevation scale on a separate sheet of paper, place it parallel to the first profile reference line and mark the corresponding elevations, then rotate it parallel to the second profile line and complete marking the remaining elevations. The resulting profile is of the mountain along its two ridges.

4. Why would contour maps and profile diagrams be important for geologists and engineers? Geologists and engineers need to understand the elevations of a mountain for planning and surveying purposes, and the profile gives them a better sense of how steep the mountain is.

Investigation
16G Topographic Maps

A *topographic map* is a map that represents the three-dimensional shape of the earth's surface. The features displayed on a topographic map are many. They include *relief* (differences in height from one point to the next), *water features* (lakes, streams, swamps, and the like), and *manmade features* (roads, bridges, tunnels, railroad tracks, landing strips, and buildings). Each map covers a *quadrangle* bounded by parallels of latitude on the north and south and by meridians of longitude on the east and west. Each quadrangle has its own name to identify it, such as "Greenwood, MI Quadrangle." The scale of the "topo map" is chosen to display the details of its terrain to the best advantage. A typical scale is 1:24,000; in this scale every distance in the real world is 24,000 times as large as the same distance measured on the map.

Relief is shown by means of contour lines. Contour lines are lines of equal elevation. If you were to walk along a contour line, you would move neither up nor down. You would stay at the same elevation. Notice the following facts about contour lines:

1. Theoretically, every contour line is a closed curve. That is, if you could follow it far enough, you would eventually come back to your starting point. But often only part of the line shows on the map you are using. You might need several maps placed together to trace a given line all the way back to your starting point.

2. Contour lines never cross each other, though two or more lines might merge together as they pass along the face of a cliff.

3. Closely spaced contour lines indicate a steep slope; widely spaced lines indicate a gentle slope.

4. Roughly circular contour lines, one inside the other, indicate a high point such as a rise, a hill, or a mountain. The same pattern, but with a number of short lines pointing inward from each contour line, indicates a depression.

5. When contour lines cross a stream, they tend to bend in the shape of a "V." The point of the "V" is always in the upstream direction. For rivers flowing over relatively level terrain, the "V" shape may be flattened.

6. The vertical spacing between contour lines is called the *contour interval* of the map (abbreviated C.I.). A commonly used contour interval is 20 feet, or 5 m for metric maps, but different values are used, depending on the local situation and the map series.

7. Every fifth contour is drawn darkly; the remaining lines are drawn lightly. For example, if the contour interval is 20 feet, the 100 ft, 200 ft, and so on, lines are dark; whereas the 20 ft, 40 ft, 60 ft, and 80 ft lines are light. The dark lines are called *index contours*, and they make map reading easier.

8. The difference in elevation between the highest and lowest points in a given area is called the *maximum relief* of the area.

9. Appendix B7 provides a listing of most topographic map symbols used on United States Geological Survey (USGS) topo maps.

Goal
Use a section of an actual USGS topographic map to develop proficiency in map reading.

Materials
ruler
drafting dividers

Introduction: Topographic maps are extremely useful to geologists, geographers, civil engineers, contractors, farmers, pilots, biologists, prospectors, surveyors, and real estate agents. Even campers, hunters, fishermen, and mountaineers make use of "topo maps" to learn more about their favorite recreational areas.

Many topographic maps show a quadrangle size that is 7.5 minutes of longitude wide and 7.5 minutes of latitude high. Another common size is 30 minutes by 60 minutes (1:100,000 scale). For regions such as Antarctica, where less detail has been charted, maps are drawn to cover as much as several degrees on a side.

Goal: You may want to review map symbols by using a topographic map of your own area. Most 7½ × 7½ quadrangle maps cost $6–$7 when purchased from the USGS.

Materials: You may choose to omit the drafting dividers in this investigation by simply placing the ruler on the map, or you may use a drawing compass to measure distances by measuring its span on the ruler. Be sure that the compasses used are tight so that the distance between the pencil and the point does not change after being adjusted.

Paragraph 2: In the case of a significant overhang, it is possible that contour lines could cross, but this would be the exception to the rule.

Paragraph 6: In mountainous regions the C.I. could be as much as 100 ft or 50 m, whereas in gently sloping regions, intervals as small as 1 ft or 1 m might be used.

The name *Passadumkeag* comes from the Abenaki Indian word for "rapids over gravel beds."

The United States Geological Survey has been gathering data for these maps since 1882. The 1:62,500 scale maps were also called the 15-minute quadrangle maps. Production and updating of these maps have been discontinued. They were replaced by the 7.5 minute (1:24,000) quadrangle series maps, which are more detailed.

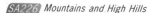
Procedure and Observations

Study the map of the Passadumkeag, Maine region, taking note of the following features.

1. The Penobscot River runs roughly north and south throughout the western part of the map. What is the name of the largest island in the river visible on this map?
   Olamon Island

2. Note that highways have been built on either side of the river, roughly parallel to it. What are the route numbers of these highways? What kind of highways are they?
   Route 116 is a secondary (or state) highway; Route 2 is a primary (or U.S.) highway.

3. In what direction does the Penobscot River flow? (*Hint*: Look for the direction of the "V" in the contour line near where Lancaster Brook enters the river. There is also an arrow indicating flow on the map.)
   Flow is north to south.

4. Note the roughly north-south coursing track of the Maine Central Railroad east of the Penobscot River. If you were to take a train from Passadumkeag to Olamon, what land and vegetation would you see to the east during the first half of the trip?
   A train passenger would see level swampy land to the east.

5. Find Vinegar Hill near the upper right-hand corner of the map.

   What is the elevation of the highest point of the hill? _622 ft_

   How high is it above Cold Stream Pond? _432 ft_ (Note that the pond spillway determines the height of the pond's surface—190 ft.)

6. An esker is a long, narrow ridge of gravel and sediment deposited by a stream flowing in or under a glacier. Enfield Horseback is probably an esker. Does it rise above or sink below the surrounding terrain? How do you know?
   It rises above the surrounding terrain and is indicated by closed, unhatched contour lines indicating points
   of higher elevation along the esker.

7. What is the contour interval of the map? _20 ft_

   What is the scale of the map? _1:62,500_

8. The distance scale of this map is provided at the bottom. Using a ruler and a pair of drafting dividers, determine the approximate aerial distance from the middle of Socs Island to the highest point on Vinegar Hill in miles and kilometers.
   _9 mi; 14.5 km_

9. Given that the Passadumkeag River is a tributary (feeder stream) of the Penobscot River, in which direction does it flow?
   southeast to northwest (or east to west)

10. What is the maximum relief of Passadumkeag Township? Note that its western border is located in the river.

    Highest point:
    340 ft (NE corner)

    Lowest point: (Find the lowest-numbered contour line in the southwest corner of the township.)
    _120 ft_

    Maximum relief: (Subtract the two numbers recorded above.)
    _220 ft_

Passadumkeag Township and Environs (part of USGS Passadumkeag Quadrangle, Maine, 1960, Scale 1:62,500)

Investigation
16H Mountains

The map for this exercise covers a portion of north-western Montana. The name *Montana* comes from the Spanish word meaning "mountainous." Quite fittingly, mountains are prominent on both the state flag and state seal of Montana. The western part of the state is characterized by especially rugged terrain. Its elevation is so great that many permanent glaciers are found in the region.

The topographic map used here comes from the top center of the Saint Mary Quadrangle, Montana, USGS 1:100,000 . It shows the northeast corner of Glacier National Park. Its northern boundary coincides with the Canadian border. Included on the map is Chief Mountain, discussed in the Facet on page 423. This mountain is a result of the alleged Lewis Overthrust. Read the Facet carefully before proceeding with this investigation. This reading will give you important background information needed for the second part of the investigation.

Goals

Study some of the distinctive features of a mountainous region from a topographic map.

Improve proficiency reading a topographic map.

Study the particulars of the so-called Lewis Overthrust and calculate the weight of material that is claimed to have been involved in the eastward movement of "older" rock over "younger" rock.

Materials

calculator
ruler
drafting dividers

Procedure

PART 1: MAP STUDY

1. The Canadian border runs along the top of the map from corner to corner. Using your dividers and the map scale, about how far south from the border is Chief Mountain located in kilometers?

   4.5 mi

2. Give the elevation of the summit of mountain peaks listed below. If a summit elevation is not provided on the map, give the elevation interval that contains the summit represented by the highest contour line visible on the map. The first peak is done as an example.

   a. Chief Mountain 2760 m (height not shown)

   b. Mount Wilbur 2841 m

   c. Mount Cleveland 3190 m

   d. Mount Cannon 2729 m

   e. Yellow Mountain 2672 m

   f. Mount Grinnel 2698 m

   g. Allen Mountain 2858 m

3. Give the elevation of each of the following bodies of water:

   Elizabeth Lake 1491 m

   Lake Sherburne 1459 m

   Glenns Lake 1482 m

   Iceberg Lake 1857 m

   McDonald Creek as it leaves the map in the lower left corner of the page (Use the last contour line it crosses.)

   1050 m

4. Assume that Questions 2 and 3 contain the highest and lowest elevations of the region covered by the map.

   a. What is the maximum relief of the area?

      2140 m

   b. Express this figure in kilometers; in miles.

      2.14 km; 1.33 mi

Make a transparency of the map on page SA231 and use it to point out features as you have students follow in their textbooks.

5. Note the road in the lower left-hand portion of the map. It has a distinctive feature called a "switchback" (hairpin turn), which results from its having been built to gain height along a very steep slope. What name has been given to the place where the road crosses the Continental Divide?

   Logan Pass

6. What is the contour interval of the map? __50 m__

   Is this a large or a small value for the contour interval? Why? __This interval is large because there is very__ steep topography with high relief on this map.

7. Locate Wynn Mountain. On which side is it steepest? __north__

   Estimate the elevation of its summit, assuming that it is halfway between contour lines. __2575 m__

8. Canyon Creek is located just to the west of Wynn Mountain. Judging by the relative elevation of Cracker Lake and Lake Sherburne, does the water in the creek flow north or south?

   Canyon Creek flows north.

9. A number of small glaciers are located in this part of the country. What is the name of the largest glacier shown on the map?

   Grinnel Glacier

10. Using the scale of kilometers, determine the aerial distance from the summit of Mount Siyeh (south of Siyeh glacier) to the summit of Chief Mountain; give the distance in miles, also.

    23.4 km; 14.5 mi

PART 2: STUDY OF ALLEGED OVERTHRUST

1. The amount of material supposedly involved in the overthrust is given on page 423. Use the metric system of measurement in your calculations. The block of rock material allegedly measured 560 km from north to south, had an average width of 36.2 km, and had a thickness of 3.04 km. Find the volume of the material in cubic kilometers by multiplying these three numbers together:

   $560 \text{ km} \times 36.2 \text{ km} \times 3.04 \text{ km} =$ __$61{,}626 \text{ km}^3 \approx 6.2 \times 10^4$__ km^3

2. There are 1000 meters in a kilometer. Find out how many cubic meters there are in a cubic kilometer by cubing the number 1000 m/km:

   $(1000 \text{ m/km})^3 =$ __1×10^9__ m^3/km^3

3. Multiply this number by the number you obtained in step 1 to get the total volume of the material in cubic meters:

   __$(6.2 \times 10^4 \text{ km}^3)$__ $\times$ __$(1 \times 10^9 \text{ m}^3/\text{km}^3)$__ $=$ __6.2×10^{13}__ m^3

4. Assume that the rock had a specific gravity of 2.75. A cubic meter of water has a mass of 1.00×10^3 kilograms. Find the mass of a cubic meter of the rock by multiplying these two numbers together:

   __2.75__ $\times$ __$(1.00 \times 10^3 \text{ kg/m}^3)$__ $=$ __2.75×10^3__ kg/m^3

5. Multiply the answer from step 3 by the answer from step 4 to get the total mass of the rock in kilograms:

   __$6.2 \times 10^{13} \text{ m}^3$__ $\times$ __$2.75 \times 10^3 \text{ kg/m}^3$__ $=$ __1.71×10^{17}__ kg

---

Explain that to cube a number means to use that number itself as a factor three times. This would be a good opportunity to discuss how to write numbers in scientific notation and the purpose and use of significant figures. See Chapter 2 of PHYSICS, Second Edition, for a thorough discussion of these topics.

The answer should be rounded to 2 significant digits: 62,000 km³; in scientific notation, 6.2×10^4 km³.

Chief Mountain Map (part of USGS Saint Mary Quadrangle, Montana, 1981. Scale 1:100,000 metric; Contour Interval 50 meters)

6. There are 1000 kilograms in a metric ton. Divide your answer from step 5 by 1000 to give the mass of the rock in metric tons:

$$\frac{1.71 \times 10^{17} \text{ kg}}{1000 \text{ kg/T}} = \underline{\quad 1.71 \times 10^{14} \quad} \text{ metric tons}$$

7. Express your answer in trillions of metric tons:

   $\underline{\quad 171 \quad}$ trillion metric tons

Observations

1. According to the Facet, what would have happened if this immense amount of rock moved 56 km (35 mi) to the east as the theory demands?

   The rock would have shattered rather than moved across the surface because the friction irregularities would have been so great. Also, the surfaces of the sliding layers would show signs of movement.

2. The material that supposedly moved to the east is Precambrian limestone. The underlying material is Cretaceous shale. According to Investigation 15E, what is the *minimum* number of years this finding would remove from the geologic time scale?

   411 million years

Summing Up

1. What factor in this terrain sustains year-round glaciers? cool climate at high elevations

2. A good theory allows the scientist to make specific predictions about data from subsequent observations. When the observations result in data vastly different from that predicted by the theory, what does that tell you about the theory?

   The theory is wrong. It must be revised or abandoned.

3. What physical evidence of overthrusting is absent in the Chief Mountain region?

   signs of previous movement at the boundary layer, such as broken rock and drag marks at the sliding boundary

4. In several parts of this map the contour lines are so close that no space can be seen between them. What does it indicate when two or more contour lines actually coincide?

   superimposed contour lines indicate a near-vertical cliff

5. Look up the definition of *continental divide* in your dictionary. Does this map seem to bear out the truth of its definition?

   Definition: An extensive stretch of high ground from each side of which the river systems of a continent flow in opposite directions (American Heritage College Dictionary, 4th ed.). Yes, the rivers on either side of the divide seem to flow more or less east and west.

Additional Resources

For additional reading on the alleged overthrust in this region, see (1) Walter E. Lammerts, "Overthrust Faults in Glacier National Park," *Creation Research Society Quarterly*, May 1966, 61–62; (2) Clifford L. Burdick, "The Lewis Overthrust," *Creation Research Society Quarterly*, September 1969, 96–106.

17 EARTHQUAKES AND VOLCANOES

Applications

17A Earthquake Effects

Directions: Listed below are ten statements concerning earthquakes. In the spaces provided, write *True* if the statement is true and *False* if the statement is false. For *False* answers, state why the answer is false in the blanks provided.

_____True_____ 1. A tsunami is an earthquake-induced ocean wave.

_____False_____ 2. The epicenter is the true center of the earthquake activity.
The focus is the true center of the earthquake. The epicenter lies on the earth's surface above the focus.

_____False_____ 3. The Richter scale goes from 1 to 9.
The Richter scale is open-ended. There is no upper magnitude limit, but no quakes larger than about 9 are likely.

_____True_____ 4. The Richter scale rates the energy released by an earthquake.

_____False_____ 5. Each whole number on the Richter scale has ten times as much energy as the next lower whole number.
Each whole number in the Richter scale represents about 31.6 times as much energy as the next lower number.

_____True_____ 6. The epicenter is the place on the earth's surface where an earthquake's energy is usually the greatest.

_____True_____ 7. If an earthquake with a magnitude of 3 occurred in your area, the residents would be able to sense it.

_____True_____ 8. Some of the geologic effects of earthquakes include landslides, vertical displacement, and horizontal displacement.

_____False_____ 9. Richtergraphs are instruments that detect and record earth waves.
Seismographs are the instruments that detect and record earthquake waves.

_____False_____ 10. The greatest magnitude that has ever been recorded for an earthquake is 8.6.
The strongest earthquake ever recorded was 9.5 in Chile in 1960 (see Table 17-2 on p. 443).

Applications
17B Earth Waves

Directions: Fill in the earth-wave chart with the correct information. Two answers have been given to you.

	P Waves	S Waves	L Waves
Complete name	Primary	Secondary	Last and large
Speed	Fast	Half as fast as P waves	Slow
Amplitude	Small	Larger than P waves	Large
Travel route	Through the earth's interior	Through the earth's interior	On the earth's surface
Ability to pass through core	Can pass through	Cannot pass through	Not Applicable

Applications

17C Volcano Structure

Directions: Label the drawing of the volcano by supplying the missing terms or definitions.

1. Volcano
   A landform built up
   by molten rock that
   has come to the
   earth's surface
   through a vent

2. _____ Lava _____
   Molten rock that has
   come to the surface

3. Parasitic cone
   A secondary cone
   that forms on the
   side of the main
   cone or is completely
   separate from it

4. _____ Magma chamber _____
   The source of magma
   at the bottom of the
   vent

8. Crater
   A depression at
   the top of the cone

   _____

   _____

   _____

7. _____ Volcanic cone _____
   Layered structure of
   lava, ash, or a combi-
   nation of the two that
   was built up by suc-
   cessive eruptions

6. _____ Vent _____
   Cylindrical opening
   that connects a source
   of molten rock with
   the surface of the
   earth

5. _____ Magma _____
   Molten rock beneath
   the earth's surface

The statements in this activity are examples of possible answers. Actual answers will vary.

Applications

17D Volcano Activity

Directions: Below are several groups of words. In each group, three of the four words (or phrases) are related to one another. Draw a line through the unrelated word and then write a sentence using the remaining related words. Your sentence should show how the words are related. You may slightly change the form of the word in your sentence (for example, *volcano* to *volcanoes*, *eruption* to *erupts*).

1. volcano / structure / activity / ~~pumice~~ _Volcanoes are classified by structure and activity._

2. lava / shield / ~~debris~~ / volcano _A shield volcano is built up from lava._

3. cinder cone / ~~carbon dioxide~~ / ejection / debris _A cinder cone is built up by the ejection of debris._

4. lava / composite / ash and cinders / ~~dormant~~ _A composite volcano is built up by layers of lava alternating with layers of ash and cinders._

5. ~~Mauna Loa~~ / Mount Etna / Fuji / Mayon _Mounts Etna, Fuji, and Mayon are all composite volcanoes._

6. eruption / ~~ashes~~ / unlikely / extinct _An extinct volcano has no historical record of any eruption and is unlikely to erupt._

7. **Mauna Loa** / **active** / **Vesuvius** / ~~**Mount Mazama**~~ _Mauna Loa and Vesuvius are active volcanoes._

8. dormant / ~~crater~~ / volcano / eruption _A dormant volcano is one that has not erupted in historical times but could do so at any time._

9. ~~oxygen~~ / water vapor / carbon dioxide / sulfur dioxide _Water vapor, carbon dioxide, and sulfur dioxide are volcanic gases._

10. dormant / Mauna Kea / Mount Shasta / ~~Mt. Tambora~~ _Mauna Kea and Mount Shasta are dormant volcanoes._

Identify each type of volcano in the diagrams by writing its name in the blank next to the corresponding letter.

11. A _Shield volcano_

12. B _Composite volcano_

13. C _Cinder cone_

Applications

17E Famous Volcanoes

Directions: Read each of the following descriptions and decide which famous volcano is being described. Then indicate your answers by writing the proper letter(s) in the blanks provided.

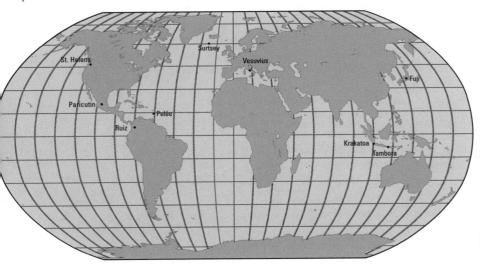

_i_	1. Located in Italy
_c_	2. Located on Martinique
_b, h_	3. Located in Indonesia
_f_	4. Located in Mexico
_g_	5. Located near Iceland
_c_	6. Killed 25,000 to 40,000 inhabitants—only two survivors
_i_	7. Buried the nearby town of Pompeii
_a_	8. A composite volcano located in Japan
_g_	9. Formed a new island
_h_	10. Largest known volcanic eruption
_f_	11. A mountain 430 m higher than the original cornfield
_g_	12. Rose from the ocean floor in recent historical times
_b, h, i_	13. Located in the Alpine-Himalayan belt
_a, d, e, f_	14. Located in the Circum-Pacific belt
_e_	15. Caused mudslides that buried thousands of people
_d_	16. Located in Washington State
_b_	17. Caused an explosion that was heard over 4800 km (3000 mi) away

a. Mount Fuji
b. Krakatoa
c. Mount Pelée
d. Mount St. Helens
e. Nevado del Ruiz
f. Parícutin
g. Surtsey
h. Tambora
i. Vesuvius

Applications
17F Heated Ground Water

Directions: In each of the following statements, circle the correct choice in the parentheses.

1. A (geyser / geyserite) is a thermal spring that forcibly ejects its water from the ground at intervals.

2. (Japan / Italy) was the first country to experiment with using geothermal energy to produce electricity.

3. The thermal gradient of the earth averages (30 °C / 30 °F) per kilometer into the crust.

4. Vents in the ground where steam and other vapors or gases escape are called (fumaroles / lahars).

5. (Carbon dioxide / Oxygen) escaping from fumaroles can be dangerous.

6. Heating homes with natural steam from the earth is an example of the use of (geothermal / geocentric) energy.

7. A whitish deposit called (travertine / geyserite) often appears around the opening of a geyser.

8. (Tephra / Travertine) deposits from evaporating water sometimes form terraces on the sides of hills.

9. When heated ground water is carried to the surface as a liquid, it becomes a (fumarole / hot spring).

10. (Algae / Mosses) growing on the travertine around hot springs color the terraces red, blue, and brown.

Investigation
17G Seismoscope

Seismographs are sensitive scientific instruments designed to measure and record the shaking of the earth during earthquakes. A seismoscope is similar to a seismograph but only indicates when an earthquake occurs. It does not produce a record of the quake. In this Investigation, you will make a simple seismoscope.

Setting Up

1. Set up the ring stand and clamp the base to one table with the C-clamp. Secure the right-angle support clamp near the top of the ring stand rod; then secure the dowel rod in the clamp. The dowel rod should extend over the second table. (See the figure.)

2. Strip 3 cm of insulation from each end of all three wires.

3. Attach the fishing sinker about 4 cm from the end of one wire. The bare wire should extend beyond the sinker. The sinker is the "inertial mass" of the instrument.

4. Tie the length of wire with the sinker to the dowel so that the weighted end hangs 2–3 mm above the second desktop. (Adjust the height by adjusting the ring-stand clamp.) Connect the free end of this wire to one of the battery terminals (the battery and lamp socket should be on the first desk).

5. Connect one end of the second wire to the other battery terminal and the other end of the same wire to one of the terminals on the light socket.

6. Bend the stripped portion of one end of the remaining third wire into a small circular loop (5–7 mm in diameter). Bend the loop so that it is perpendicular

Goal
Make and demonstrate a simple seismoscope.

Materials
desks or tables, same height (2)
ring stand
C-clamp
right angle support clamp
dowel rod, ¼ in.
dry-cell battery, 6 V
socket for 6 V light bulb
insulated wire, 0.5–1 m lengths (3)
fishing sinker (1–6 oz) (the heavier the better)
light bulb, 6 V
modeling clay (plasticene)

to the long part of the wire. Carefully insert the hanging wire through the loop; then secure the loop to the second table with a piece of clay. When all pieces are assembled and stationary, the bare end of the hanging wire should be through but not touching any part of the bare wire loop.

7. Connect the free end of the third wire to the free terminal on the light socket.

The setup easily lends itself to a great deal of substitution of materials. The underlying idea is to construct a hanging mass that completes an electrical circuit when it makes contact with a shaking electrode. In order to get across the concept of a seismic sensor, the hanging mass needs to be supported by a surface that is not shaking.

If you use a lower voltage or weak battery, the light bulb may not light every time.

For Step 4, you may want to use a light bulb designed for voltage lower than 6 V in order to get a bright flash with each weak contact. If you do so, be prepared with several spare bulbs since accidental good contacts of longer duration may burn out the bulbs. You may also substitute a voltmeter for the bulb to make the instrument even more sensitive.

Procedure

1. Gently bump the second table. What happens? The wire loop shakes and contacts the wire with the sinker, which is stationary. The electrical contact makes the light flash.

2. Shake the table harder. What happens? The flashes are more rapid, possibly brighter.

3. Bump the table hard enough to move the table on the floor. What happens? The wire loop bumps against the hanging wire, possibly making continuous contact, indicating a permanent displacement of the table.

4. How does the flashing change with the strength of the bump? The flashes occur more rapidly and perhaps more brightly with stronger shaking motion.

Summing Up

1. What does bumping the table represent? the movement of the earth during an earthquake

2. Which part of the seismoscope is moving during an "earthquake," the loop "detector" or the inertial mass?
   The inertial mass is stationary during an "earthquake." The ground moves the detector relative to the mass.

3. How could this seismoscope be made even more sensitive? Answers will vary. Possibilities include making the loop detector smaller in diameter or using a larger mass so it is not set to swinging so easily. More advanced classes might use a fixed inductive coil connected to a microammeter positioned under a hanging magnet.

4. How could the movement of the table be permanently recorded? Answers will vary. Use some sort of recording device rather than a light bulb, such as lab logging software on a computer.

5. What would this instrument be called if it were modified so that it could record earthquakes?
   It would be called a seismograph.

Investigation

17H Finding the Epicenter of an Earthquake

Natural occurrences such as rock fractures and volcanism generate sound waves within the earth or along its surface. Such waves are usually called earthquakes. But the word *earthquake* means different things to different people. To some people it means an observable, physical shaking of the earth. To others, any source of vibration (even if it is observable only with sensitive instruments) is an earthquake. For this reason all waves within the earth shall be referred to as seismic waves, and the source of those seismic waves shall be referred to as an earthquake.

The three principal types of seismic waves are classified as either body waves or surface waves. Body waves travel within the earth and consist of two principal types—P (primary) and S (secondary) waves. Surface waves, or L waves, travel along the earth's surface.

Goals

Determine the location of an earthquake's epicenter by using data from three seismic data stations.

Learn about relative energies of different quakes from Richter-scale ratings.

Materials

calculator

map or atlas of the United States

drawing compass

textbook

The word *seismic* comes from the Greek word *seismos,* meaning "to shake." Artificial sources of seismic waves include the blasting of large rocks, nuclear explosions and other large explosions, sonic booms, and landslides.

Date	Station	ID	LAT	LONG	Elev. (m)	P Wave hh:mm:ss (UTC)	S Wave hh:mm:ss (UTC)	M_n	Sensor
28JUL05	Elko, NV	ELK	40.7448	-115.2388	2210.0	18 : 11 : 57.8	18 : 12 : 55.3	7.8	BB
28JUL05	Eugene, OR	EUO	44.0294	-123.0689	160.0	18 : 11 : 41.1	18 : 12 : 46.5	7.7	BB
28JUL05	Sta Barbara, CA	SBC	34.4408	-119.7149	61.0	18 : 12 : 12.2	18 : 13 : 02.9	7.8	BB
•	•	•	•	•	•	•	•	•	•
•	•	•	•	•	•	•	•	•	•
•	•	•	•	•	•	•	•	•	•

The seismic stations in this investigation are assigned to the U.S. National Seismic Network. The data given is for a hypothetical earthquake. Note that for this reporting system, the coordinate convention used assigns west longitude as negative values. Students will need only the times and names of the stations to successfully complete the exercise.

Procedure and Observations

1. Determine the epicenter of an earthquake from the following representation of seismograph readings. (*Note:* Each record gives the arrival time of the earthquake shock waves and the relative magnitude [Richter-scale or M_R] readings of the surface waves.)

This is a simulated computer monitor display of earthquake data from three seismic stations in the western United States. The times that the P and S waves were received at each station are reported in Universal Coordinated Time (UTC), which is nearly equivalent to Greenwich Mean Time (GMT).

a. Find the time between the P waves and the S waves for each station ($t_S - t_P$). Record the times in the Data Table on the following page.

b. Find the distance from each station to the epicenter, using the following formula: $d = 9.56(t_S - t_P)$. Record the distances on the Data Table.

c. On the map on the following page, use a drawing compass to draw a circle around each station with a radius equal to the distance from each station to the epicenter.

d. Find the major city nearest the intersection of the three circles, using a map or atlas. Label this city on your map.

2. Calculate the time at which the earthquake occurred at the epicenter.

a. Use the following equation to calculate the time it took for the S and P waves to reach each station.

$$time\ of\ travel\ (t) = \frac{distance\ from\ epicenter}{speed\ of\ wave} = \frac{d}{v}$$

Record your times on the Data Table. (*Note:* Assume that the speed of a P wave is 8.5 km/s and that the speed of an S wave is 4.5 km/s.)

b. Subtract the time of travel from the time of the reading (displayed on the computer monitor) to obtain the time of occurrence at the epicenter. Perform this calculation for both the S and P waves for each station. Record the times of occurrence on the Data Table.

You may want to use the graphical method for determining the distance to the epicenter by using the graph in Visual 17-4 or Figure 17-9 in the text. Mark off the "lag time" between P and S waves in whole and decimal minutes along the vertical scale on a 3 × 5 card. Then slide the card along the P curve, keeping the edge of the card parallel to the vertical axis. At the point where the distance between the P and S curves exactly matches the "lag time" difference, read the distance off the bottom scale. Answers will vary if these graphical techniques are used.

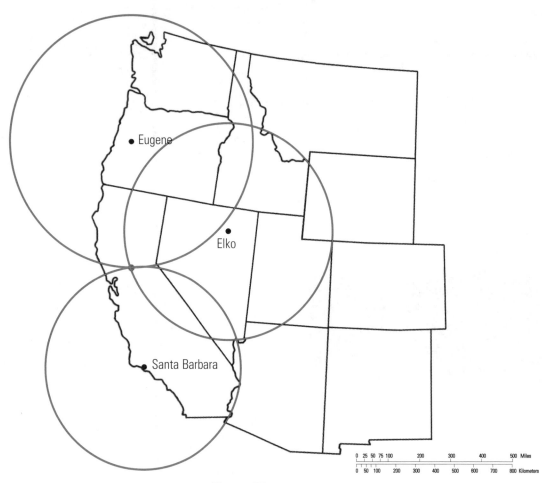

DATA TABLE

Station	$t_S - t_P$ (s)	Distance (d) from epicenter (km)	Time of travel (t)		Time of occurrence	
			P wave (s)	S wave (s)	P wave	S wave
Elko, NV	57.5	550	64.7	122.2	18:14:00.0	18:14:00.0
Eugene, OR	65.4	625	73.5	138.9	18:14:00.0	18:14:00.0
Santa Barbara, CA	50.7	485	57.1	107.8	18:14:00.0	18:14:00.0

3. Which quake had more energy, the one reported in this investigation or one rated 6.8 on the Richter scale?

   The one reported here (7.7–7.8) had more energy.

   How much more energy did the greater quake have? The greater quake had 31.6 times more energy.

Summing Up

1. What are the two main types of seismic waves? The two main types of seismic waves are body waves and surface waves.

2. What instrument detects the amplitude and wavelength of seismic waves? The seismograph detects the amplitude and wavelength of seismic waves.

3. What is the epicenter of an earthquake? The epicenter is the point on the earth's surface directly above the source of the earthquake.

Investigation
171 Types of Volcanoes

Volcanoes are classified into three groups according to their structure: shield, cinder cone, and composite volcanoes. In this investigation you will study examples of shield and composite volcanoes.

Shield volcanoes, such as those in the Hawaiian Islands, are made up entirely of solidified lava flows. In fact, the Hawaiian Islands are composed completely of shield volcanoes that have grown upward from the floor of the Pacific Ocean. The largest of these islands, called Hawaii, is an aggregation of *five* volcanoes: Mauna Kea, Mauna Loa, Hualalai, Kohala, and Kilauea. At least two of these, Mauna Loa and Kilauea, are still active. The highest peak, Mauna Kea, is a volcano that has long been dormant. The summit of Mauna Kea, at a lofty 4205 m (13,796 ft) above sea level, is the site of important national and international astronomical observatories. If you consider the fact that there is more of the mountain *below* the surface of the water than there is above it, 6002 m (19,692 ft) below compared to 4205 m (13,796 ft) above, you can understand how the actual height of the mountain at 10,203 m (33,476 ft) is greater than the actual height of Mount Everest, 8848 m (29,028 ft). In fact, if total heights are compared, Mauna Kea rates as the world's tallest mountain. Mauna Loa is a close second at 10,172 m (33,372 ft) total height.

Composite volcanoes are a combination of shield volcanoes and cinder cones. They are built of layers of lava interbedded (alternated) with layers of cinders and ash. The largest and highest volcanic mountains are generally of this type. Some composite volcanoes begin as shield volcanoes and then gradually change their behavior as time goes on. Examples of composite volcanoes are Mounts Etna and Fuji and Mayon Volcano in the Philippines. In the United States a number of examples are found in the states that border the Pacific Ocean: Mount Shasta, Mount Rainier, Mount St. Helens, Mount Hood, Mount Lassen, and the volcanic peak in which Crater Lake is located (Mount Mazama).

One additional piece of information is needed for this investigation. A *topographic profile* is a graph that shows the side view, or outline, of a portion of the earth's surface. Usually the vertical distance is exaggerated somewhat on the graph to show the differences in elevation more clearly.

Goals

Construct a topographic profile across the summit of Mauna Kea.

Study the distinctive features of the Mount St. Helens area.

Materials

ruler

Procedure and Observations

Part 1: Mauna Kea—A Shield Volcano

1. Look at the map of Hawaii on the next page.

2. Note the five volcanic peaks: Mauna Kea, 4205 m (13,796 ft); Mauna Loa, 4169 m (13,677 ft); Hualalai, 2521 m (8271 ft); Kohala, 1670 m (5480 ft); and Kilauea, 1248 m (4096 ft).

3. Use the grid provided to draw a topographic profile from west to east (from point *A* to point *B*, a distance of 93 km, or 58 mi) through the summit of Mauna Kea. (*Note*: Since points *A* and *B* are both at sea level, they are placed on the zero contour line.)

   a. Position a ruler parallel to the vertical solid lines.

   b. Directly below each intersection of the line *AB* with a contour line, indicated by a tick mark, mark a point on the grid. Be sure to place the point on the correct elevation line of the grid; note that each contour line on the map represents 1000 feet, and each line on the profile grid represents 1000 feet.

   c. Connect the points carefully to show the topographic profile when you have placed all twenty-seven points on the grid (not counting endpoints A and B).

   d. Divide each vertical distance by 3.5 and make a new plot under the one you have. This will give you a true picture of what the volcano looks like since the scale of the grid used here gives a 3.5:1 vertical exaggeration. (*Note*: Your new topographic profile tends to mask some of the detail. Because of this effect, some vertical exaggeration is generally used when drawing a topographic profile.)

Kohala
5480
4000

2000

4000

6000
8000
10000
Mauna Kea 12000
13796

Hualalai
8271
6000

4000

6000

6000

8000

10000
12000
13677
Mauna Loa

4096
Kilauea

A

B

N

Scale of Miles
0   5   10
Contour Interval: 1000 ft

Contour map of the Island
of Hawaii
Based on 1975 USGS 1:250,000 map

Topographic Profile

15,000

10,000

Elevation (ft)

5000

0

3.5:1 vertical exaggeration

1:1 profile

A   10   20   30   40   50   B   60
Miles

PART 2: MOUNT ST. HELENS—A COMPOSITE VOLCANO

Notice that the map of Mount St. Helens on the next page shows some of the effects of the cataclysmic blast of May 18, 1980. This blast occurred after two months of seismic activity and minor eruptions of steam and ash. As can be seen from the map, the destruction was directed toward the north, northeast, and northwest of the volcano. Note that the north rim of the crater has been blown away. The stippled dark area represents landslide debris that avalanched down the mountainside at speeds of up to 240 km/h (150 mi/h). The unstippled dark areas represent mudflows. The volume of material removed from the mountain has been estimated at 3 km³ (3 billion m³, or ¾ mi³). The avalanched debris quickly dammed up streams and intruded into the southwest corner of Spirit Lake, greatly raising the level of the water in the process. Debris was carried as much as 21 km (13 mi) to the northwest by the North Fork of the Toutle River, inflicting serious damage to roads, bridges, and logging equipment along the way. All told, more than 520 km² (200 mi²) of timberland and recreational areas were devastated. The "Eruption Impact Area" label at the top of the map is located at the approximate center of the affected region.

1. Several new lakes were formed when streams were dammed by debris. These are designated by arrows with a number 3 on them. How many of these features show on the map?

   _____ four _____

2. The arrow labeled 5 shows several new islands that formed in Spirit Lake at the time of the eruption. Assuming there were none before the blast, how many new islands were formed?

   _____ four _____

3. Mount St. Helens, before the eruption, possessed a picturesque cone-shaped peak. The elevation of its summit was 2950 m. The highest point on the mountain is now 2550 m. How many meters of height did it lose?

   _____ 400 m _____

   How many feet of height did it lose? (1 m = 3.28 ft) _____ 1312 ft _____

4. The bottom of the crater is 665 m below the highest part of the south rim and 46 m below what remains of the north rim. What is the difference in heights between the north and south rims?

   In meters: _____ 619 m _____

5. The former elevation of Spirit Lake was 975 m above sea level.

   a. What is it now? (Assume that it is halfway between contour lines.)

      _____ 1025 m _____

   b. How many meters did it increase in elevation?

      _____ 50 m _____

   c. How many feet did it increase in elevation?

      _____ 164 ft _____

Because of space limitations on page SA246, a large amount of the affected region covered by the map had to be omitted.

SCALE 1:100 000
1 CENTIMETER ON THE MAP REPRESENTS 1 KILOMETER ON THE GROUND
CONTOUR INTERVAL 50 METERS

Part of Mount Saint Helens and Vicinity Map (March 1981; Scale 1:100,000; Contour Interval 50 meters)

18 WEATHERING, MASS WASTING, AND EROSION

Applications

18A A Degenerating Earth

Directions: Below are several groups of words. In each group, three of the four words (or phrases) are related to one another. Draw a line through the unrelated word and then write a sentence using the remaining related words. Your sentence should show how the words are related. You may slightly change the form of the words in your sentence (for example, *eye* to *eyes*, *fingerprint* to *fingerprinting*).

1. weathering / rock / disintegrates / ~~streams~~ __Weathering is the disintegration of rocks.__
   _____

2. mass wasting / ~~streams~~ / hills / lower __Hills are lowered by mass wasting.__
   _____

3. ~~disintegrates~~ / erosion / soil / streams __Erosion by streams moves tons of soil each year.__
   _____

4. chemical / ~~erosion~~ / mechanical / weathering __The two types of weathering are chemical and mechanical.__
   _____

5. natural acids / ~~mass wasting~~ / agents / chemical weathering __Natural acids are agents of chemical weathering.__
   _____

6. weathering agents / break up / ~~dissolving~~ / physical __Mechanical weathering agents break up rocks by__
   __physical processes._____

7. ~~mechanical weathering~~ / warmth / chemical weathering / moisture __Warmth and moisture promote__
   __chemical processes._____

8. chemical weathering / ~~hinders~~ / rock surface / weathering agents __Chemical weathering is promoted by the__
   __exposure of rock surfaces to weathering agents.__

9. ~~chemical weathering~~ / physical forces / mechanical weathering / breaks __Mechanical weathering breaks up__
   __rocks into smaller pieces by physical forces.__

10. frost heaving / weathering / ~~pushes downward~~ / ice __Frost heaving is a type of weathering in which ice__
    __pushes surface material upward.__

There may be more than one correct answer for each group of words.

Applications

18B Chemical and Mechanical Weathering

Directions: Complete the missing words in the following statements by filling in the necessary letters. After you complete each question, find the matching number in the word puzzle below and then fill in the correct letter. The circled letters finish the sentence below that describes degenerative processes.

1. Carbonic acid and humic acid are two agents that promote
   <u>c</u> <u>h</u> <u>e</u> <u>m</u> <u>(i)</u> <u>c</u> <u>a</u> <u>l</u> weathering.
                         1

2. Mechanical weathering is the breaking up of rocks into smaller pieces by
   <u>p</u> <u>h</u> <u>(y)</u> <u>s</u> <u>i</u> <u>c</u> <u>a</u> <u>l</u>   <u>f</u> <u>o</u> <u>r</u> <u>c</u> <u>e</u> <u>s</u>.
                  2

3. Frost <u>h</u> <u>e</u> <u>a</u> <u>v</u> <u>i</u> <u>n</u> <u>(g)</u> is one way that freezing water
                                                   3
   causes weathering.

4. Wind carries off loose material, leaving excavated areas called
   <u>b</u> <u>l</u> <u>o</u> <u>(w)</u> <u>o</u> <u>u</u> <u>t</u> <u>s</u>.
                      4

5. Rock debris, called <u>t</u> <u>(a)</u> <u>l</u> <u>u</u> <u>s</u>, accumulates at the base of a cliff.
                                     5

6. Water <u>(e)</u> <u>x</u> <u>p</u> <u>a</u> <u>n</u> <u>d</u> <u>s</u> about nine percent when it freezes
             6
   and can exert tremendous pressure within cracks and crevasses.

7. Exfoliation, a process which involves both chemical and mechanical weathering,
   extensively weathers even extremely durable materials like <u>g</u> <u>(r)</u> <u>a</u> <u>n</u> <u>i</u> <u>t</u> <u>e</u>.
                                                                               7

8. A <u>d</u> <u>e</u> <u>s</u> <u>e</u> <u>r</u> <u>t</u>   <u>p</u> <u>a</u> <u>v</u> <u>e</u> <u>m</u> <u>e</u> <u>(n)</u> <u>t</u>
                                                                   8
   is a place where all the materials have blown away, leaving only pebbles and cobbles.

9. The earth's surface is <u>w</u> <u>e</u> <u>a</u> <u>r</u> <u>i</u> <u>n</u> <u>g</u>   <u>a</u> <u>w</u> <u>a</u> <u>y</u>.
                          4   6   5   7   1   8   3   5   4   5   2

Applications

18C Soil Science

Directions: Use the definitions to help unscramble the terms.

___silt___ 1. A fine-grained material deposited as sediment from water
LITS

___humus___ 2. Produced by the decomposition of leaves and other organic matter
UMUSH

___pedologist___ 3. A soil scientist
TOGEPIDLOS

___sand___ 4. The soil component most likely to be dominant in a region with
DASN   mainly quartz rocks

___clay___ 5. The soil component most likely to be predominant in a region
YALC   with mainly mica and feldspar minerals

___loam___ 6. An especially fertile soil, containing about equal parts of sand
MALO   and silt and about half as much clay

___irrigation___ 7. A process used by farmers in dry climates to help their crops
GATIROIRNI   grow in fertile soils

___fertilizer___ 8. Chemical or organic nutrients added to the soil by farmers to
REZITREFLI   restore the nutrients that have been removed from the soil

___profile___ 9. A cross section of the soil
EFIPOLR

___horizons___ 10. Layers of soil seen in Number 9
SHNOORIZ

Applications

18D Mass Wasting

Directions: Read each description carefully and decide which type of mass wasting is
being described. Then indicate your answers by writing the proper letters in the blanks
provided. Some descriptions have more than one answer.

___c___ 1. A sudden catastrophic slippage caused by weakness or loss of
             friction between layers of bedrock

___a, f___ 2. Example(s) of slow mass wasting

___b, c, d, e___ 3. Example(s) of rapid mass wasting

___b, e___ 4. Example(s) of a debris slide

___b, f___ 5. May occur in places having near-continuous below-freezing conditions

___b, c, d, e___ 6. Triggered sometimes by earthquakes

___a, c, d___ 7. Downhill movement of large masses of solid soil or rock as a direct result
               of gravity

___a___ 8. So slow that the cover of grass or other surface vegetation is not broken

___a, b, c, d, e___ 9. Can be triggered or accelerated by heavy rainfall.

___e___ 10. Usually involves the movement of largely unconsolidated volcanic material

a. Creep
b. Avalanche
c. Rockslide
d. Debris slide
e. Lahar
f. Rock glacier

Applications
18E Stream Erosion

Directions: Label the drawing by writing in the terms from the following list.

alluvial fan	headwaters (or source)	natural levees
base level	high-gradient stream	neck
delta	low-gradient stream	neck cutoff
drainage basin	meander	oxbow lake
flood plain	mouth	tributary

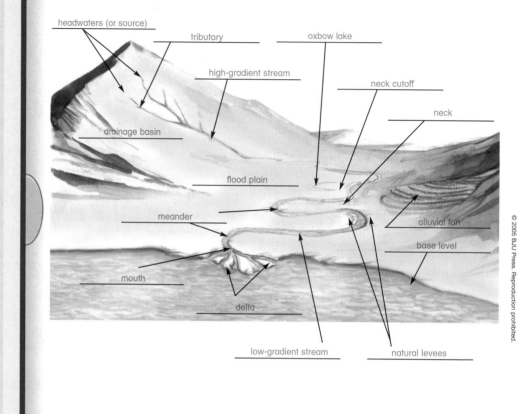

headwaters (or source)

tributary

oxbow lake

high-gradient stream

neck cutoff

neck

drainage basin

flood plain

alluvial fan

meander

base level

mouth

delta

low-gradient stream

natural levees

Investigation
18F Soil Composition

Soil is composed of solids (rocks, sand, silt, clay), liquid (water), air, and organic matter (living and nonliving). In this investigation you will determine the amount of solids, water, and organic matter in a soil sample.

Procedure

1. In an area where you have permission to dig, collect a volume of soil about 15 cm (6 in.) square and 15 cm deep. (Your teacher may have done this ahead of time.)

2. Place a sheet of weighing paper on a balance. Measure 10 g of the soil onto the paper, then remove the sample to your desk. Using a hand lens, carefully examine the sample.

3. Count the live animals (insects, worms, and so forth) you find and record this number in Table A.

4. Mix the 10 g sample of soil thoroughly with 250 mL of water in a graduated cylinder.

5. Allow the mixture to sit undisturbed for 5 minutes. Organic debris should float to the surface of the water, and the rocks and sand will settle to the bottom. Silt and clay will remain suspended in the water.

6. While the suspension is settling, label the beakers with a grease pencil or tape before measuring their masses. Beaker A is the larger beaker and Beakers B and C are the two smaller beakers. Then find the mass of each of the three beakers and record them in the blanks above Table A.

7. Slowly and carefully pour the cloudy water from the graduated cylinder through cheesecloth or a wire strainer into the larger beaker (A) and label it "silt, clay, and water." Do not pour out the material settled on the bottom of the graduated cylinder.

8. Place the organic debris that you filtered out into Beaker B. Label this beaker "organic debris."

9. Refill the graduated cylinder with fresh water and thoroughly mix it with the remaining sediment. Repeat Steps 7 and 8, adding the cloudy water and organic debris to what had previously separated.

10. Repeat Step 9 until the water is relatively clear after 5 minutes of settling.

11. Transfer the remaining sediment from the graduated cylinder to the other smaller beaker (C). You may need to rinse the graduated cylinder with water to transfer all the soil. Use as little water as possible. Label this beaker "stones and sand."

12. Slowly pour off the water in Beaker C, being careful not to lose any of the stones or sand. Count the number of stones in this wet sediment that are 2–5 mm in diameter and record this number in Table A.

Goal
Identify and measure the various components in a soil sample.

Materials
balance (accurate to at least 0.1 g)
paper, weighing
ruler, metric
beaker, 1 L
oven or hot plate
cheesecloth or wire strainer
small shovel
graduated cylinder, 250 mL
beakers, 250 mL (2)
hand lens

As an additional analysis you could use a soil test kit to perform chemical tests of the soil before separating it into its components. Test kits can be easily obtained from a home improvement or garden store.

You may want to prepare the soil yourself to eliminate any abnormal samples.

You may want to test this investigation ahead of time to determine the appropriate sample size to give measurable amounts of each component.

For Step 2, adjust the sliders on the empty balance to read 10.0 g plus the mass of a weighing paper. Students should add or remove matter from their samples as necessary to balance at this setting.

For Step 3, if you have a microscope available, use it to observe a drop of soil-water mixture. Depending on the soil and the magnification, you may be able to observe microscopic organisms such as roundworms and larvae, pollen and seeds, and various kinds of soil particles and sand grains.

For Step 4, the sample may be mixed by adding the soil to the graduated cylinder first and then adding the water. Place the palm of the hand tightly over the lip of the cylinder and grasp the center of the cylinder with the other hand. Shake the cylinder rapidly several times until the soil is well mixed, being careful not to spill the contents.

TABLE A

Mass of Beaker A: _____ g   Mass of Beaker B: _____ g   Mass of Beaker C: _____ g

Number of live animals	Mass of organic debris	Mass of rock and sand	Mass of silt, clay, and water	Number of rocks 2–5 mm in diameter
	g	g	g	

13. Heat the beakers containing the "organic debris" (B) and "stones and sand" (C) in a 150 °C (300 °F) oven or on a hot plate until they are dry (5–20 min). Be careful not to burn the organic debris.

14. Measure the mass of each beaker with its dry contents; then subtract the mass of the empty beakers recorded in Step 6 to determine the mass of the organic debris and the stones and sand. Record these masses in Table A.

Mass of Beaker B with dry organic material	−	Mass of empty Beaker B	=	Mass of organic material
_____ g	−	_____ g	=	_____ g

Mass of Beaker C with dry stones and sand	−	Mass of empty Beaker C	=	Mass of stones and sand
_____ g	−	_____ g	=	_____ g

15. You can determine the weight of the silt, clay, and water present in the original soil sample by subtracting the weights of the organic debris and rocks and sand from the beginning weight of 10 g.

Beginning weight of soil	−	Weight of dry organic debris	−	Weight of dry rock and sand	=	Weight of silt, clay, and water
10 g	−	_____ g	−	_____ g	=	_____ g

Summing Up

1. What kinds of materials make up the organic matter found in the soil? <u>Answers will vary, but students will probably find a lot of plant debris.</u>

2. What kinds of living organisms did you find in the soil? <u>Answers will vary. Organisms may include worms (both annelids and nematodes), arthropods (insects, sow bugs, centipedes, millipedes, spiders), mollusks (snails, slugs), fungi, plants, mosses, lichens, and so forth.</u>

3. What might make the amount of water in different soil samples vary? <u>Answers will vary. Possible causes are soil type and composition, depth of sample, shady vs. sunny location, plant types present, and so forth.</u>

4. What might make the amount of living plants and animals in different soil samples vary? <u>Answers will vary. Possible causes are the same as for Question 3, plus the presence of hosts, parasites, predators or prey, and so forth.</u>

5. How could the geographic location of soil samples affect your results? <u>Answers will vary. Possible causes include the parent rock material of the soil, the slope or drainage, and the climate of a region.</u>

6. How could the depth from which you take the soil samples affect your results? <u>The deeper the sample, fewer organisms, less organic matter, and more rocks would likely be found. Topsoil near the surface would be more affected by changes in the weather than soil deeper down, so organisms would move deeper in a dry spell, for example.</u>

Go a Step Further

PART 1

Dig a trench exposing all three horizons of a soil profile and repeat this investigation with samples from each horizon. Determine which horizon has the most and least of each soil component examined in the investigation.

PART 2

Determine separate masses for the amounts of silt, clay, and water present in a soil sample. Find the mass of a sample before and after heating it to evaporate the water. The difference will be due to soil water. Determine the mass of silt and clay in a sample by evaporating the water from the "silt, clay, and water" (Beaker A) used in steps 7–10 of the Procedure. Find the mass of the beaker with the dried silt and clay and subtract the mass of the empty beaker. The difference will be the weight of only the silt and clay. Compare these masses with those obtained by subtraction in the investigation.

Investigation
18G Erosion

Erosion is a process that occurs slowly. In this investigation you will develop your own methods for causing erosion and then will observe their effects on a pan of sand.

Procedure

1. Put about 5 cm of sand in one half of the dishpan. Leave the other half of the dishpan empty.

2. Create ways to move the sand to the other half of the dishpan *without directly touching the sand or dishpan.* This means that you cannot tilt the dishpan or put your fingers or a tool into the sand to push it to the other side.

3. List the ways you can move the sand without directly touching it with your hands or tools. Write this list on a separate sheet of paper.

4. Use each method and then record its effectiveness on your paper.

Goal
Identify and compare ways by which erosion can move material.

Materials
large dishpan
sand
water

Some suggested ways to move the sand: blow on it, pour water on it, use a fan of paper or an electric fan to create wind, put ice cubes in the pan and let them melt, vibrate the side of the pan (or the table the pan is sitting on), and so on. Most students will blow on the sand or pour water on it.

Summing Up

1. Which method of moving the sand worked the best? Answers will vary. The students will probably say that quickly pouring large amounts of water on the sand or blowing on it were the most efficient methods.

2. Was it possible to move the entire pile of sand? It is possible, but it may take a long time depending on the method.

3. What do your observations tell you about erosion that is going on today in the land around you?
It is constantly occurring, and it may occur rapidly.

4. What do your observations lead you to conclude about the effects of a global Flood as the bodies of water over the continents flowed rapidly back into the ocean basins?
Those students that poured water rapidly into the dishpan can conclude that the greater the quantity of water and the faster it moved, the greater the erosional effects. The erosion during the Flood must have displaced immense amounts of rock and sediment, which we now see in sedimentary rocks all over the world.

19 THE OCEANS AND SEAS

Applications
19A Wave Structure

Directions: Label the diagram of a typical wave below; then answer the questions that follow.

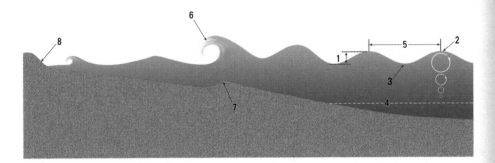

1. _____ wave height _____
2. _____ crest _____
3. _____ trough _____
4. _____ wave base _____

5. _____ wavelength _____
6. _____ breaker _____
7. _____ bar (longshore bar) _____
8. _____ berm _____

9. What causes the breaker to form at the beach? __As the wave moves through shallow water, the wave height__ __increases and the wavelength decreases. The wave falls over when the wave steepness exceeds $1/7$ or__ __0.143.__

10. Can breakers form before the wave approaches the beach? __yes__

11. Explain your answer to Question 10. __If the water is shallow enough or the wave gains enough energy from__ __the wind, a breaking wave can form far from a beach.__

Applications
19B Wave Motions

Directions: The descriptions listed below describe something about waves as they approach the shore. Some of the descriptions apply only to waves in deep water (including deep coastal waters), some only to waves in shallow water, and some can apply to either. Read each description carefully; then write either *shallow*, *deep*, or *both* in the blanks in front of the descriptions.

both	1.	Diagonal approach
deep	2.	Diagonal right up to the shoreline
shallow	3.	Parallel at the shoreline
both	4.	Longshore currents develop
both	5.	Rip currents develop
shallow	6.	Refraction occurs
shallow	7.	Flattened circular wave motion orbits
shallow	8.	Beach drifting results
deep	9.	Breaking waves are caused only by wind
both	10.	Wave forms a breaker

Applications

19C Wave Erosion and Deposition

Directions: The first diagram represents a rocky shoreline in which erosion occurs. The second diagram represents a sandy shoreline in which deposition occurs. Label the diagrams by supplying the missing terms or definitions; then draw a line from each term to the proper structure in the diagram.

Stack

Mass of rock cut off from

the mainland by erosion

_____

_____

Sea cave

Cavity in a weaker part

of a cliff

_____

_____

Sea arch

Mass of rock with the center eroded away forming a "bridge"

Barrier island

A sandy beach having

no connection with

the mainland

Tombolo

Beach of sand

connecting one or more

islands to the mainland

Bay

A body of water partly enclosed by land; named by local convention

Bay barrier

A sandy beach across

the mouth of a bay

_____

_____

Spit

An exposed sandbar extending into the mouth of a bay from a headland

Hook

An exposed sandbar extending with a sharp bend beyond a headland

A map of ocean surface currents appears on page 503. Discourage students from copying these answers directly from the map.

Applications
19D Ocean Currents

Directions: The map below shows the major surface ocean currents. Label the currents depicted on the map (Questions 1–6), then answer Questions 7–10.

1. _____ Labrador Current _____
2. _____ Gulf Stream _____
3. _____ Peru Current _____
4. _____ Kuroshio (Japan) Current _____
5. _____ California Current _____
6. _____ Brazil Current _____

7. Would you expect the northwest coast of Africa to be influenced by cold waters or warm waters? _____ cold _____
   Why? _ The current flows from the North Atlantic. _____

8. Would you expect the southern tip of South America to be influenced by cold or warm waters? _____ cold _____
   Why? _ The current is near a polar region. _____

9. The eastern coast of the United States has warmer waters than the western coast. Why? _ The Gulf Stream _
   brings warm water from the equatorial regions; the California Current brings cold water down from the
   north Pacific.

10. In which direction do the current gyres in the Northern Hemisphere flow? _____ clockwise _____
    in the Southern Hemisphere? _____ counterclockwise _____ Why? _ Ocean current gyres are formed by the _
    combined effect of prevailing winds and the Coriolis effect.

Applications

19E Ocean Topography

Directions: Write the word *True* in the blank provided if the statement is true; write *False* if the statement is false. For *False* answers, state why the answer is false in the blanks provided.

_____True_____ 1. Guyots are flat-topped seamounts.

_____False_____ 2. Abyssal plains are long, relatively narrow zones of higher elevation on the ocean floors.
  Abyssal plains are broad, flat regions within the ocean basins. Long, narrow zones of relatively higher elevation describes mid-ocean ridges.

_____True_____ 3. Scientists from nearly every scientific field study the oceans.

_____False_____ 4. The ocean basins are flat and featureless.
  The ocean basins contain more and taller mountains, broader and flatter valleys, and deeper trenches than any found on dry land.

_____True_____ 5. An island arc is a long chain of volcanic islands that is usually located near the edge of a tectonic plate.

_____True_____ 6. The term *seamount* refers to a submerged mountain that is situated on an abyssal plain.

_____False_____ 7. The *Trieste* is the first bathysphere to descend to the deepest part of the Atlantic Ocean.
  The *Trieste* was the first bathyscaph to dive to the deepest depth in the Pacific Ocean.

_____False_____ 8. Geographically, the world ocean is divided into three major basins: the Atlantic, the Indian, and the Pacific oceans.
  The world ocean is divided into at least four basins, which includes the basins mentioned above as well as the Arctic Ocean.

_____False_____ 9. Today the depth of the ocean is most accurately measured by lowering a line with a lead weight attached to it to the bottom of the ocean and measuring the length of the line.
  Today, ocean depths are measured with echo sounders.

_____False_____ 10. The Mid-Atlantic Ridge is an example of a guyot.
  The Mid-Atlantic Ridge contains guyots, but the formation is not itself a guyot.

Question 8: Students may also include the Southern Ocean (5) if you discussed this fact from the Teacher's Edition margin note on page 486.

(continued on next page)

___True___ 11. The British ship HMS *Challenger* made a four-year study of the ocean beginning in 1872.

_____

_____

___True___ 12. Echo sounding is a technique that involves sending sound waves to the ocean floor and recording the time they take to return. The depth is half the calculated distance of the round trip based on the speed of sound in water.

_____

_____

___False___ 13. The greatest obstacle to visiting the ocean floor is the temperature of the water.

The greatest obstacle facing deep-ocean explorers is the great water pressure.

_____

___True___ 14. The depth of the Mariana Trench is about 11,000 m below sea level.

_____

_____

___False___ 15. The gently sloping bottom adjacent to most continental coastlines is called the continental slope.

The gently sloping bottom adjacent to the continents is the continental shelf. The continental

slope falls away from the shelf into the abyssal plain.

Applications

19F Ocean Basins

Directions: The diagram below represents a typical ocean basin. In each box, place the letter of the term that best describes the feature.

a. Abyssal plain
b. Canyon
c. Continent
d. Continental rise
e. Continental shelf
f. Continental slope
g. Guyot
h. Island
i. Mid-ocean ridge
j. Rift
k. Seamount
l. Trench

Applications
19G Coral Reefs

Directions: Read each of the phrases about coral reefs carefully. Decide which of the following types of coral reefs is described by each phrase. Write the proper letter in the blank in front of the phrase.

a. Fringing reef   b. Barrier reef   c. Atoll

<u>c</u> 1. A ring of low coral islands surrounding a central lagoon

<u>a</u> 2. Reefs extending from the beach low-water mark into deeper water

<u>b</u> 3. Reefs that parallel the beach but have deeper open water between them and the beach

<u>c</u> 4. The type of reef found in some of the Pacific Islands such as Wake, Midway, Bikini, and Eniwetok

<u>b</u> 5. The great reef off the coast of Australia that extends for about 2000 km

<u>a</u> 6. The type of reef that occurs along the coast of Florida and the coast of Bermuda

<u>a</u> 7. Attached to the bottom of the ocean near the shoreline, leaving very little water between the reef and the mainland

<u>c</u> 8. A coral reef surrounding the top of a volcano that has either collapsed or been carried into deeper water by the motion of the ocean floor

19H Oceans Review

Directions: Select the proper terms from the list to complete the statements below. Write
your answers in the blanks provided. A term may be used only one time.

abyssal plains	cold	guyot	North Pacific	slope
arch	continental	height	plankton net	spit
atoll	density	hook	ridge	spring tide
autonomous	desalination	island	rip	stack
barrier	distillation	lagoon	rise	tide
bathyscaph	echo sounding	longshore	salt	tombolo
breaker	erosion	Mid-Atlantic	sand	upwelling
canyon	fringing	neap	seamount	wind

1. In 1960 the *Trieste*, a _____bathyscaph_____, explored water over 11,000 m (36,000 ft) below sea level.

2. The _____continental_____ shelf is the part of the ocean floor that slopes gently out from the continental shoreline at most places.

3. A/An _____tombolo_____ connects an island to the mainland.

4. A/An _____density_____ current exists where sediment-laden or salty water is sinking along a sloping bottom.

5. Waves erode rock on a shore and then redeposit the eroded materials in the form of _____sand_____.

6. _____Erosion_____ causes various shoreline features such as sea caves and sea arches.

7. The process of making seawater fit to drink is called _____desalination_____.

8. The oceans bulge at high _____tide_____ because of the pull of the moon and the sun and the momentum of the ocean waters.

9. The most straightforward but less efficient way to desalinate water is the process called _____distillation_____.

10. A sandbar that extends partway across a bay from a headland is called a/an _____spit_____.

11. A ring of low coral islands surrounding a central lagoon is called a/an _____atoll_____.

12. A flat-topped seamount is called a/an _____guyot_____.

13. A deeply eroded valley under the sea is called a submarine _____canyon_____.

14. A/An _____stack_____ is a mass of rock cut off from the mainland by erosion.

15. A drowned island or a submarine volcano is referred to as a/an _____seamount_____.

16. A barrier reef is separated from the mainland by a/an _____lagoon_____.

17. A device used to collect drifting organisms in deep water is called a/an _____plankton net_____.

18. A mass of coral following a shoreline and attached to it or to an island is called a/an _____fringing_____ reef.

19. A wave that "falls over" because it is too steep is called a/an _____breaker_____.

20. A sandy beach completely across the mouth of a bay is called a bay _____barrier_____.

21. A sandy beach with no visible connection to the nearby mainland is a barrier _____island_____.

22. The continental _____rise_____ slopes less severely away from the coninental slope to the ocean floor.

(continued on next page)

abyssal plains	cold	guyot	North Pacific	slope
arch	continental	height	plankton net	spit
atoll	density	hook	ridge	spring tide
autonomous	desalination	island	rip	stack
barrier	distillation	lagoon	rise	tide
bathyscaph	echo sounding	longshore	salt	tombolo
breaker	erosion	Mid-Atlantic	sand	upwelling
canyon	fringing	neap	seamount	wind

23. The continental _____slope_____ is the outer edge of the continental shelf where the ocean quickly deepens.

24. Waves on large lakes or oceans are usually caused by the _____wind_____.

25. A spit with a sharp bend is called a/an _____hook_____.

26. The best-known mid-ocean ridge is the _____Mid-Atlantic_____ Ridge.

27. A bridge-like formation left by coastal erosion is called a sea _____arch_____.

28. A/An _____rip_____ current is a strong surface current that courses through a gap in the breakers.

29. A more practical method to remove _____salt_____ from seawater is called reverse osmosis.

30. Flat, deep seafloors are called _____abyssal plains_____.

31. The _____North Pacific_____ Current warms the climate of western Canada.

32. _____Cold_____ water tends to sink.

33. A very high tide that results from an alignment of the sun, moon, and earth is called a/an _____spring tide_____.

34. A/An _____neap_____ tide occurs twice each month, when the moon is at the first and third quarters.

35. An unmanned submersible that is programmed to conduct research without any connection to a tending ship is called a/an _____autonomous_____ underwater vehicle.

36. A/An _____upwelling_____ occurs when cold water from the ocean bottom is forced upward to replace warmer waters that have been removed by strong prevailing winds.

37. The vertical distance from the crest of one wave to the trough of another is called the wave's _____height_____.

38. Today oceanographers use _____echo sounding_____ to measure the depths of the oceans.

39. A long, relatively narrow zone of higher elevation on the seafloor is called a mid-ocean _____ridge_____.

40. A/An _____longshore_____ current flows parallel to the shore.

Investigation

191 Desalting Seawater

Procedure and Observations

Note: If the distilled water is going to be tasted at the end of this procedure, ensure that all glassware and hose used have never been in contact with poisonous chemicals and have been thoroughly washed.

1. Obtain 3.5 g of salt (NaCl).

2. Pour the salt into the Erlenmeyer flask.

3. Measure out 100 mL of water in a graduated cylinder.

4. Add the water to the salt in the flask and stir until the salt is dissolved. This mixture will be the "seawater" in this investigation.

5. Clamp a support ring to a ring stand, and position it above a laboratory burner.

6. Place a wire gauze square on the support ring.

7. Set the flask of seawater on the wire gauze and secure it to the support stand with the flask clamp.

8. Connect the section of rubber hose to the glass tubing inserted in the stopper.

9. Fit the stopper into the mouth of the Erlenmeyer flask.

10. Place the free end of the rubber hose into the beaker.

Goal

Demonstrate the distilling of seawater to remove the minerals (salt).

Materials

table salt, 3.5 g
Erlenmeyer flask, 250 mL
graduated cylinder, 100 mL
water, 100 mL
ring stand
support ring
laboratory burner
wire gauze beaker support
flask clamp
one-hole stopper containing a short length of glass tubing
new rubber hose, 60 cm
beaker, 250 mL
matches or burner igniter

Table salt is NaCl. Note that many grocery and specialty stores sell sea salt crystals, which can be substituted.

A stove burner or hot plate will work as a heat source.

If you live near an ocean, you may use real seawater. Weigh the recovered salt to verify the 35 g/1000 g of seawater.

For Step 1, you may want to have the salt already weighed in individual containers.

For Step 10, if much steam escapes from the end of the tubing, trail the tubing through a pan of ice.

distillation apparatus

propane or Bunsen burner

Caution: Steam is hot!

11. Light the laboratory burner.

12. Boil the seawater until only a few milliliters remain.

    Caution: Avoid the steam rising from the beaker. Also, the water in the beaker is hot. Allow it to cool before proceeding.

13. The beaker should contain purified water. Taste it. (*Note*: Do *not* taste the water if the flask, hose, or beaker have ever held laboratory chemicals.) Does it taste salty?
    _____ no _____

Summing Up

1. According to your text, what is the method demonstrated in this investigation called? distillation

2. Why isn't the method demonstrated in this investigation used very much today? It is expensive because it requires fuel to boil the water.

3. What other substances (besides water) could be recovered from seawater by this process? Various minerals and salts can be recovered.

You can demonstrate that distillation retains all of the salt in the boiling flask by first taking the mass of the flask and salt sample and then adding the water. Boil the water to dryness; then take the mass of the flask and salt again and compare to the original mass. Be sure to reduce the boiling rate when only a few milliliters are left in the flask to prevent damage to the flask and to avoid spattering the salt.

19J Examining Density Currents

There are several reasons for the formation of ocean currents. The amount of material dissolved in the water determines its density. A difference in density between two depths is one cause of ocean currents. This investigation will help you to observe why different densities affect the currents.

Procedure and observations

1. Fill two bottles with plain tap water from the container indicated by your teacher.

2. Mix a saturated salt solution in a 500 mL beaker using water from the same container. Fill the other two bottles with the saturated salt water.

3. Add several drops of food coloring into both bottles of salt water.

4. Arrange the bottles according to the diagram to the right. To invert a bottle without spilling the water, place an index card over the mouth. Holding the card firmly against the mouth, turn the bottle upside down and rest it against the mouth of the other bottle. Ease the index card out from between the two bottles.

5. Observe the two bottles over several minutes and record your observations.

   Salt water tends to move downwards.
   _____
   _____
   _____

6. In the space below, make a sketch of what happened within the bottles.

Goal

Observe the formation of a density current.

Materials

glass bottles (4) (250 mL glass reagent bottles or baby food jars)

table salt

tap water

beaker, 500 mL

food coloring

index card (2)

Ensure that you have enough room-temperature water for all the teams in your class.

A *saturated* solution means that the water cannot hold any additional salt at room temperature. To prepare a saturated solution, add salt to the required amount of room-temperature water until no more salt will dissolve. Larger bottles (more water) or warmer water will take more salt to reach saturation.

You might want to expand this investigation by including temperature as one of the variables. You would need to set up several sets of bottles if you try this; then use hot and cold water in addition to the plain and salt water.

Summing Up

1. What caused the water movement in one set of bottles? The greater density of the salt water caused it to sink to the bottom.

2. Why was there no water movement in the other set of bottles? The fresh water in the top bottle was not as dense as the colored salt water below it, so no change occurred.

3. What effect does gravity have on the flow of dense liquids above less dense liquids? Denser liquids sink through less dense liquids because of gravity.

4. Could temperature have played a part in the color change? Though temperature can cause density currents, it was not a factor in this investigation.

20 GLACIERS

Applications

20A Glacier Structure

Directions: Explain the difference between the terms in each pair of terms below. Label the diagram at the bottom of the page.

1. glacier / snowfield _A glacier is a mass of flowing ice. A snowfield is the area in which the glacier forms._

2. firn / glacial ice _Both are a compact form of granular ice. Glacier ice is solid, but firn has air spaces between the crystals._

3. accumulation zone / wastage zone _The accumulation zone is the part of the glacier above the equilibrium line, whereas the wastage zone is the part of the glacier below the equilibrium line._

4. valley glaciers / piedmont glaciers _Valley glaciers are found between mountains. Piedmont glaciers are formed when two or more valley glaciers merge, usually near the bases of mountains._

5. continental glacier / icecap _A continental glacier covers a large region of a continent. An icecap usually covers much less area, such as an island._

6. zone of fracture / zone of flow _The zone of fracture is the solid, crevassed upper 50 m of a glacier consisting of brittle ice. The zone of flow is the plastic, underlying part of a glacier._

1. _____ equilibrium (snow) line

2. _____ accumulation zone

3. _____ wastage zone

4. _____ zone of fracture

5. _____ zone of flow

Applications
20B Types of Glaciers

Directions: Match the type of glacier with each description below.

<u>c</u> 1. Broad mass of ice that covers essentially all geographic features over a wide area

<u>b</u> 2. Means "at the foot of the mountain"

<u>e</u> 3. Large ice sheet covering most of a continent or large island

<u>a</u> 4. Found between mountains and in highlands

<u>c, d, e</u> 5. Spreads outward from its origin in all directions

<u>d</u> 6. Smaller type of ice sheet

<u>b</u> 7. Formed by the union of two or more valley glaciers in a broad basin or plain

<u>e</u> 8. The type of glacier covering more than four-fifths of Greenland

<u>d</u> 9. World's largest of this category is found in northern Ellesmere Island, Canada.

<u>a</u> 10. Resembles rivers of ice

a. Valley glacier
b. Piedmont glacier
c. Ice sheet
d. Icecap
e. Continental glacier

Applications
20C Effects of Glaciers

Directions: Change one word in each of the following sentences to make a correct statement. Cross out the incorrect word, and place the correct word in the blank.

<u>brittle</u> 1. The uppermost 50 m layer of a glacier, called the zone of fracture, consists of ~~plastic~~ ice.

<u>centimeters</u> 2. Most glaciers can normally move a few meters or ~~kilometers~~ per day.

<u>mountaintop</u> 3. A horn may be all that is left of a ~~valley~~ if cirques completely encircle it.

<u>fiord</u> 4. A ~~tarn~~ is an inlet or arm of the sea dug out by glacial action and bordered by steep cliffs.

<u>crevasses</u> 5. A glacier forms ~~cirques~~ to relieve the stresses of motion.

<u>continental</u> 6. The world's largest ~~valley~~ glacier covers most of the continent of Antarctica.

<u>Glaciologists</u> 7. ~~Geologists~~ are scientists who study glaciers.

<u>tarns</u> 8. Cirques that retain water after the glacier disappears are called ~~kettles~~.

Applications
20D Glacial Deposits

Directions: Answer the following questions.

1. Explain the two ways that a glacier can deposit sediment (drift). __(1) Materials can be pushed or dragged by__ ice and dropped into place as the ice melts. (2) Materials can be laid down as sediment from running meltwater.

2. When are deposits from glacier ice unsorted and unstratified? __Deposits are unstratified when they are__ dropped from melting ice without the sorting effects of meltwater streams.

3. How is till deposited by a glacier? __Till is dropped by ice as the glacier melts.__

4. Define *moraine*. List four types of moraines. __A moraine is an accumulation of ice-deposited rocks and__ other debris. Four types are (1) terminal moraines, (2) ground moraines, (3) medial moraines, and (4) lateral moraines.

5. How are eskers and kames alike? How are they different? __They are both glacial deposits that were sorted__ and stratified by flowing meltwater. Eskers are long, winding ridges that formed under glaciers; kames are steep-sided hills that formed from deposits on top of a glacier.

6. How were kettles formed? __Chunks of ice that broke free from the glacier terminus became embedded in__ outwash drift or the ground moraine. When the ice melted completely, the depression that was left is called a kettle.

7. What are varves? What events may cause varve counting to be unreliable? __Varves are thin layers of__ glacial sediment that form on the bottoms of lakes at the terminus of a glacier. Varve counting, or dating a sedimentary deposit by counting the varves, is unreliable because storms and floods may cause more than one layer to be deposited per year.

Applications
20E Glacier Review

Directions: Complete the crossword puzzle.

Across

1. An ice _____ covers a large area.
7. An ice _____ covers the tops of mountains.
9. Any glacial deposit
10. A/An _____ moraine covers the whole area that a glacier occupied.
12. Snow-covered area above the snow line
13. Process in which the glacier ice adheres to the bedrock, which is torn out when the glacier moves
17–18. A/An __17__ __18__ points to a distant bedrock source.
22. A deep fissure in a glacier
23. Steep, hollow excavation made by a glacier on a mountain
24. A glacially produced lake
25. _____ glaciers are actually found in valleys.
27. Thin layers of fine glacial sediments on lake bottoms
28. _____ moraines are found at the sides of glacier valleys.
30. Probably deposited by a stream flowing under a glacier
34. A/An _____ moraine formed when two glaciers merged.
35. An accumulation of glacial drift
36. Another name for a valley glacier

Down

2. Moraine deposited at the terminus of a glacier
3. Mountain peak surrounded by at least three cirques
4. The _____ zone is that part of a glacier that breaks up, melts, or flows away.
5. Type of glacier formed by the union of two or more valley glaciers in a broad area
6. A/An _____ glacier covers a large portion of a continent or large island.
8. Type of glacier found between mountain ridges
11. A streamlined hill of glacial till
12. Parallel scratch marks in bedrock
14. Process of forming icebergs
15. A mass of ice made by the compaction and refreezing of snow that moves under the influence of gravity
16. Coastal valley glacially eroded below sea level
19. The _____ zone is above the snow line.
20. The zone of _____ has crevasses.
21. Depression formed by a block of ice that melted
26. Dropped boulders unlike the bedrock under them
29. Unstratified glacial drift
31. A steep-sided hill of stratified glacial drift
32. Unusually rapid glacier movement
33. Granular ice

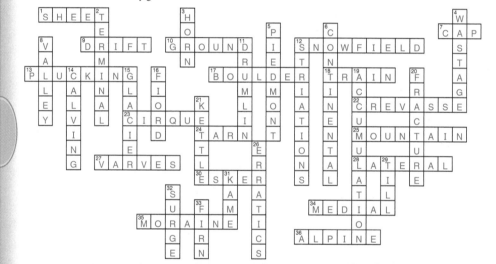

Investigation
20F Glacial Erosion

It is difficult in the average classroom to observe firsthand the action of glaciers in producing erosion. However, this investigation will help you observe a similar action.

Procedure

1. At the side of the dishpan, partially bury four or five ice cubes in the soil. Leave the tops of some of the ice cubes showing and cover others completely with soil.

2. Put several ice cubes in a row extending out from one edge of the dishpan. Push the column of cubes with your finger or with a pencil to the other end of the dishpan. Observe the results.

3. Leave all the ice cubes in place and allow them to melt.

4. After the ice cubes have melted, carefully pour water into the holes that remain.

Goal
Make a simple model of a glacier to demonstrate how glaciers may erode the landscape.

Materials
large dishpan
enough fine soil to fill the dishpan about 12–15 cm (5–6 in.) deep
ice cubes

You can speed up Step 3 by placing the pans outside on a warm day or under a heat lamp.

Summing Up

1. What erosional features were formed by pushing a row of ice cubes across the surface of the soil?
   moraines

2. What erosional features were formed by burying ice cubes and allowing them to melt? _____ kettles

3. Did it make any difference how deep the ice cubes were buried or with how much pressure they were moved across the surface of the soil?
   Yes; the deeper the cubes were buried, the deeper the holes were; more pressure meant more erosion.

4. What would the extent of glacial erosion in an area tell you about the size of the glacier that once covered it?
   Extensive erosion could mean the glacier was deep and heavy or that the glacier flowed for a long interval.

5. What does pouring water into the remaining holes demonstrate? The water-filled depressions simulate the formation of kettle lakes.

Investigation
20G Representative Glaciers

Valley glaciers are still prevalent in the northwestern United States and Alaska. By studying topographic maps of these regions, you can see both their present locations and the results of their past erosional and depositional work. The glaciers and their tributaries appear white on the maps. Glacial drift, whether riding on the surface of a glacier or left as a deposit at the sides or end of a glacier, is indicated by dotted areas. Crevasses are represented by short line segments that mark where the cracks in the glacier were located at the time the map was made. Calving (iceberg formation) may be seen on a topographic map at the point a glacier enters a body of water. Erosional remains of mountains in glaciated areas take the form of arêtes or horns. Both of these features are identifiable by their closely spaced contour lines, the horns showing as single sharp peaks and the arêtes as elongated narrow ridges.

Procedure and Observations

PART 1: MOUNT RAINIER

Mount Rainier is a massive composite volcano located in the Cascade Mountains of Washington State. Its lofty stature and numerous glaciers combine to make it a picturesque sight, visible for many miles in every direction. At present it is a model of serenity, although some small steam emissions can be seen from time to time and seismologists have noted a slight increase in the number of minor shallow earthquakes under the volcano. Approximately five hundred years have passed since its last major eruption. The 1978 USGS map on the following page shows the glaciers clearly contrasted against their surroundings. Since this is a relatively recent map, the contour lines are marked in meters. The contour interval is 50 m (about 164 ft).

1. How many named glaciers are there on the flanks of the mountain? (Count only those that have the word *glacier* included in their name.)

   Total: _____ 17 _____

2. Using the scale of kilometers, determine the length of the longest glacier, assuming that it begins at the summit and is continuous. (Give answer to the nearest half kilometer).

   _____ 10.5 km _____

   Determine the same in miles. _____ 6.5 mi _____

Goal
Study the activity of a number of present-day valley glaciers as well as several examples of continental glaciation features.

Materials
calculator
hand magnifying lens
ruler

3. The Nisqually Glacier as shown on this 1978 map was about 4 miles long, measuring from the summit of the mountain to the terminus of the glacier. It was observed to retreat a total of 4131 feet between 1857 and 1944. Note the moraine that was deposited during the retreat. What symbol is used to represent moraine material?

   _____ brown dots _____

4. Many of the glaciers exhibit three different orders of steepness: very steep near the summit, moderately sloping in the middle reaches, and gently sloping near the terminus. Using your scale of kilometers, determine the gradient for these three regions of the Winthrop Glacier.

   Gradient near the summit:

   _____ 585 _____ m/km

   Gradient at the word *Winthrop*:

   _____ 350 _____ m/km

   Gradient north of the word *Glacier*:

   _____ 218 _____ m/km

For Step 4, the answers will vary depending on where students measure the contour span.

Hint for students: From the scale of kilometers, mark off one kilometer on the edge of a piece of paper. Use this to determine how many contour intervals (not contour *lines*) are contained in one kilometer for each section of the glacier. Then multiply these numbers by the contour interval (50 m) to get the gradient in each case.

SCALE 1:100 000

KILOMETERS

MILES

FEET

Mount Rainer Map (Part of the USGS Mount Rainier Quadrangle, Washington, 1978. Scale 1:100,000; Contour Interval 50 meters)

Part 2: Cordova Map

The map on the next page shows several valley glaciers in southeastern Alaska as mapped in 1953. Literally thousands of valley glaciers are contained within the boundaries of this large state, ranging in length from 2 to 48 kilometers (1–30 mi). In addition, there are large piedmont glaciers such as the Malaspina and Columbia Glaciers. Malaspina is the largest piedmont glacier in North America, having a width of almost 65 km (40 mi). This investigation will focus on the Heney and McCune Glaciers. Note that the map is subdivided into lettered 6 × 6 mile sections and numbered 1-square-mile subsections.

1. Judging by the contour lines, in which direction does Heney Glacier move?

    Toward the _____northeast_____ (northeast, southwest)

2. Give the location and number(s) of the map subsection(s) in which calving could be taking place.

    Calving could be taking place in subsection C6.

3. A long, unnamed tributary valley glacier joins Heney Glacier from the west.

    The lateral moraines of both the glacier and its tributary merge to form a _____medial_____ moraine.

4. The margins of the glaciers are marked with small dashed lines. Note that the Mc-Cune glacier dies out; it does not reach a lake or river as does the Heney Glacier. What becomes of its wasting ice?

    Some of the ice melts and forms streams that flow out to the proglacial lake at the terminus of the

    Heney Glacier. Some of the ice sublimes to a vapor.

5. A reasonably good example of a horn appears in map subsection D2. What is the elevation of its summit?

    _____7423 ft_____

6. Several examples of arêtes appear on the map. One of the better ones is located in map subsections A24 and A25. What is the highest point on the arête?

    _____5285 ft_____

7. What kind of glacial erosional feature is shown in the eastern portion of map subsection B5?

    A cirque is found in the east side of subsection B5.

CONTOUR INTERVAL 100 FEET
NATIONAL GEODETIC VERTICAL DATUM OF 1929
TO CONVERT FEET TO METERS MULTIPLY BY 0.3048

Cordova Map (Part of the USGS Cordova D-3 Quadrangle, Alaska, 1953. Scale 1:63,360; Contour Interval 100 feet)

Part 3: Whitewater Map

The maps (on p. SA282) for this part of the exercise are of two segments of a heavily glaciated region of southern Wisconsin. Several glacial features are shown here, including drumlins, kettles, and different kinds of moraines. A major difference between this region and the last two glaciated terrains you studied is that the deposits in Wisconsin were caused by a continental glacier. The glaciation that occurred in Washington and Alaska was connected with valley glaciers.

1. Numerous drumlins appear in the upper map. In what general direction are the drumlins oriented—east-west, north-south, northeast-southwest, or northwest-southeast?

   The drumlins are oriented north-south.

2. What direction did the ice sheet move according to the orientation of the drumlins? The glacier moved from north to south. This is indicated by the highest elevations being generally on the north end of the drumlins.

3. Locate Duck Creek to the west of the city of Rome. Study the high drumlin just to the west of the word "Duck." Assuming that its summit is halfway between contour lines, what is its elevation?

   The summit of this drumlin is between the 920 and 930 ft contours (925 ft).

4. On the lower map, the irregular terrain south and east of Palmyra is part of a terminal moraine. Note that the average elevation in this region is greater than the elevation west of Palmyra. This is logical because the moraine is made up of "extra" material that was transported into the area by the glacier. What is the approximate elevation at the base of the radio tower in the northeast corner of grid square 35?

   The knoll of the hill at the tower base is between the 1010 and 1020 ft contours (1015 ft).

5. An example of a kettle appears in the west side of grid square 35. Note the hatched contour lines indicating that it is a depression. Assuming that the floor of the kettle is halfway between contour lines, what is its elevation?

   The floor is between the 930 and 940 ft contours (935 ft).

6. What kind of body of water is in the north side of grid square 31?

   This body of water is a kettle lake or pond.

(Part of the USGS Rome Quadrangle, Wisconsin, 1960/1971. Scale 1:24,000; Contour Interval 10 feet)

SCALE 1:24 000

CONTOUR INTERVAL 10 FEET

(Part of the USGS Little Prairie Quadrangle, Wisconsin, 1960/1971. Scale 1:24,000; Contour Interval 10 feet)

21 THE GROUNDWATER SYSTEM

Applications

21A The Hydrologic Cycle

Directions: Match the numbered items on the water cycle diagram with their labels by writing the proper letter choices in the blanks provided.

1. __f__
2. __h__
3. __a__
4. __i__
5. __d__
6. __e__
7. __c__
8. __b__
9. __g__

a. Evaporation
b. Groundwater to bodies of water
c. Groundwater to water table
d. Groundwater to streams
e. Groundwater to vegetation
f. Precipitation
g. Run-off
h. Transpiration
i. Cloud formation (condensation)

Applications
21B Groundwater

Directions: In the puzzle below, write the words that are described by the following statements. Each term is related to the subject of groundwater.

1. A/An ____ is a location where the water table reaches the surface.

2. A/An ____ rock contains a large number of open spaces between its particles.

3. A cone-shaped lowering of the water table around a well is called a cone of ____.

4. The zone of ____ is the water-filled region below the water table.

5. A small region between the zone of aeration and the zone of saturation where water has worked its way upward is called the capillary ____.

6. A/An ____ water table is located in strata above the regular water table.

7. The level below which all the spaces between rocks or soil particles are filled with water is called the ____ table.

8. The ground above the water table is called the zone of ____.

9. A/An ____ well occurs where the water rises to the ground surface under its own pressure in a well pipe.

10. Material that allows liquids or gases to pass through it is ____.

11. The path that water takes between the ocean, the clouds, precipitation, groundwater, and the ocean again is called the ____ cycle.

1. S P R I N <u>**G**</u>
2. P O <u>**R**</u> O U S
3. D E P R E S S I <u>**O**</u> N
4. S A T <u>**U**</u> R A T I O N
5. F R I <u>**N**</u> G E
6. P E R C H E <u>**D**</u>
7. <u>**W**</u> A T E R
8. A E R <u>**A**</u> T I O N
9. A R <u>**T**</u> E S I A N
10. P E R M <u>**E**</u> A B L E
11. H Y D <u>**R**</u> O L O G I C

Applications

21C Hard and Soft Water

Directions: In the spaces provided to the left, write *True* if the statement is true and *False* if the statement is false. For *False* answers, state why the answer is false in the blanks provided.

_____True_____ 1. Although it may look like pure water, groundwater always contains various dissolved minerals.

_____

_____

_____

_____False_____ 2. Dissolved minerals in water supplies are usually harmful to humans.

The minerals in most groundwater are at a low enough concentration that they do not present

a health hazard to humans. In most cases they are beneficial. Some people must restrict

their intake of certain minerals because of health conditions.

_____True_____ 3. Hard water contains high concentrations of dissolved calcium or magnesium compounds.

_____

_____

_____

_____True_____ 4. Soft water is low in calcium and magnesium compounds.

_____

_____

_____

_____False_____ 5. Lathering soap in soft water is difficult because a chemical reaction makes the soap less active.

This is true for hard water, not soft water.

_____

_____

_____True_____ 6. Scum that forms on bathtubs is caused by a chemical reaction between soap and hard water.

_____

_____

_____

Applications
21D Karst Topography

Directions: Match the features listed below with the corresponding areas on the diagram. Place the letter for each feature in the appropriate box. Then write a definition in the space provided for each of the terms listed.

a. Column
b. Curtain
c. Disappearing stream
d. Karst topography
e. Natural bridge
f. Shelf
g. Shield
h. Sinkhole
i. Solution cave
j. Spelunker
k. Stalactites
l. Stalagmites

1. Cave _A hollow space or opening beneath the surface of the ground_

2. Column _A cave formation that results when a stalactite growing downward and a stalagmite growing upward meet and join together_

3. Disappearing stream _A stream that disappears into a hole in the ground and becomes an underground stream_

4. Flowstone _A cave deposit that results from water flowing over a cave wall or floor rather than dripping from the ceiling_

5. Karst topography _A region that has undergone extensive chemical weathering of soluble rock both on the surface and underground_

6. Natural bridge _A stone arch that is a remnant segment of the collapsed ceiling of a solution cave_

7. Sinkhole _A hole that develops when a section of a cave roof collapses_

8. Spelunker _A person who explores caves as a hobby_

9. Stalactites _Icicle-like deposits of calcite that hang from the ceiling of a cave_

10. Stalagmites _Narrow mounds or projections of calcite that build upward from the floor of a cave_

21E Permeability

Procedure

1. Use a grease pencil to label the cups 1, 2, and 3.

2. Mix some plaster of Paris in a bucket.

3. Arrange strata of gravel, sand, clay, and plaster in each cup according to the following table. Be sure that no layer leaves any openings at the edges of the cup.

Cup	1	2	3
Strata order	gravel sand plaster clay	plaster clay sand gravel	plaster sand clay gravel

4. Allow the cups to stand until the plaster hardens.

5. Pour water into each cup and record the results (how far the water penetrates) in the table below.

6. Make a small crack in the plaster layers in cups 2 and 3. Observe the water. Record the results in the table below.

Goal

Demonstrate the permeability of different arrangements of sedimentary rock layers.

Materials

grease pencil
plastic cups (clear) (3)
plaster of Paris
bucket
gravel
sand
clay
water

Locally collected clay is most appropriate. However, modeling clay will also work.

In the Strata Order table, Cup 3 is an example of a perched water table.

In Step 5, the water should rapidly penetrate until it reaches either the clay or the plaster of Paris.

Cup	Initial water penetration	Water penetration after plaster cracked
1	gravel and sand	gravel, sand, and plaster
2	none	plaster
3	none	plaster and sand

Summing Up

1. What are sedimentary rocks? (*Hint*: Refer to Chapter 15 if necessary.) Sedimentary rocks are made up of particles that settled from water and were then bonded together by natural cements or solids.

2. What are layers of sedimentary rock called? The layers are called strata.

3. Which of the four materials in this investigation were permeable? Sand and gravel
Which were impermeable or nearly so? Clay and plaster of Paris

4. Which cup with the cracked plaster could be considered the recharge zone for a deep aquifer?
Cup 3. The aquifer is between the clay and plaster strata. The cracked plaster permits water to enter the aquifer.

Investigation
21F Mineral Water

Water picks up minerals as it moves through the ground. The presence of these minerals in water can be both desirable and undesirable. Since we need minerals for our bodies to function properly, drinking mineral water can have healthful benefits. Europeans have been "taking the waters" at spas for centuries. Today we can purchase mineral water that was bottled at its source. Although possibly healthful, waters with a mineral content may taste terrible, smell unpleasant, and cause soap to form a scum rather than a lather. For reasons such as these, most communities remove the minerals from water in their water purification process.

Water that contains high concentrations of dissolved minerals is called hard water; water that contains low concentrations of dissolved minerals is called soft water. Minerals that commonly cause hard water are calcium or magnesium compounds. These compounds may be further classified as bicarbonates, sulfates, or chlorides. There are several products on the market that can remove unwanted minerals from water.

Procedure and Observations

PART 1: SMELL AND TASTE OF MINERAL WATER

1. Pour some mineral water into a small cup. Smell the mineral water. Describe the smell.

   Answers will vary.

2. Taste the mineral water. Describe the taste.

   Answers will vary.

PART 2: EFFECT ON SOAPSUDS

1. Fill each of four test tubes about half full with one of the following types of water (each test tube gets a different kind of water): distilled water, mineral water, tap water, and distilled water with Epsom salts. (*Note*: Add a very small pinch of Epsom salts to the test tube.)

2. Add one drop of liquid soap to each test tube.

3. Cap each test tube with your thumb and shake the tube vigorously for 10 seconds to make soapsuds.

Goal
Use the senses of smell and taste to examine mineral water. Demonstrate the effect hard water has on soap's lathering.

Materials
mineral water
test tubes (4)
distilled water
tap water
Epsom salts
liquid soap (dish-washing soap, not detergent)
small cup

4. Wait 1 minute; then observe the suds in each test tube. Which test tube has the most suds?

   the one with distilled water

   How does the appearance of the water in each test tube differ?

   The one with distilled water should be clear; the

   others should be cloudy.

Epsom salts is the chemical compound magnesium sulfate heptahydrate. The formula for Epsom salts is $MgSO_4 \cdot 7H_2O$. Epsom salts is a source of magnesium ions in solution that simulates hard water.

To substitute for Epsom salts, dissolve a small piece of chalk in a few drops of an acid (vinegar or muriatic acid) and then add to a large volume of water.

Summing Up

1. Was the smell and taste of the mineral water pleasant or unpleasant? _Answers will vary._

2. What was produced after adding Epsom salts to the water? _hard water_

3. What did the presence of lots of soapsuds indicate? _soft water, or the absence of dissolved minerals_

4. What did the absence of lots of soapsuds indicate? _hard water, or the presence of minerals_

5. Where in your home would it be especially beneficial to use soft water? _Water softeners would be useful in any place where soap is used, such as for showers and for washing clothes._

6. Are benefits of bathing in mineral water primarily due to a better cleaning ability? _No; as demonstrated in this investigation, hard water interferes with the action of soap._

Investigation
21G Stalactites and Stalagmites

Procedure

1. Fill the beakers with warm water.

2. Put Epsom salts into the beakers and stir to dissolve. Continue adding Epsom salts until no more will dissolve.

3. Soak the string thoroughly in one of the beakers.

4. Set the two beakers on the tray 4 to 8 cm apart and drape the string between them, with each end of the string submerged in a separate beaker.

5. Set the tray in a place where it will be undisturbed for several days and out of direct sunlight.

6. After three to five days, inspect the apparatus and record the results.

Goal

Observe the formation of stalactites and stalagmites.

Materials

beakers (250 mL) (2)
water
Epsom salts
heavy cotton string, 30 cm
tray

The string should be heavy cotton crochet thread or even cotton knitting yarn. Avoid using synthetic yarns. The objective is to obtain a medium that will wick the solution over the edges of the beakers.

In Step 4, ensure that there is a distinct dip in the string between the beakers. This will allow the drops to collect and form at a specific place in the thread.

Summing Up

1. Where do the deposits come from? _They are Epsom salts carried in solution to the low point on the string._
   _____

2. What causes the Epsom salts to reappear? _The salts reappear when the water evaporates._
   _____

3. How does this process represent the formation of stalactites and stalagmites in caves? _Water containing_
   dissolved minerals is present in caves. As it drips from the ceiling and evaporates, it causes the precipitation
   of calcium carbonate. This process causes stalactites to form on the ceiling and stalagmites on the floor
   of the cave.

Investigation
21H Solution of Limestone

Some caves and other formations typical of karst topography are formed by the solution (dissolving) of limestone or other soluble rocks by groundwater. While the origin of solution caves is open to discussion, it is known today that groundwater can dissolve limestone because the water is slightly acidic and thus reacts with the limestone. In this investigation you will determine the amount of limestone dissolved during one week of exposure to slightly acidic water.

Procedure and Observations

1. Choose pieces of limestone for this experiment that are about the same size and shape. (*Note*: Size, shape, and weight are important since the goal is to have equal limestone surface areas in each treatment.) Rinse the limestones thoroughly in water and allow them to dry.

2. Accurately find the mass of five samples of the limestone pieces. Each sample should be about 10 g. Record the starting mass in the table and place each sample in a separate flask.

3. Prepare the slightly acidic solutions as follows:

   Water: Measure 100 mL of water, using the graduated cylinder. Pour this into one of the flasks with limestones. Label the flask "#1, Water."

   Humic Acid: Using the graduated cylinder, measure 100 mL of the water from the humus container prepared by your teacher. Pour the solution into one of the unlabeled flasks. Label the flask "#2, Humic Acid." Rinse out the graduated cylinder with tap water.

   1 N HCl: Your teacher will provide you with a 1 N solution of hydrochloric acid. Measure 100 mL of this using the graduated cylinder. Pour this into one of the unlabeled flasks. Label the flask "#3, 1 N HCl." *Caution*: Hydrochloric acid can cause irritation or burns. Avoid getting acid in your eyes.

   Vinegar: Measure 100 mL of vinegar using the graduated cylinder. Pour this into one of the unlabeled flasks. Label the flask "#4, Vinegar."

   Carbonic Acid: Measure 100 mL of carbonated water using the graduated cylinder. Pour this into the remaining unlabeled flask. Label the flask "#5, Carbonic Acid."

Goal
Measure the dissolving of limestone by slightly acidic solutions.

Materials
limestone pieces (similar-sized), 40–50 g
balance (accurate to 0.1 g)
flasks, (125 mL) (5)
graduated cylinder (100 mL)
water, 4–5 L
rubber stoppers (5)
1 N HCl (hydrochloric acid), 100 mL
vinegar, 100 mL
carbonic acid (carbonated water or soft drink), 100 mL
universal pH indicator paper or pH meter

In nature, the acidic solutions are usually carbonic and humic acids.

You may also want to test the dissolving action of rainwater. Collect at least 100 mL of rainwater using a rain gauge or a funnel-and-jar apparatus. Make sure that the collection jars and other apparatus are thoroughly cleaned before use.

Prepare the humic acid solution. Collect half a bucket of humus-rich topsoil. Soil from a forest works well. Pour in 3–4 L of water, stir it, and allow it to sit for at least 30 minutes (overnight is better). Pour the water from the humus bucket through a funnel into a 1 L graduated cylinder or a large beaker, filtering it with cheesecloth or other filtering material (see diagram).

Prepare the quantity of 1 N HCl required for your class by diluting concentrated hydrochloric acid. Concentrated HCl has a molarity (and normality) of 12.1. Divide the volume of dilute HCl you need by 12.1. This result is the amount of concentrated acid to be diluted. Subtract this volume from the total volume of dilute acid needed. This difference is the volume of water required. Add the acid to the water to avoid spattering. The pH of 1 N HCl is approximately 0.1, but your pH paper may not indicate a value of less than 1 pH. You may use muriatic acid from a hardware store, but you will need to know its concentration to make the appropriate dilution.

The pH of your tap water may be somewhat acidic. Test the pH of your water with a pH meter. If you present this investigation as a controlled experiment, you should adjust the pH of the "water" treatment to 7. You should also adjust the pH of the water you add to the humus to 7 prior to mixing the humus infusion. Add a dilute acid solution (HCl or vinegar) or a dilute basic solution (NaOH) to adjust the pH to approximately 7. Do not use a buffer because these chemicals are meant to resist pH changes.

Values in the table will vary. Change in mass = starting mass − ending mass; percent change = (change in mass) ÷ (starting mass) × 100.

Flask	Solution	pH	Starting mass	Ending mass	Change in mass	Percent change
1	Water		g	g	g	%
2	Humic acid		g	g	g	%
3	1 N HCL		g	g	g	%
4	Vinegar		g	g	g	%
5	Carbonic acid		g	g	g	%

4. Determine the pH of each solution with universal pH indicator paper or a pH meter and record the values.

5. Loosely stopper the flasks to limit evaporation. Place all the flasks in the same area so that they will encounter the same temperature and other conditions.

6. After one week pour off each solution and recover the limestone pieces. Rinse each limestone sample *separately* and allow them to dry on paper towels.

7. When the limestone samples are completely dry, measure the mass of each and record the ending mass in the table. Subtract the ending mass from the starting mass for each sample. Record the change in mass.

8. Divide the change in mass by the starting mass of each sample. Multiply the result by 100 to obtain percent change for each solution. Record this value in the last column of the table.

Summing Up

1. Which solution produced the largest percent change in mass? <u>The 1 N HCl (hydrochloric acid) treatment produced the largest change.</u>

2. Where did the lost matter go? <u>The matter was dissolved in the solution.</u>

3. Did any sample not lose any measurable mass? <u>Yes, Flask #1</u> Why? <u>Water (and perhaps others) did not dissolve the limestone.</u>

4. What was the relationship between the pH and the amount of limestone dissolved? <u>The lower the pH (more acidic), the more limestone was dissolved.</u>

5. How do the results here demonstrate how some speleothems form? <u>Acidic groundwater dissolves limestone, as these acidic solutions did, and redeposits the mineral as speleothems.</u>

6. Which of these acids are present in groundwater long after the Flood? <u>Carbonic acid and humic acid are commonly in the groundwater entering caves today.</u>

Go a Step Further

Repeat this investigation, using other kinds of rocks as well as limestone. Compare the rates of solution of the various rocks. Is limestone the only one that dissolves? <u>Answers will vary.</u>

What rocks dissolve more rapidly? <u>Answers will vary.</u>

What do your results indicate about where caves are likely to form? <u>They are more likely to form in regions with limestone or other rocks easily dissolved by acids.</u>

In Step 6, consider testing the pH of the liquids left in the five flasks after the limestone has soaked. Note any changes of pH due to reaction with the limestone.

Investigation Equipment and Materials by Item

Material	Opt.	Size/Range	Source	Invest.	Quantity	Per	Notes
alcohol, rubbing		bottle	L	10D	1	group or class	
			L	10F	30 mL	group	
		bottle	L	12G	1	group	
alum			L	14D	100 g	group	aluminum ammonium sulfate; $AlNH_4SO_4$
			L	14E	(200 g)	group	see investigation instructions
aluminum foil		15 cm square	L	4F	1	group	
		roll	L	4G	1	class	
		15 cm square	L	8G	1	student or group	
		3 cm square	L	12G	1	group	
aspirator, faucet			S	9F	1	group or class	substitute: vacuum pump (see optional equipment)
balance, laboratory			S	18F	1	group	accurate to 0.1 g
			S	21H	1	group or class	accurate to 0.1 g
balloon			L	10F	1	group	large, heavy latex
balloon, long cylindrical			L	8F	≥3	group or class	
balloon, round		≥5 cm diameter	L	9E	1	group or class	
battery		6 volt	L	17G	1	group or class	dry cell
beaker		1 L	S	9E	2	group or class	
		500 mL	S	10D	1	group or class	substitute: wide-mouth quart jar
		1 L	S	10F	1	group	substitute: wide-mouth quart jar
		250–300 mL	S	12G	1	group	
		250 mL	S	14D	3	group	Pyrex
		250 mL–1 L	S	14F	1	group or class	substitute: deep cup
		250 mL–1 L	S	15D	1	group	
		250 mL–1 L	S	16E	1	group or class	substitute: water pitcher
		1 L	S	18F	1	group	
		250 mL	S	18F	2	group	
		250 mL	S	19I	1	group	
		500 mL	S	19J	1	group or class	
		250 mL	S	21G	2	group or class	substitute: large drinking glasses

Material	Opt.	Size/Range	Source	Invest.	Quantity	Per	Notes
bolt		⅛ × 2 in. long	L	12I	1	group	
		⅛ × 6 in. long	L	12I	1	group	
bucket			L	21E	1	class	
			L	21H	1	class	to collect humus topsoil
burner, laboratory			S	12G	1	group	substitute: hot plate
			S	19I	1	group	
burner igniter			L/S	19I	1	group	substitute: safety matches
calculator			L	3K	1	student	standard calculator OK
			L	4E	1	group or class	standard calculator OK
			L	5I	1	student	standard calculator OK
			L	6F	1	student	standard calculator OK
			L	7F	1	student or group	standard calculator OK
			L	7G	1	student or group	pi key preferred but not necessary
			L	8F	1	group or class	standard calculator OK
			L	17H	1	student	standard calculator OK
	X		L	17I	1	student	standard calculator OK
			L	20G	1	student	standard calculator OK
calculator, scientific			L	5G	1	group	for determining square and cube roots
			L	8H	1	group	for trigonometric calculations
			L	16H	1	student	for calculations in scientific notation
camera tripod			L	2E	1	class or group	
can			L	10E	1	group	shiny metal can or drinking glass
candle			L	3G	1	group	
			L	11G	1	group or class	
carbonic acid			S/L	21H	100 mL	group or class	substitute: carbonated water
card, index		3 × 5 in.	L	7F	1	student or group	
		3 × 5 in.	L	7I	8	class	
		3 × 5 in.	L	16F	1	student	
		3 × 5 in.	L	19J	2	group or class	
cardboard, corrugated		10 × 10 cm	L	4E	2	group or class	
		≥8½ × 11 in.	L	5E	1	student	

Material	Opt.	Size/Range	Source	Invest.	Quantity	Per	Notes
cardboard, corrugated (cont.)			L	8G	1	student or group	large enough to cover a desk
		20 × 20 cm	L	3J	1	class	
			L	4F	1	group	substitute: large dishpan
cardboard box		8½ × 11 in.	L	5H	1	student	
card stock, stiff		8½ × 11 in.	L	3G	1	group	
		≥8½ × 11 in.	L	4G	1	group	must be white
card stock, white		8½ × 11 in.	L	11G	1	group or class	substitute: cereal box panel
C-clamp		≥3 in.	L	17G	1	group or class	
cellophane, colored	X	15 cm square	L	4F	4	group	4 different colors per group
ceramic tile			L/S	14F	1	group	substitute: mineralogical streak plate
cheesecloth			L	18F	1	group	substitute: wire strainer
			L	21H	1	class	substitute: wire strainer; for preparing humic acid solution
clamp, flask			S	4E	1	group or class	3- or 4-finger, adjustable
		large	S	12H	1	group	must be able to clamp vacuum bottle
			S	19I	1	group	to fit Erlenmeyer flask
clamp, knife edge, & support base			S	10D	1	group or class	to support meter stick balance
clamp, right angle support			S	17G	1	group or class	
clay, modeling		4 oz package	L	2F	1	class or group	
		4 oz package	L	3J	1	class	
			L	17G	2 oz	group or class	
			L	21E	2 oz	group or class	
clay, modeling, waterproof		large package	L	16E	1	group or class	
clay tool			L	16E	1	group or class	substitute: pencil or old ballpoint pen
clip, document			L	7F	1	student or group	spring type
clip, paper			L	8F	2	group or class	same size clips
			L	10D	2	group or class	
clock or watch			L	2H	1	student or group	digital or quartz
compass, drawing			L	17H	1	student	

Material	Opt.	Size/Range	Source	Invest.	Quantity	Per	Notes
cup		small	L	12H	1	group	substitute: 150 mL beaker
cup, clear plastic			L	21E	3	group or class	
cup, foam		8 oz	L	4F	4	group	
			L	14E	3	group	
cup, paper			L	12I	1	group	substitute: any kind of cup or small beaker
		small	L	21F	1	group	disposable preferred
dishpan		deep	L	16E	1	group or class	
		large	L	18G	1	class	
		large	L	20F	1	group or class	
dividers, drafting			L	16G	1	student	
			L	16H	1	student	
drill, electric			L	12I	1	class	
drill bit		⁵⁄₃₂ in.	L	12I	1	class	
drinking straw		large	L	8F	1	group or class	
		large	L	8H	1	group or class	
Epsom salts			L	14D	100 g	group	magnesium sulfate heptahydrate; $MgSO_4 \cdot 7\,H_2O$
			L	14E	(200 g)	group	see investigation instructions
			L	21F	2 g	group	to make hard water
		box	L	21G	1	group or class	
eyedropper			L/S	12I	1	group	
			L/S	15D	1	group	
fastener, split tack			L	3I	1	group	
fishing line		10 m	L	8F	1	group or class	
fishing sinker			L	8H	1	group	substitute: machine nut
		1–6 oz	L	17G	1	group or class	
flask, Erlenmeyer, Pyrex	X	500 mL	S	9F	1	group or class	
		250 mL	S	19I	1	group	
		125 mL	S	21H	5	group or class	
		500 mL	S	9F	1	group or class	
food coloring		bottle	L	4F		group	several colors, mix to get black

Material	Opt.	Size/Range	Source	Invest.	Quantity	Per	Notes
food coloring (cont.)		bottle	L	12G	1	class	1 color
	X	bottle	L	12H	1	group	1 color
	X	bottle	L	14D	1	group	1 color
fossil, trilobite			S	15F	≥1	group	more than one kind preferred
funnel		10 cm diam.	L/S	12J	1	group	
			L/S	21H	1	class	for preparing humic acid solution
gauze, surgical		15 × 15 cm piece	L	12I	1	group	
glass jar		narrow (5 cm diam.)	L	12J	1	group	e.g., olive jar
		large (1 gal)	L	12J	1	group	wide mouth
glass plate		thin	L	4F	1	group	sized to cover a foam cup
			L	14F	1	group	
globe, desk		≥20 cm diam.	S	2F	1	class or group	
glue, polystyrene	X	tube	L	8G	1	student or group	if finishing rockets in classroom
glue, white		bottle	L	3H	1	student or group	
		bottle	L	3I	1	student or group	
		bottle	L	4E	1	group or class	
	X	bottle	L	8G	1	student or group	if finishing rockets in classroom
		bottle	L	11G	1	group or class	
graduated cylinder		50–250 mL	S	4F	1	group	
		250 mL	S	18F	1	group	
		100 mL	S	19I	1	group	
		1 L	S	21H	1	class	for preparing humic acid solution
		100 mL	S	21H	1	group or class	
graph paper		1 mm ruled, sheet	L	4E	1	group or class	
		¼ in. ruled, sheet	L	6F	1	student	
		¼ in. ruled	L	12H	1	student	
gravel		fine	L	21E	120 cm³	group or class	pea gravel is preferred
hair dryer			L	10D	1	group or class	substitute: small fan
heat source			L	10D	1	group or class	e.g., hot plate, Bunsen burner
hole punch			L	7F	1	student or group	

Material	Opt.	Size/Range	Source	Invest.	Quantity	Per	Notes
hot plate			L	14D	1	group	substitute: stove burner
			S/L	14E	1	group	substitute: stove burner
hydrochloric acid		bottle, 2 N or 2 M	S	15D	1	group	a few drops of HCl per group
		1 N or 1 M	S	21H	100 mL	group or class	
ice			L	9E	500 mL	group or class	
			L	10D	1	group or class	cube
			L	10E	sufficient	group	several pieces, directly from freezer
			L	10F	1 bag	group	fill plastic bags directly from freezer
			L	12G	200 mL	group	crushed
			L	14E	sufficient	class	substitute: refrigerator
	X		L	19I	sufficient	class	
			L	20F	several	group or class	cubes
insulating material			L	4F	sufficient	group	vermiculite, shredded foam, fiberglass
iron support ring			S	12G	1	group	NA if hot plate used
			S	19I	1	group	
knife (steel)			L	14F	1	group	
lamp, heat			L	11G	1	group or class	
lamp, high intensity			L/S	2F	1	class or group	300 watt, overhead projector, etc.
			L/S	7I	1	class	
lamp bulb		6 volt	L/S	17G	1	group or class	
launching pad and launch switch			L	8G	≥1	class	fresh batteries required
			L	8H	1	class	
lens, convex		known focal length	S	3G	2	group	
lens, convex—large		38 mm × 300 mm f.l.	S	3H	1	group	
lens, convex—small			S	3H	1	student or group	substitute: 10× magnifier w/o tripod
lens, hand magnifying			L/S	14D	1	group	substitute: stereo microscope
			L/S	14E	1	group	substitute: stereo microscope
			L/S	14F	1	group	substitute: stereo microscope
			L/S	15D	1	group	substitute: stereo microscope
			L/S	15F	1	group	stereo microscope preferred

Material	Opt.	Size/Range	Source	Invest.	Quantity	Per	Notes
lens, hand magnifying (cont.)	X		L/S	16G	1	student	if required by student to read map
			L/S	18F	1	group	
			L/S	20G	1	student	
limestone, gravel			L	21H	40–50 g	group or class	similar sized pieces
liquid soap		bottle	L	21F	1	class	dish washing, non-detergent
lumber, milled	X	1 × 4 × 12 in.	L	3H	1	group	for optional mounting attachment
magnet			L/S	14F	1	group	permanent horseshoe or bar magnet
map or atlas of the United States			L	17H	1	class	
mass, hooked		50 g	S	2E	1	class or group	
matches, safety		box	L	3G	1	group	
		box	L	10F	1	group	
		box	L	11G	1	group or class	
meter stick			S/L	3G	1	group	substitute: metric tape measure
			S/L	7F	1	student or group	
			S/L	7I	1	class	
			S/L	10D	1	group or class	
mirror, concave		known focal length	S	3G	1	group	
mirror, flat	X	large	L/S	4G	1	class	
model rocket			L/S	8H	≥1	group	purchased or assembled from kit
model rocket engine			L/S	8G	1	student or group	size according to rocket kit instructions
			L/S	8H	1	group	size according to rocket kit instructions
model rocket engine igniter			L/S	8H	sufficient	group or class	
			L/S	8G	sufficient	class	
model rocket kit			L/S	8G	1	student or group	available from hobby and toy stores
moving box, large	X		L	4G	1	group	wardrobe-sized box
newspaper		full page	L	11G	1	group or class	
nut, machine		⅛ in.	L	12I	8	group	nut thread must match bolts
oven			L	18F	1	class	substitute: hot plate
paint, spray, enamel	X	can	L	8G	several	class	various colors
paint, spray, flat black		can	L	4F	1	class	

Material	Opt.	Size/Range	Source	Invest.	Quantity	Per	Notes
paintbrush	X	small	L	8G	1	student or group	for applying sealer (not needed for a spray sealer)
paint thinner	X		L	8G	sufficient	class	substitute: mineral spirits (for cleaning brushes)
paper, construction		23 × 30 cm	L	3I	3	student	
paper, printer		8½ × 11 in.	L	5E	3	student	
		8½ × 11 in.	L	14D	1	group	
paper, weighing			S	18F	2	group	
paper toweling		roll	L	8G	1	class	
		roll	L	10D	1	class	
		roll	L	15D	1	class	
		roll	L	21H	1	class	
paper towel tube			L	3H	2	group	
pencil			L	5E	1	student	mechanical pencil is best
			L	5H	1	student	mechanical pencil is best
pencil, china marker			L	12G	1	group	
			L	12H	1	group	
			L	18F	1	group	
			L	21E	1	group or class	
			L	21H	1	group or class	
pencil, colored			L	6G	2	student	2 different colors
			L	11H	5	student	
			L	12H	2	student	2 different colors
pencil, wooden			L	3J	1	class	substitute: thin wooden dowel
penny			L	14F	1	group	pre-1983, or substitute: solid copper materials
pH indicator paper, universal		package	S	21H	1	class	substitute: pH meter
pin, push	X		L	2H	1	student or group	
			L	5E	2	student	substitute: thumbtacks
pin, round headed			L	3J	2	class	
pin, straight			L	4E	1	group or class	
			L	4G	1	group	

Material	Opt.	Size/Range	Source	Invest.	Quantity	Per	Notes
plaster of Paris			L	21E	sufficient	group or class	
plastic bag			L	10F	1	group	large enough to hold several cubes of ice
plastic wrap		roll	L	4F	1	class	
plate, foam		small	L	14E	1	group	
projection screen, solar	X		S	4G	1	telescope	
protractor			L	2F	1	class or group	
			L	3J	1	class	
			L	5D	1	student	
			L	8H	1	group or class	
protractor, chalkboard			S	5F	1	class	
			S	7I	1	class	
razor blade, single edge			L	8G	1	student or group	
reagent bottle		250 mL	S/L	19J	4	group or class	substitute: baby food jars
recovery wadding			L/S	8G	1	student or group	
rock and mineral collection			S	14F	1	group	recommended: 50 specimen set from Scott Resources (BJU Press #63396)
			S	15D	1	group or class	recommended: 50 specimen set from Scott Resources (BJU Press #63396)
rock/stone		palm-sized	L	5F	21	class	substitute: weighted paper cups, pieces of chalk, etc.
rope		≥24 m	L	5F	1	class	
rubber band			L	3H	1	group	
			L	10F	1	group	heavy duty, large enough to fit over mouth of jar
rubber cement		bottle	L	4E	1	group or class	substitute: glue or tape
		bottle	L	8G	1	student or group	
ruler			L	6G	1	student	for straight edge only
			L	13H	1	student	for straight edge only
			L	16F	1	student	for straight edge only
			L	16G	1	student	for straight edge only
			L	16H	1	student	for straight edge only
ruler, English			L	6F	1	student	
ruler, metric			L	4E	1	group or class	
			L	4F	1	group	substitute: a meter stick or metric tape

Material	Opt.	Size/Range	Source	Invest.	Quantity	Per	Notes
ruler, metric (cont.)			L	5D	1	student	
			L	5E	1	student	
			L	7F	1	student or group	
			L	12G	1	group	
			L	12J	1	group	
			L	16E	1	group or class	plastic
			L	17I	1	student	
			L	18F	1	group	to measure soil sample in place in the field
			L	20G	1	student	
salt			L	10E	100 g	group	rock salt or table salt
			L	19I	3.5 g	group	table or rock salt (NaCl)
			L	19J	sufficient	group or class	table or rock salt (NaCl), to make a saturated solution
sand			L	18G	sufficient	class	about 2 in. deep in dishpan
			L	21E	sufficient	group or class	
sanding sealer		can	L	8G	1	student or group	
sandpaper		sheet	L	8G	1	student or group	fine grade
saucepan			L	14D	1	group	substitute: 500 mL Pyrex beaker
			L	14E	1	group	substitute: 500 mL Pyrex beaker
scissors			L	3I	1	group	
			L	5H	1	student	
			L	11G	1	group or class	
scissors, fine tip			L	8G	1	student or group	
serving tray			L	21G	1	group or class	
shovel, small			L	18F	1	class	
socket, lamp			S/L	17G	1	group or class	must accept 6 V light bulb
soil			L	18F	15 cm³	group	
soil, humus			L	21H	1 bucket	class	humus-rich top soil
soil, sifted			L	20F	sufficient	group or class	12–15 cm deep in dishpan; substitute: clean sand
sponge		5 × 10 cm	L	10D	2	group or class	must be same size

Material	Opt.	Size/Range	Source	Invest.	Quantity	Per	Notes
spring scale			S	14F	1	group or class	substitute: mass balance
stake, wooden		1–2 m long	L	2H	2	student or group	
stapler			L	3I	1	group or class	
			L	7F	1	student or group	
stirring rod			L/S	10E	1	group	
			L/S	14D	3	group	glass, metal, or substitute: pencil
			L/S	14E	2	group	glass, metal, or substitute: pencil
stopper, one-hole			S	9F	1	group or class	fitted with short glass tube
			S	12G	1	group	to fit test tube
		large	S	12H	1	group	to fit thermos bottle
			S	19I	1	group	to fit 250 mL Erlenmeyer flask
stopper, solid			S	21H	5	group or class	to fit 125 mL Erlenmeyer flasks
stopper, two-hole	X		S	9F	1	group or class	fitted with two glass tubing elbows and one additional thick-walled rubber tubing, 30 cm
stopwatch			L/S	4F	1	group	substitute: digital watch with seconds display
			L/S	5F	1	class	substitute: digital watch with seconds display
			L/S	8F	1	group or class	substitute: digital watch with seconds display
			L/S	8H	1	group	substitute: digital watch with seconds display
			L/S	10D	1	group or class	substitute: digital watch with seconds display
			L/S	11G	1	group or class	substitute: digital watch with seconds display
			L/S	12I	1	group	substitute: digital watch with seconds display
string			L	5E	25 cm	student	
			L	12I	1 m	group	
string, surveyor's			L	3J	1	class	long enough to stretch across room
sugar			L	14D	200 g	group	sucrose
			L	14E	(400 g)	group	sucrose; see investigation instructions
sun shield, telescope			L/S	4G	1	telescope	
support rod		≥20 cm	S	17G	1	group or class	steel rod or ¼ in. wooden dowel

Material	Opt.	Size/Range	Source	Invest.	Quantity	Per	Notes
support rod and clamp	X		S	14F	1	group	required only if using mass balance for specific gravity test
support stand, laboratory			S	4E	1	group or class	
			S	12G	1	group	NA if hot plate used
			S	12H	1	group	
	X		S	14F	1	group or class	required only if using mass balance for specific gravity test
			S	17G	1	group or class	
			S	19I	1	group	
table or desk			L	17G	2	group or class	must be same height
tape, cellophane		roll	L	5H	1	class	
tape, masking		roll	L	3H	1	student or group	
		roll	L	3I	1	group	
		roll	L	3J	1	class	
		roll	L	4G	1	class	
		roll	L	5E	1	student	
		roll	L	7I	1	class	
		roll	L	8F	1	group or class	
		roll	L	8G	1	student or group	
		roll	L	8H	1	group or class	
		roll	L	11G	1	class	
		roll	L	12G	1	class	
		roll	L	12H	1	class	
			L	12J	1	class	
tape measure, metric			L/S	2F	1	class	
			L/S	3G	1	group	substitute: meter stick
			L/S	3J	1	class	
			L/S	5F	1	class	
		5–10 m long	L/S	8F	1	group or class	
		≥20 m long	L/S	8H	1	class	
tape measure, metric, cloth			L/S	9E	1	group or class	

Material	Opt.	Size/Range	Source	Invest.	Quantity	Per	Notes
telescope			L/S	2H	1	student or group	
			L/S	4G	1	group	substitute: binoculars
			L/S	7H	1	student or group	substitute: binoculars
test tube, Pyrex		10–15 cm	S	12G	1	group	
		10–15 cm	S	21F	4	group	
thermometer, card mounted		0–100 °C or equiv.	S	12I	2	group	mounted on metal, plywood, or stiff cardboard
thermometer, laboratory, Celsius			L/S	4F	4	group	
		–20 to 110 °C	L/S	10E	1	group	
thread, sewing		see notes	L	2E	1	class or group	length to match height of tripod
		5 m	L	2F	1	class or group	
thread or string			L	14F	50 cm	group or class	
thread or string, cotton		15 cm long	L	14D	3	group	
		15 cm long	L	14E	2	group	
thread or string, cotton, heavy			L	21G	30 cm	group or class	
thread or string, heavy sewing		35 cm	L	8H	1	group or class	
thumbtack			L	5H	1	student	
tongs, test tube			S	12G	1	group	
tubing, glass or rigid plastic		6 mm O.D.	S/L	12G	40 cm	group	must fit hole in stopper
		6 mm O.D.	S/L	12H	30–40 cm	group	must fit hole in stopper
		6 mm O.D. × 8 cm	S/L	19I	1	group	must fit hole in stopper; length is approximate
tubing, natural rubber			S/L	19I	60 cm	group	
tubing, rubber, thick walled		30 cm long	S/L	9F	1	group or class	sized to fit glass tubing
turntable			L	2E	1	class or group	lazy Susan, record player, etc.
vacuum bottle		1 pt–1 qt	L	12H	1	group	thermos, etc.; narrow-mouth
	X		L/S	9F	1	group or class	motor operated
vinegar			L	21H	100 mL	group or class	
volleyball			L	7I	1	class	substitute: any sports ball
washer, metal		⅛ in.	L	12I	10	group	

Material	Opt.	Size/Range	Source	Invest.	Quantity	Per	Notes
watch glass		large	S	10D	1	group or class	to cover beaker
water, distilled			L	21F	10 mL	group	
water, mineral			L	21F	10 mL	group	
water container		5 gal	L/S	19J	1	class	for uniform temperature water supply
weather instrument station	X		S	12K	1	class	anemometer, barometer, thermometer, etc.
wire, insulated		24 AWG or finer, 50–100 cm	L/S	17G	3	group or class	AWG stands for American Wire Gauge
wire gauze square			S	12G	1	group	NA if hot plate used
			S	19I	1	group	
wood splint		≥10 cm long	L/S	2F	2	class or group	
			L/S	8G	1	student or group	flame test splints can be used

Investigation Equipment and Materials by Activity

Invest.	Material	Opt.	Size/Range	Source	Quantity	Per	Notes
1C	none			NA	NA	NA	read and complete activity
1D	none			NA	NA	NA	read and complete activity
2E	camera tripod			L	1	class or group	
	mass, hooked		50 g	S	1	class or group	
	thread, sewing		see notes	L	1	class or group	length to match height of tripod
	turntable			L	1	class or group	lazy Susan, record player, etc.
2F	clay, modeling		4 oz package	L	1	class or group	
	globe, desk		≥20 cm diam.	S	1	class or group	
	lamp, high intensity			L/S	1	class or group	300 watt, overhead projector, etc.
	protractor			L	1	class or group	
	tape measure, metric			L/S	1	class	
	thread, sewing		5 m	L	1	class or group	
	wood splint		≥10 cm long	L/S	2	class or group	
2G	none			NA	NA	NA	read and complete activity
2H	clock or watch			L	1	student or group	digital or quartz
	pin, push	X		L	1	student or group	
	stake, wooden		1–2 m long	L	2	student or group	
	telescope			L/S	1	student or group	
3G	candle			L	1	group	
	card stock		8½ × 11 in.	L	1	group	
	lens, convex		known focal length	S	2	group	
	matches, safety		box	L	1	group	
	meter stick			S/L	1	group	substitute: metric tape measure
	mirror, concave		known focal length	S	1	group	
	tape measure, metric			L/S	1	group	substitute: meter stick
3H	glue, white		bottle	L	1	student or group	
	lens, convex—large		38 mm × 300 mm f.l.	S	1	group	
	lens, convex—small			S	1	student or group	substitute: 10× magnifier w/o tripod

Invest.	Material	Opt.	Size/Range	Source	Quantity	Per	Notes
3H (cont.)	lumber, milled	X	1 × 4 × 12 in.	L	1	group	for optional mounting attachment
	paper towel tube			L	2	group	
	rubber band			L	1	group	
	tape, masking		roll	L	1	student or group	
3I	fastener, split tack			L	1	group	
	glue, white		bottle	L	1	student or group	
	paper, construction		23 × 30 cm	L	3	student	
	scissors			L	1	group	
	stapler			L	1	group or class	
	tape, masking		roll	L	1	group	
3J	cardboard, corrugated		20 × 20 cm	L	1	class	
	clay, modeling		4 oz package	L	1	class	
	pencil, wooden			L	1	class	substitute: thin wooden dowel
	pin, round headed			L	2	class	
	protractor			L	1	class	
	string, surveyor's			L	1	class	long enough to stretch across room
	tape measure, metric			L/S	1	class	
	tape, masking		roll	L	1	class	
3K	calculator			L	1	student	standard calculator OK
4E	calculator			L	1	group or class	standard calculator OK
	cardboard, corrugated		10 × 10 cm	L	2	group or class	
	clamp, flask			S	1	group or class	3- or 4-finger, adjustable
	glue, white		bottle	L	1	group or class	
	graph paper		1 mm ruled, sheet	L	1	group or class	
	pin, straight			L	1	group or class	
	rubber cement		bottle	L	1	group or class	substitute: glue or tape
	ruler, metric			L	1	group or class	
	support stand, laboratory			S	1	group or class	
4F	aluminum foil		15 cm square	L	1	group	
	cardboard, corrugated			L	1	group	substitute: large dishpan
	cellophane, colored	X	15 cm square	L	4	group	4 different colors per group

Invest.	Material	Opt.	Size/Range	Source	Quantity	Per	Notes
4F (cont.)	cup, foam		8 oz	L	4	group	
	food coloring		bottle	L		group	several colors, mix to get black
	glass plate		thin	L	1	group	sized to cover a foam cup
	graduated cylinder		50–250 mL	S	1	group	
	insulating material			L	sufficient	group	vermiculite, shredded foam, fiberglass
	paint, spray, flat black		can	L	1	class	
	plastic wrap		roll	L	1	class	
	ruler, metric			L	1	group	substitute: a meter stick or metric tape
	stopwatch			L/S	1	group	substitute: digital watch with seconds display
	thermometer, laboratory, Celsius			L/S	4	group	
4G	aluminum foil		roll	L	1	class	
	card stock, stiff		≥8½ × 11 in.	L	1	group	must be white
	mirror, flat	X	large	L/S	1	class	
	moving box, large	X		L	1	group	wardrobe-sized box
	pin, straight			L	1	group	
	projection screen, solar	X		S	1	telescope	
	sun shield, telescope			L/S	1	telescope	
	tape, masking		roll	L	1	class	
	telescope			L/S	1	group	substitute: binoculars
5D	protractor			L	1	student	
	ruler, metric			L	1	student	
5E	cardboard, corrugated		≥8½ × 11 in.	L	1	student	
	paper, printer		8½ × 11 in.	L	3	student	
	pencil			L	1	student	mechanical pencil is best
	pin, push			L	2	student	substitute: thumbtacks
	ruler, metric			L	1	student	
	string			L	25 cm	student	
	tape, masking		roll	L	1	student	
5F	protractor, chalkboard			S	1	class	
	rock/stone		palm-sized	L	21	class	substitute: weighted paper cups, pieces of chalk, etc.

Invest.	Material	Opt.	Size/Range	Source	Quantity	Per	Notes
5F (cont.)	rope		≥24 m	L	1	class	
	stopwatch			L/S	1	class	substitute: digital watch with seconds display
	tape measure, metric			L/S	1	class	
5G	calculator, scientific			L	1	group	for determining square and cube roots
5H	cardboard box		8½ × 11 in.	L	1	student	
	pencil			L	1	student	mechanical pencil is best
	scissors			L	1	student	
	tape, cellophane		roll	L	1	class	
	thumbtack			L	1	student	
5I	calculator			L	1	student	standard calculator OK
6F	calculator			L	1	student	standard calculator OK
	graph paper		¼ in. ruled, sheet	L	1	student	
	ruler, English			L	1	student	
6G	pencil, colored			L	2	student	2 different colors
	ruler			L	1	student	for straight edge only
7F	calculator			L	1	student or group	standard calculator OK
	card, index		3 × 5 in.	L	1	student or group	
	clip, document			L	1	student or group	spring type
	hole punch			L	1	student or group	
	meter stick			S/L	1	student or group	
	ruler, metric			L	1	student or group	
	stapler			L	1	student or group	
7G	calculator			L	1	student or group	pi key preferred but not necessary
7H	telescope			L/S	1	student or group	substitute: binoculars
7I	card, index		3 × 5 in.	L	8	class	
	lamp, high intensity			L/S	1	class	
	meter stick			S/L	1	class	
	protractor, chalkboard			S	1	class	
	tape, masking		roll	L	1	class	
	volleyball			L	1	class	substitute: any sports ball

Invest.	Material	Opt.	Size/Range	Source	Quantity	Per	Notes
8F	balloon, long cylindrical			L	≥3	group or class	
	calculator			L	1	group or class	standard calculator OK
	clip, paper			L	2	group or class	same size clips
	drinking straw		large	L	1	group or class	
	fishing line		10 m	L	1	group or class	
	stopwatch			L/S	1	group or class	substitute: digital watch with seconds display
	tape measure, metric		5–10 m long	L/S	1	group or class	
	tape, masking		roll	L	1	group or class	
8G	aluminum foil		15 cm square	L	1	student or group	
	cardboard, corrugated			L	1	student or group	large enough to cover a desk
	glue, polystyrene	X	tube	L	1	student or group	if finishing rockets in classroom
	glue, white	X	bottle	L	1	student or group	if finishing rockets in classroom
	launching pad and launch switch			L	≥1	class	fresh batteries required
	model rocket engine			L/S	1	student or group	size according to rocket kit instructions
	model rocket engine igniter			L/S	sufficient	class	
	model rocket kit			L/S	1	student or group	available from hobby and toy stores
	paint thinner	X		L	sufficient	class	substitute: mineral spirits (for cleaning brushes)
	paint, spray, enamel	X	can	L	several	class	various colors
	paintbrush	X	small	L	1	student or group	for applying sealer (not needed for a spray sealer)
	paper toweling		roll	L	1	class	
	razor blade, single edge			L	1	student or group	
	recovery wadding			L/S	1	student or group	
	rubber cement		bottle	L	1	student or group	
	sanding sealer		can	L	1	student or group	
	sandpaper		sheet	L	1	student or group	fine grade
	scissors, fine tip			L	1	student or group	
	tape, masking		roll	L	1	student or group	
	wood splint			L/S	1	student or group	flame test splints can be used

Invest.	Material	Opt.	Size/Range	Source	Quantity	Per	Notes
8H	calculator, scientific			L	1	group	for trigonometric calculations
	drinking straw		large	L	1	group or class	
	fishing sinker			L	1	group	substitute: machine nut
	launching pad and launch switch			L	1	class	
	model rocket			L/S	≥1	group	purchased or assembled from kit
	model rocket engine			L/S	1	group	size according to rocket kit instructions
	model rocket engine igniter			L/S	sufficient	group or class	
	protractor			L	1	group or class	
	stopwatch			L/S	1	group	substitute: digital watch with seconds display
	tape measure, metric		≥20 m long	L/S	1	class	
	tape, masking		roll	L	1	group or class	
	thread or string, heavy sewing		35 cm	L	1	group or class	
9E	balloon, round		≥5 cm diameter	L	1	group or class	
	beaker		1 L	S	2	group or class	
	ice			L	500 mL	group or class	
	tape measure, metric, cloth			L/S	1	group or class	
9F	aspirator, faucet			S	1	group or class	substitute: vacuum pump (see optional equipment)
	flask, Erlenmeyer, Pyrex	X	500 mL	S	1	group or class	
	flask, Florence, Pyrex		500 mL	S	1	group or class	
	stopper, one-hole			S	1	group or class	fitted with short glass tube
	stopper, two-hole	X		S	1	group or class	fitted with two glass tubing elbows and one additional thick-walled rubber tubing, 30 cm
	tubing, rubber, thick-walled		30 cm long	S/L	1	group or class	sized to fit glass tubing
	vacuum pump	X		L/S	1	group or class	motor operated
10D	alcohol, rubbing		bottle	L	1	group or class	
	beaker		500 mL	S	1	group or class	substitute: wide-mouth quart jar
	clamp, knife edge, & support base			S	1	group or class	to support meter stick balance

Invest.	Material	Opt.	Size/Range	Source	Quantity	Per	Notes
10D (cont.)	clip, paper			L	2	group or class	
	hair dryer			L	1	group or class	substitute: small fan
	heat source			L	1	group or class	e.g., hot plate, Bunsen burner
	ice cubes			L	1	group or class	
	meter stick			S/L	1	group or class	
	paper toweling		roll	L	1	class	
	sponge		5 × 10 cm	L	2	group or class	must be same size
	stopwatch			L/S	1	group or class	substitute: digital watch with seconds display
	watch glass		large	S	1	group or class	to cover beaker
10E	can			L	1	group	shiny metal can or drinking glass
	ice			L	sufficient	group	several pieces, directly from freezer
	salt			L	100 g	group	rock salt or table salt
	stirring rod			L/S	1	group	
	thermometer, laboratory, Celsius		–20 to 110 °C	L/S	1	group	
10F	alcohol, rubbing			L	30 mL	group	
	balloon			L	1	group	large, heavy latex
	beaker		1 L	S	1	group	substitute: wide-mouth quart jar
	ice			L	1 bag	group	fill plastic bags directly from freezer
	match, safety		box	L	1	group	
	plastic bag			L	1	group	large enough to hold several ice cubes
	rubber band			L	1	group	heavy duty, large enough to fit over mouth of jar
11G	candle			L	1	group or class	
	card stock, white		8½ × 11 in.	L	1	group or class	substitute: cereal box panel
	glue, white		bottle	L	1	group or class	
	lamp, heat			L	1	group or class	
	matches, safety		box	L	1	group or class	
	newspaper		full page	L	1	group or class	
	scissors			L	1	group or class	
	stopwatch			L/S	1	group or class	substitute: digital watch with seconds display
	tape, masking		roll	L	1	class	

Invest.	Material	Opt.	Size/Range	Source	Quantity	Per	Notes
11H	pencil, colored			L	5	student	
11I	none			NA	NA	NA	read and complete ativity
12G	alcohol, rubbing		bottle	L	1	group	
	aluminum foil		3 cm square	L	1	group	
	beaker		250–300 mL	S	1	group	
	burner, laboratory			S	1	group	substitute: hot plate
	food coloring		bottle	L	1	class	1 color
	ice			L	200 mL	group	crushed
	iron support ring			S	1	group	NA if hot plate used
	pencil, china marker			L	1	group	
	ruler, metric			L	1	group	
	stopper, one-hole			S	1	group	to fit test tube
	support stand, laboratory			S	1	group	NA if hot plate used
	tape, masking		roll	L	1	class	
	test tube, Pyrex		10–15 cm	S	1	group	
	tongs, test tube			S	1	group	
	tubing, glass or rigid plastic		6 mm O.D.	S/L	40 cm	group	must fit hole in stopper
	wire gauze square			S	1	group	NA if hot plate used
12H	clamp, flask		large	S	1	group	must be able to clamp vacuum bottle
	cup		small	L	1	group	substitute: 150 mL beaker
	food coloring	X	bottle	L	1	group	1 color
	paper, graph		¼ in. ruled	L	1	student	
	pencil, china marker			L	1	group	
	pencil, colored			L	2	student	2 different colors
	stopper, one-hole		large	S	1	group	to fit thermos bottle
	support stand, laboratory			S	1	group	
	tape, masking		roll	L	1	class	
	tubing, glass or rigid plastic		6 mm O.D.	S/L	30–40 cm	group	must fit hole in stopper
	vacuum bottle		1 pt–1 qt	L	1	group	thermos, etc.; narrow-mouth

Invest.	Material	Opt.	Size/Range	Source	Quantity	Per	Notes
12I	bolt		⅛ × 2 in. long	L	1	group	
	bolt		⅛ × 6 in. long	L	1	group	
	cup, paper			L	1	group	substitute: any kind of cup or small beaker
	drill bit		5/32 in.	L	1	class	
	drill, electric			L	1	class	
	eyedropper			L/S	1	group	
	gauze, surgical		15 × 15 cm piece	L	1	group	
	nut, machine		⅛ in.	L	8	group	nut thread must match bolts
	stopwatch			L/S	1	group	substitute: digital watch with seconds display
	string			L	1 m	group	
	thermometer, card mounted		0–100 °C or equiv.	S	2	group	mounted on metal, plywood, or stiff cardboard
	washer, metal		⅛ in.	L	10	group	
12J	funnel		10 cm diam.	L/S	1	group	
	glass jar		narrow (5 cm diam.)	L	1	group	e.g., olive jar
	glass jar		large (1 gal)	L	1	group	wide mouth
	ruler, metric			L	1	group	
	tape, masking			L	1	class	
12K	weather instrument station	X		S	1	class	anemometer, barometer, thermometer, etc.
13H	ruler			L	1	student	for straight edge only
14D	alum			L	100 g	group	aluminum ammonium sulfate; $AlNH_4SO_4$
	beaker		250 mL	S	3	group	Pyrex
	Epsom salts			L	100 g	group	magnesium sulfate heptahydrate; $MgSO_4 \cdot 7\, H_2O$
	food coloring	X	bottle	L	1	group	1 color
	hot plate			L	1	group	substitute: stove burner
	lens, hand magnifying			L/S	1	group	substitute: stereo microscope
	paper, printer		8½ × 11 in.	L	1	group	
	saucepan			L	1	group	substitute: 500 mL Pyrex beaker
	stirring rod			L/S	3	group	glass, metal, or substitute: pencil

Invest.	Material	Opt.	Size/Range	Source	Quantity	Per	Notes
14D (cont.)	sugar			L	200 g	group	sucrose
	thread or string, cotton		15 cm long	L	3	group	
14E	alum			L	(200 g)	group	aluminum ammonium sulfate; $AlNH_4SO_4$; see investigation instructions
	cup, foam			L	3	group	
	Epsom salts			L	(200 g)	group	$MgSO_4 \cdot 7 H_2O$; see investigation instructions
	handheld magnifying lens			L/S	1	group	substitute: stereo microscope
	hot plate			S/L	1	group	substitute: stove burner
	ice			L	sufficient	class	substitute: refrigerator
	plate, foam		small	L	1	group	
	saucepan			L	1	group	substitute: 500 mL Pyrex beaker
	stirring rod			L/S	2	group	glass, metal, or substitute: pencil
	sugar			L	(400 g)	group	sucrose; see investigation instructions
	thread or string, cotton		15 cm long	L	2	group	
14F	beaker		250 mL–1 L	S	1	group or class	substitute: deep cup
	ceramic tile			L/S	1	group	substitute: mineralogical streak plate
	glass plate			L	1	group	
	knife (steel)			L	1	group	
	lens, hand magnifying			L/S	1	group	
	magnet			L/S	1	group	permanent horseshoe or bar magnet
	penny			L	1	group	pre-1983, or substitute: solid copper materials
	rock and mineral collection			S	1	group	recommended: 50 specimen set from Scott Resources (BJU Press #63396)
	spring scale			S	1	group or class	substitute: mass balance
	support rod and clamp	X		S	1	group	required only if using mass balance for specific gravity test
	support stand, laboratory	X		S	1	group or class	required only if using mass balance for specific gravity test
	thread or string			L	50 cm	group or class	
15D	beaker		250 mL–1 L	S	1	group	
	eyedropper			L/S	1	group	

Invest.	Material	Opt.	Size/Range	Source	Quantity	Per	Notes
15D (cont.)	hydrochloric acid		bottle, 2 N or 2 M	S	1	group	a few drops of HCl per group
	lens, hand magnifying			L/S	1	group	substitute: stereo microscope
	paper toweling		roll	L	1	class	
	rock and mineral collection			S	1	group or class	recommended: 50 specimen set from Scott Resources (BJU Press #63396)
15E	none			NA	NA	NA	read and complete activity
15F	fossil, trilobite			S	≥1	group	more than one kind preferred
	lens, hand magnifying			L/S	1	group	stereo microscope preferred
16E	beaker		250 mL–1 L	S	1	group or class	substitute: water pitcher
	clay tool			L	1	group or class	substitute: pencil or old ballpoint pen
	clay, modeling, waterproof		large package	L	1	group or class	
	dishpan		deep	L	1	group or class	
	ruler, metric			L	1	group or class	plastic
16F	card, index		3 × 5 in.	L	1	student	
	ruler			L	1	student	for straight edge only
16G	dividers, drafting			L	1	student	
	lens, hand magnifying	X		L/S	1	student	if required by student to read map
	ruler			L	1	student	for straight edge only
16H	calculator, scientific			L	1	student	for calculations in scientific notation
	dividers, drafting			L	1	student	
	ruler			L	1	student	for straight edge only
17G	battery		6 volt	L	1	group or class	dry cell
	C-clamp		≥3 in.	L	1	group or class	
	clamp, right angle support			S	1	group or class	
	clay, modeling			L	2 oz	group or class	
	fishing sinker		1–6 oz	L	1	group or class	
	lamp bulb		6 volt	L/S	1	group or class	
	socket, lamp			S/L	1	group or class	must accept 6 V light bulb
	support rod		≥20 cm	S	1	group or class	steel rod or ¼ in. wooden dowel
	support stand, laboratory			S	1	group or class	

Invest.	Material	Opt.	Size/Range	Source	Quantity	Per	Notes
17G (cont.)	table or desk			L	2	group or class	must be same height
	wire, insulated		24 AWG or finer, 50–100 cm	L/S	3	group or class	AWG stands for American Wire Gauge
17H	calculator			L	1	student	standard calculator OK
	compass, drawing			L	1	student	
	map or atlas of the United States			L	1	class	
17I	calculator	X		L	1	student	standard calculator OK
	ruler, metric			L	1	student	
18F	balance, laboratory			S	1	group	accurate to 0.1 g
	beaker		1 L	S	1	group	
	beaker		250 mL	S	2	group	
	cheesecloth			L	1	group	substitute: wire strainer
	graduated cylinder		250 mL	S	1	group	
	lens, hand magnifying			L/S	1	group	
	oven			L	1	class	substitute: hot plate
	paper, weighing			S	2	group	
	pencil, china marker			L	1	group	
	ruler, metric			L	1	group	to measure soil sample in place in the field
	shovel, small			L	1	class	
	soil			L	15 cm^3	group	
18G	dishpan		large	L	1	class	
	sand			L	sufficient	class	about 2 in. deep in dishpan
19I	beaker		250 mL	S	1	group	
	burner igniter			L/S	1	group	substitute: safety matches
	burner, laboratory			S	1	group	
	clamp, flask			S	1	group	to fit Erlenmeyer flask
	flask, Erlenmeyer, Pyrex		250 mL	S	1	group	
	graduated cylinder		100 mL	S	1	group	
	ice	X		L	sufficient	class	
	iron support ring			S	1	group	

Invest.	Material	Opt.	Size/Range	Source	Quantity	Per	Notes
19I (cont.)	salt			L	3.5 g	group	table or rock salt (NaCl)
	stopper, one-hole			S	1	group	to fit 250 mL Erlenmeyer flask
	support stand, laboratory			S	1	group	
	tubing, glass or rigid plastic		6 mm O.D. × 8 cm	S/L	1	group	must fit hole in stopper; length is approximate
	tubing, natural rubber			S/L	60 cm	group	
	wire gauze square			S	1	group	
19J	beaker		500 mL	S	1	group or class	
	card, index		3 × 5 in.	L	2	group or class	
	reagent bottle		250 mL	S/L	4	group or class	substitute: baby food jars
	salt			L	sufficient	group or class	table or rock salt (NaCl), to make a saturated solution
	water container		5 gal	L/S	1	class	for uniform temperature water supply
20F	dishpan		large	L	1	group or class	
	ice cubes			L	several	group or class	
	soil, sifted			L	sufficient	group or class	12–15 cm deep in dishpan; substitute: clean sand
20G	calculator			L	1	student	standard calculator OK
	lens, hand magnifying			L/S	1	student	
	ruler, metric			L	1	student	
21E	bucket			L	1	class	
	clay, modeling			L	2 oz	group or class	
	cup, clear plastic			L	3	group or class	
	gravel		fine	L	120 cm^3	group or class	pea gravel is preferred
	pencil, china marker			L	1	group or class	
	plaster of Paris			L	sufficient	group or class	
	sand			L	sufficient	group or class	
21F	cup, paper		small	L	1	group	disposable preferred
	Epsom salts			L	2 g	group	magnesium sulfate heptahydrate; $MgSO_4 \cdot 7\,H_2O$; to make hard water
	liquid soap		bottle	L	1	class	dish washing, non-detergent
	test tube, Pyrex		10–15 cm	S	4	group	

Invest.	Material	Opt.	Size/Range	Source	Quantity	Per	Notes
21F (cont.)	water, distilled			L	10 mL	group	
	water, mineral			L	10 mL	group	
21G	beaker		250 mL	S	2	group or class	substitute: large drinking glasses
	Epsom salts		box	L	1	group or class	magnesium sulfate heptahydrate; $MgSO_4 \cdot 7\, H_2O$
	serving tray			L	1	group or class	
	thread or string, cotton, heavy			L	30 cm	group or class	
21H	balance, laboratory			S	1	group or class	accurate to 0.1 g
	bucket			L	1	class	to collect humus topsoil
	carbonic acid			S/L	100 mL	group or class	substitute: carbonated water
	cheesecloth			L	1	class	substitute: wire strainer; for preparing humic acid solution
	flask, Erlenmeyer, Pyrex		125 mL	S	5	group or class	
	funnel			L/S	1	class	for preparing humic acid solution
	graduated cylinder		1 L	S	1	class	for preparing humic acid solution
	graduated cylinder		100 mL	S	1	group or class	
	hydrochloric acid		1 N or 1 M	S	100 mL	group or class	
	limestone, gravel			L	40–50 g	group or class	similar sized pieces
	paper toweling		roll	L	1	class	
	pencil, china marker			L	1	group or class	
	pH indicator paper, universal		package	S	1	class	substitute: pH meter
	soil, humus			L	1 bucket	class	humus-rich top soil
	stopper, solid			S	5	group or class	to fit 125 mL Erlenmeyer flasks
	vinegar			L	100 mL	group or class	